D1206445

PHOTOELASTICITY

PHOTOELASTICITY

Volume I. 411 pages. 6 by 9. 349 figures, 6 colored inserts. Cloth.

Volume II. 505 pages. 6 by 9. 425 figures, 1 colored insert. Cloth.

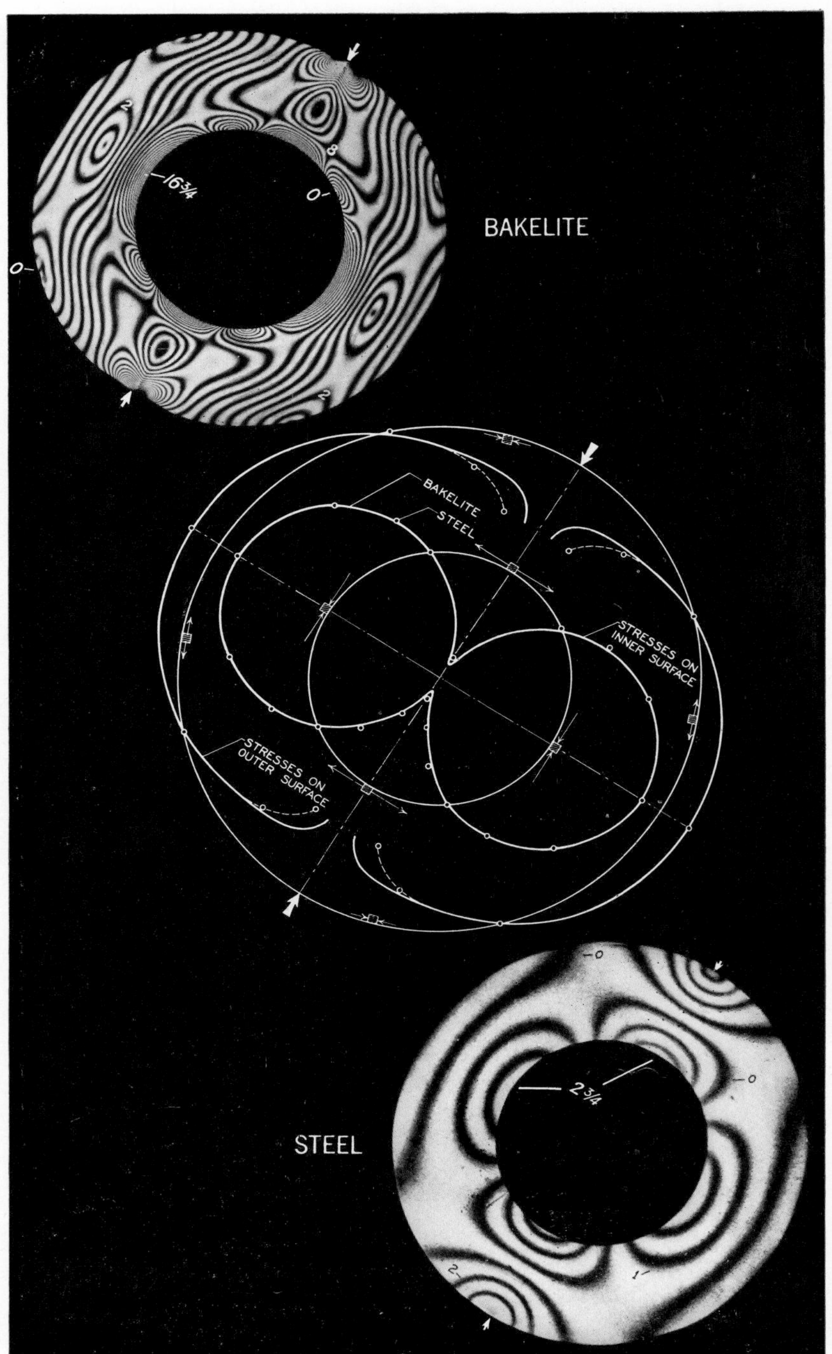

Frontispiece

PHOTOELASTICITY

BY

MAX MARK FROCHT, Ph. D.

Research Professor of Mechanics
Director of Experimental Stress Analysis
Illinois Institute of Technology
Consultant, Armour Research Foundation

VOLUME II

NEW YORK
JOHN WILEY & SONS, INC.
London: CHAPMAN & HALL, Limited

PRINTED IN THE UNITED STATES OF AMERICA

PREFACE

This book is a continuation of, and companion volume to, *Photoelasticity*, Volume I, which was published in 1941. Taken together these two books cover the theoretical principles and laboratory procedures of modern photoelasticity. Selected applications to practical problems of stress concentration are also included.

The six-year interval between the publication of the two volumes was not without benefit. In spite of the interruptions caused by the war, some new work was done during this period in this country[1] which is incorporated in the present volume. This includes several interesting developments in three-dimensional photoelasticity, such as the applications of oblique incidence to Saint Venant torsion and to the separation of principal stresses, the application of the rotational effect to bending stresses, the studies in three-dimensional stress concentrations, and progress in three-dimensional techniques. Improvements have also been made in the numerical solution of Laplace's equation. The most important single achievement is no doubt the very recent announcement by the Westinghouse Research Laboratories of a new material, known as Fosterite, especially suitable for three-dimensional photoelasticity. This is a contribution of far-reaching importance. It will stand out as a landmark in the history of the optical method of stress analysis. When Fosterite becomes commercially available, the scope and power of three-dimensional photoelasticity will be vastly increased. Fosterite is essentially free of time stresses and has already been successfully cast into cylinders 30 in. long and 6 in. in diameter. Although there still are difficulties to be overcome, one can envisage the time when it will be possible to study photoelastically complicated machine parts such as pistons, camshafts, and even crankshafts.

The book consists of fourteen chapters and an appendix, which may be divided into three parts. The first part, comprising the first six chapters, is intended as a brief introduction to the theory of elasticity for engineers. Although photoelasticity is an experimental method of

[1] Foreign work done during this period has not come to the author's attention.

stress analysis, its effective utilization requires an understanding of the fundamentals of the theory of elasticity. Also, in this part, the applicability of photoelastic results to structural materials is considered. The basic question of the influence of the material on the state of stress is here examined, and it is shown that, for practical purposes, this state is independent of the elastic constants.

A parallel study of a rather large number of problems is made both mathematically and photoelastically. The two sets of results are presented side by side in the form of comparative stress patterns. These parallel studies should contribute much to the better understanding of both photoelasticity and the theory of elasticity. In addition, there are presented direct comparisons between the results from steel and aluminum with those from Bakelite and Celluloid.

A special effort has been made to attain clarity and simplicity. The arrangement of the topics differs somewhat from that traditionally followed in works on elasticity. It is hoped that this new arrangement will result in a greater measure of unity. Theoretical topics are treated with more than usual mathematical detail. One full chapter is thus devoted to each of the three topics: the semi-infinite plate, the wedge, and the disk.

Chapters 7, 8, and 9 constitute the second part of the book. In these chapters we consider methods for determining the sums of the principal stresses at isolated points, as well as complete isopachic patterns in two-dimensional problems beyond those treated in Volume I.

Chapters 8 and 9 are, perhaps, of special interest. They contain a systematic treatment of the numerical methods for the solution of Laplace's equation. These methods have in recent years been much improved and appear preferable to most other methods in the general problem of determining isopachic patterns. In addition, the numerical solution of Laplace's equation finds many applications in other fields of engineering and physics, such as heat transfer, electricity, hydrodynamics, and elasticity. For completeness the theory of conformal transformations and its uses in the numerical solution of Laplace's equation are treated in Chapter 9.

The last five chapters, i.e., Chapters 10–14 inclusive, and the appendix, make up the third part of this volume. This part is devoted to the theory, technique, and applications of three-dimensional photoelasticity. Here are included a new demonstration of the general stress-optic law in three dimensions which is made possible by the development of the frozen stress pattern, a discussion of laboratory technique, the theory and some applications of oblique incidence, studies in stress concentrations including a correlation with results from fatigue tests and strain measurements, an exposition of the method of scattered light, and a description of Fosterite.

Unfortunately, space did not permit a treatment of many applied phases of photoelasticity. We were thus compelled to omit the interesting applications to structural problems and most of the material on stress concentrations.

Some material in this book appears in print for the first time. To these topics belong all the comparative stress patterns, a good many aspects of the numerical solution of Laplace's equation, the demonstration of the stress-optic law in Chapter 10, and the appendix on the new material.

Much work remains to be done. The possibilities in the methods of scattered and convergent light are still to be explored. The rotational effects need further investigation. Greater efforts must be made to apply photoelasticity to dynamical and impact problems and also to fluid flow. The extension of the optical method into the field of plasticity is one of the challenging tasks for the future. These are but a few of the problems before us. In addition, there are numerous practical problems that can be solved with present-day methods and materials.

There remains the pleasant task of acknowledging the assistance which the author generously received from his colleagues and friends. Dr. D. C. Drucker read all the material on three-dimensional photoelasticity and made many important corrections and suggestions. The introduction to the theory of elasticity was read by Dr. D. Moskovitz, Dr. E. Saibel, and Dr. E. Sternberg, all of whom made valuable suggestions.

Early drafts of Chapters 8 and 9 on the numerical solution of Laplace's equations were also read by Dr. T. L. Smith and Dr. D. Moskovitz. The author has also had valuable conversations with Dr. L. H. Donnell. To all these he expresses his deep appreciation.

The author has freely drawn upon numerous publications and books, reference to which is made in the footnotes. In particular he drew upon the investigations by Drucker, Mindlin, and Weller. He also derived great benefit from the *Theory of Elasticity* by S. Timoshenko, and the *Theory of Elasticity* by R. V. Southwell.

The author's work was sponsored by the Carnegie Institute of Technology and carried out in its Photoelastic Laboratory. In these investigations he was assisted by M. M. Leven and J. R. McDowell, who made most valuable contributions. Mr. A. C. Otto assisted in preparing the tables for Chapter 8. The author also wishes to thank all those who helped in the reading of the proof and in the checking of the drawings, and in particular Dr. Le Van Griffis for providing much of this help.

The author deems it a pleasure to record his indebtedness to Messrs. R. E. Peterson and M. M. Leven from the Westinghouse Research Laboratories for making available to him the data, curves, and stress patterns on Fosterite which appear in the Appendix.

Finally, the author wishes to thank his wife, not only for editorial and secretarial assistance, but perhaps even more for the patience shown during the years required to bring the manuscript to completion.

MAX MARK FROCHT

Laboratory of Experimental
Stress Analysis
Mechanics Department
Illinois Institute of Technology
December 16, 1947

CONTENTS

CHAPTER 1: THE COMPATIBILITY EQUATION AND ELEMENTARY STRESS FUNCTIONS IN TWO DIMENSIONS

PART I THE COMPATIBILITY EQUATION AND THE STRESS FUNCTION

PART II ELEMENTARY RECTANGULAR STRESS FUNCTIONS — SAINT VENANT'S PRINCIPLE

CHAPTER 2: RADIAL STRESSES IN THE SEMI-INFINITE PLATE

CHAPTER 13: CIRCULAR SHAFTS IN TENSION AND BENDING

Part I Introduction

CHAPTER I

THE COMPATIBILITY EQUATION AND ELEMENTARY STRESS FUNCTIONS IN TWO DIMENSIONS

PART I THE COMPATIBILITY EQUATION AND THE STRESS FUNCTION

§1.1 Introduction. In the first several chapters of this book we treat some problems of the mathematical theory of elasticity which are of immediate interest to photoelasticians. Although photoelasticity is an experimental method of stress analysis the interpretations of the stress data obtained from the polariscope frequently rest on propositions and relations developed in the theory of elasticity.

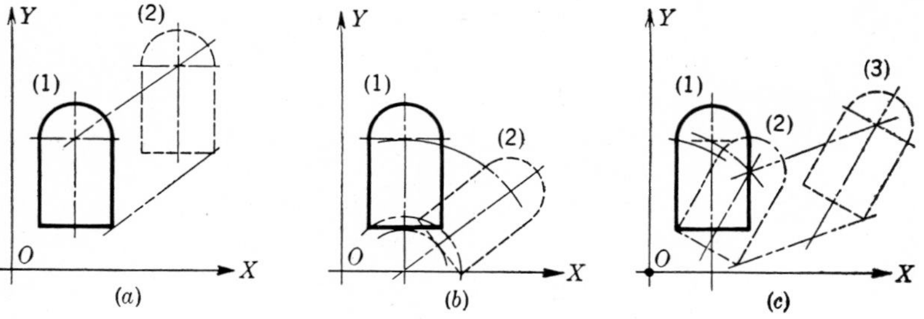

FIG. 1.1 Sketches Showing Rigid Body Motions. (*a*) Pure translation; (*b*) pure rotation; (*c*) plane motion.

This theory concerns itself with basic relations between stresses and strains, and the loads which produce them. The concept of strain is derived from that of deformation, which in turn is associated with the displacements of points. Here we must distinguish between rigid-body displacements and the displacements which give rise to deformations and strains.

In rigid-body motions the shape and size remain unchanged. The distances between any two points in a body stay unaltered, and so do the angles between any two lines. Fig. 1.1 shows the three basic types of plane rigid-body motions, i.e., pure translation, pure rotation, and their combination (general plane motion). These are motions of fictitious bodies which remain free from all stress and strain. Rigid-body motions are treated in dynamics.

The theory of elasticity deals with displacements resulting in deformations. Here, the shape, size, distances between points, and angles between lines always change, although in metals the changes in the dimensions may at times be extremely difficult to measure. Bars in tension, beams in bending, shafts in torsion are simple examples of strained or deformed bodies.

The scope of the theory of elasticity is generally confined to homogeneous isotropic bodies in the elastic range where Hooke's law holds. In this range there is complete recovery of stress and deformation when the loads are removed. Deformations beyond the eleastic range are treated in the theory of plasticity.

§1.2 Components of Strain in Rectangular Coordinates. Fig. 1.2 shows a section of a strained body and a set of fixed reference axes OX and OY. Consider now the two intersecting straight lines OA and OB, which, before the loads are applied, coincide with the coordinate axes. The application of the loads will cause points O, A, and B to be displaced to new positions O', A', and B' and the right angle AOB to change to an angle $A'O'B'$. The displacement of a point will be represented by three rectangular components u, v, w parallel respectively to the X, Y, and Z axes. These displacements will be assumed to be continuous functions of the coordinates x, y, z.[1] Limiting ourselves to two dimensions, let u, v denote the displacements of the origin O. The components u_a, v_a, u_b, v_b of the displacements at A and B respectively are then given by

$$u_a = u + \frac{\partial u}{\partial x} dx,$$

$$v_a = v + \frac{\partial v}{\partial x} dx,$$

$$u_b = u + \frac{\partial u}{\partial y} dy,$$

$$v_b = v + \frac{\partial v}{\partial y} dy,$$

[1] It is further assumed that the partial derivatives of these displacements with respect to the coordinates are small, in the sense that all higher powers of these derivatives may be neglected in comparison with their first powers. This is usually referred to as the assumption of infinitesimal deformations.

as shown in Fig. 1.2. The length $O'A''$ is given by

$$O'A'' = dx + u_a - u = dx + u + \frac{\partial u}{\partial x}\,dx - u$$
$$= dx + \frac{\partial u}{\partial x}\,dx.$$

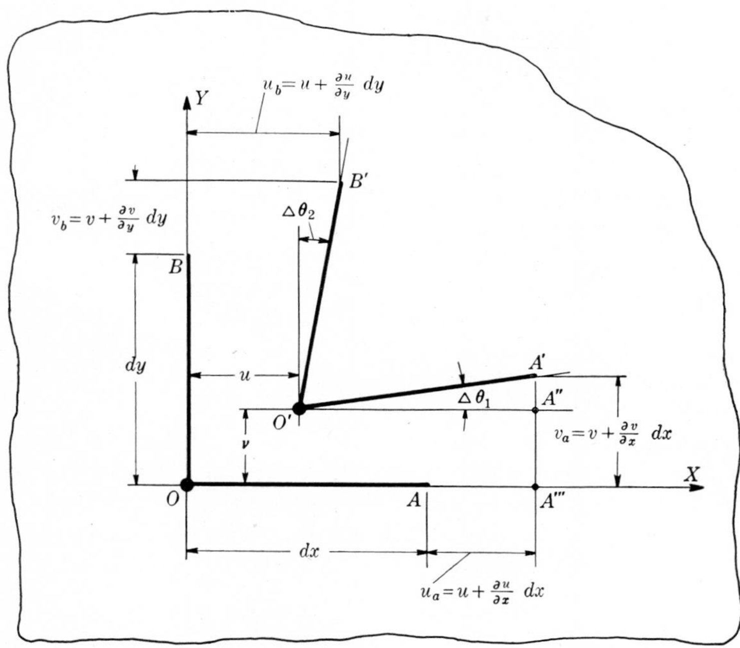

FIG. 1.2 Sketch Showing Displacement and Notation in Cartesian Coordinates

Assuming the angle $\Delta\theta_1$ between $O'A'$ and $O'A''$ to be small so that its cosine may be taken as unity, the length $O'A'$ may be taken as equal to that of $O'A''$. Hence the deformation δ_x in the length OA is

$$\delta_x = O'A'' - OA = dx + \frac{\partial u}{\partial x}\,dx - dx = \frac{\partial u}{\partial x}\,dx,$$

and the strain ϵ_x is by definition given by

$$\epsilon_x = \frac{\delta_x}{dx} = \frac{\partial u}{\partial x}. \qquad (a)$$

In like manner (1.1)

$$\epsilon_y = \frac{\partial v}{\partial y}. \qquad (b)$$

Further, remembering that $\Delta\theta_1$ and $\Delta\theta_2$ are small angles, we have

$$\tan \Delta\theta_1 = \Delta\theta_1 = \left(\frac{\partial v}{\partial x} dx\right)\frac{1}{dx} = \frac{\partial v}{\partial x} \quad \text{approximately,}$$

$$\tan \Delta\theta_2 = \Delta\theta_2 = \left(\frac{\partial u}{\partial y} dy\right)\frac{1}{dy} = \frac{\partial u}{\partial y} \quad \text{approximately.}$$

Hence, the shear strain γ_{xy} at the origin O, which is defined as the angular change in the right angle AOB (§1.18, Vol. I), is

$$\boldsymbol{\gamma}_{xy} = \boldsymbol{\Delta\theta}_1 + \boldsymbol{\Delta\theta}_2 = \frac{\partial \boldsymbol{u}}{\partial \boldsymbol{y}} + \frac{\partial \boldsymbol{v}}{\partial \boldsymbol{x}}. \tag{1.2}$$

In general in three-dimensional problems there are six components of strain which are given by

$$\epsilon_x = \frac{\partial u}{\partial x}, \quad \epsilon_y = \frac{\partial v}{\partial y}, \quad \epsilon_z = \frac{\partial w}{\partial z};$$

$$\gamma_{xy} = \frac{\partial u}{\partial y} + \frac{\partial v}{\partial x}, \quad \gamma_{xz} = \frac{\partial u}{\partial z} + \frac{\partial w}{\partial x}, \quad \gamma_{yz} = \frac{\partial v}{\partial z} + \frac{\partial w}{\partial y}.$$

In two-dimensional or plane problems two states are distinguished: *plane strain* and *plane stress*. Plane strain is defined as a state of strain in which the displacements u and v are functions of x and y alone and the displacement w vanishes. The strain components ϵ_z, γ_{xz}, and γ_{yz} therefore vanish, leaving only

$$\boldsymbol{\epsilon}_x = \frac{\partial \boldsymbol{u}}{\partial \boldsymbol{x}}, \quad \boldsymbol{\epsilon}_y = \frac{\partial \boldsymbol{v}}{\partial \boldsymbol{y}}, \quad \boldsymbol{\gamma}_{xy} = \frac{\partial \boldsymbol{u}}{\partial \boldsymbol{y}} + \frac{\partial \boldsymbol{v}}{\partial \boldsymbol{x}}.$$

The stress components resulting from plane strain are σ_x, σ_y, σ_z, and τ_{xy}, all of which are functions of x and y only.

An essential characteristic of the state of plane strain thus lies in the fact that ϵ_z vanishes but the corresponding stress σ_z does not vanish.

Plane stress, on the other hand, is defined as the state of stress in which

$$\sigma_z = \tau_{xz} = \tau_{yz} = 0.$$

This means that the existing stresses are all parallel to the XY plane. The stress components σ_x, σ_y, and τ_{xy} will in general be functions of the coordinates x, y, z. However, in very thin plates the stresses may be treated as functions of x and y only, i.e., as constant across the thickness at each point.[1]

§1.3 Components of Strain in Polar Coordinates. Let $ABCD$, Fig. 1.3, represent the position of an unstrained element, and let $A'B'C'D'$ be the position of the same element after deformation. We denote the

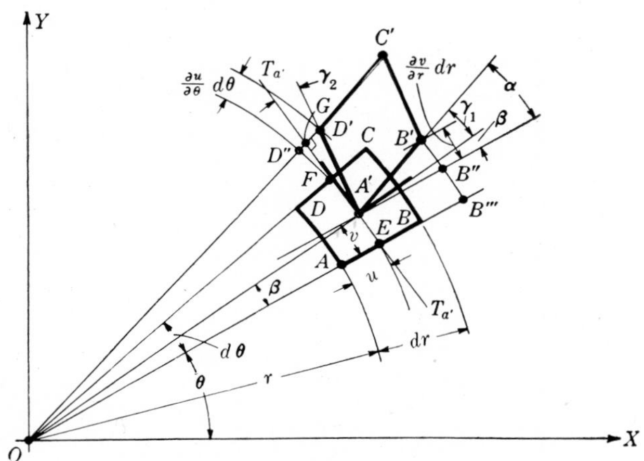

FIG. 1.3 Sketch Showing Displacements and Notation in Polar Coordinates.

radial and tangential displacements of point A by u and v respectively, and the corresponding strains by ϵ_r and ϵ_θ. The shear strain we denote by $\gamma_{r\theta}$. By inspection we have

$$A'B'' = dr + \frac{\partial u}{\partial r} dr.$$

Hence the deformation in the radial direction is

$$A'B'' - AB = \delta_r = \frac{\partial u}{\partial r} dr,$$

and the expression for the radial strain becomes

$$\epsilon_r = \frac{\delta_r}{dr} = \frac{\partial u}{\partial r}. \tag{1.3}$$

[1] Filon introduced the concept of generalized plane stress in which the mean stresses across the thickness replace the actual stresses. The mean stresses can be shown to satisfy the differential equations of equilibrium and other basic relations. See *Treatise on Photoelasticity* by Coker and Filon, §2.23.

In order to obtain the expression for the tangential strain we observe that the element AD has a twofold deformation: one due to the displacement in the radial direction and the other due to tangential displacements. Thus let the arc AD first be displaced in the radial direction to the position EF. Its length would then be $(r + u)\, d\theta$. Next let us displace the element EF to the position $A'D''$. The length ED'' would then be

$$ED'' = (r + u)\, d\theta + v + \frac{\partial v}{\partial \theta}\, d\theta.$$

The tangential deformation δ_θ in the length AD is then given by

$$\begin{aligned}\delta_\theta &= (r + u)\, d\theta + v + \frac{\partial v}{\partial \theta}\, d\theta - r\, d\theta - v \\ &= u\, d\theta + \frac{\partial v}{\partial \theta}\, d\theta\end{aligned}$$

and the tangential strain ϵ_θ becomes

$$\boldsymbol{\epsilon_\theta = \frac{\delta_\theta}{r\, d\theta} = \frac{u}{r} + \frac{1}{r}\frac{\partial v}{\partial \theta}}. \tag{1.4}$$

We thus see that ***the strain in the tangential direction is a function not only of the tangential displacement v but also of the radial displacement u.***

Lastly we determine the shear strain $\gamma_{r\theta}$, that is the angular change in the right angle at A'. This angle is made up of two parts: γ_1 which represents the angle between the side $A'B'$ and the radial line through A', and γ_2 which is the angle between the side $A'D'$ and the tangent $T_{a'}$ to the circle at A'. We draw an auxiliary line $A'B''$ through point A' parallel to the side AB and denote the angle between it and the radial line through A' by β. This angle represents the rigid-body rotation of the element as a whole.

Let

$$\gamma_1 + \beta = \alpha.$$

From Fig. 1.3 we have, considering α a small angle,

$$\begin{aligned}\tan \alpha = \alpha &= \frac{B''B'}{B''A'} \\ &= \left(\frac{\partial v}{\partial r}\, dr\right) \cdot \frac{1}{dr} = \frac{\partial v}{\partial r}, \quad \text{approximately.}\end{aligned}$$

Similarly

$$\tan \beta = \beta = \frac{v}{r},$$

whence

$$\gamma_1 = \frac{\partial v}{\partial r} - \frac{v}{r}. \tag{1.5}$$

Further, in the limit

$$\frac{GD'}{GA'} = \tan \gamma_2 = \gamma_2.$$

But the limiting value of GD' is $(\partial u/\partial \theta)\,d\theta$, and for purposes of division GA' may be taken as $r\,d\theta$, approximately. Hence

$$\frac{GD'}{GA'} = \left(\frac{\partial u}{\partial \theta}\,d\theta\right)\frac{1}{r\,d\theta},$$

and

$$\gamma_2 = \frac{\partial u}{\partial \theta}\cdot\frac{1}{r}, \quad \text{approximately.} \tag{1.6}$$

The value of the shear strain is thus

$$\begin{aligned}\gamma_{r\theta} &= \gamma_1 + \gamma_2 \\ &= \frac{\partial u}{\partial \theta}\cdot\frac{1}{r} + \frac{\partial v}{\partial r} - \frac{v}{r}.\end{aligned} \tag{1.7}$$

§1.4 The Compatibility Equation in Terms of Rectangular Strain Components. In §§1.18 and 1.19, Vol. I, it was shown that given ϵ_x, ϵ_y, and γ_{xy} it is possible to calculate ϵ_θ, the linear strain in any arbitrary direction, as well as γ_θ, the angular change between any two perpendicular lines, or for that matter the angular change between any two lines. However, in those articles the components of strain were treated as if they were independent quantities. That they are not independent can be seen both from physical and from mathematical considerations. If a body be thought of as consisting of small cubes, these cubes will be deformed in shape and size but they must fit together if the body has not failed by rupture. The components of the strain must therefore be interrelated. Considered mathematically the problem can be stated thus. In plane strain problems there are three strain components ϵ_x, ϵ_y, γ_{xy} related to u and v by the expressions

$$\epsilon_x = \frac{\partial u}{\partial x}, \quad \epsilon_y = \frac{\partial v}{\partial y}, \quad \gamma_{xy} = \frac{\partial u}{\partial y} + \frac{\partial v}{\partial x}.$$

It is clear therefore that a particular set of u and v functions determines not only ϵ_x and ϵ_y but also the shear strain γ_{xy}.

In order to obtain the specific relations between the strain components we form

$$\frac{\partial^2 \epsilon_x}{\partial y^2}, \quad \frac{\partial^2 \epsilon_y}{\partial x^2}, \quad \text{and} \quad \frac{\partial^2 \gamma_{xy}}{\partial x\, \partial y}.$$

Thus[1]

$$\frac{\partial^2 \epsilon_x}{\partial y^2} = \frac{\partial^3 u}{\partial x\, \partial y^2},$$

$$\frac{\partial^2 \epsilon_y}{\partial x^2} = \frac{\partial^3 v}{\partial x^2\, \partial y},$$

$$\frac{\partial^2 \gamma_{xy}}{\partial x\, \partial y} = \frac{\partial^3 u}{\partial x\, \partial y^2} + \frac{\partial^3 v}{\partial x^2\, \partial y}.$$

Adding, we obtain

$$\frac{\partial^2 \epsilon_x}{\partial y^2} + \frac{\partial^2 \epsilon_y}{\partial x^2} = \frac{\partial^2 \gamma_{xy}}{\partial x\, \partial y}. \tag{1.8}$$

This equation is known as the compatibility or continuity equation. It marks the essential difference between the elementary methods used in calculating nominal stresses and the rigorous methods of the mathematical theory of elasticity. In the first instance a simple distribution of the stress is assumed and the analysis is based exclusively upon the laws of equilibrium; in the second instance the solution rests not only on the laws of statics but also on the compatibility equation. Here the distribution of the stress is not assumed but is determined analytically.[2]

§1.5 The Compatibility Equation in Terms of Rectangular Stress Components. (*a*) *Plane Stress.* In §1.2 we defined plane stress as a state of stress in which $\sigma_z = 0$. The equations of Hooke's Law for this case are

$$\left.\begin{aligned} \epsilon_x &= \frac{1}{E}(\sigma_x - \nu\sigma_y), \qquad (a) \\ \epsilon_y &= \frac{1}{E}(\sigma_y - \nu\sigma_x), \qquad (b) \end{aligned}\right\} [(1.36), \text{Vol. I}]$$

$$\gamma_{xy} = \frac{\tau_{xy}}{G} = \frac{2(1+\nu)}{E}\tau_{xy}. \qquad [(1.41), \text{Vol. I}]$$

[1] We assume that all functions used are continuous functions and that they have continuous partial derivatives of sufficiently high order to insure that all partial derivatives used are independent of the order of differentiation. These conditions will be satisfied if the functions are analytic.

[2] It can be shown that the average strains associated with the state of generalized plane stress are also characterized by eq. (1.8). See *Treatise on Photoelasticity* by Coker and Filon, §3.23. It should be noted that eq. (1.8) is independent of ϵ_z; it is valid whether ϵ_z is zero or not.

Substituting these expressions in eq. (1.8), the continuity equation from the preceding article, and multiplying by E we have

$$\frac{\partial^2}{\partial y^2}(\sigma_x - \nu\sigma_y) + \frac{\partial^2}{\partial x^2}(\sigma_y - \nu\sigma_x) = 2(1+\nu)\frac{\partial^2 \tau_{xy}}{\partial x\,\partial y},$$

or

$$\frac{\partial^2 \sigma_x}{\partial y^2} + \frac{\partial^2 \sigma_y}{\partial x^2} - \nu\left(\frac{\partial^2 \sigma_x}{\partial x^2} + \frac{\partial^2 \sigma_y}{\partial y^2}\right) = 2(1+\nu)\frac{\partial^2 \tau_{xy}}{\partial x\,\partial y}. \tag{1.9}$$

Further, from the equations of equilibrium

$$\frac{\partial \sigma_x}{\partial x} + \frac{\partial \tau_{xy}}{\partial y} + X_b = 0, \qquad [(2.5), \text{Vol. I}]$$

$$\frac{\partial \sigma_y}{\partial y} + \frac{\partial \tau_{yx}}{\partial x} + Y_b = 0, \qquad [(2.6), \text{Vol. I}]$$

it follows from differentiation and addition that

$$\frac{\partial^2 \sigma_x}{\partial x^2} + 2\frac{\partial^2 \tau_{xy}}{\partial x\,\partial y} + \frac{\partial^2 \sigma_y}{\partial y^2} + \frac{\partial X_b}{\partial x} + \frac{\partial Y_b}{\partial y} = 0, \tag{1.10}$$

whence

$$2\frac{\partial^2 \tau_{xy}}{\partial x\,\partial y} = -\left(\frac{\partial^2 \sigma_x}{\partial x^2} + \frac{\partial^2 \sigma_y}{\partial y^2}\right) - \left(\frac{\partial X_b}{\partial x} + \frac{\partial Y_b}{\partial y}\right). \tag{1.11}$$

Substituting the last expression for $2(\partial^2 \tau_{xy}/\partial x\,\partial y)$ in eq. (1.9) we obtain

$$\frac{\partial^2 \sigma_x}{\partial y^2} + \frac{\partial^2 \sigma_y}{\partial x^2} - \nu\left(\frac{\partial^2 \sigma_x}{\partial x^2} + \frac{\partial^2 \sigma_y}{\partial y^2}\right) = -(1+\nu)\left(\frac{\partial^2 \sigma_x}{\partial x^2} + \frac{\partial^2 \sigma_y}{\partial y^2}\right) - (1+\nu)\left(\frac{\partial X_b}{\partial x} + \frac{\partial Y_b}{\partial y}\right),$$

whence

$$\frac{\partial^2 \sigma_x}{\partial x^2} + \frac{\partial^2 \sigma_y}{\partial x^2} + \frac{\partial^2 \sigma_x}{\partial y^2} + \frac{\partial^2 \sigma_y}{\partial y^2} = -(1+\nu)\left(\frac{\partial X_b}{\partial x} + \frac{\partial Y_b}{\partial y}\right), \tag{1.12}$$

or

$$\left(\frac{\partial^2}{\partial x^2} + \frac{\partial^2}{\partial y^2}\right)(\sigma_x + \sigma_y) = -(1+\nu)\left(\frac{\partial X_b}{\partial x} + \frac{\partial Y_b}{\partial y}\right). \tag{1.13}$$

This is the compatibility equation for plane stress for general body forces X_b, Y_b. When the body forces are constant or absent this equation reduces to

$$\left(\frac{\partial^2}{\partial x^2} + \frac{\partial^2}{\partial y^2}\right)(\sigma_x + \sigma_y) = 0. \tag{1.14a}$$

Recalling that at a given point [see eq. (1.9), Vol. I]

$$\sigma_x + \sigma_y = p + q = \Sigma, \quad \text{a constant,}$$

we may write the last equation as

$$\frac{\partial^2 \Sigma}{\partial x^2} + \frac{\partial^2 \Sigma}{\partial y^2} = 0, \tag{1.14b}$$

i.e., ***the sum of the principal stresses satisfies Laplace's equation.***

(*b*) *Plane Strain.* In §1.2 we defined plane strain as a state of strain in which $\epsilon_z = 0$, that is, a plane transverse to the longitudinal axis of the body, the Z axis, remains a plane. Since

$$\epsilon_z = \frac{1}{E}[\sigma_z - \nu(\sigma_x + \sigma_y)], \qquad [(1.35c), \text{Vol. I}]$$

it follows that for plane strain

$$\sigma_z = \nu(\sigma_x + \sigma_y). \tag{1.15}$$

The expressions for ϵ_x and ϵ_y given by eq. (1.35), Vol. I, then become

$$\epsilon_x = \frac{1 + \nu}{E}[(1 - \nu)\sigma_x - \nu\sigma_y], \tag{1.16}$$

$$\epsilon_y = \frac{1 + \nu}{E}[(1 - \nu)\sigma_y - \nu\sigma_x]. \tag{1.17}$$

Substituting these in eq. (1.8) and replacing γ_{xy} by $[2(1 + \nu)\tau_{xy}]/E$ and $2(\partial^2\tau_{xy}/\partial x\, \partial y)$ by the expression from eq. (1.11) we obtain upon simplification

$$\left(\frac{\partial^2}{\partial x^2} + \frac{\partial^2}{\partial y^2}\right)(\sigma_x + \sigma_y) = -\frac{1}{1 - \nu}\left(\frac{\partial X_b}{\partial x} + \frac{\partial Y_b}{\partial y}\right). \tag{1.18}$$

Comparison of eqs. (1.13) and (1.18) shows that, ***when body forces are absent or constant, the compatibility equation for plane stress is identical with that for plane strain.***

§1.6 Boundary Conditions. The equations of equilibrium [eqs. (2.7), (2.8) of Vol. I] express the relation between the stresses acting on a small rectangular element free of body forces. At a boundary an element which includes a portion of the boundary among its faces is generally not rectangular, and the relations must be modified to take into account the shape of the boundary and the surface forces acting upon it. Equilibrium must exist between the stresses acting on the internal faces of the element and the surface forces or tractions acting on the outside face.

Consider, for example, the prismatic element ABC, Figs. 1.4(a) and (b), in which $\bar{X}$ and $\bar{Y}$ represent the average components of the surface forces on CB. Neglecting infinitesimals of higher order, a small curved segment CB may be treated as a straight line, regardless of the curvature at the boundary.

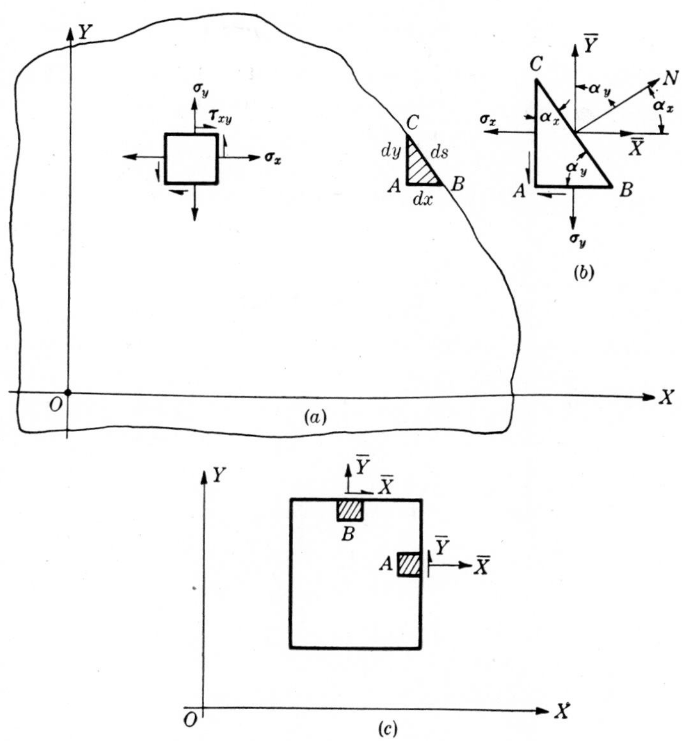

FIG. 1.4 Sketch for Boundary Conditions.

Summing forces in the X and Y directions, respectively, and neglecting body forces, we have

$$\bar{X}t\,ds - \sigma_x t\,ds\cos\alpha_x - \tau_{xy}t\,ds\cos\alpha_y = 0, \tag{1.19}$$

$$\bar{Y}t\,ds - \sigma_y t\,ds\cos\alpha_y - \tau_{xy}t\,ds\cos\alpha_x = 0, \tag{1.20}$$

in which t is the thickness of the prism perpendicular to the plane of the paper and the angles α_x and α_y are as shown in Fig. 1.4. Simplifying and replacing cos α_x and cos α_y by l and m respectively, we get

$$\left.\begin{aligned} \bar{X} &= l\sigma_x + m\tau_{xy}, && (a)\\ \bar{Y} &= m\sigma_y + l\tau_{xy}. && (b)\end{aligned}\right\} \quad (1.21)$$

These equations express the boundary conditions necessary for equilibrium. When the boundary is rectangular we take the coordinate axes parallel to the sides of the rectangle and thereby simplify materially eqs. (1.21).

Thus, at a point, such as A, on the vertical edges, Fig. 1.4(c), $l = 1$, $m = 0$, and the above equations reduce to

$$\bar{X} = \sigma_x, \quad \bar{Y} = \tau_{xy}. \tag{1.22a}$$

Similarly at a point B on the horizontal edges

$$\bar{X} = \tau_{xy}, \quad \bar{Y} = \sigma_y. \tag{1.22b}$$

This means that for equilibrium the surface forces per unit area must in this case coincide with the stresses at the boundary. It is to be noted that eqs. (1.21) remain valid even when body forces are present.

§1.7 The Airy Stress Components and the Stress Function. (a) *Cartesian Coordinates.* Let $\phi(x, y)$ be an arbitrary function[1] of the coordinates (x, y). Direct substitution in the equations of equilibrium below,

$$\frac{\partial \sigma_x}{\partial x} + \frac{\partial \tau_{xy}}{\partial y} = 0, \qquad [(2.7), \text{Vol. I}]$$

$$\frac{\partial \sigma_y}{\partial y} + \frac{\partial \tau_{xy}}{\partial x} - \rho g = 0, \qquad [(2.6), \text{Vol. I}]$$

which contain the weight $-\rho g$, as the only body force, shows that they can be satisfied by a system of stress components σ_x, σ_y, τ_{xy}, formed in the following manner:[2]

$$\left.\begin{aligned} \sigma_x &= \frac{\partial^2 \phi}{\partial y^2} && (a)\\ \sigma_y &= \frac{\partial^2 \phi}{\partial x^2}, && (b)\\ \tau_{xy} &= -\frac{\partial^2 \phi}{\partial x\, \partial y} + \rho g x. && (c)\end{aligned}\right\} \quad (1.23)$$

[1] See footnote, p. 13.

[2] It can be shown that eqs. (1.23) are in reality the general solution of the equations of equilibrium for the plane problem. See *Theory of Elasticity* by R. V. Southwell, §4.02, Oxford University Press.

Thus, substituting the above stress components into eq. (2.7), Vol. I, we obtain

$$\frac{\partial}{\partial x}\left(\frac{\partial^2 \phi}{\partial y^2}\right) - \frac{\partial}{\partial y}\left(\frac{\partial^2 \phi}{\partial x\, \partial y} - \rho g x\right) = 0,$$

or

$$\frac{\partial^3 \phi}{\partial x\, \partial y^2} - \frac{\partial^3 \phi}{\partial x\, \partial y^2} = 0,$$

which is obviously true. In like manner it can be verified that eq. (2.6), Vol. I, is satisfied.

There is thus no difficulty in satisfying the laws of statics at each internal point. An infinite variety of rectangular stress components can be found, all of which would be in equilibrium. However, in addition to satisfying the laws of statics, which is automatically effected by eqs. (1.23), the stresses σ_x, σ_y, and τ_{xy} must also fit the compatibility equation

$$\left(\frac{\partial^2}{\partial x^2} + \frac{\partial^2}{\partial y^2}\right)(\sigma_x + \sigma_y) = 0, \tag{1.14a}$$

as well as the boundary conditions given by eqs. (1.21). The last requirements furnish the greatest mathematical difficulties in the solution of problems by the theory of elasticity.

The function ϕ, from which the stresses are formed, is called the *Airy stress function*, or briefly the *stress function*, named after Professor Airy,[1] who was the first to suggest this approach.

(*b*) *Polar Coordinates.* In a similar manner we find that, neglecting body forces, the equations of equilibrium in polar coordinates, i.e.,

$$r\frac{\partial \sigma_r}{\partial r} + (\sigma_r - \sigma_\theta) + \frac{\partial \tau_{r\theta}}{\partial \theta} = 0, \qquad [(2.9),\ \text{Vol. I}]$$

$$\frac{\partial \sigma_\theta}{\partial \theta} + r\frac{\partial \tau_{r\theta}}{\partial r} + 2\tau_{r\theta} = 0, \qquad [(2.10),\ \text{Vol. I}]$$

are satisfied if the stress components are chosen as follows:

$$\left.\begin{aligned} \sigma_r &= \frac{1}{r}\frac{\partial \phi}{\partial r} + \frac{1}{r^2}\frac{\partial^2 \phi}{\partial \theta^2}, && (a)\\ \sigma_\theta &= \frac{\partial^2 \phi}{\partial r^2}, && (b)\\ \tau_{r\theta} &= \frac{1}{r^2}\frac{\partial \phi}{\partial \theta} - \frac{1}{r}\frac{\partial^2 \phi}{\partial r\, \partial \theta} = -\frac{\partial}{\partial r}\left(\frac{1}{r}\frac{\partial \phi}{\partial \theta}\right). && (c) \end{aligned}\right\} (1.24)$$

[1] See G. B. Airy, *British Assoc. Adv. Sci. Rept.*, 1862.

It is left to the reader to show that this is true. Eqs. (1.23) and (1.24) represent basic steps in the mathematical solution of a stress problem.

§1.8 The Compatibility Equation in Terms of the Stress Function. (*a*) *Cartesian Coordinates.* The compatibility eq. (1.14*a*) can now be readily expressed in terms of the stress function.

Thus, if, in the equation below,

$$\left(\frac{\partial^2}{\partial x^2} + \frac{\partial^2}{\partial y^2}\right)(\sigma_x + \sigma_y) = 0, \tag{1.14a}$$

we replace σ_x and σ_y by $\partial^2\phi/\partial y^2$ and $\partial^2\phi/\partial x^2$ respectively, which are their values in terms of the stress function ϕ, eqs. (1.23), we obtain

$$\left(\frac{\partial^2}{\partial x^2} + \frac{\partial^2}{\partial y^2}\right)\left(\frac{\partial^2\phi}{\partial x^2} + \frac{\partial^2\phi}{\partial y^2}\right) = 0, \qquad (a)$$

or

$$\frac{\partial^4\phi}{\partial x^4} + 2\frac{\partial^4\phi}{\partial x^2\partial y^2} + \frac{\partial^4\phi}{\partial y^4} = 0. \qquad (b) \qquad (1.25)$$

A more condensed way of writing this is

$$\nabla^4\phi = 0 \tag{1.26}$$

in which $\nabla^4\phi$ is read del^4 ϕ.

(*b*) *Polar Coordinates.* Among the most useful stress functions are those given in polar coordinates. We therefore proceed to transform the expression (1.26) into the corresponding polar coordinate form.

The basic relations between the two sets of coordinates, Fig. 1.5(*a*), are furnished by

$$r^2 = x^2 + y^2 \tag{1.27}$$

$$\tan\theta = \frac{y}{x} \tag{1.28}$$

or

$$\theta = \text{arc tan}\,\frac{y}{x}\cdot$$

From these, as well as from inspection of Fig. 1.5(*b*), it follows that

$$\frac{\partial r}{\partial x} = \cos\theta, \tag{1.29}$$

$$\frac{\partial r}{\partial y} = \sin\theta. \tag{1.30}$$

From Fig. 1.5(*c*) we note that, if x be given a positive increment Δx, the radial line OA turns clockwise, making $\Delta\theta$ negative. We further note that

$$\frac{r\,\Delta\theta}{\Delta x} = -\sin\theta,$$

whence

$$\frac{\partial\theta}{\partial x} = -\frac{\sin\theta}{r}. \tag{1.31}$$

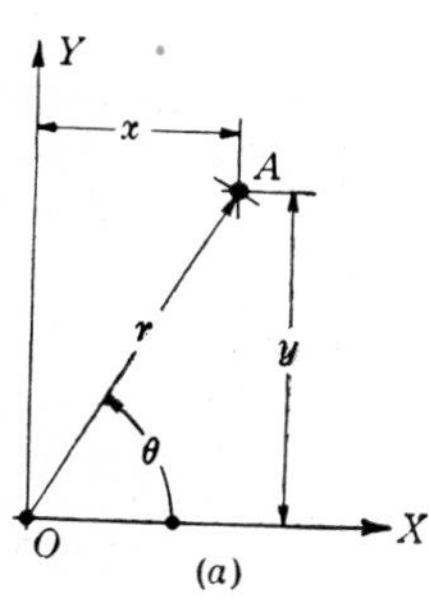

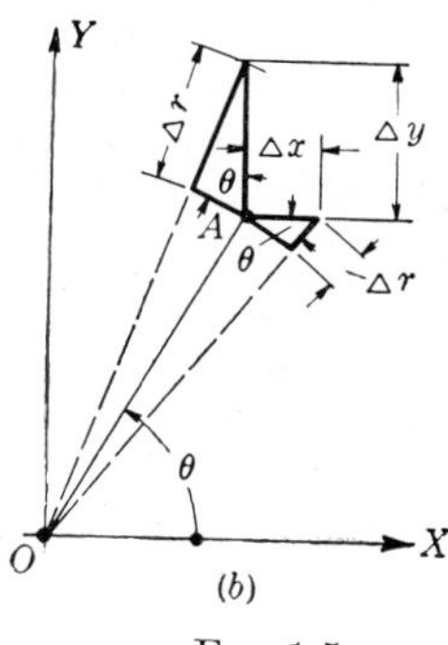

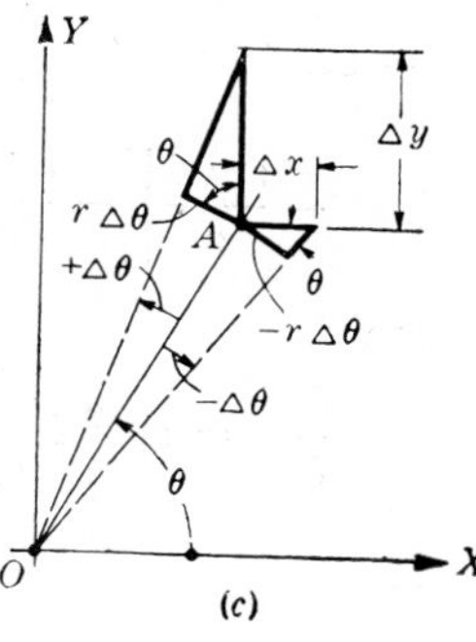

FIG. 1.5

Similarly, if y be given a positive increment Δy, the radial line turns counterclockwise, and $\Delta\theta$ is therefore positive, Fig. 1.5(c), and

$$\frac{r\,\Delta\theta}{\Delta y} = \cos\theta,$$

whence

$$\frac{\partial\theta}{\partial y} = \frac{\cos\theta}{r}. \tag{1.32}$$

These expressions also follow directly from eqs. (1.27) and (1.28) by differentiation.

Treating ϕ as a function of r and θ we recall that

$$\frac{\partial\phi}{\partial x} = \frac{\partial\phi}{\partial r}\frac{\partial r}{\partial x} + \frac{\partial\phi}{\partial\theta}\frac{\partial\theta}{\partial x}, \tag{1.33}$$

which in terms of the expressions obtained above becomes

$$\frac{\partial\phi}{\partial x} = \frac{\partial\phi}{\partial r}\cos\theta - \frac{\partial\phi}{\partial\theta}\frac{\sin\theta}{r} = \phi_1. \tag{1.34}$$

By analogy

$$\frac{\partial\phi_1}{\partial x} = \frac{\partial\phi_1}{\partial r}\cos\theta - \frac{\partial\phi_1}{\partial\theta}\frac{\sin\theta}{r}. \tag{1.35}$$

Remembering that r and θ are independent variables, i.e., $\partial\theta/\partial r = \partial r/\partial\theta = 0$, we have

$$\frac{\partial^2\phi}{\partial x^2} = \frac{\partial\phi_1}{\partial x} = \cos\theta\,\frac{\partial}{\partial r}\left(\frac{\partial\phi}{\partial r}\cos\theta - \frac{\partial\phi}{\partial\theta}\frac{\sin\theta}{r}\right) - \frac{\sin\theta}{r}\frac{\partial}{\partial\theta}\left(\frac{\partial\phi}{\partial r}\cos\theta - \frac{\partial\phi}{\partial\theta}\frac{\sin\theta}{r}\right)$$

$$= \cos\theta\left[\cos\theta\,\frac{\partial^2\phi}{\partial r^2} - \left(-\frac{\partial\phi}{\partial\theta}\frac{\sin\theta}{r^2} + \frac{\sin\theta}{r}\frac{\partial^2\phi}{\partial\theta\,\partial r}\right)\right] - \frac{\sin\theta}{r}\left[-\frac{\partial\phi}{\partial r}\sin\theta + \cos\theta\,\frac{\partial^2\phi}{\partial r\,\partial\theta} - \frac{1}{r}\left(\frac{\partial\phi}{\partial\theta}\cos\theta + \sin\theta\,\frac{\partial^2\phi}{\partial\theta^2}\right)\right].$$

Hence

$$\frac{\partial^2\phi}{\partial x^2} = \cos^2\theta\,\frac{\partial^2\phi}{\partial r^2} + 2\,\frac{\sin\theta\cos\theta}{r^2}\frac{\partial\phi}{\partial\theta} - 2\,\frac{\sin\theta\cos\theta}{r}\frac{\partial^2\phi}{\partial\theta\,\partial r} + \frac{\sin^2\theta}{r}\frac{\partial\phi}{\partial r} + \frac{\sin^2\theta}{r^2}\frac{\partial^2\phi}{\partial\theta^2}. \tag{1.36}$$

We next write

$$\frac{\partial\phi}{\partial y} = \frac{\partial\phi}{\partial r}\frac{\partial r}{\partial y} + \frac{\partial\phi}{\partial\theta}\frac{\partial\theta}{\partial y} \tag{1.37}$$

$$= \frac{\partial\phi}{\partial r}\sin\theta + \frac{\partial\phi}{\partial\theta}\frac{\cos\theta}{r} = \phi_2. \tag{1.38}$$

Therefore

$$\frac{\partial^2\phi}{\partial y^2} = \frac{\partial\phi_2}{\partial y} = \frac{\partial\phi_2}{\partial r}\sin\theta + \frac{\partial\phi_2}{\partial\theta}\frac{\cos\theta}{r}. \tag{1.39}$$

Differentiating and simplifying we obtain

$$\frac{\partial^2\phi}{\partial y^2} = \sin^2\theta\,\frac{\partial^2\phi}{\partial r^2} - 2\,\frac{\sin\theta\cos\theta}{r^2}\frac{\partial\phi}{\partial\theta} + 2\,\frac{\sin\theta\cos\theta}{r}\frac{\partial^2\phi}{\partial\theta\,\partial r} + \frac{\cos^2\theta}{r}\frac{\partial\phi}{\partial r} + \frac{\cos^2\theta}{r^2}\frac{\partial^2\phi}{\partial\theta^2}. \tag{1.40}$$

By addition of (1.36) and (1.40) we get

$$\frac{\partial^2\phi}{\partial x^2} + \frac{\partial^2\phi}{\partial y^2} = \frac{\partial^2\phi}{\partial r^2} + \frac{1}{r}\frac{\partial\phi}{\partial r} + \frac{1}{r^2}\frac{\partial^2\phi}{\partial\theta^2}. \tag{1.41}$$

Thus the compatibility equation may be written either as

$$\left(\frac{\partial^2}{\partial x^2} + \frac{\partial^2}{\partial y^2}\right)\left(\frac{\partial^2\phi}{\partial x^2} + \frac{\partial^2\phi}{\partial y^2}\right) = 0, \tag{1.25a}$$

or in terms of polar coordinates as

$$\left(\frac{\partial^2}{\partial r^2} + \frac{1}{r}\frac{\partial}{\partial r} + \frac{1}{r^2}\frac{\partial^2}{\partial \theta^2}\right)\left(\frac{\partial^2 \phi}{\partial r^2} + \frac{1}{r}\frac{\partial \phi}{\partial r} + \frac{1}{r^2}\frac{\partial^2 \phi}{\partial \theta^2}\right) = 0, \qquad (1.42a)$$

which can also be written as

$$\frac{\partial^2 \phi_1}{\partial r^2} + \frac{1}{r}\frac{\partial \phi_1}{\partial r} + \frac{1}{r^2}\frac{\partial^2 \phi_1}{\partial \theta^2} = 0, \qquad (1.42b)$$

where

$$\phi_1 = \frac{\partial^2 \phi}{\partial r^2} + \frac{1}{r}\frac{\partial \phi}{\partial r} + \frac{1}{r^2}\frac{\partial^2 \phi}{\partial \theta^2}. \qquad (1.42c)$$

§1.9 **The State of Stress in a Bar of Finite Thickness.** Thus far we have considered the two ideal states of plane stress and plane strain, which can be well approximated in practice in very thin, long bars subjected to axial loads, and in infinitely long cylinders under uniform transverse pressures along the axis, respectively.

It is of some interest also to consider a bar of finite thickness, say t, subjected to axial tensile loads P, Fig. 1.6(a). The bisecting planes A–A and B–B are inherently planes of symmetry which remain planes and undergo no lateral deformation even when the bar contains a discontinuity, such as a central hole or slot. The total lateral deformation, δ, in the thickness t, may be viewed as the sum of the accumulated or integrated deformations which start at the plane A–A and gradually build up to a value of $\delta/2$ for each half of the bar.

Photoelastic experiments[1] with thin slotted plates, Fig. 1.6(a), 3 in. by 0.1 in. in cross section, subjected to pure tension in the region surrounding the slot failed to reveal the presence of a transverse stress, σ_z, i.e., a state of plane stress is approximated in such plates even at the roots of the slot. Here then the deformation is given by the familiar expression

$$\delta = \frac{-\nu t(\sigma_x + \sigma_y)}{E} = -\frac{\nu t(p + q)}{E}, \qquad [1.37(c), \text{Vol. I}]$$

the graph of which is clearly a straight line, Fig. 1.6(b).

However, in thick bars with small[2] discontinuities the state of stress

[1] The photoelastic results quoted in this section are from an investigation made by the author for the David Taylor Model Basin of the U. S. Navy. The author is indebted to Dr. D. F. Windenburg, chief physicist for the Basin, who secured permission to publish the findings.

[2] The state of stress in a thick plate is no doubt a function of the ratio of the critical dimension of the discontinuity (the radii of curvature) to the thickness of the plate. When these critical dimensions are larger in comparison with the thickness the three-dimensional effects no doubt diminish.

near the discontinuity is in general three-dimensional. Experiments show that in such plates:

1. The stresses σ_x and σ_y, in the plane of the plate, are essentially the same as in similar thin plates. They have the same distribution, essentially the same magnitudes, and are substantially constant across the thickness.

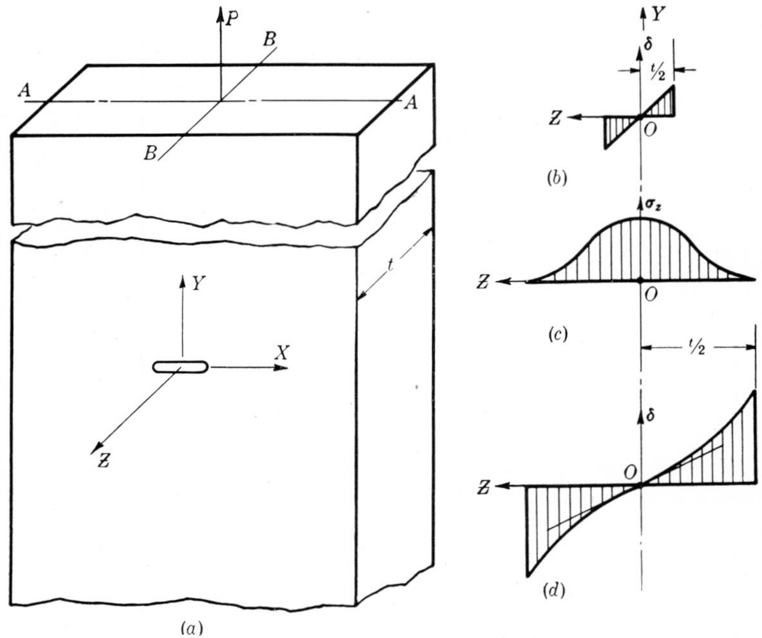

Fig. 1.6 Sketches Showing Variation in the Transverse Displacements and Stresses in Thick Slotted Plates.

2. A transverse stress is developed which follows a curve of the type shown in Fig. 1.6(*c*).

3. The sign of the transverse stress σ_z is the same as the sign of the main longitudinal stress σ_y.

From the general Hooke's Law we then have

$$\delta = \frac{-\nu t(\sigma_x + \sigma_y)}{E} + \frac{2}{E}\int_0^{t/2} \sigma_z \, dz$$

$$= \frac{-\nu t(\sigma_x + \sigma_y)}{E} + \frac{(\sigma_z)_{\text{ave.}} t}{E}. \tag{1.43}$$

Eq. (1.43) shows that the effect of σ_z is to reduce the lateral deformation. Since σ_z is a maximum at the center of the plate it follows that the central core of the plate contributes least to this deformation, which is in the main due to the external layers of the bar. The graph of δ is therefore as shown in Fig. 1.6(*d*). The slopes of this curve represent the lateral strains ϵ_z.

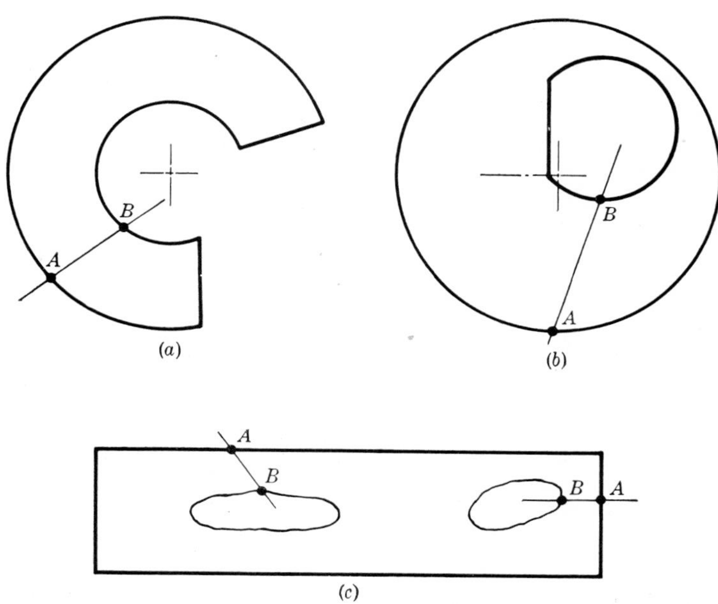

FIG. 1.7 (*a*) Simply Connected Body; (*b*) and (*c*) Multiply Connected Bodies. In (*a*), line *AB* divides the body into two distinct and separate parts. In (*b*) and (*c*) the bodies remain unseparated by sections *AB*.

The existence of the transverse stresses in thick plates has an important bearing on the methods which employ lateral extensometers for the determination of the sum of the principal stresses at a point. See §7.7.

§1.10 Simply and Multiply Connected Bodies. If a plate has no hole it is said to be *simply connected*; if it is perforated by holes it is *multiply connected*. A simply connected body is said to have one boundary; a multiply connected body has more than one boundary. Fig. 1.7 shows examples of simply and multiply connected bodies. In a simply connected body every closed curve can be shrunk down to a point. This is not true in a multiply connected body. In a simply connected body a section passing through any two points on the boundary cuts the body into two separate pieces. Inspection of Fig. 1.7 shows that such is not the case in a multiply connected body.

§1.11 The Mathematical Conditions for an Exact Solution in Two-Dimensional Elasticity. *We can now formulate the mathematical conditions which an exact solution of two-dimensional stress problems must fulfill. The stresses must first obey the laws of statics, i.e., the differential equations of equilibrium,* (*2.5*), (*2.6*), (*2.9*), *and* (*2.10*), *Vol. I. They must also satisfy the compatibility or continuity requirements given by eqs.* (*1.25*) *or* (*1.42*). *Lastly, the stresses, which necessarily have to be single valued, must agree with the boundary conditions expressed by eqs.* (*1.21*).

The mathematical procedure in the solution of a stress problem thus consists of assuming, or finding, a function ϕ *which satisfies the requirements of compatibility, and to form from it the stress components by means of eqs.* (*1.23*) *or* (*1.24*), *which inherently satisfy the conditions of equilibrium. When the stresses so obtained also meet the boundary conditions we have obtained the required solution.*[1]

Inspection shows that the only physical constant which enters into these equations is Poisson's ratio ν, and that it appears only in the compatibility equation. Further, even this constant vanishes for constant body forces. This leads us to an observation about stress distributions which is of fundamental importance in photoelasticity. *We conclude that, neglecting body forces, and assuming all boundary forces to be given, the stress distribution in two-dimensional problems is independent of the material.* The equations cited above constitute the theoretical justification for the employment of transparent plastic or glass models for the study of stresses in structural materials. This conclusion is valid for simply connected bodies in which the boundary conditions are expressed in terms of stresses. In such cases single-valued stresses of necessity produce single-valued strains and displacements. It can be shown, however, that *in multiply connected bodies the possibility exists that the strains may be many valued even when the stresses are single valued; see §5.2. In such problems, not only must the mathematical solution satisfy the conditions stated in this article, but in addition the expressions for the displacements must be examined to see that they are single valued. The stresses in multiply connected bodies, in contrast to those in simply connected bodies, may be functions of the physical constants of the material, although the numerical*

[1] For a proof that this solution is unique see *Theory of Elasticity* by S. Timoshenko, §64, McGraw-Hill Book Co.

effect of these constants is, from a practical point of view, negligible. An understanding of the influence of the material on the stress distribution is of such vital importance in the optical method of stress analysis that further, and more direct, evidence substantiating the above conclusion will be presented in Chapter 6.

PART II ELEMENTARY RECTANGULAR STRESS FUNCTIONS

Saint Venant's Principle

§1.12 Stress Function for Pure Tension. Consider a prismatic bar subjected to a uniform tensile stress p, acting on the vertical planes

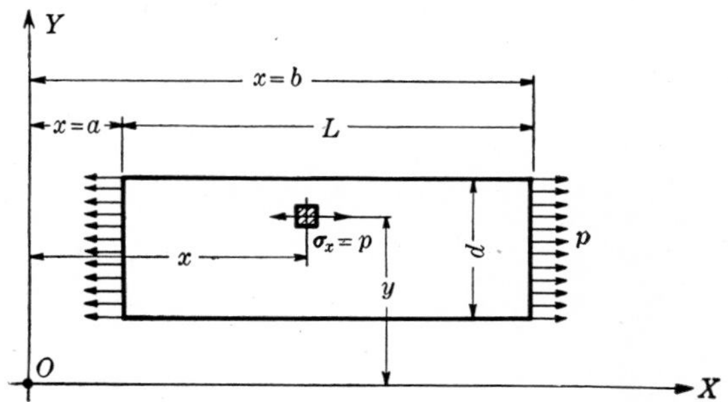

FIG. 1.8 Prismatic Bar in Pure Tension.

$x = a$ and $x = b$, Fig. 1.8. We wish to find the rectangular stress system at any point within the bar.

We assume the function

$$\phi(x, y) = \frac{C}{2} y^2, \tag{1.44}$$

and observe that it satisfies the compatibility equation (1.26). Thus

$$\frac{\partial^4 \phi}{\partial x^4} = 0, \quad \frac{\partial^4 \phi}{\partial y^4} = 0, \quad \frac{\partial^4 \phi}{\partial x^2 \, \partial y^2} = 0.$$

Hence

$$\nabla^4 \phi = 0. \tag{1.26}$$

In general, any integral power function of x and y not higher than the third degree will always satisfy the condition of compatibility.

We next form the stress components σ_x, σ_y, and τ_{xy} in accordance with eqs. (1.23) on the assumption of no body forces. Thus

$$\sigma_x = \frac{\partial^2 \phi}{\partial y^2} = C,$$

$$\sigma_y = \frac{\partial^2 \phi}{\partial x^2} = 0,$$

$$\tau_{xy} = -\frac{\partial^2 \phi}{\partial x\, \partial y} = 0.$$

(*a*)

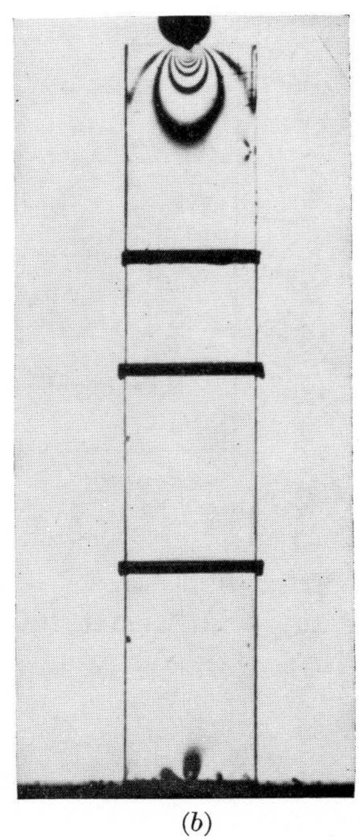

(*b*)

FIG. 1.9 Stress Patterns of Four Struts Separated by Cardboard Gaskets in Compression.

The stress patterns show that uniformly applied loads are transmitted as uniform stresses even in extremely short blocks. (*a*) Load, $P = 50.5$ lb. (*b*) $P = 36.1$ lb.; thickness, $t = 0.266$ in.; model fringe value, $F = 162$ psi. shear; width $= 0.401$ in.; length of blocks from top to bottom $= 0.641$ in., 0.320 in., 0.587 in., and 0.641 in.

Hence, if we put C equal to the applied tension p the boundary conditions become satisfied. We thus see that uniform tension applied to the boundary is transmitted without change through a rectangular bar,

Fig. 1.8. The same conclusion evidently holds for compression. The resulting stress system is

$$\left.\begin{aligned} \sigma_x &= p, & (a)\\ \sigma_y &= 0, & (b)\\ \tau_{xy} &= 0. & (c) \end{aligned}\right\} \quad (1.45)$$

The conclusion regarding the state of stress produced by pure tensile or compressive forces acting on a prismatic bar is clearly corroborated by the photoelastic stress patterns shown in Fig. 1.9. It is seen that ***even in very short blocks the state of stress produced by uniformly distributed loads is one of pure compression.***

§1.13 Stress Function for Pure Bending. Consider next a prismatic bar, Fig. 1.10, bent only by two couples M formed by longitudinal boundary stresses $\sigma_x = ky$, in which k is a constant and y is the distance from the axis of the bar to the stressed point. The state of stress produced by a constant bending moment is generally defined as pure bending.

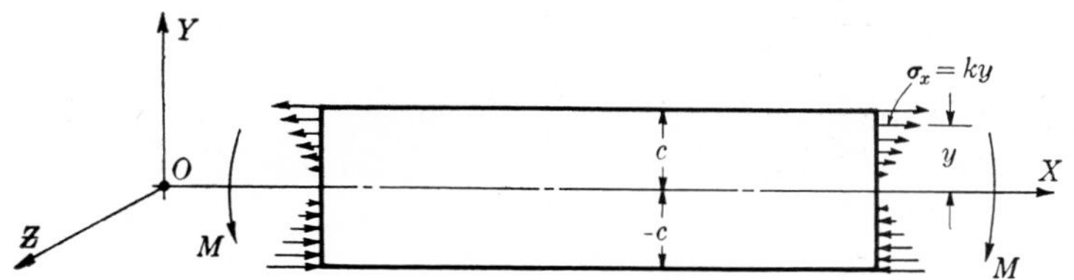

FIG. 1.10 Prismatic Bar in Pure Bending.

In order to find the true state of stress in this bar, we choose

$$\phi(x, y) = \frac{C}{6} y^3. \quad (1.46)$$

It can be easily verified that the function $\phi(x, y)$ satisfies the compatibility equation $\nabla^4\phi = 0$. We now form the Airy stress components

$$\sigma_x = \frac{\partial^2\phi}{\partial y^2} = Cy,$$

$$\sigma_y = \frac{\partial^2\phi}{\partial x^2} = 0,$$

$$\tau_{xy} = -\frac{\partial^2\phi}{\partial x\,\partial y} = 0.$$

In order to satisfy the boundary conditions, we put $C = k$, so that

$$\left.\begin{aligned} \sigma_x &= ky, & (a)\\ \sigma_y &= 0, & (b)\\ \tau_{xy} &= 0. & (c) \end{aligned}\right\} \quad (1.47)$$

Since the stresses do not depend upon x it means that all transverse sections are subjected to identical systems of stresses. The solution further shows that these stresses follow exactly the same linear distribution as the applied forces. They are positive or tensile in the upper fibers where y is positive and negative or compressive in the lower fibers where y is negative. In every transverse section the points on the line through the centroid parallel to the Z axis are free from stresses, and these points form the neutral axis. ***As in pure tension, the applied boundary tractions are here also transmitted without change.***

In order to identify this solution with that from the elementary beam theory, we take moments about the neutral axis. The bending moment is then given by

$$M = \int_{-c}^{c} y\sigma_x \, dA = k \int_{-c}^{c} y^2 \, dA = kI,$$

in which I is the moment of inertia of the area of a transverse section about the neutral axis. The constant k is then given by

$$k = \frac{M}{I},$$

and therefore

$$\sigma_x = ky = \frac{My}{I},$$

which is the well-known flexure formula derived in first courses of strength of materials. It follows that, ***for beams of uniform cross section in pure bending, the solution from the elementary beam theory agrees with that of the mathematical theory of elasticity.*** It will be shown later that, in beams subjected also to shear, the stresses may differ radically from those given by the elementary theory. Moreover, even in pure bending, the longitudinal stresses do not follow a linear law unless the beam is of uniform cross section. When a beam has discontinuities such as fillets, grooves, or holes, there are pronounced deviations from this linear law which are characterized by high local stresses, known as stress concentrations. (See example 8.4, Vol. I.)

§1.14 Stress Function for Pure Shear. We next consider the problem of pure shear, Fig. 1.11. Letting

$$\phi(x, y) = -Cxy, \tag{1.48}$$

we find that the compatibility equation is satisfied. The Airy stress components are

$$\left.\begin{aligned}\sigma_x &= \frac{\partial^2 \phi}{\partial y^2} = 0, &\quad (a)\\ \sigma_y &= \frac{\partial^2 \phi}{\partial x^2} = 0, &\quad (b)\\ \tau_{xy} &= -\frac{\partial^2 \phi}{\partial x\, \partial y} = C. &\quad (c)\end{aligned}\right\} \quad (1.49)$$

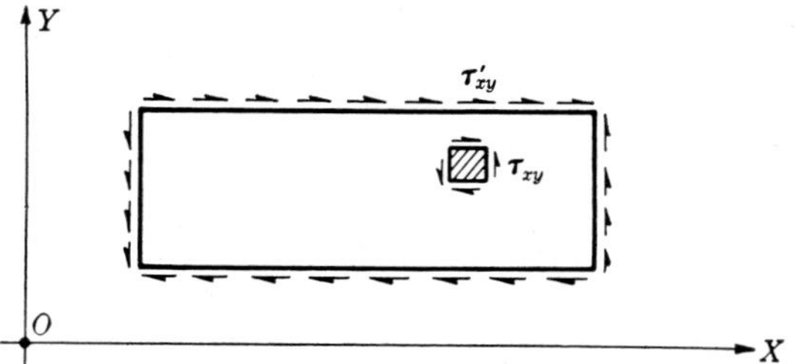

FIG. 1.11 Bar in Pure Shear.

Choosing $C = \tau_{xy}'$, the value of the applied shear stress on the boundary, we satisfy all the requirements for the exact solution of the problem. ***As in pure tension, and pure bending, we see that also in pure shear the applied stresses are transmitted without change.*** Every rectangular element within the body is subjected to the same shear stresses as the boundaries. This conclusion has been verified experimentally by Tuzi.[1,2]

§1.15 Equivalent Systems. ***Two systems of forces are said to be statically equivalent if their resultants are equal. In coplanar systems this means that ΣX, ΣY, and ΣM must be the same for both systems.***

[1] See "The Effect of a Circular Hole in the Uniform Shear Field and the Stresses of Stiff Frames," by Ziro Tuzi, Institute of Physical and Chemical Researches, Tokyo, Japan, 1930, or *Proc. of International Congress for Metallic Structures*, Liége, September, 1930.

[2] See also "Stress Distribution around a Circular Discontinuity in any Two-Dimensional System of Combined Stress," by A. J. Durelli and W. M. Murray, *Proc. of the Fourteenth Semi-Annual Eastern Photoelasticity Conference*, Yale University, December, 1941.

Consider, for example, the three sets of forces shown in Fig. 1.12. In (*a*) the force is assumed to be concentrated and to have a value P. In (*b*) the forces are compressive and uniformly distributed over a semicircular groove of diameter d and thickness t and have an intensity P/td. In (*c*) the compressive forces are also distributed over a semicircular groove, but they vary in accordance with the expression

$$\sigma_r = \frac{4P \cos \theta}{\pi t d},$$

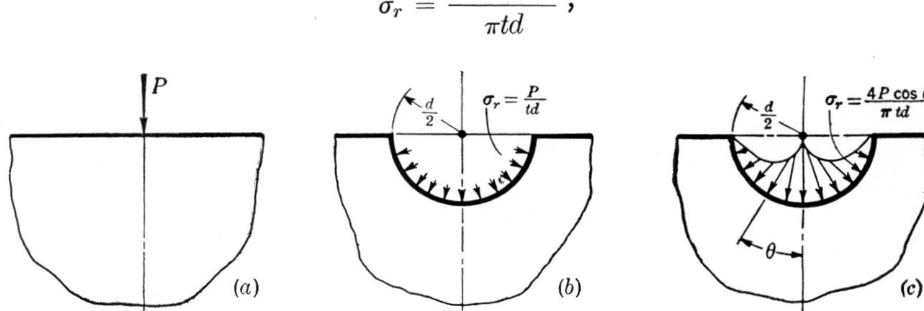

FIG. 1.12 Three Statically Equivalent Systems.

in which θ is as shown. In spite of the differences in the distribution, ***the three systems are statically equivalent because their resultants are equal.*** It is left to the reader to show that this is true.

§1.16 Saint Venant's Principle. ***Saint Venant's principle states that, if the forces acting on a small area be replaced by a statically equivalent system on the same area, the new system will only produce changes in the immediate vicinity of the applied loads, but that it will not affect the stresses at distances which are large compared with the linear dimensions of the area on which the boundary forces act.*** This principle rests in the main on general plausibility and experimental verification, although it has been pointed out that it follows from the broader principle of conservation of energy.[1]

An experimental illustration and corroboration is furnished by the disk of Fig. 1.13, in which the load at the top is applied through a cylindrical pin and the support is provided by a flat bar. The distribution of the forces at the top is therefore different from that at the bottom. The resultant forces are, however, clearly equal so that, except for direction, the downward and upward forces are statically equivalent.

Inspection of the magnified portion of the stress patterns, Fig. 1.14, shows that in the immediate vicinity of the loads there are several differ-

[1] See J. N. Goodier, *Phil. Mag.*, series 7, Vol. xxiii, p. 607, 1937; also Vol. 24, p. 325, 1937.

(a)

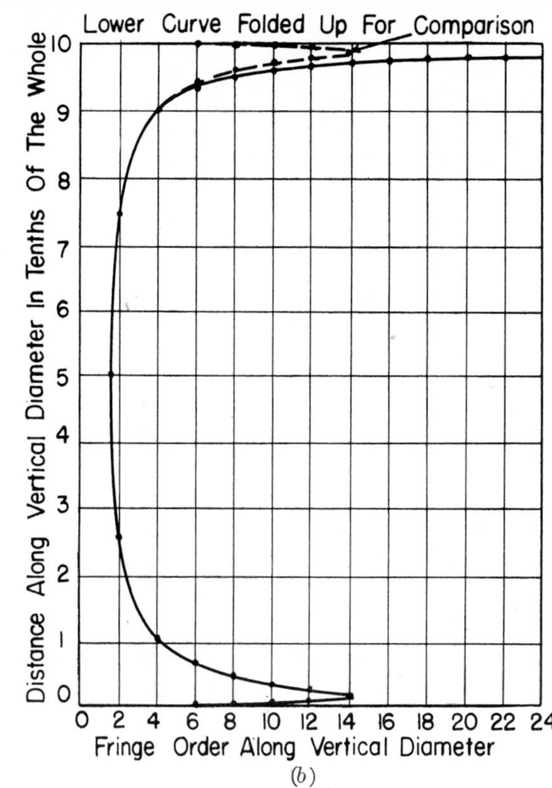

(b)

FIG. 1.13 Illustration of Saint Venant's Principle.

(a) Stress pattern of a disk resting on a flat bar and compressed by means of a pin at the top. (b) Curve showing effect of loading conditions on stress distribution. Diameter of disk = 2.00 in.; thickness = 0.200 in.; load = 99 lb.; material fringe value = 43 psi. shear stress.

ences in the stress distribution. At the pin there is a pronounced concentrated plastic zone, while at the flat support this zone is much smaller and diffused. The shapes of the fringes are also different. At the pin the fringes are circular and merge with the plastic zone, whereas at the base the fringes are more nearly horizontal ovals. Lastly, at the top the maximum fringe order is right at the pin, whereas at the bottom it is in the center of the oval, which is at some distance above the line of contact with the bar.

It is to be observed, however, that these differences in the stress distribution are confined to a very small region close to the loads and that they rapidly die away. Thus, at points A and B distant $0.1D$ from the loads the stresses are the same. Except for small regions near the loads the stress distribution in the upper half is the same as in the lower half, as can be seen from the curves of Figs. 1.13 and 1.14. It is also to be noted that the restriction on the absolute equality of the areas on which the forces act is not altogether necessary. The result is nearly the same even if the areas are somewhat different, which is obviously the case in the disk under consideration.

It should, however, be added that, when the differences in the areas on which the loads act are pronounced, the regions in which the stresses are disturbed are markedly increased. Thus, when a bar is compressed by means of concentrated axial loads instead of uniformly distributed loads, the ratio of the length of the bar to the width must be at least 2.5 before a state of uniform compression is developed, Fig. 1.15; whereas for uniformly distributed loads the bar may be extremely short, Fig. 1.9.

The solution obtained in §1.13 for a beam bent by linearly distributed forces may be extended by Saint Venant's principle to any kind of pure bending, regardless of the manner in which the bending moment is applied. From the stress pattern in Fig. 1.16 it is seen that even when the couples are formed by concentrated vertical loads the stresses become linear at sections fairly close to the inner pin. The validity of this principle in pure bending has also been investigated theoretically. Thus, Goodier[1] analyzed the stress distribution in short beams bent by forces on the ends of an intensity proportional to the cube of the distance from the neutral axis and found that linear distributions are probably attained at distances from the ends equal to half the depth of the beam. This conclusion evidently agrees with the photoelastic results from Fig. 1.16.

[1] See "Compression of Rectangular Blocks and the Bending of Beams by Non-Linear Distributions of Bending Forces" by J. N. Goodier, *Trans. A.S.M.E.*, December, 1931.

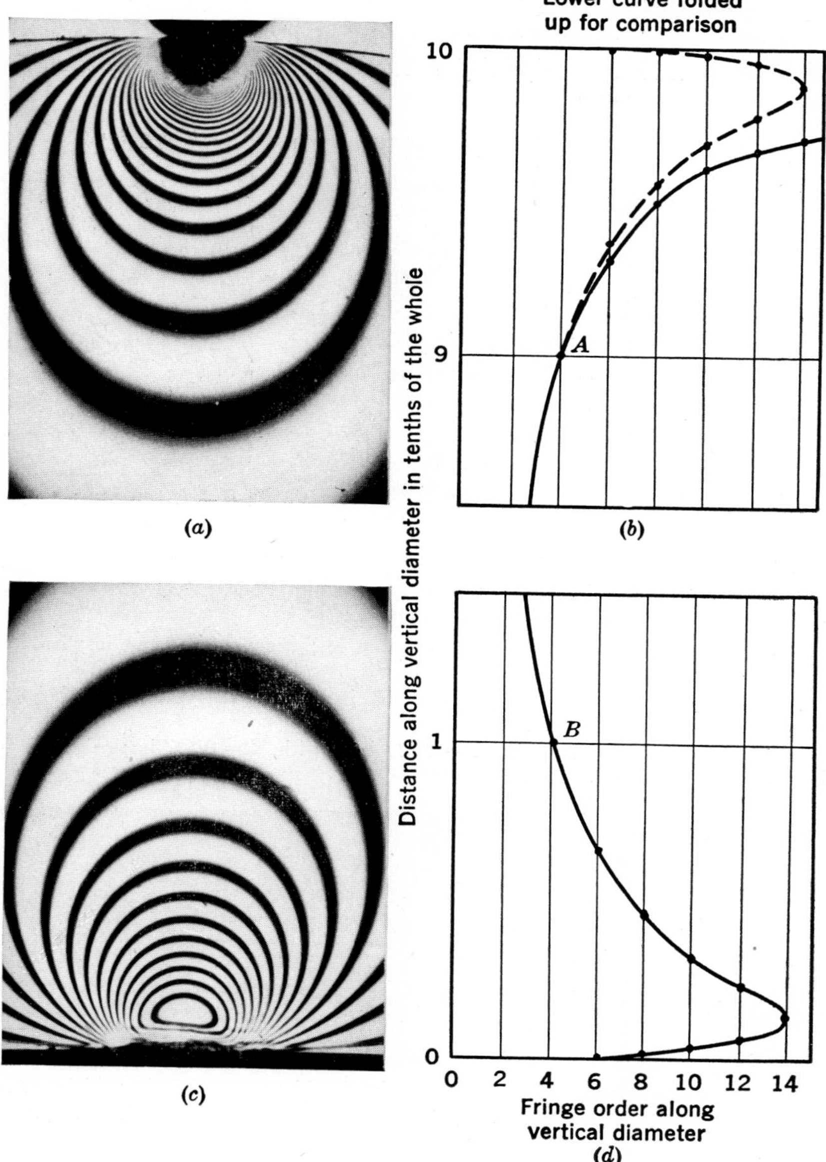

FIG. 1.14 Stress Patterns and Curves Illustrating Saint Venant's Principle. Dimensions and loads are the same as in Fig. 1.13. Region near pin and flat surface enlarged for better comparison of stress distribution. It is seen that at points distant $D/10$ from the load the stresses become identical.

There are variations in the statements of Saint Venant's principle. One statement is as follows: ***the stresses that are produced in a body by the application to a small part of its surface of a system of forces stati-***

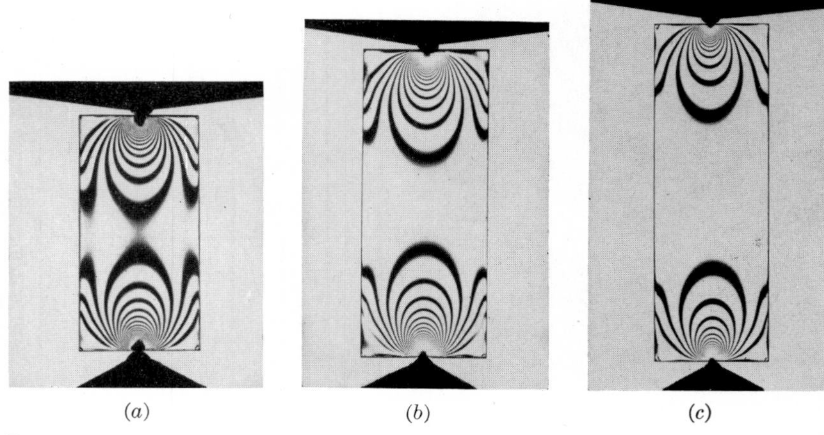

(a) (b) (c)

FIG. 1.15 Stress Patterns of Short Struts Compressed by Means of Concentrated Loads, Showing that Pure or Uniform Compression is Not Developed unless the Ratio of Height to Width is at Least about 2.5.

(a) Load, $P = 112.2$ lb.; thickness $= 0.253$ in.; width, $d = 0.459$ in.; height, $h = 0.919$ in.; ratio $h/d = 2$.

(b) Load, $P = 133$ lb.; thickness $= 0.253$ in.; width, $d = 0.522$ in.; height, $h = 1.298$ in.; ratio $h/d = 2.5$.

(c) Load, $P = 98.9$ lb.; thickness $= 0.253$ in.; width, $d = 0.567$ in.; height, $h = 1.699$ in.; ratio $h/d = 3$.

FIG. 1.16 Stress Pattern of a Straight Beam Subjected to Pure Bending.

Applied bending moment $= 50.0$ lb.-in.; depth of beam $= 0.763$ in.; thickness $= 0.250$ in.; distance between downward loads $= 3.00$ in.; distance between upward reactions $= 4.00$ in. Loads were applied by means of pins.

cally equivalent to zero force and zero couple are of negligible magnitude at distances which are large compared with the linear dimensions of the area on which the forces are acting. This statement is upon reflection seen to be equivalent to the statement given in the beginning of this article.

Saint Venant's principle is of great value both in the mathematical theory of elasticity and in photoelasticity. In elasticity it enables us to extend the theoretical solution obtained for idealized boundary forces to more realistically applied statically equivalent systems. In photoelasticity, and for that matter in other experimental methods of stress analysis, it provides a method to produce certain desired states of stress by means of simplified boundary stresses.

CHAPTER 2

RADIAL STRESSES IN THE SEMI-INFINITE PLATE

§2.1 Radial Stresses. Notation. When a concentrated load acts on the straight edge of a semi-infinite plate[1] the stress distribution is purely

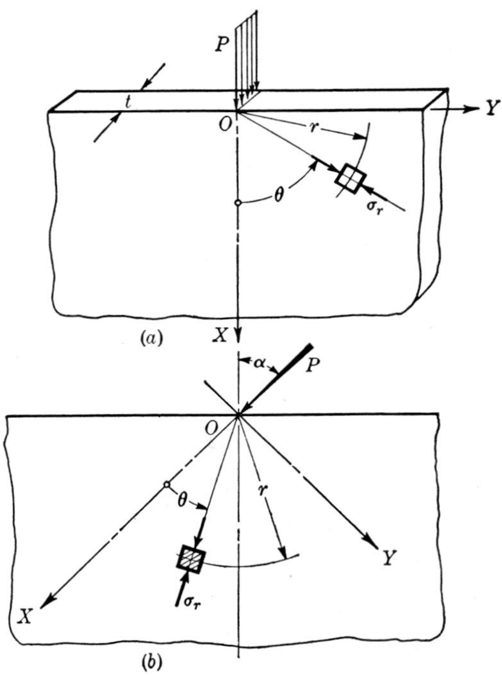

Fig. 2.1 Sketches Showing Concentrated Loads on a Semi-Infinite Plate and the Resulting Radial Stresses.

radial, Fig. 2.1. One of the principal stresses vanishes, and the other, which may be a tension or compression, acts along the radial line r connecting the stressed point with the point of application of the load.

[1] A semi-infinite plate will be defined as any portion of an infinite plate separated from it by a transverse plane section, Fig. 2.1(*a*).

The general expression for these stresses is

$$\sigma_r = \frac{A \cos \theta}{r}, \tag{2.1}$$

in which θ and r are polar coordinates, and A is a constant.

Throughout this chapter we have consistently followed the simple rule of placing the origin of the coordinate system at the point of application of the load and choosing the direction of the X axis parallel to that of the load. The positive branch of this axis is taken into the body of the plate and the positive branch of the Y axis 90° counterclockwise from it, Fig. 2.1. The angle θ is a directed angle and is always measured from the positive branch of the X axis to the radius vector r connecting the stressed point with the origin. The usual convention of treating the angle as positive when it is counterclockwise is followed. The sign of a concentrated force will be taken as positive if its direction is the same as that of the positive branch of the X axis, so that a normal force, for example, which produces compressive stresses will be called positive, Fig. 2.1. In this chapter only positive concentrated loads are treated, although the results are equally applicable to negative forces.

When boundary forces are distributed they are generally specified by their intensities, that is, by the load per unit area of external surface or per unit length. The intensities of external boundary loading, therefore, have all the characteristics of internal stresses and must coincide in magnitude and direction with these stresses as the latter approach the boundary. It would, therefore, seem convenient and proper to speak of intensities of distributed loads as external or boundary stresses. A more conventional terminology, however, is *traction, or intensity of boundary loading.*

Since it is generally agreed to treat compressive stresses as negative and tensions as positive not only in the interior of a body but also at the boundaries, it follows that the sign of a system of distributed boundary forces or tractions is opposite to the sign of their resultant. For example, in Fig. 2.2 the boundary forces on the semicircular groove are negative because they are compressive, but their resultant will be treated as a positive quantity because its direction is the same as that of the positive branch of the X axis.

A state of radial stress exists also in wedges when the loads act at the apexes. Those problems will be treated in the next chapter. Here we will discuss only the basic cases arising in connection with the semi-infinite plate, and we will treat these both theoretically and photoelastically.

§2.2 Stresses Produced by a Concentrated Load Acting on Edge of a Semi-Infinite Plate. Flamant's Solution.[1] Fig. 2.2 shows a portion of a semi-infinite plate of uniform thickness t, on the straight boundary of which there is a small semicircular groove of radius r_o. We assume that the straight portion of the plate is free, and that external forces act only on the semicircular groove. We further assume that the forces on the groove are compressive, and that their distribution is given by

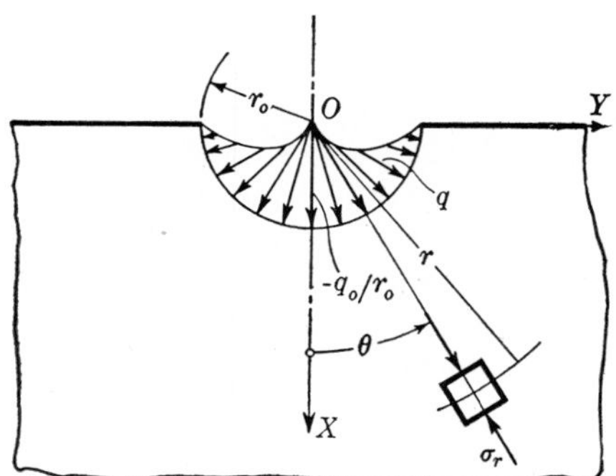

FIG. 2.2 Sketch Showing Boundary Forces on a Semicircular Groove of a Semi-Infinite Plate Distributed According to Eq. (2.2).

These boundary forces are statically equivalent to a normal concentrated load.

$$q = -q_o \frac{\cos\theta}{r_o} \qquad (2.2)$$

in which $(-q_o/r_o)$ is the pressure at the center, and θ is measured from the X axis, which is normal to the straight edge.

In order to find the exact state of stress in this plate we choose a function

$$\boldsymbol{\phi = Cr\theta \sin \theta,} \qquad (2.3)$$

in which C is a constant. This function satisfies the compatibility equation.

$$\left.\begin{aligned} &\frac{\partial^2\phi_1}{\partial r^2} + \frac{1}{r}\frac{\partial\phi_1}{\partial r} + \frac{1}{r^2}\frac{\partial^2\phi_1}{\partial\theta^2} = 0, && (b) \\ &\text{in which} \\ &\phi_1 = \frac{\partial^2\phi}{\partial r^2} + \frac{1}{r}\frac{\partial\phi}{\partial r} + \frac{1}{r^2}\frac{\partial^2\phi}{\partial\theta^2}. && (c) \end{aligned}\right\} (1.42)$$

Differentiating eq. (2.3) we have

$$\frac{\partial^2\phi}{\partial r^2} = 0,$$

$$\frac{1}{r}\frac{\partial\phi}{\partial r} = \frac{C\theta\sin\theta}{r},$$

[1] This solution was found by Flamant from the more general solution obtained by J. Boussinesq for the case of a concentrated load acting on the boundary of a semi-infinite body. See *Compt. rend.*, Vol. 114, p. 1465, 1892, Paris.

and

$$\frac{1}{r^2}\frac{\partial^2 \phi}{\partial \theta^2} = \frac{C}{r}(2 \cos \theta - \theta \sin \theta).$$

Hence

$$\phi_1 = \frac{2C \cos \theta}{r}. \tag{2.4}$$

Again by differentiation,

$$\frac{\partial^2 \phi_1}{\partial r^2} = \frac{4C \cos \theta}{r^3},$$

$$\frac{1}{r}\frac{\partial \phi_1}{\partial r} = -\frac{2C \cos \theta}{r^3},$$

$$\frac{1}{r^2}\frac{\partial^2 \phi_1}{\partial \theta^2} = -\frac{2C \cos \theta}{r^3}.$$

Substituting in eq. (1.42*b*) we find that the compatibility equation is satisfied.

The stress components are given by eqs. (1.24)

$$\left.\begin{aligned} \sigma_r &= \frac{1}{r}\frac{\partial \phi}{\partial r} + \frac{1}{r^2}\frac{\partial^2 \phi}{\partial \theta^2}, && (a) \\ \sigma_\theta &= \frac{\partial^2 \phi}{\partial r^2}, && (b) \\ \tau_{r\theta} &= -\frac{\partial}{\partial r}\left(\frac{1}{r}\frac{\partial \phi}{\partial \theta}\right), && (c) \end{aligned}\right\} \tag{1.24}$$

which yield the following expressions:

$$\left.\begin{aligned} \sigma_r &= \frac{2C \cos \theta}{r}, && (a) \\ \sigma_\theta &= 0, && (b) \\ \tau_{r\theta} &= 0. && (c) \end{aligned}\right\} \tag{2.5}$$

Each element is thus seen to be in a state of pure radial compression as shown in Fig. 2.2.

Next, we examine the boundary conditions. We consider first the straight edge of the semi-infinite plate. This edge is by assumption free from external loads. This necessitates that the normal stress σ_θ and the shear stress $\tau_{r\theta}$ vanish, for $\theta = \pm\pi/2$. Since σ_θ and $\tau_{r\theta}$ are zero everywhere, eqs. (2.5*b* and *c*), it follows that the boundary conditions on the straight edge are completely satisfied.

The boundary forces on the portions of the plate which are at infinity are by assumption approaching zero, and the same is true of the radial stresses σ_r, since

$$\operatorname*{Limit}_{r\to\infty} \frac{2C \cos\theta}{r} = 0.$$

Lastly, we consider the semicircular groove. The compressive radial forces on this groove have been assumed to be distributed in accordance with the expression

$$q = -q_o \frac{\cos\theta}{r_o}, \tag{2.2}$$

and to be free from shears. Since the radial stresses are given by eq. (2.5*a*) it follows that by making $2C$ equal to $(-q_o)$ the radial stresses become equal to the applied forces, and the boundary conditions are everywhere satisfied. Consequently, ***the stresses given by eqs.*** (*2.5*), ***which were obtained from the stress function***

$$\boldsymbol{\phi = Cr\theta \sin\theta}, \tag{2.3}$$

provide an exact solution for the grooved semi-infinite plate shown in Fig. 2.2.

Now, by Saint Venant's principle, the same system of stresses would be produced at all points in the body, except those in the immediate vicinity of the groove, by a statically equivalent system acting on the same area. In order to obtain the statical equivalent of the applied forces, we form ΣX and ΣY for the forces on the groove. The horizontal components ΣY obviously vanish. Hence, the resultant is furnished by ΣX. The statical equivalent of the boundary forces is therefore a concentrated load acting normally to the straight edge of the boundary, and passing through the origin O.

The stresses given by eqs. (*2.5*), ***and derived from the stress function*** (*2.3*), ***may thus be looked upon as representing the state of stress produced by a concentrated load acting normally to the straight edge of the semi-infinite plate.*** This state of stress is one of pure radial compression and is inversely proportional to r, i.e., it varies from infinity to zero as r goes from zero to infinity. Along any semicircle of radius r with center at the point of application of the load the stresses follow a cosine distribution, Fig. 2.3. It follows that, in the immediate vicinity of a concentrated load, there must be a region, however small, in which the stresses exceed the yield point. It will later be shown that experiments substantiate this conclusion. See Fig. 2.11.

We now proceed to evaluate the constant C, which appears in eq. (2.5), in terms of the applied load P. To this end we consider a semicircular

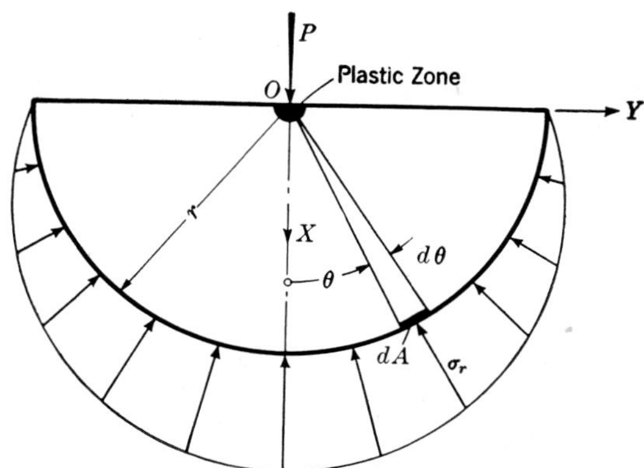

FIG. 2.3 Sketch Showing the Radial Pressure Distribution Produced by a Concentrated Load.

section of arbitrary radius r and sum all the forces in the X direction, Fig. 2.3. Denoting the thickness of the plate by t we have

$$P - 2\int_0^{\pi/2} \cos\theta\, \sigma_r\, dA = 0,$$

$$P = 2\int_0^{\pi/2} \cos\theta\, \sigma_r tr\, d\theta$$

$$= 4Ct\int_0^{\pi/2} \cos^2\theta\, d\theta$$

$$= Ct\pi, \tag{2.6}$$

whence

$$C = \frac{P}{\pi t}. \tag{2.7}$$

Substituting this expression for C in eqs. (2.5) we obtain

$$\left.\begin{aligned} \sigma_r &= -\frac{2P}{\pi t}\frac{\cos\theta}{r}, & (a)\\ \sigma_\theta &= 0, & (b)\\ \tau_{r\theta} &= 0, & (c) \end{aligned}\right\}(2.8)$$

the minus sign indicating compression, which will always be produced by a normal load P directed toward the edge of the plate. ***These are the final expressions for the stresses produced by a concentrated load P acting normally to the straight edge of a semi-infinite plate of thickness t.***[1] It may be argued that the concentrated load P is also the statical

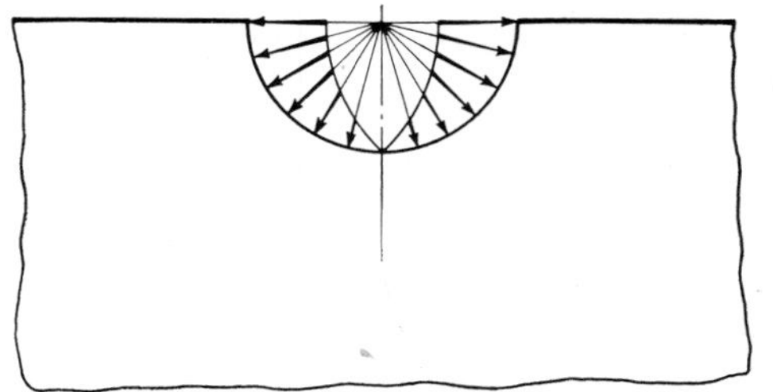

FIG. 2.4 Another System of Boundary Forces on a Semicircular Groove Which is also Equivalent to a Concentrated Load.

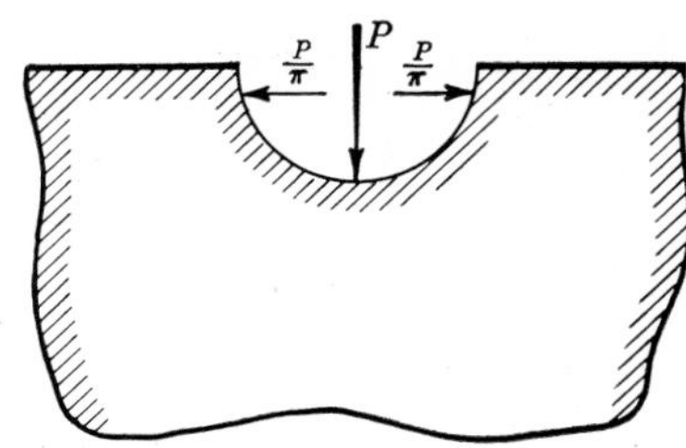

FIG. 2.5 Usual Representation of Boundary Forces Equivalent to a Normal Concentrated Load Acting on the Straight Edge of a Semi-Infinite Plate.

equivalent of other symmetrically distributed systems of pressures acting on the groove, such as shown in Fig. 2.4, for example. This is no doubt true, and it means that at distances far from the groove all such systems of forces would produce the same state of radial compression, although in the immediate vicinity of the groove there might be distinctly different stresses. Experiments show that when the load approaches a truly concentrated state the radial system holds well nigh to the boundary itself. From this we conclude that a concentrated load is best approximated by the cosine distribution of forces shown in Fig. 2.2. Other mathematical approaches, which do not rest on Saint Venant's principle, lead to the same conclusions. See §2.15.

In order to eliminate the difficulties due to plastic flow in the immediate vicinity of the concentrated load it is often desirable to replace such loads by radial pressures acting on a groove of small radius and distributed in accordance with the cosine law, eq. (2.2.) Fig. 2.5 shows the usual representation of forces statically equivalent to this distribution.

[1] It is interesting to observe that the above theoretical solution was suggested by the results from a photoelastic investigation made by Carus Wilson. See *Phil. Mag.*, Vol. 32, p. 481, 1891. The theoretical developments are due to Boussinesq, Flamant, and J. H. Michell. See, respectively, *Compt rend.*, Vol. 114, pp. 1510 and 1465, 1892; and *Proc. London Math. Soc.*, Vol. 32, p. 35, 1900.

The horizontal thrust Y is obtained from

$$Y = \int_0^{\pi/2} \sin\theta\,\sigma_r\,dA$$

$$= \frac{P}{\pi}\int_0^{\pi/2} \sin 2\theta\,d\theta,$$

$$Y = \frac{P}{\pi}. \tag{2.9}$$

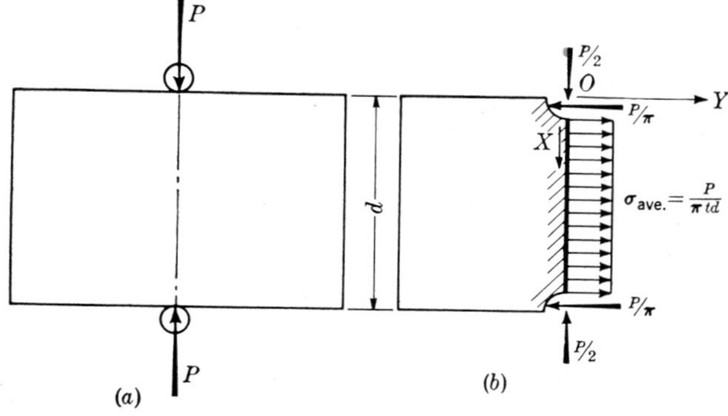

FIG. 2.6 Sketch Showing a Rectangular Block Subjected to Concentrated Loads and the Induced Tensions.

A concentrated load acting on the straight edge of a thin, large plate may therefore be replaced by an equal force on a semicircular groove of small radius accompanied by two thrusts, numerically equal to P/π, and acting at right angles to the force P, Fig. 2.5. An interesting application of the thrusts produced by concentrated loads is found in rectangular blocks subjected to concentrated forces, Fig. 2.6(a). In the immediate vicinity of these loads the distribution of the stresses is the same as those produced by a concentrated load acting normally to the straight edge of a semi-infinite plate. Hence, if small grooves be removed from around the points of application of the loads the resultant of the stresses acting on each groove would consist of a vertical component P accompanied by equal and opposite horizontal thrusts P/π. It follows that, across the vertical section of symmetry passing through the X axis, Fig. 2.6(b), there are set up tensile stresses of an average magnitude $P/\pi td$. Another application is found in the rolling of metals.

§2.3 Photoelastic Corroboration of Flamant's Solution. ***Let us define a theoretical stress pattern for a body under the action of specific***

external loads as a pattern giving the loci of equal maximum shear stresses in planes perpendicular to the plane of the loads. Since the maximum shear is given by $(p - q)/2$ these loci would also represent paths of constant $(p - q)$, and would correspond to the fringes or isochromatics in photoelastic stress patterns.

It is relatively easy to determine the theoretical stress pattern for the problem discussed in the preceding article. Thus, if

$$\left.\begin{aligned} \sigma_r &= -\frac{2P}{\pi t}\frac{\cos\theta}{r}, && (a) \\ \sigma_\theta &= 0, && (b) \\ \tau_{r\theta} &= 0, && (c) \end{aligned}\right\} \quad (2.8)$$

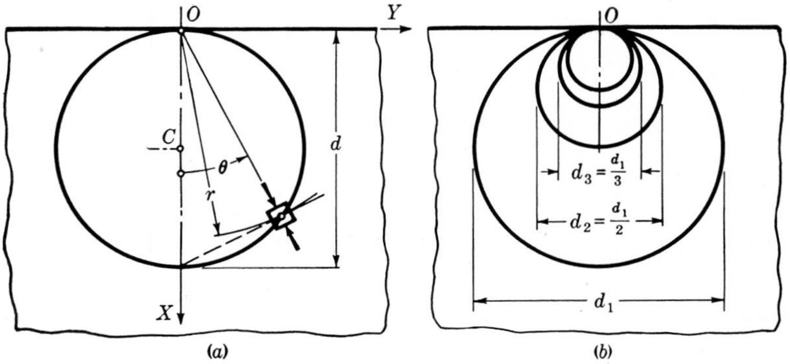

FIG. 2.7 Sketch of the Theoretical Stress Pattern for a Normal Concentrated Load on a Semi-Infinite Plate.

then

$$\tau_{\text{max.}} = \frac{\sigma_\theta - \sigma_r}{2}$$

$$= \frac{P}{\pi t}\frac{\cos\theta}{r}. \quad (2.10)$$

Now let us draw a circle of diameter d from a center on the line of the load P, and tangent to the straight edge of the boundary, Fig. 2.7(a) Inspection of this circle clearly shows that for any point on the circle

$$\frac{\cos\theta}{r} = \frac{1}{d}, \quad \text{a constant.}$$

Substituting in eq. (2.10) we get for the shears along the circle

$$\tau_{\text{max.}} = \frac{P}{\pi t}\frac{1}{d}, \quad \text{a constant.} \tag{2.11}$$

This means that the shear stresses $\tau_{\text{max.}}$ are equal everywhere along the circle. Moreover, eq. (2.11) clearly shows that $\tau_{\text{max.}}$ is inversely proportional to the diameter d. Hence, if τ_1 denotes the shear stresses on a circle of diameter d_1, then these stresses are doubled on a circle of diameter $d_2 = d_1/2$ and tripled on a circle of diameter $d_3 = d_1/3$. The theoretical stress pattern is therefore as shown in Fig. 2.7(*b*). ***The essential characteristics are the circular shapes of the fringes and the ratios of the diameters of the circles.***

The corresponding photoelastic stress pattern is shown in Fig. 2.8. It is seen that the fringes are quite circular, are approximately tangent to the boundary, and are of decreasing diameters. The comparison between the ratios of the diameters is shown in Fig. 2.9, in which the diameter of the largest theoretical circle is arbitrarily taken to equal the diameter of the first photoelastic fringe. It is seen that the diameters of the photoelastic fringes of higher order equal very closely the diameters of the corresponding theoretical fringes. ***The photoelastic and mathematical results are thus seen to be in good agreement.***

§2.4 Isoclinics and Stress Trajectories. ***Since the stress system is radial the isoclinics must also be radial; i.e., they are straight lines converging at the point of application of the load, Fig. 2.10(a). Photoelastic observations support this conclusion. The principal stress trajectories form a system of concentric circles with centers at the point of application of the load, intersected by radial lines passing through the centers of the circles,*** Fig. 2.10(*b*). It is also useful to have the shear trajectories, i.e., curves giving the directions of the maximum shear stresses. Since these stresses are always inclined 45° to the directions of the principal stresses the shear trajectories can easily be constructed either from the isoclinics or from the principal isostatics. Fig. 2.10(*c*) shows the shear trajectories for a normal concentrated load.

The equations of the shear trajectories can be readily determined. Referring to Fig. 2.10(*c*), let ψ denote the angle between an isoclinic of parameter θ and the tangent to a shear trajectory at some point A. Inspection of the figure shows that

$$\tan \psi = \frac{r\,d\theta}{dr}.$$

Since the shear trajectory intersects the principal stress trajectories

Fig. 2.8 Stress Pattern of a Semi-Infinite Plate under a Normal Concentrated Load of 39.3 Lb. Thickness of plate is 0.241 in.

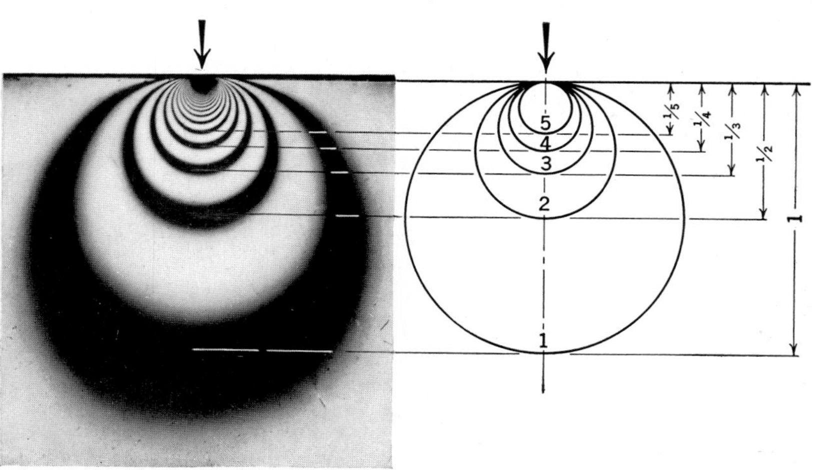

Fig. 2.9 Comparison of Theoretical and Photoelastic Stress Patterns.

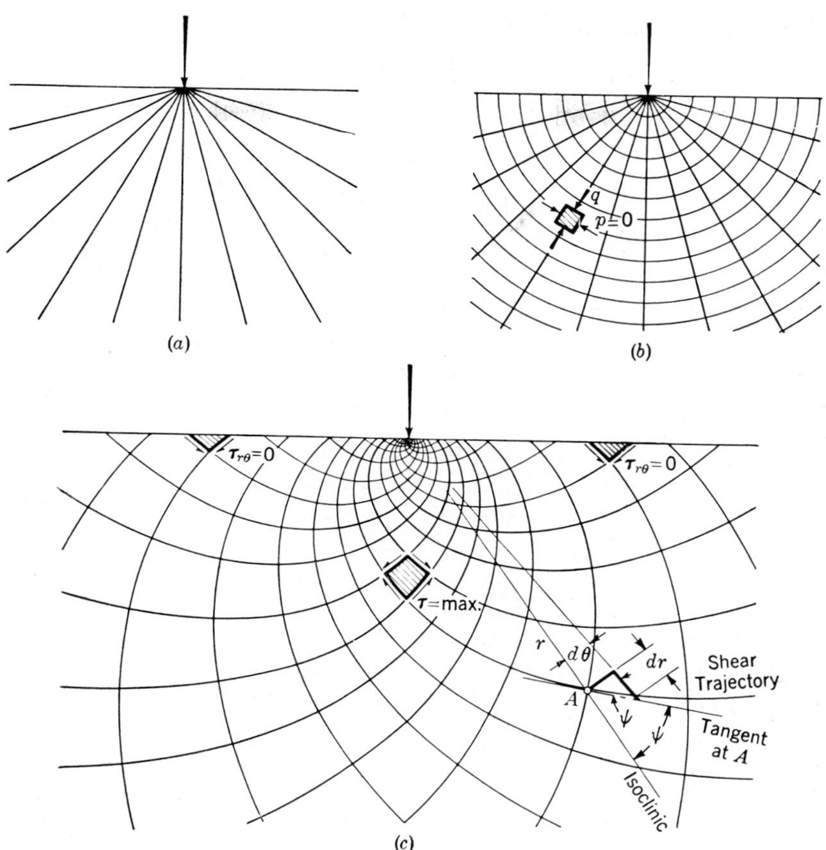

FIG. 2.10 Concentrated Load on a Semi-Infinite Plate.
(*a*) Theoretical isoclinics; (*b*) principal stress trajectories; (*c*) maximum shear trajectories.

everywhere at 45° it follows that

$$\tan \psi = \tan 45° = 1, \quad \text{a constant.}$$

Substituting and separating variables we obtain

$$\frac{dr}{r} = d\theta.$$

Integrating we have

$$\log r - \log C = \theta,$$

where C is a constant. Hence

$$\frac{r}{C} = e^{\theta}$$

and

$$r = Ce^{\theta}.$$

These curves are known as logarithmic spirals.

These shear trajectories find an important application in the study of plasticity, yielding generally occurring first on these planes. They also throw much light on the phenomena of metal cutting, such as turning and planing.

Further corroboration of the Flamant's solution giving the stresses produced by a concentrated load on a semi-infinite plate can be obtained from plasticity by examining the slip lines produced by such a load in a plate of mild steel and revealed by the well-known Fry's etching process. These slip lines represent plastic zones and follow approximately the directions of the maximum shear stresses. A comparison of the theoretical shear stress trajectories with the flow line pattern bears, therefore, on the validity of both the theoretical and photoelastic solutions. The flow line patterns are in substantial agreement with the photoelastic and theoretical results,[1] Fig. 2.11.

§2.5 Inclined or Oblique Concentrated Loads.[2] It is now a simple matter to extend the solution from §2.2 to include other problems. We begin with an oblique concentrated load acting at an arbitrary angle α with the normal to the straight edge of the semi-infinite plate, Fig. 2.12(a). We will show that the stress system in this case is identical with that discussed in §2.2 in which the load was normal, provided we again measure the angle θ from the line of action of the load. Specifically the stresses here are

$$\left.\begin{aligned} \sigma_r &= -\frac{2P\cos\theta}{\pi t r}, & (a)\\ \sigma_\theta &= 0, & (b)\\ \tau_{r\theta} &= 0. & (c) \end{aligned}\right\} \quad (2.8)$$

As in the preceding case we again remove a semicircular groove from

[1] See also *Plasticity* by A. Nadai, McGraw-Hill Book Co., New York, Figs. 322, 323, 324.

[2] The extension of Flamant's solution to the case of an inclined load was made by J. Boussinesq, whose original work on the three-dimensional problem was used by Flamant. See *Compt. rend.*, Vol. 114, p. 1510, 1892. See also paper by J. H. Michell, *Proc. London Math. Soc.* Vol. 32, p. 35, 1900.

the plate and subject it to radial forces only defined by $q = -q_o(\cos \theta / r_o)$, Fig. 2.12(*b*).

The stresses given by eqs. (2.8) fully satisfy the new boundary condi-

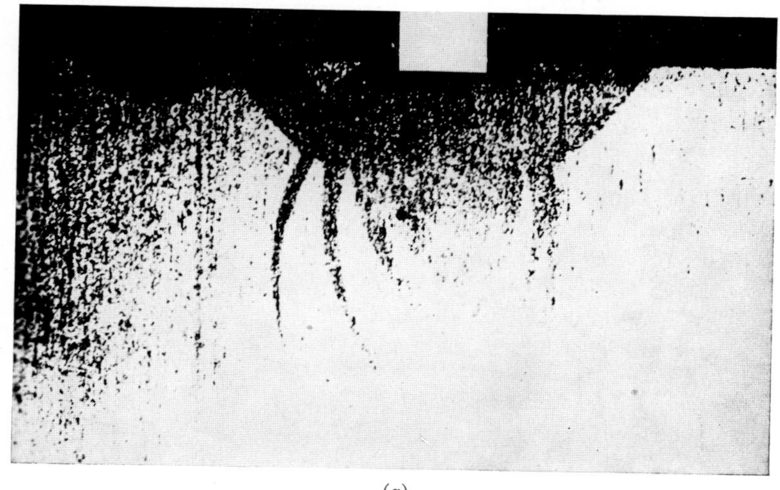

(*a*)

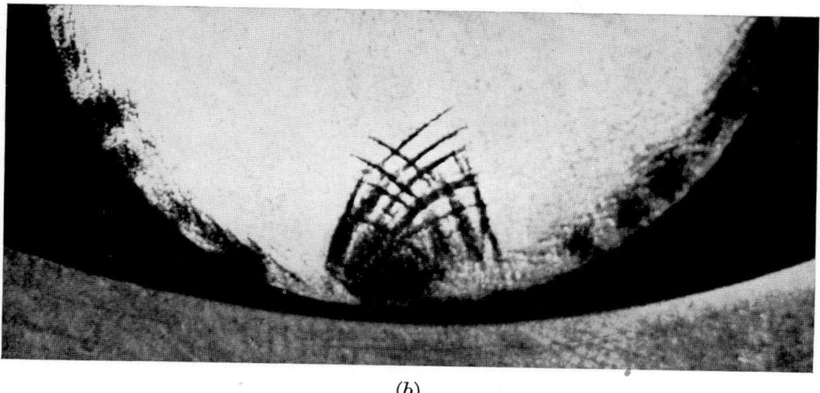

(*b*)

FIG. 2.11 (*a*) Photograph of a Plate of Mild Steel under a Concentrated Load Showing Slip Lines as Revealed by Fry's Etching Process. From *Plasticity* by Dr. A. Nadai. (*b*) Slip Lines in a Circular Disk Compressed by Diametral Loads.

tions. The straight edge remains free since σ_θ and $\tau_{r\theta}$ vanish everywhere. On the semicircular groove the stresses σ_r become equal to the assumed pressures q. Lastly all stresses vanish at infinity. Furthermore, the assumed forces on the groove are statically equivalent to a concentrated load parallel to the X axis. These forces are compressive on the arc ABC, vanish at C, and change into tension on the arc CD so that all the X components are positive. The Y components, on the other hand, vanish because the components of the tensile forces on CD plus those of

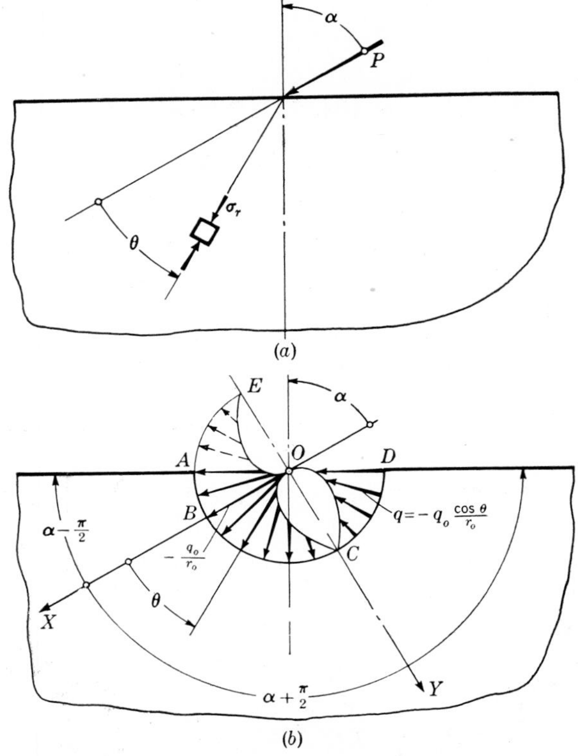

FIG, 2.12 Sketches Showing Inclined Concentrated Load on a Semi-Infinite Plate, also Equivalent Cosine Distribution and Notation.

the compressions on AB balance the effect of the compressions on BC. The same conclusions can, of course, be obtained analytically. Thus, summing forces parallel to the X and Y axes respectively, we have for the numerical values

$$\Sigma X = \int_{\alpha-\pi/2}^{\alpha+\pi/2} \cos\theta \, \sigma_r \, dA$$

$$= \frac{2P}{\pi} \int_{\alpha-\pi/2}^{\alpha+\pi/2} \cos^2\theta \, d\theta$$

$$\Sigma X = \frac{P}{\pi}\left[\theta + \frac{1}{2}\sin 2\theta\right]_{\alpha-\pi/2}^{\alpha+\pi/2} = P.$$

$$\Sigma Y = \int_{\alpha-\pi/2}^{\alpha+\pi/2} \sin\theta\,\sigma_r\,dA$$

$$= \frac{P}{\pi}\int_{\alpha-\pi/2}^{\alpha+\pi/2} 2\sin\theta\cos\theta\,d\theta$$

$$= \frac{P}{\pi}\left[\sin^2\theta\right]_{\alpha-\pi/2}^{\alpha+\pi/2} = 0.$$

The statical equivalent of the distributed forces on the groove is therefore a concentrated load parallel to the X axis. It follows that ***the stresses produced by the inclined concentrated load are also given by eqs. (2.8), provided the angle θ is measured from the direction of the load.***

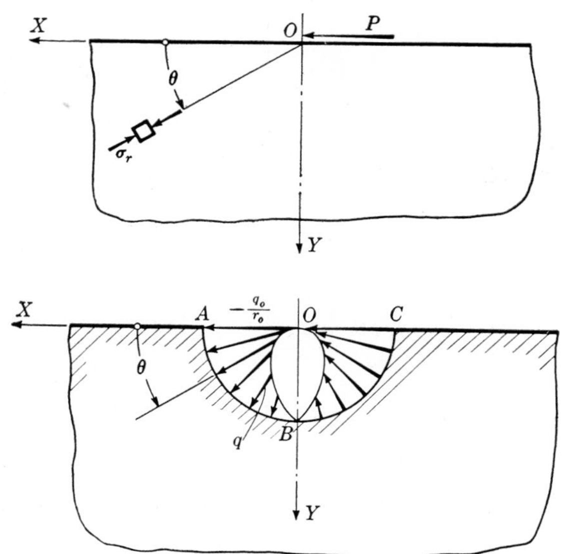

FIG. 2.13 Sketches Showing a Concentrated Load Parallel to Edge of Semi-Infinite Plate and Its Statically Equivalent System on a Semicircular Groove.

§2.6 Load Parallel to Straight Edge of Plate. A state of pure radial stress also exists when the concentrated load is parallel to the edge of the plate. Here the load P, Fig. 2.13, is the statical equivalent of a distributed system of boundary forces on the groove defined by eq. (2.2),

θ being measured from the direction of the applied load, which coincides here with the straight edge of the plate. This gives compressive forces on the arc AB and tensile forces on BC. The Y components vanish and the X components combine into a positive concentrated load. It is clear that the stress components derived from the Flamant function give radial stresses exactly equal to the boundary forces. Hence ***eqs. (2.8) also represent an exact solution for this system of boundary forces, and for their statically equivalent concentrated load acting parallel to the edge.***

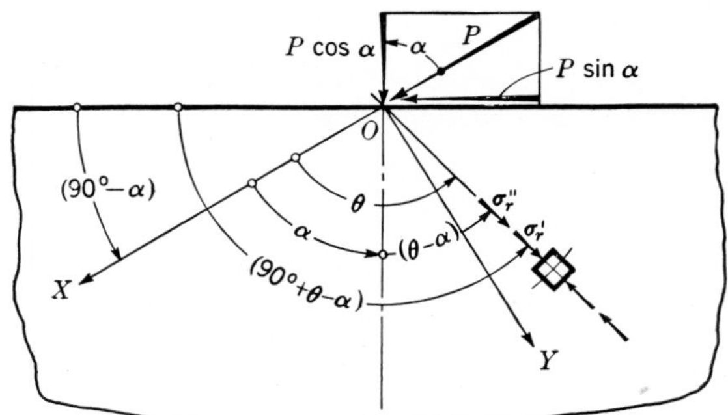

FIG. 2.14 Sketch Showing Method of Superposition for Finding Stresses Due to an Inclined Concentrated Load.

It is interesting to point out that the solution for the oblique load P, Fig. 2.12, can be obtained by superimposing the solutions for the normal and parallel loads. Thus, resolving the inclined force P, Fig. 2.14, into two components $P \cos \alpha$ and $P \sin \alpha$, normal and parallel to the straight edge of the plate, we get for the radial stresses $\sigma_r{}'$ and $\sigma_r{}''$, respectively produced by them, the following

$$\sigma_r{}' = -\frac{2P \cos \alpha}{\pi t} \frac{\cos (\theta - \alpha)}{r}, \tag{2.12}$$

$$\sigma_r{}'' = -\frac{2P \sin \alpha}{\pi t} \frac{\cos [90° + (\theta - \alpha)]}{r}$$

$$= \frac{2P \sin \alpha \sin (\theta - \alpha)}{\pi t r}, \tag{2.13}$$

since

$$\cos [90° + (\theta - \alpha)] = -\sin (\theta - \alpha).$$

Hence

$$\sigma_r = \sigma_r' + \sigma_r'' = -\frac{2P}{\pi tr}[\cos\alpha\cos(\theta-\alpha) - \sin\alpha\sin(\theta-\alpha)]$$

$$= -\frac{2P}{\pi tr}\cos[\alpha + (\theta-\alpha)]$$

$$= -\frac{2P}{\pi t}\frac{\cos\theta}{r}, \tag{2.8a}$$

which is clearly identical with the expression for the stress resulting from a normal load. We thus see that ***eqs. (2.8) define the state of stress in the semi-infinite plate due to a concentrated load acting on its straight edge regardless of whether this load is normal, inclined, or parallel to this edge.***

§2.7 Photoelastic Corroboration for Oblique and Parallel Loads. (*a*) *Oblique Loads.* In Fig. 2.15 the origin is at the point of application of the load, the X axis along its direction, and the Y axis at right angles. We draw circles from centers on the line of the load and tangent to the Y axis. Such circles are clearly loci of equal radial stresses and therefore of maximum shear stresses. Along such circles

$$\frac{\cos\theta}{r} = \frac{1}{d}, \quad \text{a constant,}$$

and therefore

$$\tau_{\text{max.}} = \frac{P}{\pi t}\frac{\cos\theta}{r} = \frac{P}{\pi t}\frac{1}{d}, \quad \text{a constant.} \tag{2.11}$$

The circles are therefore theoretical fringes. Furthermore, the transverse plane through the Y axis is a neutral surface, since σ_r vanishes for $\theta = \pi/2$. This axis divides the plate into distinct regions of compressive and tensile stresses. The circles in front of the load, marked C in Fig. 2.15(*b*), represent loci of equal radial compression, and those back of it, marked T, are loci of equal radial tension. It is interesting to note that a tensile arc added to a compressive arc of the same diameter completes a circle.

The stresses in this instance are also inversely proportional to the diameter of the circle, so that the stress on a circle of diameter d/n is n times the stress on the circle of diameter d. The diameters of the fringes therefore decrease rapidly for large values of n and the circles become rather crowded as we approach the point of application of the load, Fig. 2.15(*b*).

A corresponding photoelastic stress pattern, with the load in a vertical position and the edge of the plate inclined, is shown in Fig. 2.16. It is seen that the fringes follow the theoretically determined shapes quite closely. The agreement between the diameters of the fringes of different orders can be seen more clearly from Fig. 2.17.

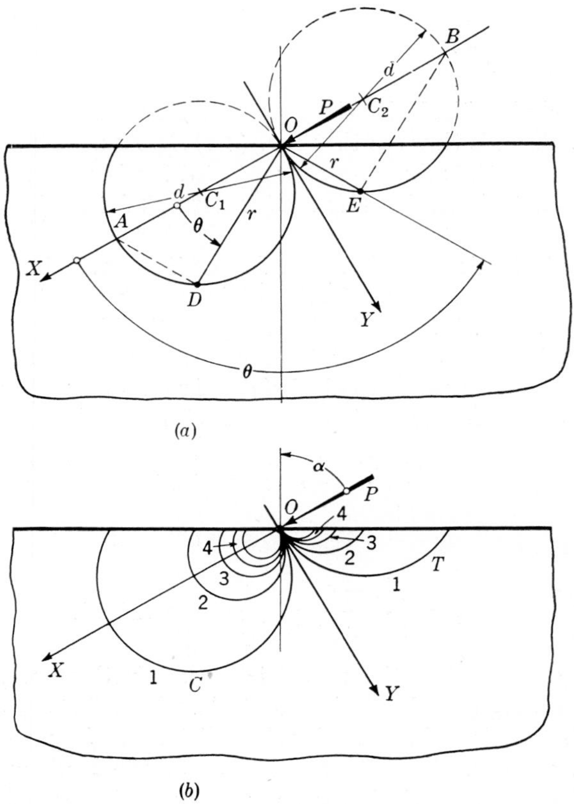

FIG. 2.15 Theoretical Stress Pattern for an Inclined Concentrated Load on a Semi-Infinite Plate.

(*b*) *Load Parallel to Edge of Plate.* In this case ***the theoretical fringes are semicircles the centers of which lie on the straight edge,*** Fig. 2.18. The corresponding photoelastic stress pattern is shown in Fig. 2.19. We note that the neutral surface is slightly deviated into the compression side. This can be readily explained. In order to apply the load to the plate it was found necessary to leave a small ridge on the compression

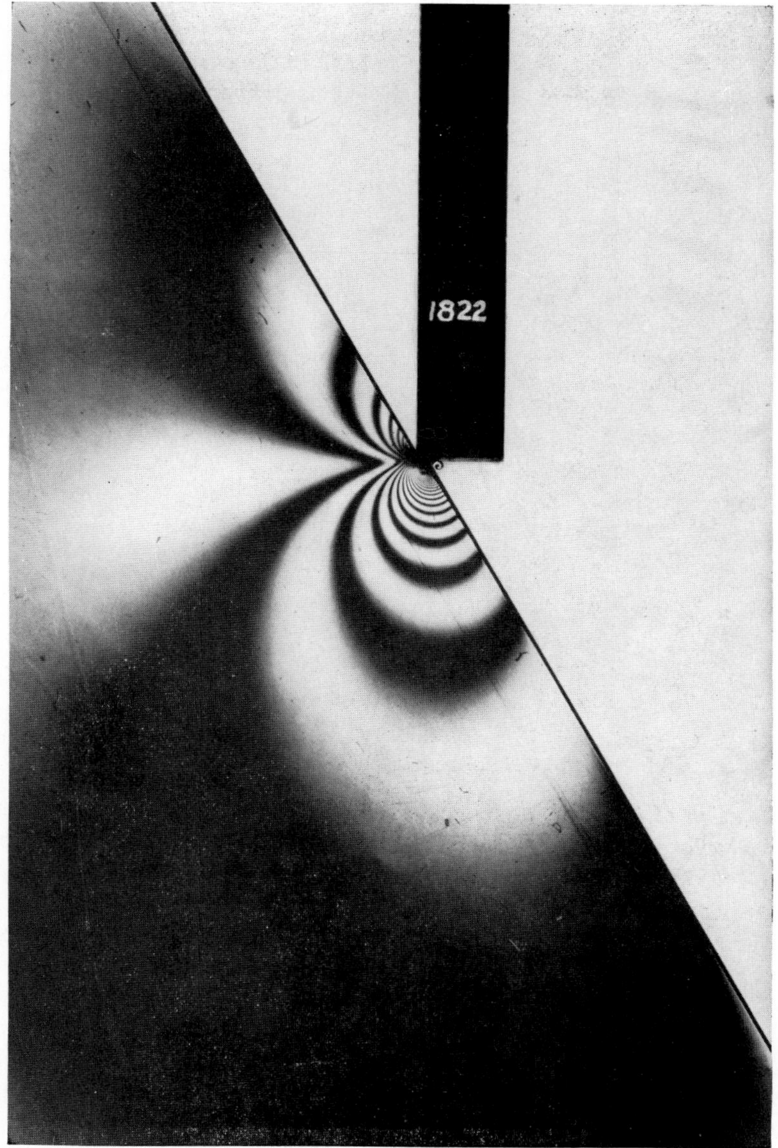

FIG. 2.16 Photoelastic Stress Pattern of a Semi-Infinite Plate under an Inclined Concentrated Load of 39.95 Lb.

Angle of inclination of load to edge of plate = 30°. Thickness of plate = 0.277 in.

side, so that this edge is a few thousandths of an inch higher than the tension side, and the straight edge is, strictly speaking, not quite straight.

(c) *Isoclinics and Stress Trajectories.* ***As in the case of a normal concentrated load the isoclinics are radial lines converging at the point of***

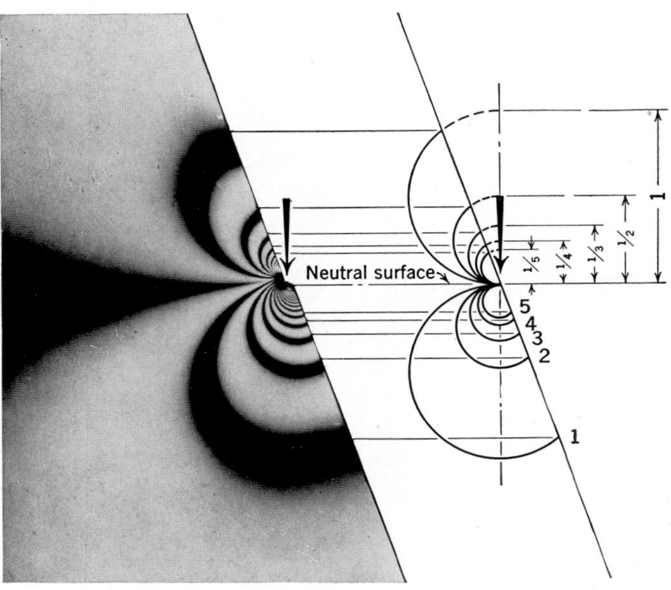

FIG. 2.17 Comparison of Photoelastic and Theoretical Stress Patterns for an Inclined Concentrated Load on a Semi-Infinite Plate.

application of the load, and the principal stress trajectories are concentric circular arcs with centers at the point of application of the load. Fig. 2.20 shows the shear trajectories for a load parallel to the edge. The shear trajectories for this case have a direct application to the formation of a metal chip both in turning and planing. The equations of these trajectories are the same as those for a normal load discussed in §2.4.

§2.8 Rectangular Stress Components. It is desirable to have expressions for the stress components σ_x, σ_y, and τ_{xy} in the directions of the X and Y axes, Fig. 2.21 (a). These can be derived from the basic formula giving σ_r, eq. (2.8). Thus, by eqs. (1.1) and (1.2), Vol. I, in which σ_x corresponds to our radial stress σ_r, and σ_θ to either σ_x or σ_y, we have

$$\left.\begin{aligned} \sigma_x &= \sigma_r \cos^2 \theta, & (a) \\ \sigma_y &= \sigma_r \sin^2 \theta, & (b) \\ \tau_{xy} &= \sigma_r \sin \theta \cos \theta. & (c) \end{aligned}\right\} (2.14)$$

Substituting the expression for σ_r, eq. (2.8a), we obtain

$$\left.\begin{aligned} \sigma_x &= -\frac{2P\cos^3\theta}{\pi tr}, && (a) \\ \sigma_y &= \frac{-2P\sin^2\theta\cos\theta}{\pi tr}, && (b) \\ \tau_{xy} &= \frac{-2P\sin\theta\cos^2\theta}{\pi tr}. && (c) \end{aligned}\right\} (2.15)$$

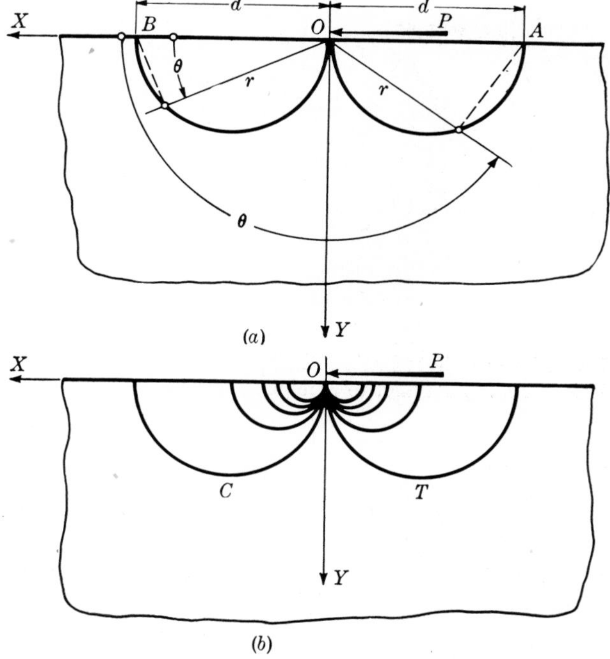

FIG. 2.18 Theoretical Stress Pattern for a Concentrated Load Acting Parallel to Straight Edge of Semi-Infinite Plate.

These equations give the rectangular stress components at any point of the plate in terms of r and θ, the polar coordinates of the point. If we denote the rectangular coordinates of the point by x and y, and observe that

$$\cos\theta = \frac{x}{r},$$

$$\sin\theta = \frac{y}{r},$$

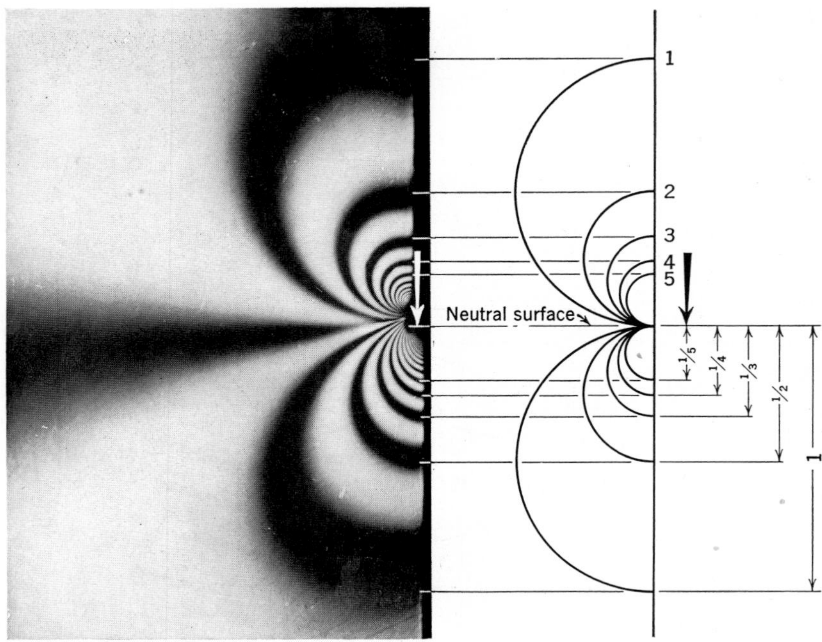

FIG. 2.19 Comparison of Photoelastic and Theoretical Stress Patterns for a Concentrated Load Acting Parallel to Straight Edge of Semi-Infinite Plate.

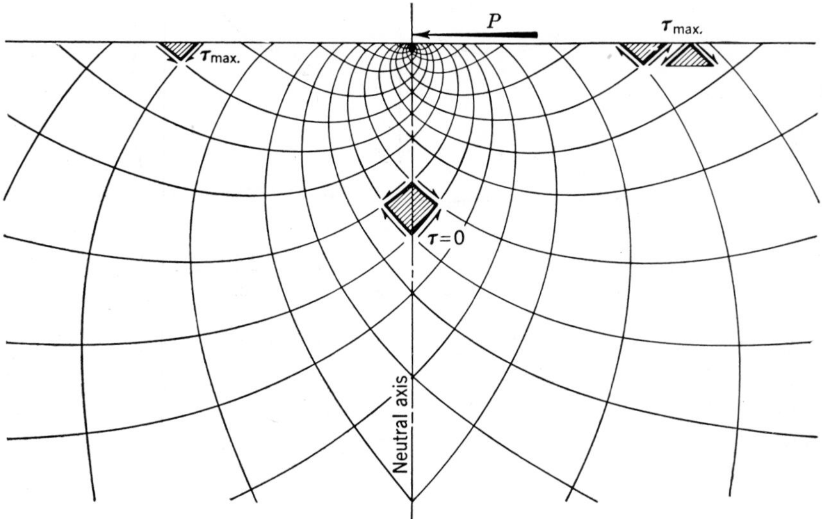

FIG. 2.20 Shear Trajectories in a Semi-Infinite Plate Subjected to a Concentrated Load Acting Parallel to Straight Edge.

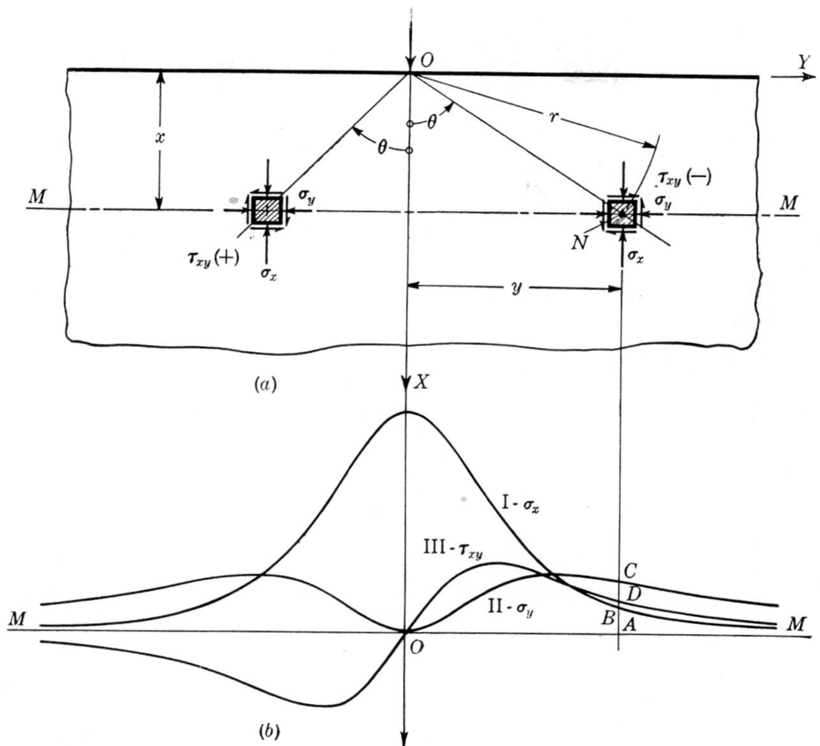

FIG. 2.21 Sketch Showing Rectangular Stress Components in a Semi-Infinite Plate under a Concentrated Normal Load; also Curves Showing Stress Distribution along Section MM, Distant x below the Straight Edge.

and

$$r = \sqrt{x^2 + y^2},$$

we obtain the following expressions for the rectangular stress components in terms of the rectangular coordinates of the point:

$$\left.\begin{aligned} \sigma_x &= \frac{-2Px^3}{\pi t(x^2 + y^2)^2}, & (a) \\ \sigma_y &= \frac{-2Pxy^2}{\pi t(x^2 + y^2)^2}, & (b) \\ \tau_{xy} &= \frac{-2Px^2y}{\pi t(x^2 + y^2)^2}. & (c) \end{aligned}\right\} \quad (2.16)$$

The expressions given in eqs. (2.15 and 2.16) are valid whether the concentrated load P is normal, parallel, or inclined to the straight edge of the plate, provided the X axis is always taken parallel to the load and the positive branch of the Y axis by a counterclockwise rotation of 90° from it. The directions of the stress components are in all cases parallel to the directions of the X and Y axes. It should be noted that for an inclined load neither axis is parallel to the edge of the plate, Fig. 2.12. For a normal load the distributions of these stress components on a section M–M parallel to the straight edge and x units from it are shown graphically in Fig. 2.21 (b), in which the ordinates AB, AC, and AD, directly under a point N, represent respectively the stresses σ_x, σ_y, τ_{xy} at that point.

§2.9 Influence Curves. Consider next the case in which we wish to find the stresses at any point N due to a moving load of unit magnitude normal to the straight edge of the plate, Fig. 2.22 (a). We choose the origin of the coordinate system at point O, directly above N on the straight edge, and denote by σ_x', σ_y', τ_{xy}' the rectangular stress components caused by the unit load. The expressions for these stress components follow directly from eqs. (2.16) if we observe that with respect to point O_1, the point of application of the unit load, the coordinates of N are $(x, -y)$. Substituting these coordinates in eqs. (2.16) and replacing P by unity we obtain

$$\left.\begin{aligned} \sigma_x' &= -\frac{2x^3}{\pi t(x^2 + y^2)^2}, & (a)\\ \sigma_y' &= -\frac{2xy^2}{\pi t(x^2 + y^2)^2}, & (b)\\ \tau_{xy}' &= \frac{2x^2 y}{\pi t(x^2 + y^2)^2}. & (c) \end{aligned}\right\} \quad (2.17)$$

The graphs of these expressions for a fixed value of x, which we will call influence curves, are shown in Fig. 2.22 (b). The ordinates AB, AC, AD directly under the unit load represent the stress components at the point N. It follows that the stresses σ_x, σ_y, τ_{xy} at N caused by an arbitrary normal load P can be obtained by multiplying the ordinates directly under the load by its magnitude P.

§2.10 Several Concentrated Normal Loads. Assume now that several normal loads, say three, P_1, P_2, and P_3, are acting on the plate, Fig. 2.23. By the principle of superposition the stresses at any point N would be given by the algebraic sum of the stresses produced by each load separately. We can obtain these stresses at N graphically by using the

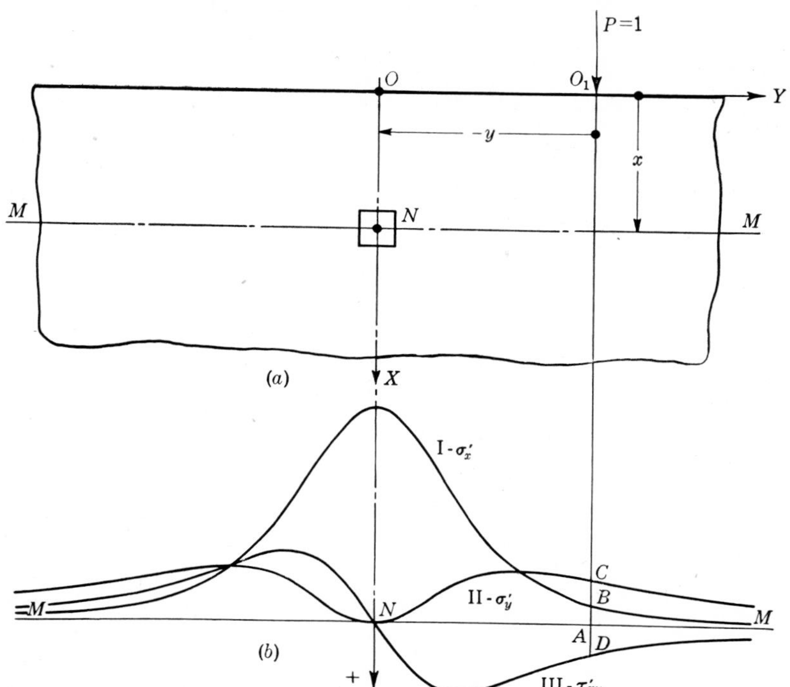

FIG. 2.22 Sketch Showing Method of Using the Influence Curves of Fig. 2.21(*b*) to Obtain Stresses Due to Concentrated Loads on a Semi-Infinite Plate.

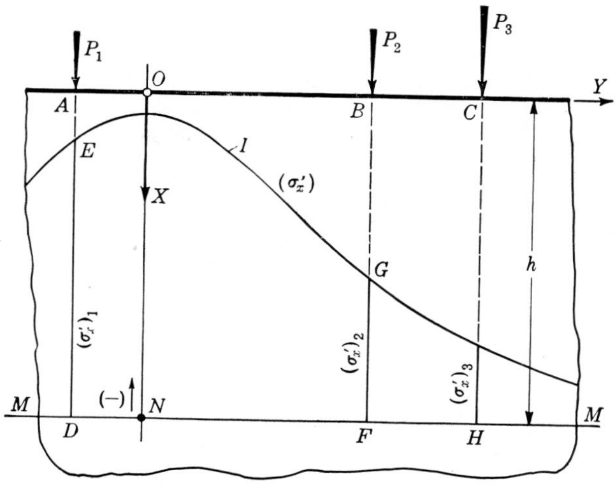

FIG. 2.23 Sketch for the Superposition of σ_x for Several Concentrated Loads on a Semi-Infinite Plate Using the Influence Curve from Fig. 2.21(*b*).

influence curves of Fig. 2.22(*b*). For example, on curve I of Fig. 2.23, which is the same as that shown in Fig. 2.22(*b*), the ordinates at D, F, and H represent the stresses $(\sigma_x')_1$, $(\sigma_x')_2$, and $(\sigma_x')_3$ produced by unit normal loads at the points A, B, and C. The resultant stress σ_x at N due to the three loads P_1, P_2, and P_3 is therefore given by

$$\sigma_x = P_1(\sigma_x')_1 + P_2(\sigma_x')_2 + P_3(\sigma_x')_3,$$

or

$$\sigma_x = \sum_{i=1}^{i=3} P_i(\sigma_x')_i.$$

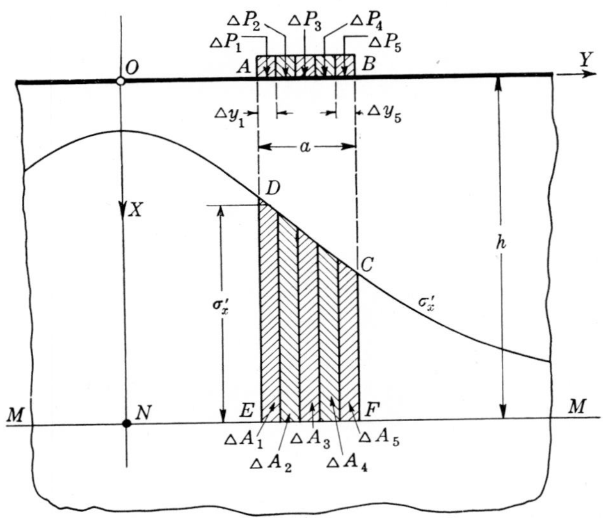

FIG. 2.24 Sketch Showing Graphical Method for Determining the Stresses Caused by a Uniformly Distributed Load Using Influence Curve from Fig. 2.21(*b*).

This method can obviously be extended to any number of loads. Thus for n loads

$$\left.\begin{aligned} \sigma_x &= \sum_{i=1}^{i=n} P_i(\sigma_x')_i, && (a)\\ \sigma_y &= \sum_{i=1}^{i=n} P_i(\sigma_y')_i, && (b)\\ \tau_{xy} &= \sum_{i=1}^{i=n} P_i(\tau_{xy}')_i. && (c) \end{aligned}\right\} (2.18)$$

§2.11 Uniformly Distributed Pressure on a Finite Interval (Graphical Solution). The method of superposition can also be used to determine the stresses caused by a uniformly distributed load of intensity, say q_o per unit length of the straight edge, Fig. 2.24. To this end we divide the interval on which the load is acting into an arbitrary number of equal increments Δy and treat the load $q_o\,\Delta y$ on each increment as a concentrated load. The stress $(\sigma_x)_1$ at some point N produced by the first load $(q_o\,\Delta y_1)$ would then be

$$\begin{aligned}(\sigma_x)_1 &= (q_o\,\Delta y_1)\sigma_x{}',\\ &= q_o(\Delta y_1 \sigma_x{}'),\\ &= q_o\,\Delta A_1.\end{aligned}$$

This stress is given by the product of the area ΔA_1 under the influence curve multiplied by the load intensity q_o. Similarly the stress developed by the second load $(q_o\,\Delta y_2)$ would be given by $(q_o\,\Delta A_2)$, etc. The resultant stress caused by the distributed load acting on the interval AB is thus given by the shaded area $EFCD$ under the influence curve multiplied by the load intensity q_o. An analytical solution of the same problem follows.

§2.12 Analytical Solution for Uniformly Distributed Pressures. In Fig. 2.25(a) let dP denote the load on an infinitesimal length dy, i.e.,

$$dP = q_o\,dy.$$

Inspection of the figure shows that

$$dy = \frac{r\,d\theta}{\cos\theta},$$

so that

$$dP = q_o\frac{r\,d\theta}{\cos\theta}.$$

The rectangular stress components $d\sigma_x$, $d\sigma_y$, and $d\tau_{xy}$ produced by the differential load dP can be obtained from eqs. (2.15) by replacing P by the above value of dP. This gives

$$\left.\begin{aligned} d\sigma_x &= -\frac{2q_o}{\pi t}\cos^2\theta\,d\theta, &\quad (a)\\ d\sigma_y &= -\frac{2q_o}{\pi t}\sin^2\theta\,d\theta, &\quad (b)\\ d\tau_{xy} &= -\frac{q_o}{\pi t}\sin 2\theta\,d\theta, &\quad (c)\end{aligned}\right\}(2.19)$$

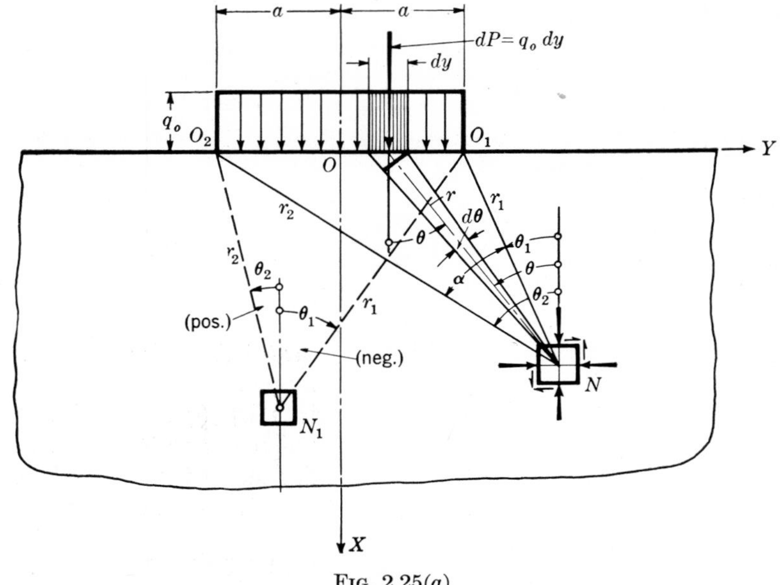

FIG. 2.25(a)

whence

$$\left.\begin{aligned}\sigma_x &= -\frac{2q_o}{\pi t}\int_{\theta_1}^{\theta_2}\cos^2\theta\,d\theta, & (a)\\ \sigma_y &= -\frac{2q_o}{\pi t}\int_{\theta_1}^{\theta_2}\sin^2\theta\,d\theta, & (b)\\ \tau_{xy} &= -\frac{q_o}{\pi t}\int_{\theta_1}^{\theta_2}\sin 2\theta\,d\theta. & (c)\end{aligned}\right\}\quad(2.20)$$

Upon integration these yield

$$\left.\begin{aligned}\sigma_x &= -\frac{q_o}{2\pi t}[2(\theta_2-\theta_1)+(\sin 2\theta_2-\sin 2\theta_1)], & (a)\\ \sigma_y &= -\frac{q_o}{2\pi t}[2(\theta_2-\theta_1)-(\sin 2\theta_2-\sin 2\theta_1)], & (b)\\ \tau_{xy} &= -\frac{q_o}{2\pi t}(\cos 2\theta_1-\cos 2\theta_2). & (c)\end{aligned}\right\}\quad(2.21)$$

In using these equations it must be remembered that the angles are directed. Thus in Fig. 2.25(a) at point N the angles θ_1 and θ_2 are both positive, whereas, at point N_1, θ_1 is negative and θ_2 is positive.

It should be noted that eqs. (2.21) are valid also for inclined loading, Fig. 2.25(b), provided q_o represents the load intensity per unit length measured along the Y axis and provided further that the angles θ_1 and θ_2 are as shown.

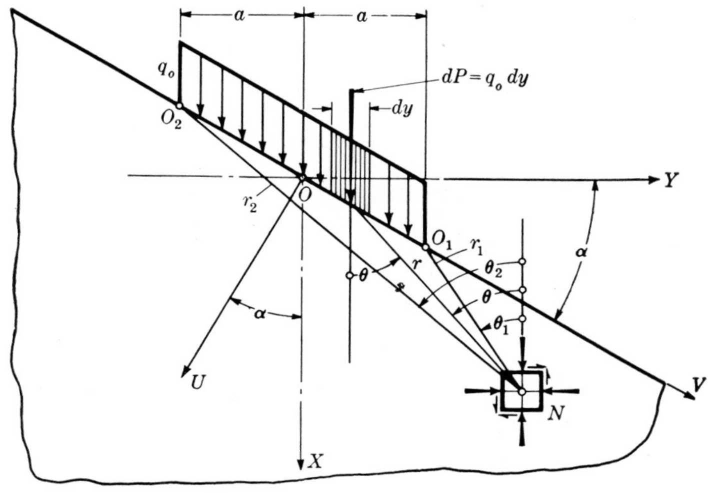

FIG. 2.25(b)

For tangentially distributed loads of uniform intensity q_o, Fig. 2.25(c) the expressions for the stress components are

$$\left.\begin{aligned}
\sigma_x &= -\frac{q_o}{2\pi t}\left[4\log\frac{\sin\theta_2}{\sin\theta_1} - (\cos 2\theta_1 - \cos 2\theta_2)\right], && (a)\\
\sigma_y &= -\frac{q_o}{2\pi t}(\cos 2\theta_1 - \cos 2\theta_2), && (b)\\
\tau_{xy} &= -\frac{q_o}{2\pi t}[2(\theta_2 - \theta_1) + (\sin 2\theta_2 - \sin 2\theta_1)]. && (c)
\end{aligned}\right\} \quad (2.22)$$

The derivation of these equations is left to the reader.

Returning to the case of the inclined loads, it is now possible to find the stress components parallel to the U and V axes, Fig. 2.25(b). To this end it is only necessary to resolve the load intensity q_o into components normal and parallel to the straight edge of the plate and to apply eqs. (2.21) to the normal component q_u and eqs. (2.22) to the tangential component q_v, and then to apply superposition. The resultant stresses

σ_u and σ_v are then given by

$$\sigma_u = \sigma_{x(u \text{ components})} + \sigma_{y(v \text{ components})},$$

$$\sigma_v = \sigma_{y(u \text{ components})} + \sigma_{x(v \text{ components})}.$$

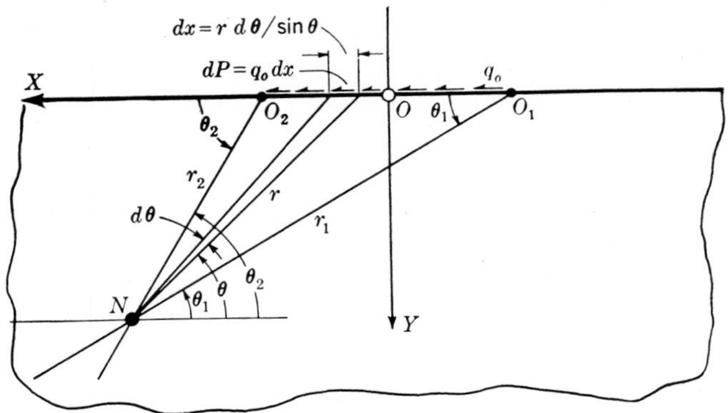

FIG. 2.25(c)

FIG. 2.25 Notation in the Analytical Method for Computing the Resultant Stress Components at any Point of a Semi-Infinite Plate under Uniformly Distributed Loads on a Finite Segment $2a$. (a) Normal loads. (b) Inclined loads. (c) Tangential loads.

It should also be noted that

$$q_u = q_o \cos^2 \alpha \quad \text{and} \quad q_v = q_o \frac{\sin 2\alpha}{2},$$

where α is the angle which the straight edge of the plate makes with the horizontal.

Maximum Shears. The maximum shear stress is given by

$$\tau_{\text{max.}} = \tfrac{1}{2}\sqrt{(\sigma_x - \sigma_y)^2 + 4\tau_{xy}^{\ 2}}. \qquad [(1.14), \text{Vol. I}]$$

From eqs. (2.21a) and (2.21b)

$$\sigma_x - \sigma_y = -\frac{q_o}{\pi t}(\sin 2\theta_2 - \sin 2\theta_1).$$

Therefore

$$(\sigma_x - \sigma_y)^2 + 4\tau_{xy}^{\ 2}$$
$$= \frac{q_o^{\ 2}}{\pi^2 t^2}[(\sin 2\theta_2 - \sin 2\theta_1)^2 + (\cos 2\theta_1 - \cos 2\theta_2)^2]$$

$$= \frac{2q_o^2}{\pi^2 t^2}[1 - (\sin 2\theta_1 \sin 2\theta_2 + \cos 2\theta_1 \cos 2\theta_2)]$$

$$= \frac{2q_o^2}{\pi^2 t^2}[1 - \cos 2(\theta_2 - \theta_1)]$$

$$= \frac{4q_o^2}{\pi^2 t^2}\sin^2(\theta_2 - \theta_1), \tag{2.23}$$

whence

$$\tau_{\text{max.}} = \frac{1}{2}\sqrt{\frac{4q_o^2}{\pi^2 t^2}\sin^2(\theta_2 - \theta_1)}$$

$$= \frac{q_o}{\pi t}\sin(\theta_2 - \theta_1)$$

$$\boldsymbol{\tau_{\text{max.}} = \frac{q_o}{\pi t}\sin\alpha,} \tag{2.24}$$

where α is the angle between r_1 and r_2, Fig. 2.25(a).

Principal Stresses. The principal stresses p, q are given by eqs. (1.12), Vol. I, from which

$$p, q = \frac{\sigma_x + \sigma_y}{2} \pm \tau_{\text{max}}$$

$$= \frac{q_o}{\pi t}[-(\theta_2 - \theta_1) \pm \sin(\theta_2 - \theta_1)],$$

$$\boldsymbol{p, q = \frac{q_o}{\pi t}(-\alpha \pm \sin\alpha),} \tag{2.25}$$

where α is the same as in eq. (2.24). From the last equation it follows that p and q are both compression.

Stress Trajectories. It will now be shown that ***the principal stress trajectories for a uniformly distributed load consist of confocal ellipses intersected by an orthogonal system of hyperbolas with foci at the extremities of the distributed load,*** Fig. 2.26. Thus, if β is the angle which a principal stress makes with the X axis, then

$$\tan 2\beta = \frac{2\tau_{xy}}{\sigma_x - \sigma_y}. \qquad [(1.13), \text{Vol. I}]$$

Substituting the expressions from eqs. (2.21) we have

$$\tan 2\beta = -\frac{2(\cos 2\theta_2 - \cos 2\theta_1)}{2(\sin 2\theta_2 - \sin 2\theta_1)}$$

$$= \frac{2 \sin (\theta_2 - \theta_1) \sin (\theta_2 + \theta_1)}{2 \sin (\theta_2 - \theta_1) \cos (\theta_2 + \theta_1)}$$

$$= \tan (\theta_2 + \theta_1).$$

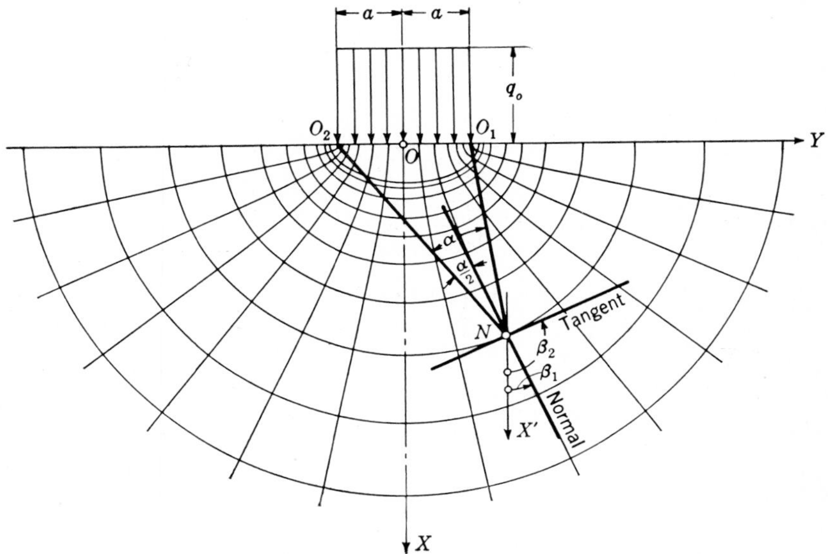

FIG. 2.26 Drawing of the Principal Stress Trajectories for a Uniformly Distributed Load Acting on a Finite Segment on the Straight Edge of a Semi-Infinite Plate.

Hence

$$2\beta = \theta_2 + \theta_1 \quad \text{or} \quad 2\beta = \theta_2 + \theta_1 + 180°.$$

Denoting the two possible values of β by β_1 and β_2 we have

$$\beta_1 = \tfrac{1}{2}(\theta_2 + \theta_1)$$

and

$$\beta_2 = \tfrac{1}{2}(\theta_2 + \theta_1) + 90°.$$

From the last equation it follows that the lines defined by β_1 and β_2 are perpendicular to each other. Hence the line defined by β_1 is normal to one of the stress trajectories passing through point N. Furthermore, this line bisects the angle α.

Consider now an ellipse with foci at the extremities of the distributed load, points O_1 and O_2, Fig. 2.26, and passing through point N. It is shown in analytic geometry that the normal to an ellipse at a point N bisects the angle O_1NO_2. Since there exists only one pair of principal stress directions at a point it follows that the ellipse is one of the stress trajectories. Consequently ***one set of stress trajectories is a family of confocal ellipses with foci at O_1 and O_2.***

The other set of stress trajectories must be orthogonal to the ellipses at every point of intersection. It can be shown that the set of curves which have this property is a family of confocal hyperbolas with the same foci as the ellipses.

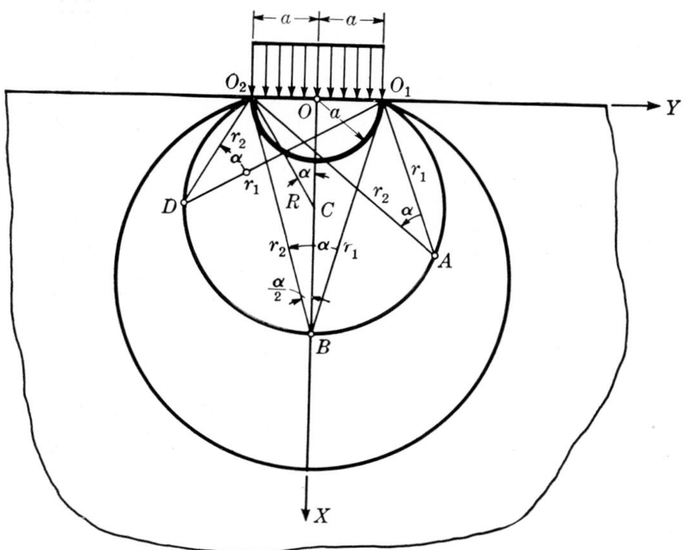

FIG. 2.27 Theoretical Stress Pattern for a Uniformly Distributed Load Acting over a Finite Interval of a Semi-Infinite Plate.

§2.13 Theoretical and Photoelastic Stress Patterns. If a circle be drawn from a center C on a line normal to the straight edge of the plate bisecting the interval O_1O_2, Fig. 2.27, on which the uniformly distributed load is acting, then the angle α between r_1 and r_2 would clearly be the same for all points on this circle, such as points A, B, D. Since, at any point

$$\tau_{\text{max.}} = \frac{q_o \sin \alpha}{\pi t}, \tag{2.24}$$

it follows that on a circle of a given radius the maximum shear is constant. These circles, therefore, represent theoretical fringes.

Furthermore, the maximum shear in the plate would clearly occur on the circle for which $\alpha = \pi/2$, and would be given by

$$(\tau_{\text{max.}})_{\alpha=\pi/2} = \frac{q_o}{\pi t}. \tag{2.26}$$

This value of α is found on the circle of diameter O_1O_2, which has its center at the origin O on the edge of the plate, Fig. 2.27. ***This fringe or isochromatic is of highest order, and its theoretical shape is semicircular.*** It is the heavy semicircle with center at O.

The straight interval O_1O_2 represents the limiting position of arcs of circles the radii of which approach infinity. The angle α on this interval O_1O_2 is then zero, and so the shear stress vanishes. The shear stress is also zero on the remaining portions of the straight edge, i.e., from O_1 to the right and from O_2 to the left.

It is also interesting to compare the ratios of the diameters of the circles of successive fringe orders. Inspection of Fig. 2.27 shows that

$$\sin\alpha = \frac{a}{R},$$

in which $2a$ is the length of the interval on which the load is acting and R is the radius of the circle. Substituting in eq. (2.24) we have

$$\tau_{\text{max.}} = \frac{q_o}{\pi t}\frac{a}{R}. \tag{2.27}$$

The maximum shear stresses on different circles are thus inversely proportional to the radii of the circles. The stress, or fringe order, on a circle of radius $2a$ is one-half of the stress, or fringe order, on the circle of radius a.

The experimental verification of these conclusions is not easy, owing to the difficulties of producing a uniform load on the boundary. The stress patterns of Figs. 2.28 and 2.29 show several attempts at such verification. In Fig. 2.28 the load was applied through a steel block and was equalized by means of a gasket. Under higher load the fringes in the vicinity of the load are seen to approach a circular shape and the fringe of highest order is approximately semicircular. A different method to produce uniform loading is shown in Fig. 2.29. Here the load was equally distributed among four small Bakelite blocks and subsequently equalized by means of a gasket.

The best approximation to uniform distribution was, however,

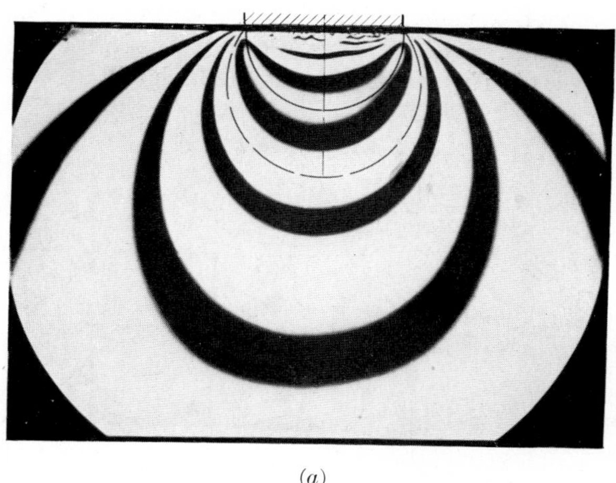

(a)

(b)

Fig. 2.28 Photoelastic Stress Patterns Produced by Approximately Uniform Loads on a Finite Interval of a Large Bakelite Plate.

The loads act on a steel die and are equalized by a layer of cardboard. Dimensions of Bakelite plate: 12 in. by 6 in. by 0.247 in. (a) Load = 430 lb.; length of die = 0.69 in. (b) Load = 1052 lb.; length of die = 0.761 in. Bakelite plate and cardboard same as in (a).

obtained from an hydraulic loading through a rubber sack glued to a rectangular metal box, using water as weights and gelatin, which is vastly more sensitive than Bakelite, as a model. The resulting pattern is shown in Fig. 2.30. This stress pattern, although still imperfect, corroborates the theoretical conclusions. The fringes are approximately circular and converge at the ends of the loaded zone.

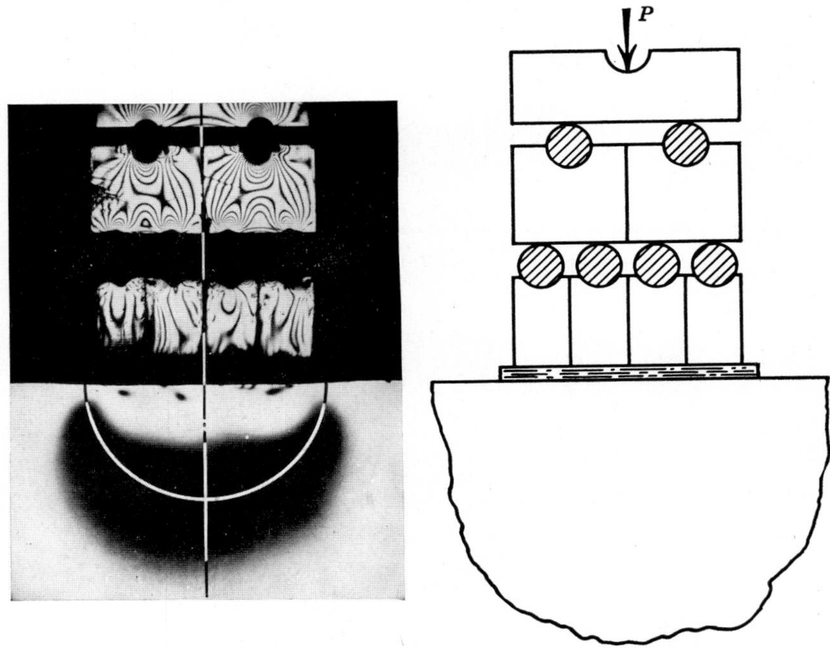

FIG. 2.29 Stress Pattern of a Uniformly Distributed Load on a Large Plate.

The load is transmitted through steel pins acting on small Bakelite blocks which in turn rest on a cardboard gasket.

In Fig. 2.30 the maximum fringe order in the region marked A is $3\frac{1}{2}$. This region corresponds to the semicircular arc of diameter $2a$ equal to the interval on which the load is acting. It can be seen that the fringe order on the circle of radius $2a$ is very nearly $1\frac{3}{4}$ or $\frac{1}{2}$ of what it is on the semicircle of radius a, which agrees with eq. (2.27). The deviations from the theoretical pattern are probably due to the large deformations of the gelatin surface and the restraining effect which the metal walls of the rectangular box exerted on the flat rubber bottom, which reduces the load intensity on the model near the edges.

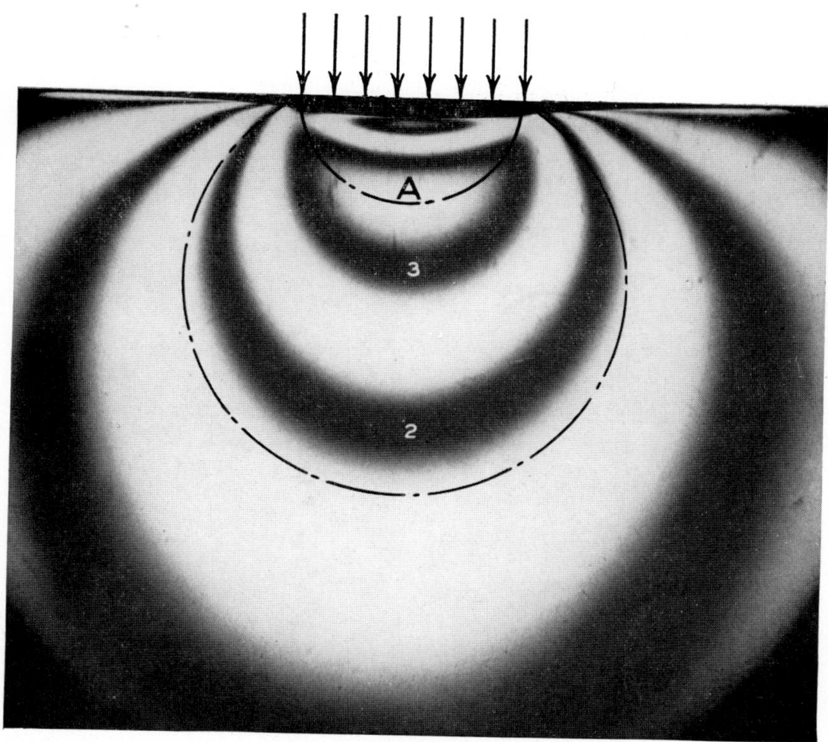

FIG. 2.30 Comparison of Photoelastic and Theoretical Stress Patterns for a Large Gelatin Plate Subjected to a Sensibly Uniform Pressure on a Small Region. For details of model see Fig. 10.16, Vol. I.

§2.14 The Stress Function $\phi = Cr^2\theta$. Consider an infinite semicircular plate of thickness t with the following boundary forces, Fig. 2.31: (1) a uniform tension per unit area of intensity $q_o/2t$ along the straight positive branch of the Y axis, (2) an equal uniform compression on the negative branch of the Y axis, (3) radial stresses on the semicircular arc given by $q_o\theta/\pi t$, and (4) a constant negative shear of magnitude $q_o/2\pi t$ per unit area on the whole boundary.

The stresses produced by such boundary forces can be found from the stress function

$$\phi = Cr^2\theta, \tag{2.28}$$

in which C is a constant and r, θ polar coordinates. This function satisfies the compatibility equation (1.42), and by eqs. (1.24) the stress components are

$$\left.\begin{aligned}\sigma_r &= \frac{1}{r}\frac{\partial\phi}{\partial r} + \frac{1}{r^2}\frac{\partial^2\phi}{\partial\theta^2} = 2C\theta, && (a)\\ \sigma_\theta &= \frac{\partial^2\phi}{\partial r^2} = 2C\theta, && (b)\\ \tau_{r\theta} &= -\frac{\partial}{\partial r}\left(\frac{1}{r}\frac{\partial\phi}{\partial\theta}\right) = -C. && (c)\end{aligned}\right\}(2.29)$$

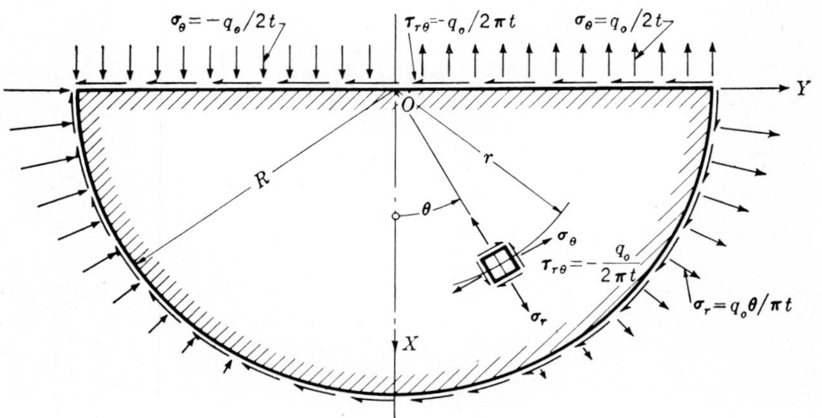

FIG. 2.31 Sketch Showing Boundary Forces on a Semicircular Plate, Resulting from the Stress Function Given by Eq. (2.28).

Choosing

$$C = \frac{q_o}{2\pi t}, \tag{2.30}$$

we have

$$\left.\begin{aligned}\sigma_r &= \frac{q_o\theta}{\pi t}, && (a)\\ \sigma_\theta &= \frac{q_o\theta}{\pi t}, && (b)\\ \tau_{r\theta} &= -\frac{q_o}{2\pi t}. && (c)\end{aligned}\right\}(2.31)$$

Boundary Conditions. On the straight edge of the plate, the Y axis, Fig. 2.31, $\theta = \pm\pi/2$, and the tangential stresses σ_θ become

$$\sigma_\theta = \frac{q_o}{2t}$$

for the positive branch, and

$$\sigma_\theta = -\frac{q_o}{2t}$$

for the negative branch. On the semicircular arc the radial stresses σ_r are clearly the same as the boundary stresses. They are positive when θ is positive, and negative when θ is negative. The shear stresses $\tau_{r\theta}$ are constant and equal $-q_o/2\pi t$ on the whole boundary. It follows that the stress system given by eq. (2.31) obtained from the stress function (2.28) fully satisfies the assumed boundary conditions shown in Fig. 2.31.

The rectangular stress components corresponding to eqs. (2.31) can be obtained from eqs. (1.7) and (1.8), Vol. I, or by superposition and inspection. The results are

$$\left.\begin{aligned} \sigma_x &= \frac{q_o}{2\pi t}(2\theta + \sin 2\theta), & (a)\\ \sigma_y &= \frac{q_o}{2\pi t}(2\theta - \sin 2\theta), & (b)\\ \tau_{xy} &= -\frac{q_o}{2\pi t}\cos 2\theta. & (c) \end{aligned}\right\} \quad (2.32)$$

§2.15 Uniform Load on a Finite Portion of a Semi-Infinite Plate. (Alternative Treatment.) We consider again the case of a uniformly distributed load of intensity q_o per unit length or q_o/t per unit area acting on the finite interval O_1O_2, Fig. 2.32(a), of a semi-infinite plate. This type of loading can be obtained by superimposing the two sets of boundary forces shown in Figs. 2.32(b) and 2.32(c). The boundary forces in Fig. 2.32(b) are identical with those shown in Fig. 2.31 with O_1 as an origin. Those shown in Fig. 2.32(c) have O_2 as an origin and are equal and opposite to those in Fig. 2.31. By this superposition all boundary forces are reduced to zero except those in the interval O_1O_2, where they combine to give a resultant compression of an intensity q_o. Therefore the stresses produced by the uniform loading of Fig. 2.32(a) can be obtained by adding algebraically the stresses produced by the two sets of forces shown in Figs. 2.32(b) and 2.32(c) which are obtainable from eqs. (2.32). The formulas for the resulting stresses are the same as

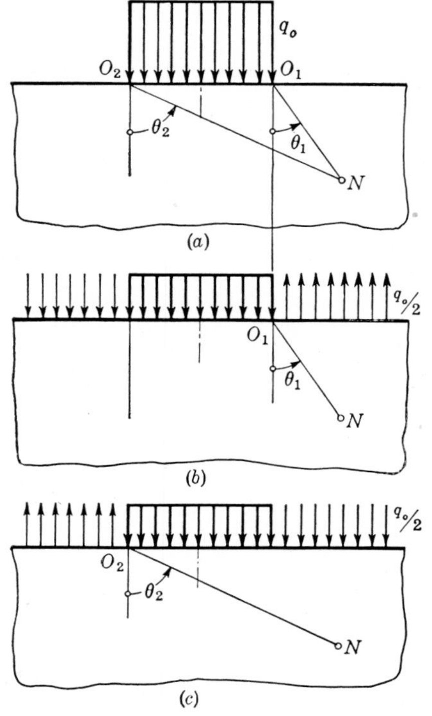

FIG. 2.32 Sketches Illustrating Method of Combining Two Sets of Opposite Forces to Obtain a Uniform Load on a Finite Interval of a Semi-Infinite Plate.

those given by eqs. (2.21) of §2.12. It follows that the expressions for the principal stresses are the same as those given by eq. (2.25).

It is interesting to point out that ***the solution for a normal concentrated load obtained in §2.2 also follows from eqs. (2.21).*** Thus, let a normal concentrated load P be viewed as the limiting resultant force of a uni-

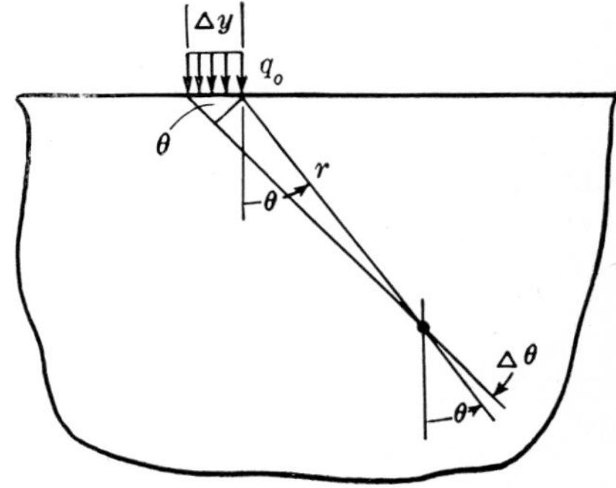

FIG. 2.33 Sketch Illustrating Limiting Resultant Force of a Uniformly Distributed Load Acting on a Small Interval Δy.

formly distributed load of intensity q_o acting on a very small interval Δy of the straight boundary, and corresponding to a small angle $\Delta\theta$, Fig. 2.33, so that

$$P = q_o \, \Delta y$$

and

$$q_o = \frac{P}{\Delta y} \cdot$$

As pointed out above, the principal stresses are here given by eq. (2.25), i.e.,

$$p, q = \frac{q_o}{\pi t} (-\alpha \pm \sin \alpha).$$

Substituting $\Delta\theta$ for α and $P/\Delta y$ for q_o, we have

$$p, q = \frac{P}{\Delta y \pi t}(-\Delta\theta \pm \sin \Delta\theta).$$

Inspection of Fig. 2.33 shows that

$$\Delta y = \frac{r\,\Delta\theta}{\cos\theta}.$$

Substituting in the expressions for p and q given above, we obtain

$$p, q = \frac{P\cos\theta}{\pi t r}\left(-1 \pm \frac{\sin\Delta\theta}{\Delta\theta}\right).$$

Since

$$\underset{\alpha \to 0}{\text{limit}} \frac{\sin\alpha}{\alpha} = 1,$$

it follows that as θ approaches zero

$$p = \sigma_\theta = 0$$

and

$$q = \sigma_r = -\frac{2P\cos\theta}{\pi t r},$$

which are the same expressions as those given by eqs. (2.8).

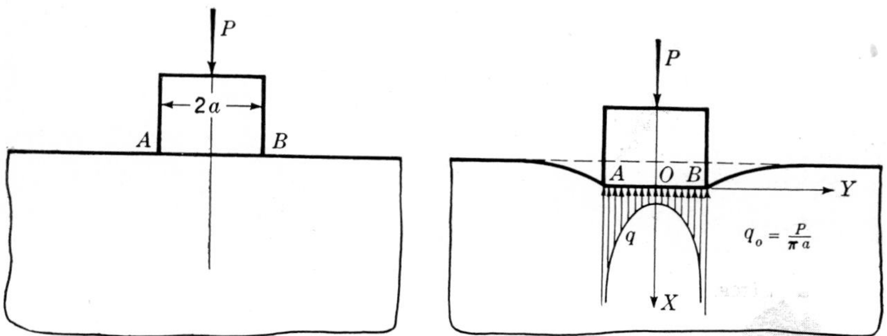

FIG. 2.34 Sketches Showing the Pressure Distribution under a Rigid Die Pressing on a Semi-Infinite Plate.

§2.16 Stresses Produced by a Concentrated Load Acting through a Rigid Die.[1] It can be shown that when a load is applied through a rigid flat die, so that the deflections under it are constant, Fig. 2.34, the dis-

[1] See article by M. A. Sadowsky, *Zeitschrift angew. Math. Mech.*, Vol. 8, p. 107, 1928.

tribution of the pressures under it is given by

$$q = \frac{P}{\pi\sqrt{a^2 - y^2}}. \tag{2.34}$$

This expression shows that $q = P/\pi a$ when $y = 0$, and q becomes infinite when y equals $\pm a$, Fig. 2.34. There are thus marked stress concentra-

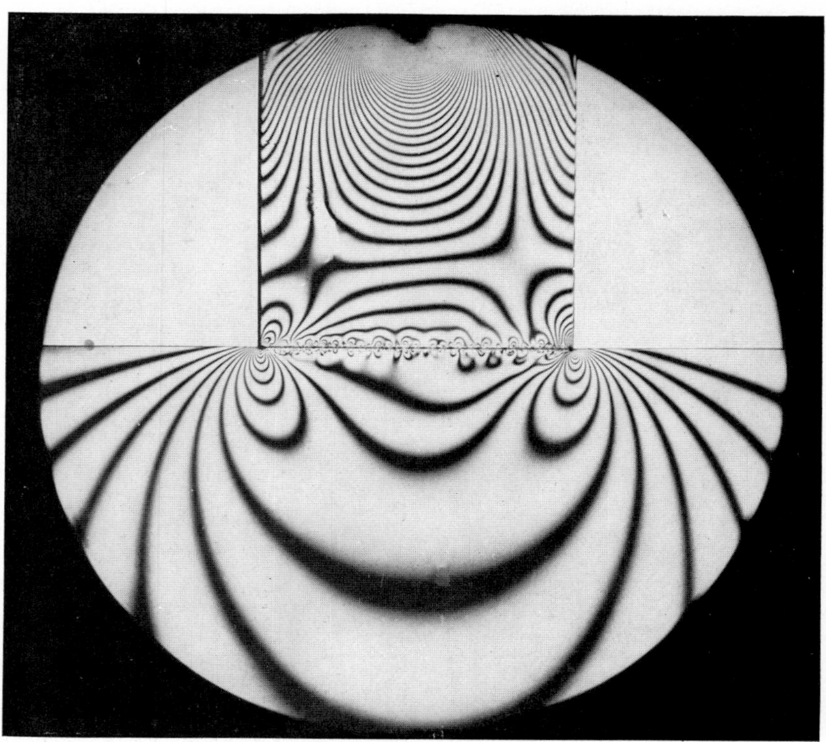

FIG. 2.35 Stress Pattern of a Large Bakelite Plate Compressed by a Bakelite Die, Showing Stress Concentrations at Ends of Die.

Load = 991.0 lb.; thickness of plate = 0.247 in.; length of die = 1.140 in.; thickness of die = 0.352 in.; model fringe value = 174 psi. shear.

tions at the ends of the die, points A and B. These conclusions are clearly corroborated by the photoelastic stress pattern of Fig. 2.35.

§2.17 Transmission of a Concentrated Load through a Long Plank on an Elastic Foundation. Consider a long rectangular block or beam subjected to two collinear equal and opposite concentrated loads,

Fig. 2.36. The section through the X axis is clearly a section of symmetry, and as such it remains free from shear stresses and does not change its shape, i.e., it remains horizontal and flat. This section acts like a rigid plane.

It can be shown mathematically[1] that the vertical stresses σ_y across this section follow the distribution shown in Fig. 2.36. They are compressive between points A and B where $x = \pm 1.35b$ approximately, and then change into small tensions which rapidly approach zero.

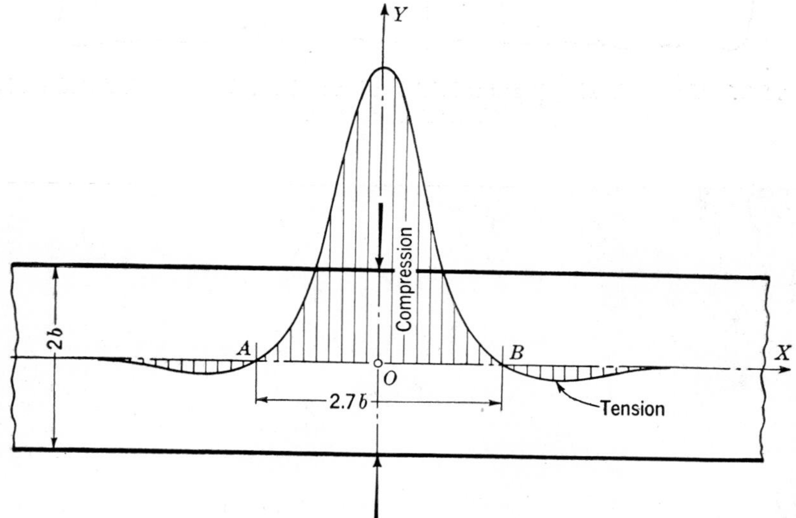

FIG. 2.36 Curve Showing Stress Distribution in a Long Plank Subjected to Collinear Concentrated Loads.

From this it is concluded that if a long plank or beam be placed on a smooth rigid plane base and pressed down by means of a normal central concentrated load, Fig. 2.37, this plank could not be in contact with the base across its full length; but this contact would be limited to a central interval approximately 2.7 times the height of the block, because, in order to maintain full contact, that is, in order for the base to remain flat, the ends would have to carry tensile stresses which the base clearly cannot exert. It follows that if the block is longer than 2.7 times its height the ends would rise off the base.

A photoelastic stress pattern bearing on this point is shown in Fig. 2.38. It shows a block about 4.5 times as long as its height which was pressed

[1] See §5.10, pp. 436–438, *Treatise on Photoelasticity*, by Coker and Filon.

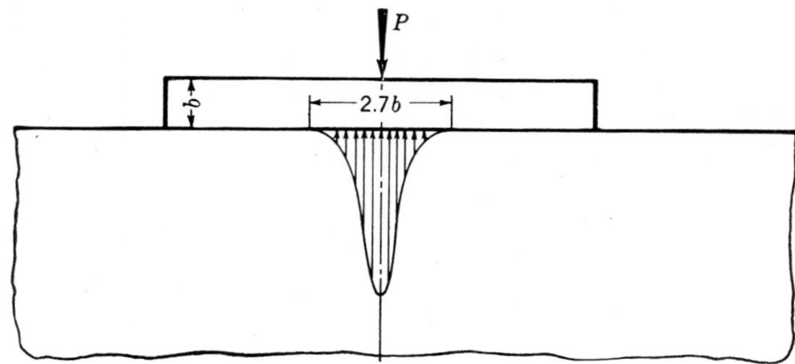

FIG. 2.37 Curve Showing Pressure Distribution under a Long Plank Acted on by Concentrated Load.

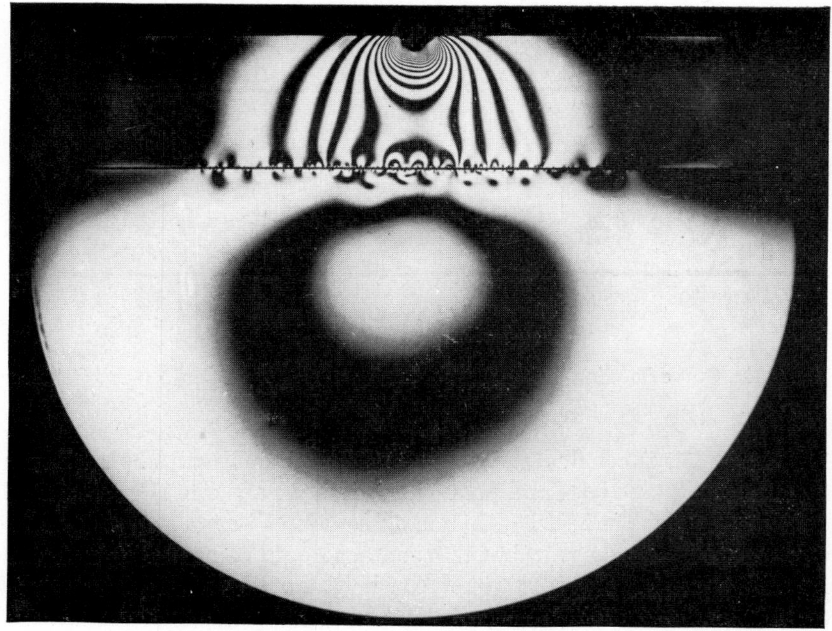

FIG. 2.38 Stress Pattern of a Large Bakelite Plate Compressed by a Concentrated Load Acting through a Long Plank. The pattern clearly indicates that the pressures drop to zero at points approximately equal to $\pm$ 1.35b from the center of the plank.

Height of plank = 0.481 in.; length of plank = 2.198 in.; thickness of plank = 0.244 in.; thickness of plate = 0.247 in.; material fringe value = 43 psi. shear; load = 13.47 lb.

down on a flat base. The surfaces of contact were machined but not polished. Nevertheless the photograph clearly shows that the ends of the block have separated from the base and that the length of contact is approximately as predicted by the theory. The distribution of the pressure under the block follows approximately the curve of Fig. 2.37. These pressures differ radically from those that would exist if the height of the block was considerably greater; see Fig. 2.35, where we found extremely large stress concentration at the ends of the block.

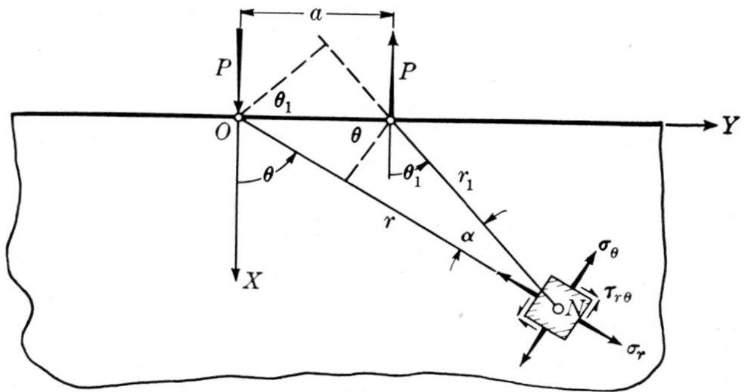

FIG. 2.39 Notation for a Couple on a Semi-Infinite Plate.

§2.18 Stresses Due to a Couple. Consider again the semi-infinite plate and assume a couple of moment Pa to be acting on the straight edge, Fig. 2.39. Using eqs. (2.8) and superposition the resultant stresses are

$$\left.\begin{aligned}\sigma_r &= \frac{2P}{\pi t}\left(-\frac{\cos\theta}{r} + \frac{\cos\theta_1}{r_1}\cos^2\alpha\right), &&(a)\\ \sigma_\theta &= \frac{2P\cos\theta_1}{\pi t r_1}\sin^2\alpha, &&(b)\\ \tau_{r\theta} &= \frac{P}{\pi t}\frac{\cos\theta_1}{r_1}\sin 2\alpha. &&(c)\end{aligned}\right\}(2.35)$$

Assume now that the moment arm a gets smaller and force P gets proportionately greater in such a manner that the product stays constant, i.e.,

$$Pa = M, \quad \text{a constant.}$$

This would represent the limiting condition of a couple acting on an infinitesimal area. In order to find the stresses resulting from the couple in this limiting case we observe that, Fig. 2.39,

$$\left.\begin{aligned} r_1 \cos\theta_1 &= r\cos\theta, && (a)\\ r\cos\alpha &= r_1 + a\sin\theta_1 && (b)\\ r_1\sin\alpha &= a\cos\theta. && (c)\end{aligned}\right\} \quad (2.36)$$

The expressions for the stress components may then be written as

$$\left.\begin{aligned} \sigma_r &= \frac{2P\cos\theta}{\pi t r}\left(-1 + \frac{r^2}{{r_1}^2}\cos^2\alpha\right)\\ &= \frac{2Pa}{\pi t r}\cos\theta\left(\frac{2\sin\theta_1}{r_1} + \frac{a\sin^2\theta_1}{{r_1}^2}\right), && (a)\\ \sigma_\theta &= \frac{2Pa^2\cos^3\theta_1}{\pi t r_1 r^2}, && (b)\\ \tau_{r\theta} &= \frac{2P\cos\theta_1\cos\alpha\sin\alpha}{\pi t r_1}. && (c)\end{aligned}\right\} \quad (2.37)$$

Approaching the limit

$$a \rightarrow 0, \quad \alpha \rightarrow 0, \quad Pa = M, \quad r_1 \rightarrow r, \quad \text{and} \quad \theta \rightarrow \theta_1.$$

At the limit, observing that $r_1 \sin\alpha = a\cos\theta$, the expressions for the stress components become

$$\left.\begin{aligned} \sigma_r &= \frac{2M\sin 2\theta}{\pi t r^2} && (a)\\ \sigma_\theta &= 0, && (b)\\ \tau_{r\theta} &= \frac{2M\cos^2\theta}{\pi t r^2}. && (c)\end{aligned}\right\} \quad (2.38)$$

An application of these equations is found in a cantilever protruding from a large wall, Fig. 2.40. If the lever be cut off along the edge of the wall, the wall will be acted upon by a shear force and a couple. The stresses in the wall can then be found by superimposing the stresses induced by the shear force upon the stresses produced by the couple.

The stress components of eqs. (2.38) can also be obtained from the stress function

$$\phi = -\frac{M}{\pi t}\left(\theta + \sin\frac{2\theta}{2}\right). \quad (2.39)$$

Owing to the approximations made, the final results for the stresses are

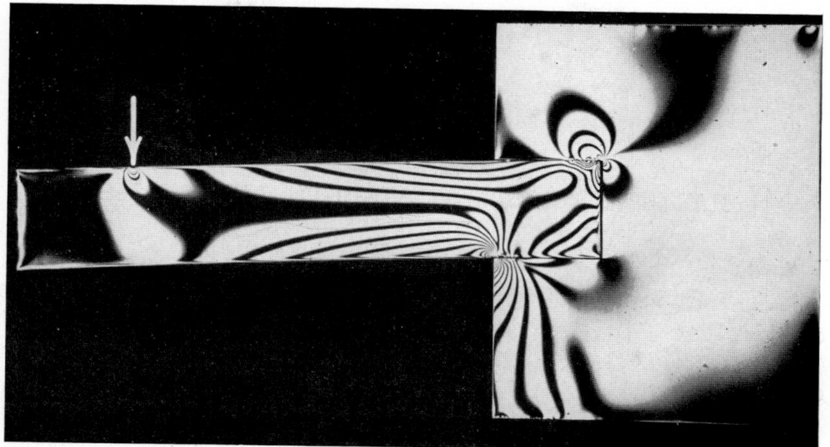

FIG. 2.40 Stress Pattern of a Cantilever Beam.

Load = 14.84 lb.; bending moment = 29.68 lb.-in.; dimensions of beam = 3.315 in. by 0.592 in. by 0.196 in.

valid only at points whose distance from the origin are large in relation to the magnitude of the moment arm $\Delta y = a$.

The stresses produced by concentrated loads acting on a semi-infinite plate at some distance below the straight edge have been investigated mathematically by E. Melan.[1]

[1] See *Zeitschrift angew. Math. Mech.*, Vol. 12, p. 343, 1932.

CHAPTER 3

RADIAL STRESSES IN WEDGES AND BEAMS

PART I WEDGES

§3.1 Introduction. This chapter consists of two parts. In Part I we consider the state of stress in a wedge subjected to concentrated loads at the apex. This state of stress is radial similar to that developed in Chapter 2 for the semi-infinite plate.

The apex of the wedge will be taken as the origin of the coordinate system, and the axis of symmetry of the wedge as the X axis. The polar

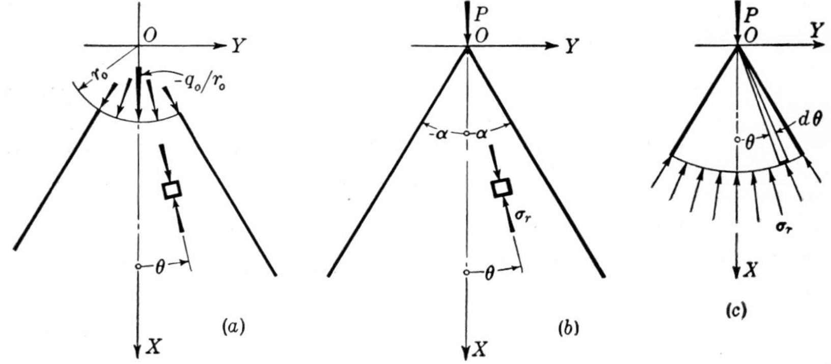

Fig. 3.1 Sketches Showing a Wedge with a Concentrated Load at the Vertex Acting along the Axis of Symmetry; Also the Statical Equivalent of That Load and Resulting Radial Stresses.

coordinates of a point will be denoted by r and θ, the angle θ being measured from the X axis counterclockwise positive and clockwise negative. Forces parallel to the coordinate axes will be called positive when their directions are the same as the positive directions of the axes.

In Part II we discuss the effect of radial stresses on simply supported beams carrying concentrated loads at the center.

§3.2 Concentrated Load Acting at the Apex of a Wedge along the Line of Symmetry. We consider first a wedge of infinite length, Fig. 3.1(a), with a small groove of radius r_o removed from the apex, and assume this groove to be subjected to boundary forces defined by the expression

$$q = -q_o \frac{\cos \theta}{r_o}, \tag{2.2}$$

in which q_o is a constant. The state of stress in this wedge can be obtained from the same stress function

$$\boldsymbol{\phi = Cr\theta \sin \theta} \tag{2.3}$$

which was found effective in Chapter 2 for the semi-infinite plate, and which yields the stress components

$$\left.\begin{aligned} \boldsymbol{\sigma_r} &= \boldsymbol{2C \frac{\cos \theta}{r}}, & (a)\\ \boldsymbol{\sigma_\theta} &= \boldsymbol{0}, & (b)\\ \boldsymbol{\tau_{r\theta}} &= \boldsymbol{0}. & (c) \end{aligned}\right\} \tag{2.5}$$

These stresses evidently satisfy all boundary conditions in the wedge. They vanish at infinity, leave the straight edges free, and on the groove of radius r_o they reduce to the assumed boundary forces q if C is taken equal to $-q_o/2$.

Furthermore, the statical equivalent of the forces on the groove is a concentrated load parallel to the plane of symmetry of the wedge and acting at the apex, Fig. 3.1(b). ***It follows that eqs. (2.5) represent the solution for such a concentrated load.***

In order to determine the constant C of eq. (2.5a) in terms of the load P we set out a sector of the wedge as a free body, Fig. 3.1(c), and write $\Sigma X = 0$. Thus

$$P - \int_{-\alpha}^{\alpha} \sigma_r \cos \theta \, dA = 0. \tag{3.1}$$

Hence, denoting the thickness by t, we have

$$\begin{aligned} P &= \int_{-\alpha}^{\alpha} 2C \frac{\cos \theta}{r} tr \cos \theta \, d\theta \\ &= 2Ct \int_{-\alpha}^{\alpha} \cos^2 \theta \, d\theta \\ &= Ct(2\alpha + \sin 2\alpha), \end{aligned} \tag{3.2}$$

and

$$C = \frac{P}{t(2\alpha + \sin 2\alpha)}. \tag{3.3}$$

Substituting in eq. (2.5a) and remembering that σ_r is a compressive stress, we have

$$\sigma_r = -\frac{2P\cos\theta}{rt(2\alpha + \sin 2\alpha)}. \tag{3.4}$$

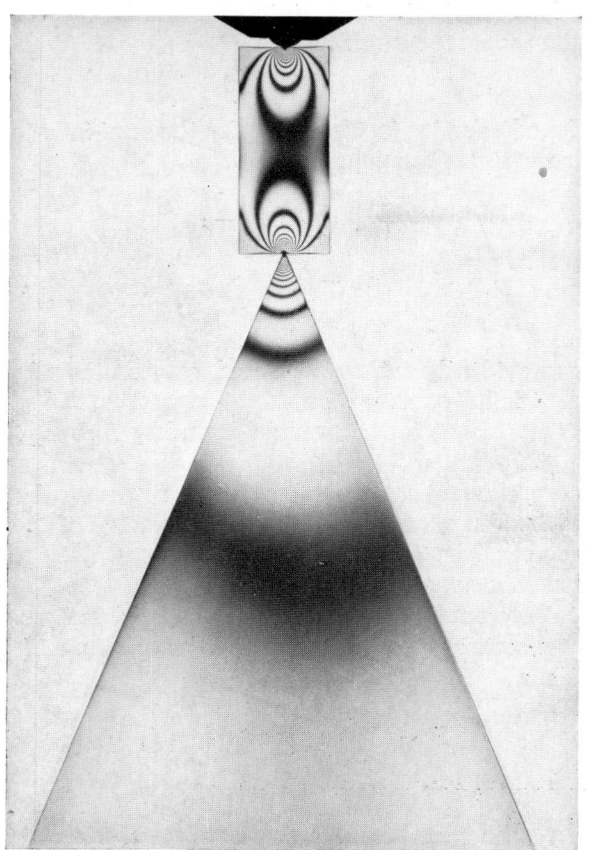

FIG. 3.2 Stress Pattern of a Wedge Subjected to a Load at Its Vertex along the Axis of Symmetry.

Load = 34.3 lb.; angle of wedge = 44° 30′; thickness of wedge = 0.176 in.; fringe value of model = 244 psi. shear. Dimensions of bar: width = 0.290 in.; length = 0.677 in.; thickness = 0.171 in.

Putting $\alpha = \pi/2$, we obtain the stresses for a load acting normally to the straight edge of a semi-infinite plate, which agree with the previous results given by eq. (2.8a).

The theoretical fringes are arcs of circles having their centers on the line of symmetry of the wedge and passing through the apex. The diameters of these circles are inversely proportional to the fringe order. A photoelastic stress pattern of such a wedge is shown in Fig. 3.2. Such photoelastic wedges have been used in the measurement of pressures.[1]

§3.3 A Simplified Permanent Compensator. The radial state of stress developed in a wedge and discussed in the preceding article can be utilized to make a simplified compensator, which would simultaneously contain a large range of stresses similar to those existing in bending. This type of compensator was suggested by Coker and Filon.[2]

The recent developments of the frozen stress pattern provide a means for making permanent compensators, thereby dispensing completely with the need for a special instrument for this purpose. A stress pattern of such a fixed or frozen, wedge-like compensator is shown in Fig. 3.3. The stress in the shank of this strip may be treated as approximately radial. Such a compensator is permanent in nature, and the fringe orders can be readily identified. It has the additional advantage that it can be brought in direct contact with the model, thereby simplifying the problem of focusing, and is easily oriented with respect to the boundary of the model. It remains to be added that a permanent compensator of variable stresses can also be made from a beam in pure bending. This compensator might have some further advantages. It would contain a clear neutral surface as well as a range of stress varying from pure tension to an equal pure compression.

§3.4 Concentrated Load Acting at the Apex of a Wedge in a Direction Perpendicular to Its Axis, Fig. 3.4(*a*). We again consider a wedge of infinite length with a groove removed from the apex, Fig. 3.4(*b*), and assume the boundary forces on the groove to follow the distribution

$$q = -q_o \frac{\cos \theta'}{r_o}, \tag{3.5}$$

the directed angle θ' being measured from the direction of the Y axis which coincides with the direction of the load, Figs. 3.4(*a*) and (*b*). The groove is thus subjected to compressions below the axis of the wedge and to tensions above it. It is clear that ***all boundary conditions are satisfied by the simple state of radial stress given by eqs.*** (*2.5*) with $\boldsymbol{\theta'}$ replac-

[1] See "Application of Photo-Elastic Effect to Measurement of Pressure," by F. Takabeya and T. Shingo, *Memoirs of the Faculty of Engineering, Hokkaido Imperial University*, Vol. 3, No. 1, March, 1932.

[2] See *Treatise on Photoelasticity* by Coker and Filon, §4.21.

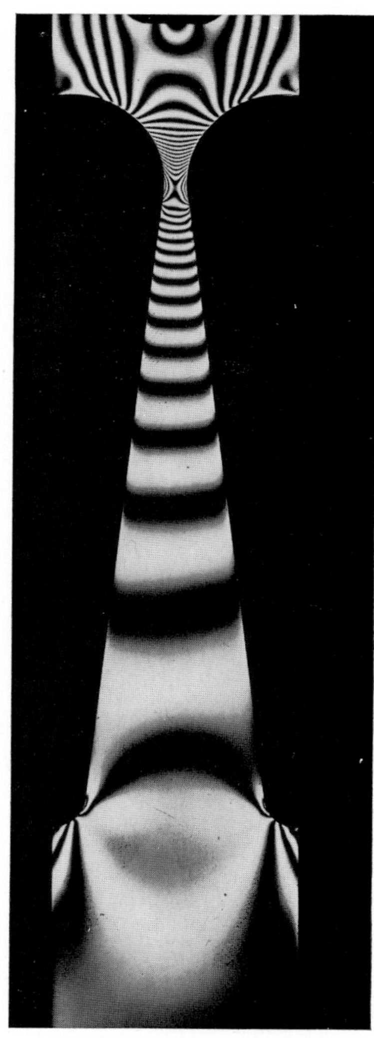

FIG. **3.3** Stress Pattern of a Wedge-Shaped Bar in Tension Which **Can Be Used as** a Permanent Compensator.

Number of fringes varies from 3 in the wide part of the shank to **18 near the neck.** Load = 172.5 lb.; width, lower end = 0.725 in.; width at neck = **0.102 in.**; thickness of bar = 0.243 in.; length of taper = 2.62 in.; fringe value of model = **177** psi. shear.

ing θ, i.e.,

$$\left.\begin{aligned} \sigma_r &= 2C\frac{\cos\theta'}{r}, && (a)\\ \sigma_\theta &= 0, && (b)\\ \tau_{r\theta} &= 0. && (c) \end{aligned}\right\} \quad (3.6)$$

Furthermore, the statical equivalent of the boundary forces is a concentrated load perpendicular to the axis of the wedge and equal to the applied load P.

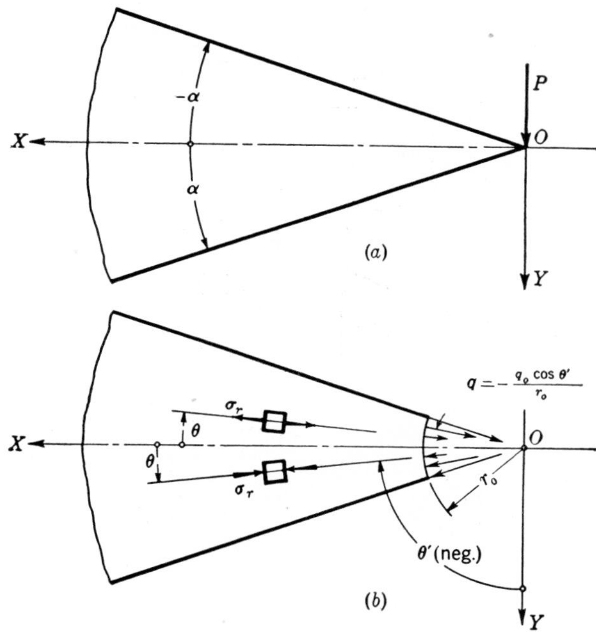

FIG. 3.4 Sketches of a Wedge Subjected to a Concentrated Load at the Vertex Normal to the Axis of Symmetry, and Statically Equivalent System; also Resulting Radial Stresses.

It is left to the reader to show that in this case

$$C = \frac{P}{t(2\alpha - \sin 2\alpha)}. \quad (3.7)$$

Substituting in eq. (3.6), we obtain

$$\sigma_r = -\frac{2P\cos\theta'}{rt(2\alpha - \sin 2\alpha)}. \quad (3.8)$$

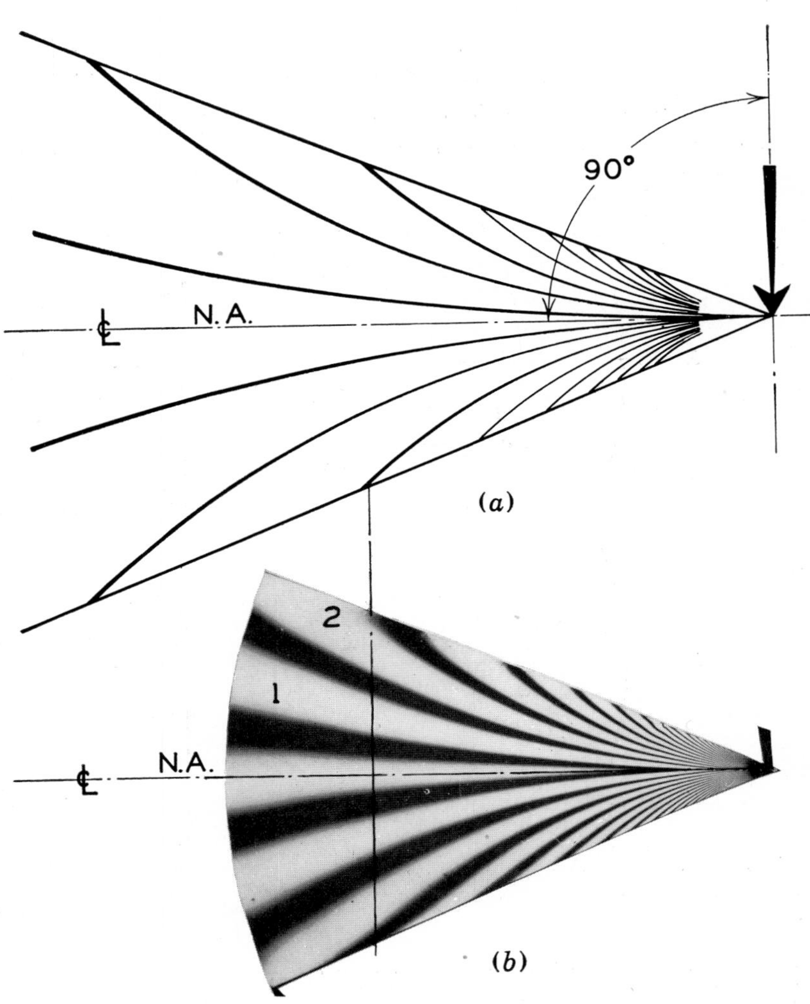

FIG. 3.5 Comparison of Theoretical and Photoelastic Stress Patterns Obtained from a Wedge Subjected to a Load at the Vertex Normal to the Axis of Symmetry. $P = 37.9$ lb.; $t = 0.250$ in.; $F = 172$ psi. shear.

The minus sign is inserted in order to satisfy the boundary conditions on the groove, where σ_r is negative when $\cos \theta'$ is positive, and vice versa. In terms of the angle θ which is measured from the X axis

$$\left.\begin{aligned} \sigma_r &= -\frac{2P \sin \theta}{rt(2\alpha - \sin 2\alpha)}, && (a)\\ \sigma_\theta &= 0, && (b)\\ \tau_{r\theta} &= 0, && (c) \end{aligned}\right\} (3.9)$$

since

$$\theta' = \theta - 90°$$

and

$$\cos \theta' = \sin \theta.$$

The theoretical fringes are arcs of circles tangent to the X axis with centers on the line of the load, and the diameters of these circles are inversely proportional to the fringe orders. These arcs are symmetrically distributed about the X axis, which lies in the neutral surface, Fig. 3.5(a). A corresponding photoelastic stress pattern is shown in Fig. 3.5(b).

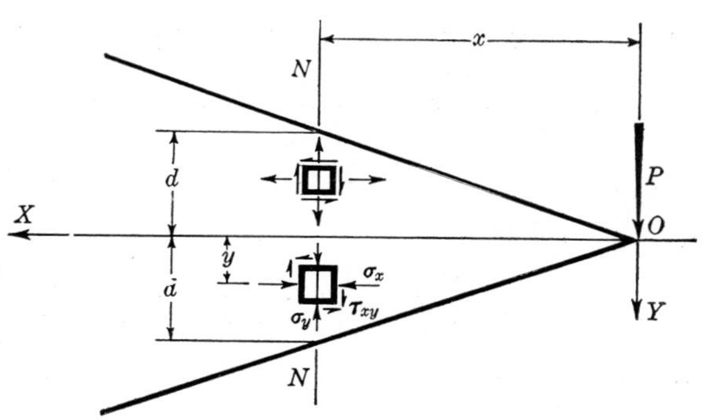

Fig. 3.6 Sketch Showing Notation for Rectangular Stress Components in a Wedge with a Concentrated Load at the Vertex Normal to Its Axis of Symmetry.

§3.5 Rectangular Stress Components for a Load Perpendicular to Axis of Wedge. It is useful to have expressions for the rectangular stress components σ_x, σ_y, τ_{xy} for an infinite wedge subjected to a concentrated load at the apex perpendicular to the axis, Fig. 3.6. These can be obtained directly from the formula for σ_r. Thus, by eqs. (2.14), we have

$$\left.\begin{aligned} \sigma_x &= \sigma_r \cos^2\theta, & (a)\\ \sigma_y &= \sigma_r \sin^2\theta, & (b)\\ \tau_{xy} &= \sigma_r \sin\theta\cos\theta. & (c) \end{aligned}\right\}(2.14)$$

Introducing the expression for σ_r from eq. (3.9a) and noting that

$$r^2 = x^2 + y^2, \quad \sin\theta = \frac{y}{r}, \quad \text{and} \quad \cos\theta = \frac{x}{r}, \tag{3.10}$$

we can write

$$\left.\begin{aligned} \sigma_x &= -\frac{Ax^2y}{(x^2+y^2)^2}, & (a)\\ \sigma_y &= -\frac{Ay^3}{(x^2+y^2)^2}, & (b)\\ \tau_{xy} &= -\frac{Axy^2}{(x^2+y^2)^2}, & (c) \end{aligned}\right\}(3.11)$$

in which

$$A = \frac{2P}{t(2\alpha - \sin 2\alpha)}. \tag{3.12}$$

Values of A as a function of α for $P = 1$, $t = 1$ are given by the curve of Fig. 3.7.

It will be useful to examine the variations of the stresses across a transverse section where x is constant. Putting the partial derivatives of the stresses equal to zero we can determine the existence and the positions of the critical values. Thus

$$\frac{\partial\sigma_x}{\partial y} = -\frac{Ax^2}{(x^2+y^2)^3}\left[(x^2+y^2) - 4y^2\right] = 0.$$

This derivative is zero when

$$(x^2+y^2) - 4y^2 = 0,$$

or

$$r^2 = 4y^2.$$

Hence the numerical value of σ_x is a maximum at

$$\frac{y}{r} = \sin\theta = \pm\tfrac{1}{2},$$

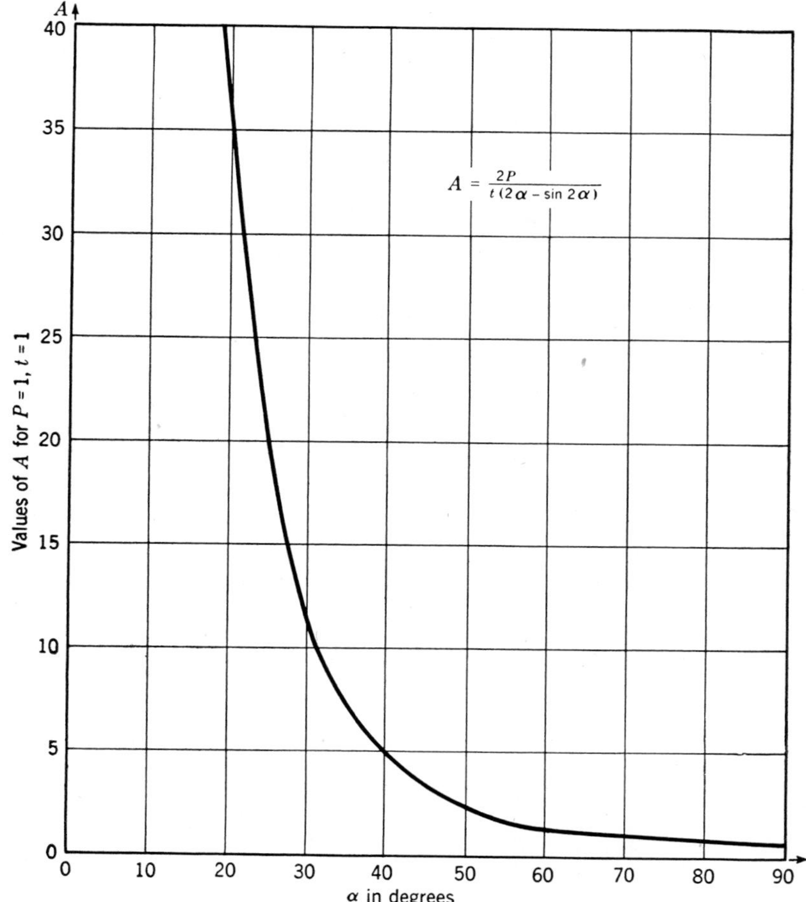

FIG. 3.7 Curve Giving Values of Constant A, in Eq. (3.12), as a Function of α, for $P = 1, t = 1$.

i.e., where

$$\theta = \pm 30°.$$

Similarly $\partial\sigma_y/\partial y = 0$ when

$$3(x^2 + y^2) - 4y^2 = 0,$$

and σ_y reaches a numerical maximum at

$$\theta = \pm 60°.$$

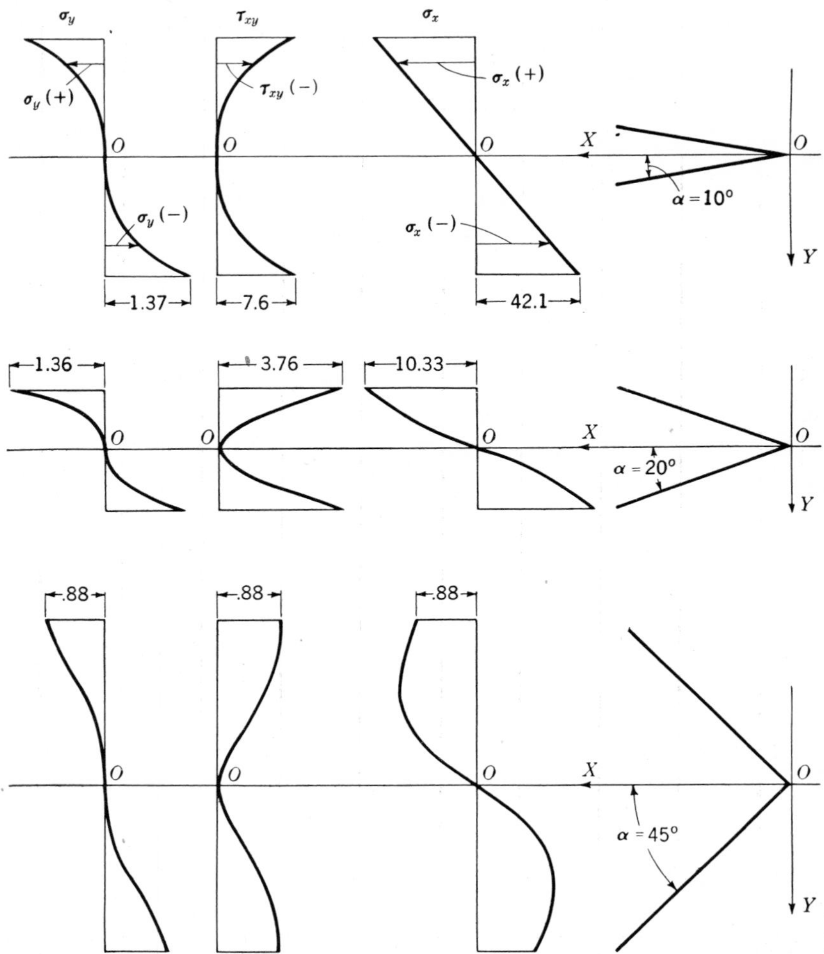

FIG. 3.8 Curves Showing Distribution of Rectangular Stress Components in a Wedge with a Concentrated Load at the Vertex Normal to Its Axis of Symmetry. Arbitrary values used are: $P = 1$ lb., $t = 1$ in., $x = 1$ in.

Lastly $\partial\tau_{xy}/\partial y = 0$ when

$$(x^2 + y^2) - 2y^2 = 0,$$

and τ_{xy} reaches a numerical maximum at

$$\theta = \pm 45°.$$

The distribution of the rectangular stresses for several values of α is given in Fig. 3.8.

§3.6 Triangular Cantilever Beams. The infinite wedge discussed in the preceding two articles may be viewed as a cantilever beam loaded at the apex and restrained at infinity. It is interesting to compare the results from the exact theory with those from elementary solutions. For this purpose it will be convenient to express the stresses in terms of the moment of inertia I of the area of a transverse section about the neutral axis and the bending moment M at the section.

(*a*) *Expression for* σ_x. Denoting the depth of the transverse section N–N, Fig. 3.6, by $2d$, and the thickness of the beam by t, the moment of inertia is given by

$$I = \tfrac{2}{3}td^3.$$

Eq. (3.11*a*) may therefore be written

$$\begin{aligned}\sigma_x &= -\frac{2Pxy}{t(2\alpha - \sin 2\alpha)}\frac{x}{(x^2+y^2)^2}\frac{2td^3}{3I} \\ &= -\frac{My}{I}\frac{4}{3(2\alpha - \sin 2\alpha)}\left[\frac{xd^3}{(x^2+y^2)^2}\right], \end{aligned} \tag{3.13}$$

in which $M = Px$ is the bending moment considered positive when P is positive, i.e., downward. Since

$$d = x \tan \alpha,$$

$$r^2 = x^2 + y^2,$$

$$x = r \cos \theta,$$

the bracketed factor in eq. (3.13) reduces to

$$\tan^3 \alpha \cos^4 \theta.$$

Upon substitution in eq. (3.13), we obtain

$$\left.\begin{aligned}\boldsymbol{\sigma}_x &= -\frac{4}{3}\frac{\tan^3 \boldsymbol{\alpha} \cos^4 \boldsymbol{\theta}}{(2\boldsymbol{\alpha} - \sin 2\boldsymbol{\alpha})}\frac{\boldsymbol{My}}{\boldsymbol{I}} && (a)\\ &= -k\frac{My}{I}, && (b)\end{aligned}\right\} \tag{3.14}$$

in which

$$k = \frac{4}{3}\frac{\tan^3 \alpha \cos^4 \theta}{(2\alpha - \sin 2\alpha)}$$

is a correction factor to the well-known flexure formula

$$\sigma_x = \frac{My}{I}.$$

On the extreme fibers where $\theta = \pm\alpha$ the constant k becomes

$$k_1 = \frac{4}{3} \frac{\sin^3 \alpha \cos \alpha}{(2\alpha - \sin 2\alpha)} \cdot \tag{3.15}$$

Values of k_1 as a function of α are given by curve I of Fig. 3.9. Inspection of this curve shows that for small values of α the value of k_1 is

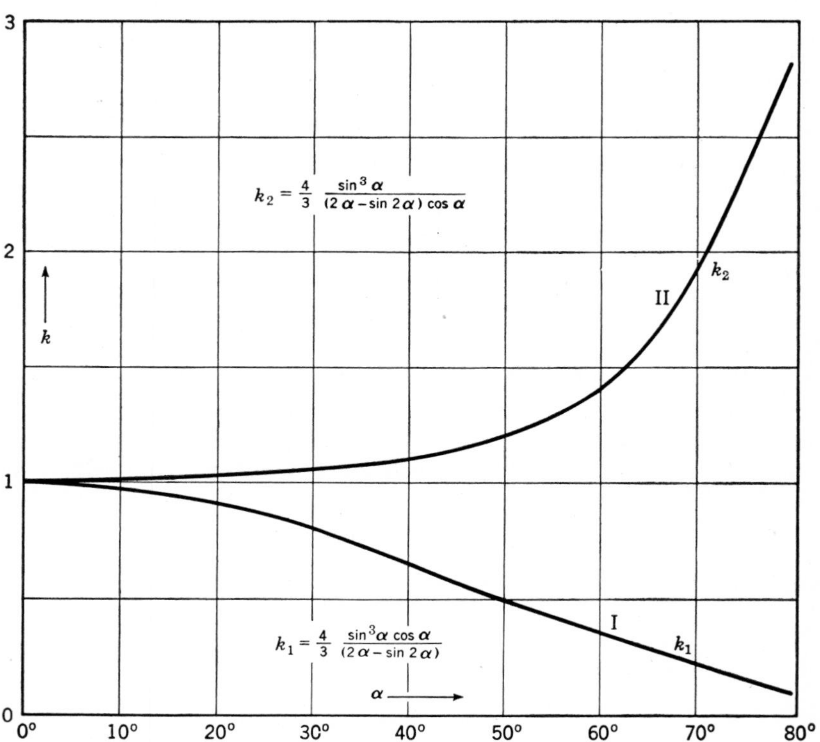

FIG. 3.9 Curves Giving Factors k_1 and k_2, in Eqs. (3.15) and (3.19), for Wedges of Various Angles with Concentrated Loads Normal to Axis of Symmetry.

approximately equal to unity. This also follows from eq. (3.15). Thus, expanding into a power series, we have

$$\sin 2\alpha = 2\alpha - \frac{(2\alpha)^3}{3!} + \frac{(2\alpha)^5}{5!} - \cdots.$$

For small values of α only the first two terms are significant, so that

$$3(2\alpha - \sin 2\alpha) = 4\alpha^3.$$

Also, for small angles

$$\sin \alpha = \alpha \quad \text{and} \quad \cos \alpha = 1,$$

approximately. With these simplifications the value of k_1 given by eq. (3.15) approaches unity as α approaches zero. Hence, ***for small angles the elementary flexure formula gives essentially the same values for the longitudinal stresses σ_x as the theory of elasticity.***

(b) *Maximum Tension or Compression.* The maximum stress in the beam is the radial stress on the extreme fibers of the beam. This stress can be found from eq. (3.9*a*) by putting $\theta = \pm\alpha$, i.e.,

$$(\sigma_r)_{\text{max.}} = \mp \frac{2P \sin \alpha}{rt(2\alpha - \sin 2\alpha)} \cdot$$

Since

$$\sigma_r = \frac{\sigma_x}{\cos^2 \theta}, \tag{3.16}$$

it follows that, for small values of α, $\sigma_r = \sigma_x$, approximately. Although, for very large values of α, σ_r on the extreme fibers is much greater than σ_x, nevertheless the maximum σ_r can still be obtained from the ordinary flexure formula for an appreciable range of α. In order to show this we express σ_r in terms of M and I. Substituting in eq. (3.16) the expression for σ_x from eq. (3.14*a*), we obtain

$$\sigma_r = -\frac{4}{3} \frac{\tan^3 \alpha \cos^2 \theta}{(2\alpha - \sin 2\alpha)} \frac{My}{I} \cdot \tag{3.17}$$

On the extreme fibers

$$\theta = \pm\alpha,$$

and

$$\begin{aligned} (\sigma_r)_{\text{max.}} &= -\frac{4}{3} \frac{\tan^3 \alpha \cos^2 \alpha}{(2\alpha - \sin 2\alpha)} \frac{My}{I} \\ &= -\frac{4}{3} \frac{\sin^3 \alpha}{(2\alpha - \sin 2\alpha) \cos \alpha} \frac{My}{I} \\ &= -k_2 \frac{My}{I}, \end{aligned} \tag{3.18}$$

in which the correction factor

$$k_2 = \frac{4}{3} \frac{\sin^3 \alpha}{(2\alpha - \sin 2\alpha) \cos \alpha} \cdot \tag{3.19}$$

Values of k_2 as a function of α are given by curve II of Fig. 3.9. Inspection of this curve shows that, for beams in which 2α is less than 45°, σ_r exceeds My/I by less than 4 per cent. Hence, ***for triangular beams in which 2α does not exceed 45°, the maximum normal stress may be assumed as being closely approximated by the ordinary flexure formula.***

(c) *Expression for τ_{xy} in Terms of P and I.* Following the same procedure as in deriving eq. (3.14a) from (3.11a), we transform eq. (3.11c) to give

$$\tau_{xy} = -\frac{4}{3}\frac{\tan^3\alpha\cos^4\theta}{(2\alpha - \sin 2\alpha)}\frac{Py^2}{I}. \tag{3.20}$$

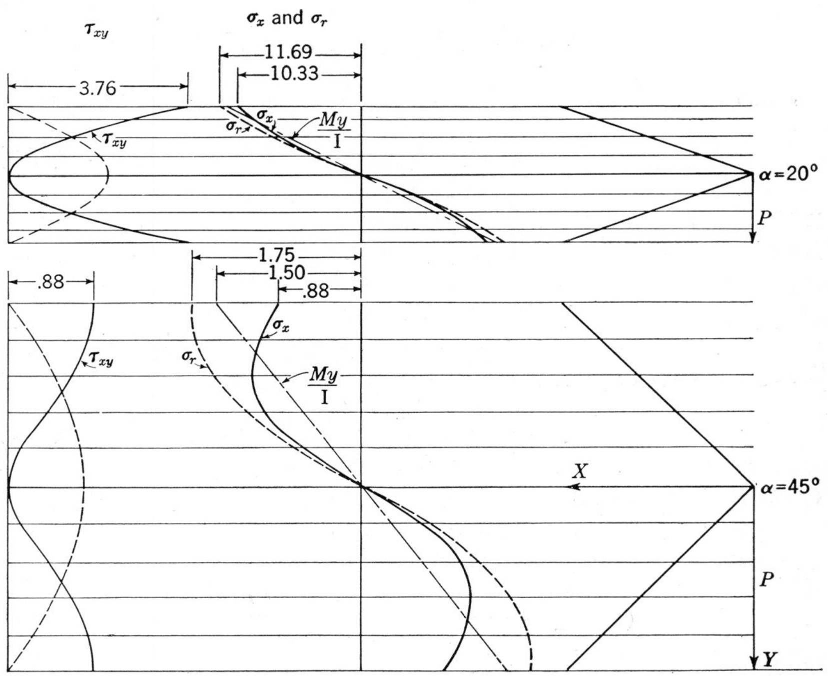

FIG. 3.10 Curves Giving a Comparison of Stresses Found by the Ordinary Flexure Formula and the True Stress Distribution in Wedge-Shaped Cantilever Beams for Two Values of α.

On the extreme fibers, where $\theta = \pm\alpha$ and $y = \pm d$, this becomes

$$\tau_{xy} = -k_1\frac{Pd^2}{I}, \tag{3.21}$$

where k_1 is given by eq. (3.15).

By the elementary parabolic formula the maximum shear stress occurs at the neutral axis, and its magnitude, using conventional notation, is given by

$$\tau_{xy} = \frac{VA\bar{y}}{tI}, \tag{3.22}$$

which for our notation reduces to

$$\tau_{xy} = \frac{Pd^2}{2I}. \tag{3.23}$$

Comparison of eqs. (3.21) and (3.23) shows that even for small angles, when k_1 is nearly unity, ***the numerical value of the maximum shear stress from the exact theory is twice as great as that from the elementary theory.*** Moreover, this critical shear occurs at the extreme fibers and not at the neutral axis. The curves of Fig. 3.10 clearly show the differences between the theoretical or true stresses and the approximate results obtained from the elementary beam theory.

It is seen that the linear distribution of the longitudinal stresses holds only for small angles α. As these angles get larger this distribution may differ radically from the assumed linear law. We further note that the shear stresses do not follow the elementary parabolic law in which the maximum is developed at the neutral surface. At that surface the shear stresses vanish, and for beams in which α does not exceed 45° the greatest shear stress is developed at the extreme fibers. Lastly we observe the presence of lateral stresses σ_y, Fig. 3.8, which are entirely neglected in the elementary theory.

§3.7 Concentrated Load of Arbitrary Direction Acting at the Apex of a Wedge. We consider next a concentrated load acting at the apex of an infinitely long wedge and making an arbitrary angle β with the axis of symmetry of the wedge from which it is measured. This angle β is the angle between the positive side of the X axis and the vector P which represents the force, laid off from the origin of the coordinate system. The angle β is positive when counterclockwise and negative when clockwise, Fig. 3.11(a). We again form a groove at the apex and assume it to be subjected to pressures given by eq. (3.5), Fig. 3.11(b). In the preceding cases the boundary forces q acting on the groove were in every instance equivalent to the concentrated load P applied at the apex; see Figs. 3.1 and 3.4. In the problem under consideration these boundary forces, Fig. 3.11(b), are not statically equivalent to the applied load P. This is due to the fact that the components normal to the direction of the load do not vanish. It follows that the stresses given by eqs. (3.6), although representing an exact solution for the assumed boundary forces q, do not directly give the stresses produced by the concentrated load P.

If, however, we resolve the given load into components respectively parallel and perpendicular to the X axis, Fig. 3.12, we can apply eqs.

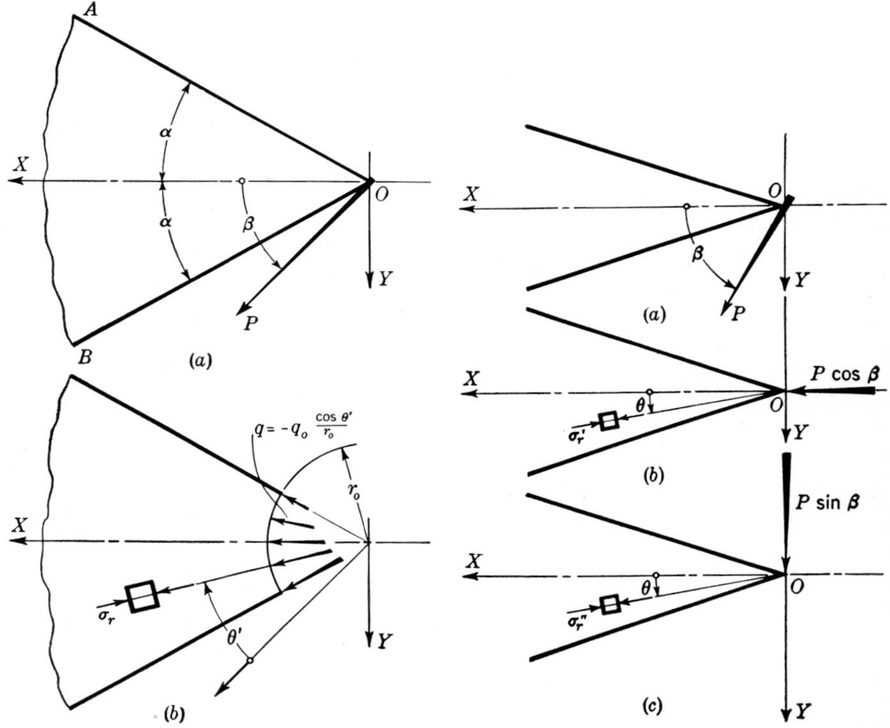

FIG. 3.11 Sketches Showing a Concentrated Load at the Vertex of a Wedge in an Arbitrary Direction; also Statically Equivalent System and Notation.

FIG. 3.12 Sketches Showing Rectangular Components of a Load Acting in an Arbitrary Direction.

(3.6) to each component separately and then find the total stress system by superposition. The X and Y components of P respectively are $P \cos \beta$, and $P \sin \beta$. The stresses $\sigma_r{}'$ produced by $P \cos \beta$ are by eq. (3.4) given by

$$\sigma_r{}' = -\frac{2P \cos \beta \cos \theta}{rt(2\alpha + \sin 2\alpha)} \cdot \tag{3.24}$$

Similarly the stresses $\sigma_r{}''$ produced by the component $P \sin \beta$ are by eq. (3.9a)

$$\sigma_r'' = -\frac{2P \sin \beta \sin \theta}{rt(2\alpha - \sin 2\alpha)}. \tag{3.25}$$

The total stress σ_r produced by the concentrated load equals the algebraic sum of σ_r' and σ_r'', i.e.,

$$\sigma_r = -\frac{2P}{rt}\left(\frac{\cos \beta \cos \theta}{2\alpha + \sin 2\alpha} + \frac{\sin \beta \sin \theta}{2\alpha - \sin 2\alpha}\right). \tag{3.26}$$

From eq. (3.26) it follows that the stress σ_r vanishes for the angle θ_o defined by the expression

$$\tan \theta_o = -\frac{1}{\tan \beta}\frac{2\alpha - \sin 2\alpha}{2\alpha + \sin 2\alpha}. \tag{3.27}$$

§3.8 Theoretical and Photoelastic Stress Patterns. The theoretical fringes are again circular arcs. The centers of the circles do not, however, lie on the line of the load, as they did in all the preceding cases. In order to show the circular character of the fringes we transform the expression (3.26) in the following manner.

Let

$$\frac{\sin \beta}{2\alpha - \sin 2\alpha} = m \sin \gamma, \qquad (a)$$

and

$$\frac{\cos \beta}{2\alpha + \sin 2\alpha} = m \cos \gamma, \qquad (b) \qquad (3.28)$$

so that

$$m^2 = \frac{\sin^2 \beta}{(2\alpha - \sin 2\alpha)^2} + \frac{\cos^2 \beta}{(2\alpha + \sin 2\alpha)^2}, \tag{3.29}$$

and

$$\tan \gamma = \tan \beta \frac{2\alpha + \sin 2\alpha}{2\alpha - \sin 2\alpha}. \tag{3.30}$$

From eqs. (3.27) and (3.30) it follows that

$$\tan \theta_o = -\frac{1}{\tan \gamma}. \tag{3.31}$$

Hence the lines defined by the angles θ_o and γ are mutually perpendicular.

Substituting the expressions from eqs. (3.28) into eqs. (3.26), we obtain

$$\sigma_r = -\frac{2Pm}{rt}(\sin\theta \sin\gamma + \cos\theta \cos\gamma)$$

$$= -\frac{2Pm}{t}\frac{\cos(\theta - \gamma)}{r}. \tag{3.32}$$

It follows that σ_r vanishes when $\theta = \theta_o$, for $\theta_o - \gamma = 90°$. This means that the line defined by θ_o is a neutral axis.[1] Also, ***for constant values of σ_r, eq. (3.32) represents circles with centers on the line defined by the angle γ and tangent at the origin O to the neutral axis defined by the angle θ_o.*** Along such a circle

$$\frac{\cos(\theta - \gamma)}{r} = \frac{1}{d}, \quad \text{a constant.}$$

It follows that along the arc of this circle which falls in the wedge the radial stresses, and therefore the maximum shear stresses, are constant. Hence ***the fringes or isochromatics corresponding to an arbitrary concentrated load acting at the apex O of a wedge are arcs of circles the centers of which lie on the line defined by the angle γ, i.e., on a line perpendicular to the neutral axis.*** Furthermore, as in the preceding cases,

$$d_n = \frac{d_1}{n}, \tag{3.33}$$

in which d_1, d_n denote respectively the diameters of the first and the nth fringes. Thus the diameter of fringe two is half the diameter of fringe one, etc. Theoretical stress patterns for a wedge in which $2\alpha = 60°$, and $\beta = 45°$ and $-15°$, are shown in Figs. 3.13(a) and 3.13(b) respectively. Photoelastic and corresponding theoretical stress patterns for three different wedges are shown in Figs. 3.14, 3.15, and 3.16. The direction of the load is in each case given by the axis of the bar through which the load was applied. Inspection of these figures shows that the theoretical and experimental results are in substantial agreement.

Fig. 3.17 shows a sketch of a wedge in which $\alpha = 45°$, $\beta = -45°$, i.e., the apex of the wedge is a right angle and the load is parallel to the vertical edge. This may be thought of as representing a column resting at the edge of a wall or foundation. The neutral axis is given by eq. (3.27).

[1] The term neutral axis is here used not only in the conventional sense but also to denote the trace of the neutral surface in the plane of the paper.

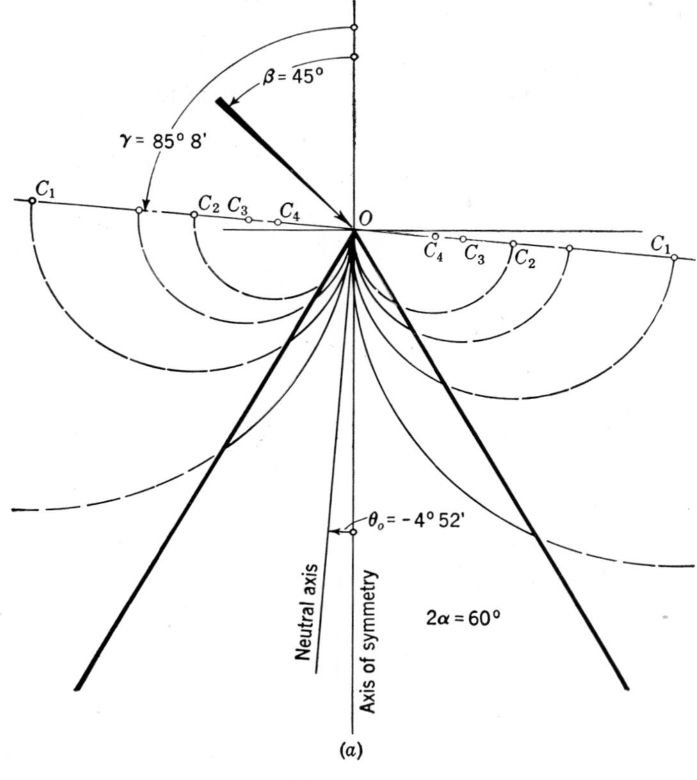

FIG. 3.13(a)

Thus

$$\tan \theta_o = -\frac{1}{\tan(-45°)} \frac{\pi/2 - \sin \pi/2}{\pi/2 + \sin \pi/2}$$

$$= \frac{\pi - 2}{\pi + 2} = 0.222, \text{ approximately,}$$

or

$$\theta_o = 12° \, 30'.$$

A neutral axis thus exists which makes an angle of 57° 30′ with the vertical edge, Fig. 3.17. All the region above this neutral axis is in a state of pure radial tension, and the region below is in a state of pure radial compression. The centers of the fringes lie on the line C_1–C_1 perpendicular to the neutral axis, Fig. 3.17.

The corresponding photoelastic stress pattern is shown in Fig. 3.18. Except for the distortions produced by plastic flow, machining, and time stresses ***the theoretical and experimental fringes are in good agreement.*** In order to obtain the pattern it was found desirable to apply the load

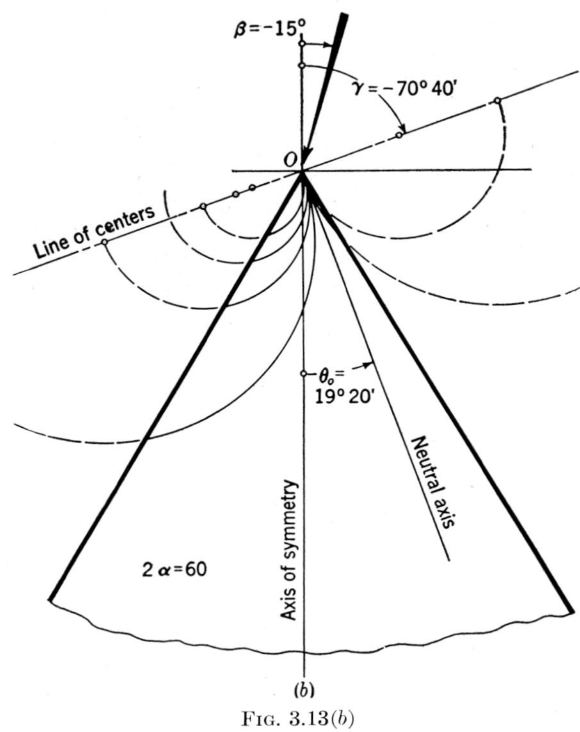

FIG. 3.13(*b*)

FIG. 3.13 Sketches Showing Notation and Method of Drawing Theoretical Stress Patterns for Wedges with Concentrated Loads at the Vertices Acting along Arbitrary Directions.

(*a*) $\beta = 45°$; (*b*) $\beta = 15°$.

through a small Bakelite block which was machined to rest with small shoulders on two identical walls. This produced a good approximation to a concentrated load of the desired direction.

Fig. 3.19 shows a stress pattern of a triangular cantilever, in which the load is normal to one edge.

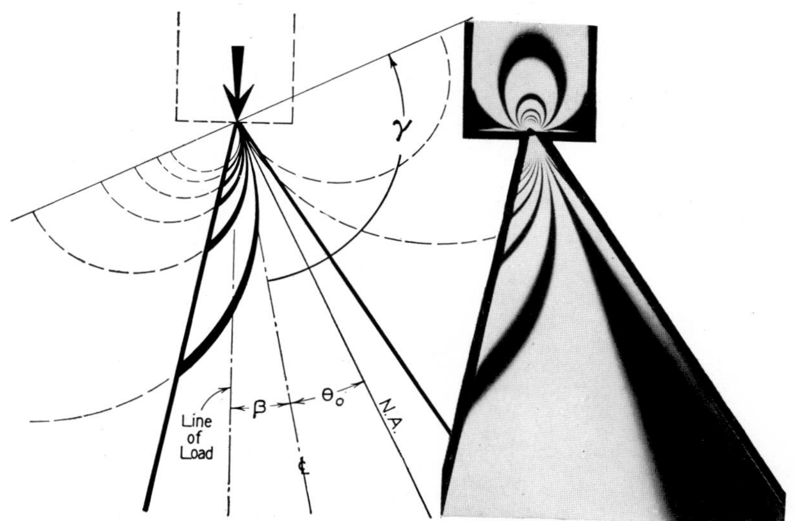

FIG. 3.14 Comparison of Theoretical and Photoelastic Stress Patterns of a Wedge with a Concentrated Load at the Vertex with Angles $2\alpha = 44° 30'$, $\beta = -11° 20'$, $\theta_0 = 14° 35'$, $\gamma = 104° 35'$.
$P = 19.86$ lb.; $t = 0.176$ in.; $F = 244$ psi. shear.

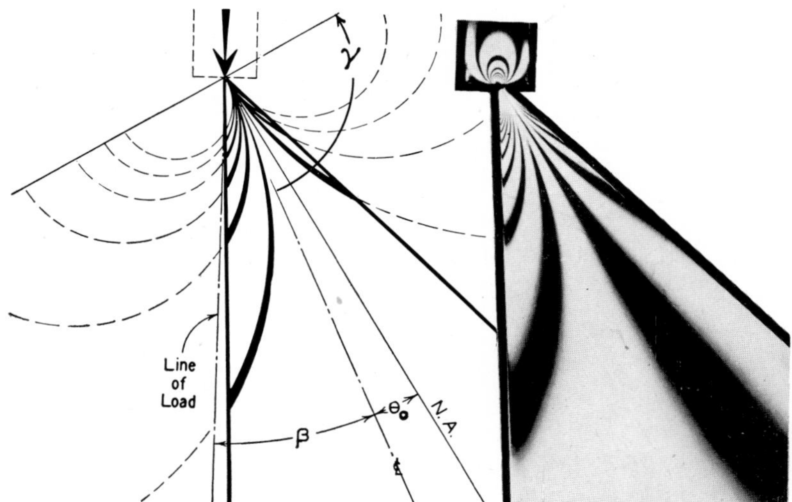

FIG. 3.15 Comparison of Theoretical and Photoelastic Stress Patterns for a Wedge with a Concentrated Load at the Vertex with Angles $2\alpha = 45°$, $\beta = -24° 15'$, $\theta_0 = 7° 20'$, $\gamma = 97° 20'$.
$P = 18.4$ lb.; $t = 0.248$ in.; $F = 173$ psi. shear.

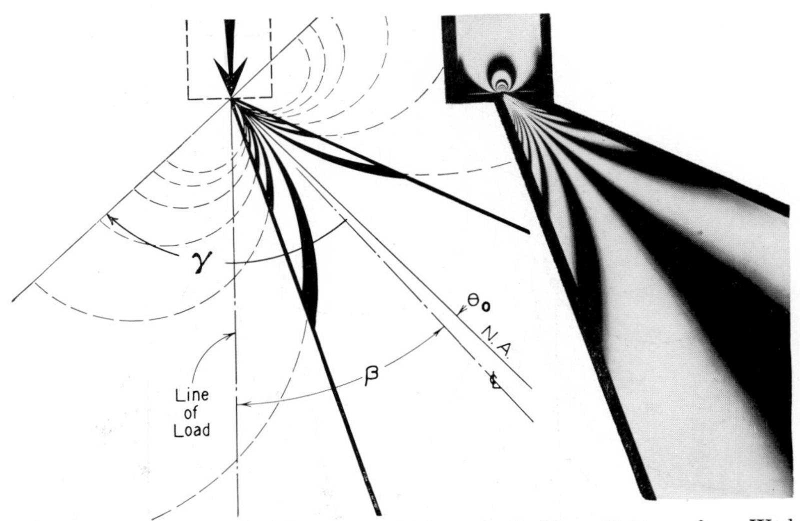

FIG. 3.16 Comparison of Theoretical and Photoelastic Stress Patterns for a Wedge with a Concentrated Load at the Vertex with Angles $2\alpha = 44° \, 30'$, $\beta = -40° \, 30'$, $\theta_0 = 2° \, 50'$, $\gamma = -87° \, 10'$.
$P = 11.54$ lb.; $t = 0.176$ in.; $F = 244$ psi. shear.

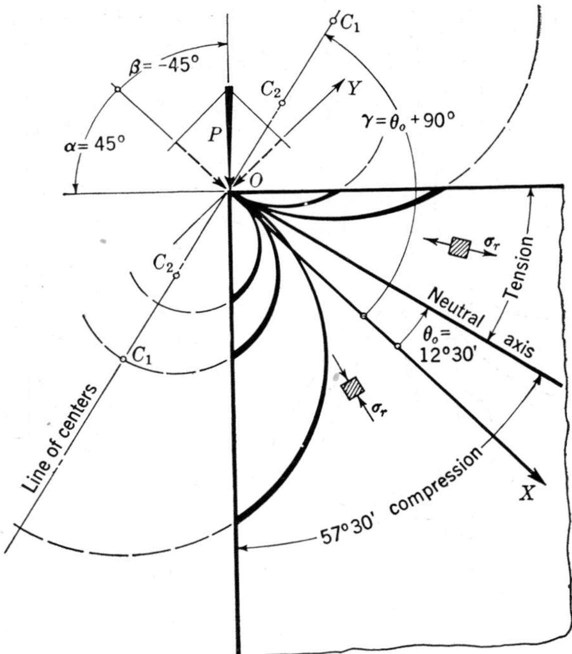

FIG. 3.17 Theoretical Stress Pattern for a Square Corner of a Large Plate Subjected to a Vertical Concentrated Load.
See Fig. 3.18 for corresponding experimental pattern.

FIG. 3.18 Stress Patterns of Square Corners of Large Plates Subjected to Concentrated Loads Approximately Vertical.

Load on each wedge, $P = 17$ lb.; $t = 0.343$ in.; $F = 125$ psi. shear.

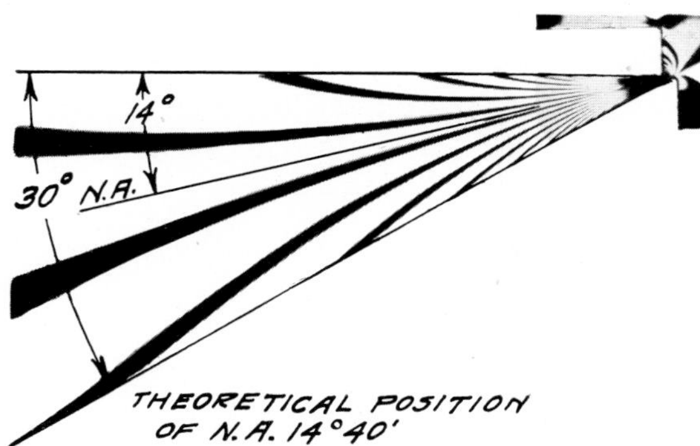

FIG. 3.19 Stress Pattern of a Wedge with a Concentrated Load at the Vertex Perpendicular to the Horizontal Edge.

$P = 4.30$ lb.; $2\alpha = 30°$; $t = 0.240$ in.; $F = 179$ psi. shear.

PART II CONCENTRATED LOADS ON RECTANGULAR BEAMS

§3.9 Effect of Concentrated Loads. Two types of beams have previously been discussed. In §1.13 we treated pure bending of straight bars, and in §3.6 we discussed wedge-shaped beams subjected to concentrated loads at the apex. Here we consider the radial stresses in a simply supported rectangular beam carrying a concentrated load at the center. We compare the experimental and photoelastic stress patterns and discuss the formation of the isotropic points along the transverse section of symmetry.

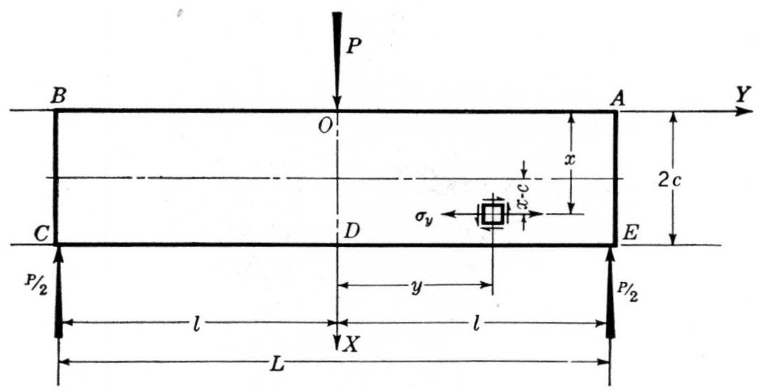

FIG. 3.20 Sketch Showing a Beam with a Concentrated Load at the Center.

In the elementary beam theory, the so-called *Bernoulli-Euler theory*, the effect of concentrated loads is neglected and the rectangular stress components, using the notation of Fig. 3.20, are assumed to be given by the expressions[1]

$$\left.\begin{aligned} \sigma_x &= 0, && (a)\\ \sigma_y &= \frac{M(x-c)}{I}, && (b)\\ \tau_{xy} &= \frac{VA\bar{y}}{tI}. && (c)\end{aligned}\right\}\quad(3.34)$$

In terms of P and l these stresses, which we designate by σ_x', σ_y', and τ_{xy}', are

[1] It can be shown that at sections far from the applied loads and reactions of the supports eqs. (3.34) represent the true solution.

$$\left.\begin{aligned}\sigma_x' &= 0, & (a)\\ \sigma_y' &= \frac{3P}{4tc^3}(l-y)(x-c), & (b)\\ \tau_{xy}' &= -\frac{3P}{8tc^3}(2c-x)x. & (c)\end{aligned}\right\}(3.35)$$

The exact solution of this problem is rather difficult and involved. A better approximation to the true stresses than that furnished by eqs. (3.35) can, however, be obtained by superimposing over this simple elementary stress system a radial set of stresses emanating from the point of application of the concentrated load as a source, treating the central region of the beam as if it were a part of a semi-infinite plate.

The rectangular stress components developed by the concentrated load P acting on a semi-infinite plate were derived in §2.8. Denoting these by σ_x'', σ_y'', and τ_{xy}'', we found that

$$\left.\begin{aligned}\sigma_x'' &= -\frac{2P}{\pi t}\frac{x^3}{(x^2+y^2)^2}, & (a)\\ \sigma_y'' &= -\frac{2P}{\pi t}\frac{xy^2}{(x^2+y^2)^2}, & (b)\\ \tau_{xy}'' &= -\frac{2P}{\pi t}\frac{x^2y}{(x^2+y^2)^2}. & (c)\end{aligned}\right\}(2.16)$$

Combining the stresses given by eqs. (3.35) and (2.16), we obtain

$$\left.\begin{aligned}\sigma_x &= -\frac{2P}{t}\frac{x^3}{\pi(x^2+y^2)^2}, & (a)\\ \sigma_y &= \frac{2P}{t}\left[\frac{3}{8c^3}(l-y)(x-c) - \frac{1}{\pi}\frac{xy^2}{(x^2+y^2)^2}\right], & (b)\\ \tau_{xy} &= -\frac{2P}{t}\left[\frac{3}{16c^3}(2cx-x^2) + \frac{1}{\pi}\frac{x^2y}{(x^2+y^2)^2}\right]. & (c)\end{aligned}\right\}(3.36)$$

It should be remembered that in these equations the X axis is parallel to the load P, and that l denotes half of the span L.

Maximum Shear Stresses. The maxium shear stress is given by

$$\tau_{\text{max.}} = \tfrac{1}{2}\sqrt{(\sigma_x - \sigma_y)^2 + (2\tau_{xy})^2}. \qquad [(1.14), \text{Vol. I}]$$

Subtracting eq. (3.36b) from (3.36a) we get

$$\sigma_x - \sigma_y = -\frac{2P}{t}\left[\frac{3}{8c^3}(l-y)(x-c) + \frac{1}{\pi}\frac{(x^3 - xy^2)}{(x^2+y^2)^2}\right]. \quad (3.37)$$

Substituting eqs. (3.36c) and (3.37) in eq. (1.14), Vol. I, we obtain

$$\tau_{\text{max.}} =$$

$$\frac{P}{t}\sqrt{\left[\frac{3}{8c^3}(l-y)(x-c)+\frac{1}{\pi}\frac{x(x^2-y^2)}{(x^2+y^2)^2}\right]^2 + 4\left[\frac{3x(2c-x)}{16c^3}+\frac{1}{\pi}\frac{x^2y}{(x^2+y^2)^2}\right]^2}. \quad (3.38)$$

§3.10 Approximate Theoretical Stress Patterns. From eq. (3.38) it is possible to determine the distribution of the maximum shear stress across any transverse section of a rectangular beam having arbitrary dimensions. Fig. 3.21 shows the distribution of the maximum shear stresses for ten transverse sections in the interval $y = 2c$ of a beam 6 in. long, 1 in. deep, and ¼ in. thick carrying a load of 500 lb. These curves form the basis for the construction of the approximate theoretical stress pattern for the central portion of the beam. The intersection of a transverse line, i.e., a line parallel to the X axis, with these curves gives the loci of equal maximum shear stresses. For example, if a transverse line be drawn corresponding to a stress of 2000 psi. the intersection of such a line with the above set of curves would give the locus of points on all sections where the maximum shear stress is 2000 psi. The stress pattern shown in Fig. 3.22(a) has been constructed in this manner. The fringe or curve value in this pattern is 750 psi. shear stress. The corresponding photoelastic pattern is shown in Fig. 3.22(b). Comparison of the theoretical and experimental patterns shows a substantial degree of agreement between the shapes and spacings of the curves.[1]

§3.11 Stresses along the Section of Symmetry. In §3.9 we superimposed the stress components produced by a concentrated load over the elementary bending stresses. This correction would have greater justification if in addition to the concentrated load and reactions the boundary of the beam also carried radial pressures defined by eq. (2.8a), Fig. 3.23. Since no such forces are acting on the beam it is clear that the solution given by eqs. (3.36) is still incomplete. In order to obtain a better approximation the radial boundary forces of Fig. 3.23 must be eliminated. This can be done by superimposing the two systems of boundary forces shown in Figs. 3.24(a) and (c), which clearly combine to give the

[1] Figs. 3.21 and 3.22(a) and all calculations on which they are based are due to Arthur C. Bates. They were made in 1933 during a summer course in photoelasticity given by the author at the Carnegie Institute of Technology.

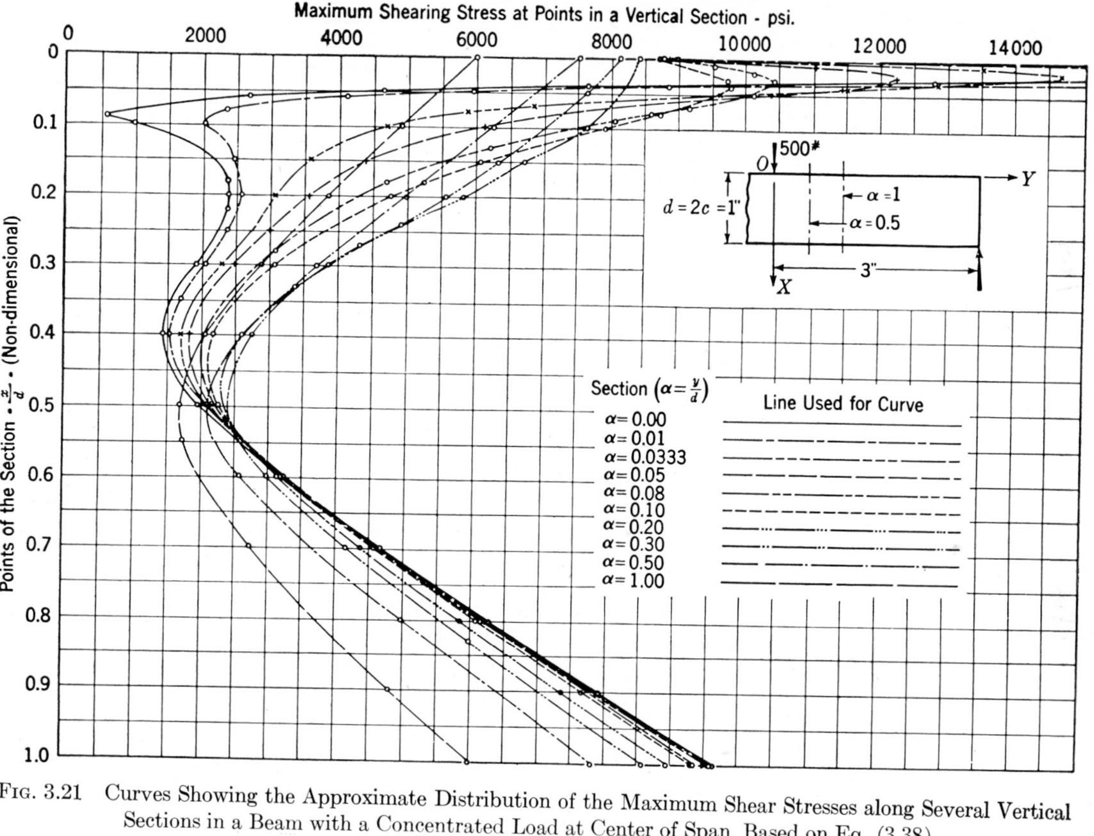

FIG. 3.21 Curves Showing the Approximate Distribution of the Maximum Shear Stresses along Several Vertical Sections in a Beam with a Concentrated Load at Center of Span, Based on Eq. (3.38).

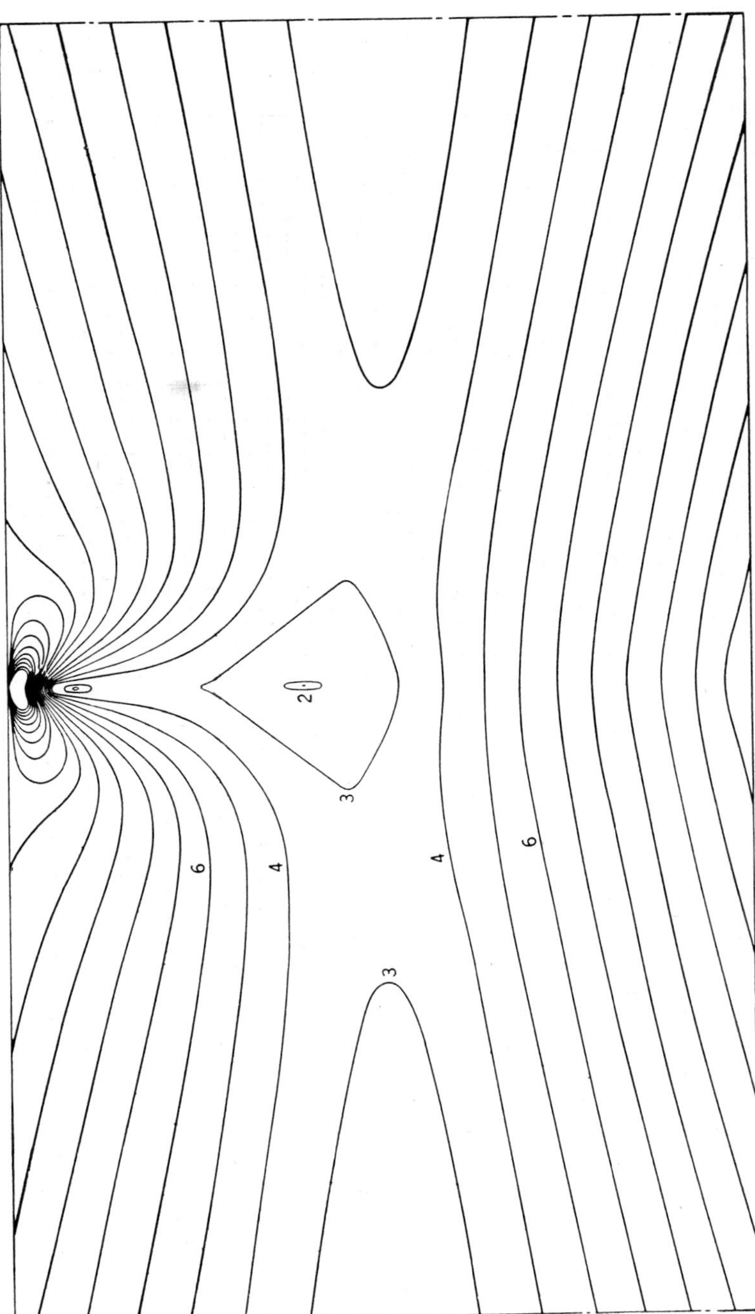

FIG. 3.22(*a*) Comparison between Photoelastic and Approximate Theoretical Stress Patterns for a Beam Subjected to a Central Concentrated Load; Ratio $l/c = 6$. Theoretical pattern was calculated using an arbitrary load of 500 lb., a fringe value of 750 psi. shear stress, and the stress distribution given by curves of Fig. 3.21.

FIG. 3.22(*b*) A Photoelastic Stress Pattern for a Beam in Central Bending in Which $l/c = 6$.

Dimensions of model: $2l = 5.028$ in.; $2c = 0.838$ in.; $t = 0.2185$ in.; $P = 140$ lb.; $F = 198$ psi. shear.

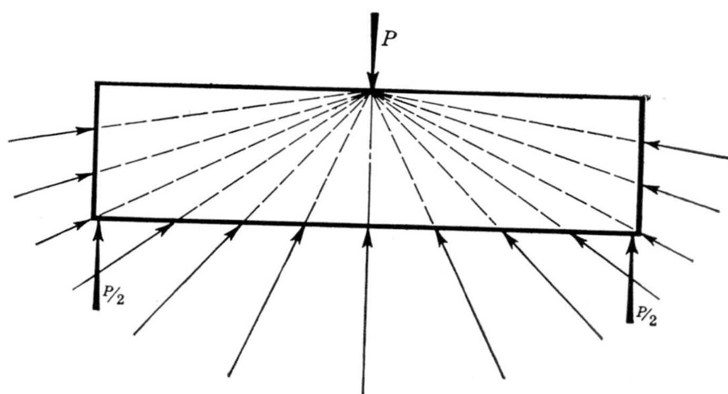

FIG. 3.23 Sketch Showing Boundary Forces Assumed in Calculating Theoretical Stress Pattern for Fig. 3.22(*a*).

three forces acting on the beam of Fig. 3.20. The stress system produced by the boundary forces shown in Fig. 3.24(a) is given by eqs. (2.16), and this represents an exact solution. However, the stresses produced by the boundary forces containing the radial tensions, Fig. 3.24(c), are not given by any simple stress function and will only be approximated.

Effect of Radial Tensions on Vertical Compressions. Confining our attention to the section of symmetry we observe that the vertical compression due to the concentrated load must be modified so as to make it vanish at point D of the lower fibers CE, Fig. 3.20. The effect of the radial tensions is therefore to reduce the vertical stresses. This correction will be assumed to be a linear function of x, so that

$$(\sigma_x)_{y=0} = -\frac{2P}{\pi t x} + kx. \tag{3.39}$$

Since

$$(\sigma_x)_{\substack{x=2c\\y=0}} = 0,$$

it follows that

$$k = \frac{P}{\pi t 2c^2}\cdot \tag{3.40}$$

Hence, along the section of symmetry

$$\sigma_x = -\frac{2P}{\pi t x} + \frac{Px}{\pi t 2c^2}$$

$$= \frac{2P}{\pi t}\left(\frac{x}{4c^2} - \frac{1}{x}\right)\cdot \tag{3.41}$$

Effect of Correction on Bending Stresses σ_y. We first observe that the radial boundary tensions acting on the three straight sides BC, CE, EA, as shown in Fig. 3.24(c), form a system statically equivalent to the compressive forces acting on the semicircular groove in the center of the beam, Fig. 3.24(a). These tensions are by assumption equal and opposite to the radial compressive boundary forces acting on the corresponding straight sides of the beam shown in Fig. 3.24(a), which are in equilibrium with the boundary forces on the groove. It follows that the radial tensions are statically equivalent to two horizontal thrusts P/π and to a vertical force P, Fig. 3.24(b), see §2.2. The bending moment M of the forces shown in Fig. 3.24(c), about the neutral axis of the section of symmetry, is therefore given by

$$M = \frac{P}{2}l - \frac{P}{\pi}c$$

$$= P\left(\frac{l}{2} - \frac{c}{\pi}\right). \tag{3.42}$$

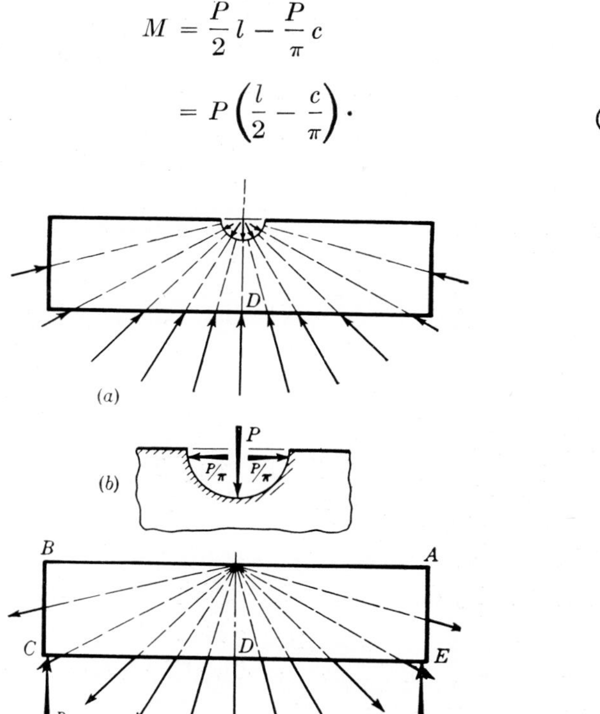

FIG. 3.24 Sketches Illustrating Boundary Forces Which Combine to Give Exact Solution to the Three Forces Acting on Actual Beam.

The bending stresses σ_y' will be approximated by the ordinary flexure formula, so that, along the section of symmetry,

$$\sigma_y' = P\left(\frac{l}{2} - \frac{c}{\pi}\right)\frac{(x - c)}{I}$$

$$= \frac{3P}{2tc^3}\left(\frac{l}{2} - \frac{c}{\pi}\right)(x - c). \tag{3.43}$$

It is to be noted that in both eqs. (3.41) and (3.43) the quantity c is inherently a positive number. We further observe that the horizontal force P/π which was included in the bending moment acts as an eccentric load, and that it will therefore produce an additional tensile stress σ_u across the section of symmetry, which we assume to be uniformly distributed, i.e.,

$$\sigma_u = \frac{P}{\pi 2ct}. \tag{3.44}$$

The resultant horizontal stress σ_y across the section of symmetry therefore is

$$(\sigma_y)_{y=0} = \frac{3}{2}\frac{P}{tc^3}\left(\frac{l}{2} - \frac{c}{\pi}\right)(x - c) + \frac{P}{\pi 2ct}. \tag{3.45}$$

This solution may be called *the Wilson-Stokes solution.* Carus Wilson[1] was the first to make a photoelastic investigation of the effect of a concentrated load acting on the edge of a straight beam. These investigations led him to introduce a correction for the radial stresses, eq. (3.41). G. G. Stokes[2] observed that the concentrated load also affected the longitudinal bending stresses, and eq. (3.45) represents his improvements. This problem has received theoretical attention from Boussinesq,[3] Filon,[4] Lamb,[5] and others.

§3.12 Isotropic Points in Beams. The Wilson-Stokes theory, although still imperfect, is sufficient to explain the formation of the isotropic points along the section of symmetry of centrally loaded beams, and the results to which it leads are in good quantitative agreement with experiments. By definition an isotropic point is one where

$$p = q \neq 0.$$

Along the section of symmetry isotropic points will exist where $\sigma_x = \sigma_y$, i.e., at the points of intersection A and B of the curves giving these stresses, Fig. 3.25. In terms of eqs. (3.41) and (3.45), this gives

$$\frac{2}{\pi}\left(\frac{x}{4c^2} - \frac{1}{x}\right) = \frac{3}{2c^3}\left(\frac{l}{2} - \frac{c}{\pi}\right)(x - c) + \frac{1}{2\pi c},$$

which can be reduced to

$$\frac{x}{4c} - \frac{c}{x} = \left(\frac{\pi l}{2c} - 1\right)\frac{3}{4}\frac{x}{c} - \frac{3}{8}\frac{\pi l}{c} + 1. \tag{3.46}$$

Transposing, rearranging, and factoring we obtain

$$\left(1 - \frac{x}{c}\right)\left(1 - \frac{3\pi l}{8c}\right) = -\frac{c}{x}$$

[1] See Carus Wilson, *Phil. Mag.*, Vol. 32, p. 481, 1891.

[2] See G. G. Stokes, *Mathematics and Physics Papers*, Vol. 5, p. 238.

[3] See *Compt. rend.*, Vol. 114, p. 1510, 1892.

[4] See *Phil. Trans.*, Vol. 201, p. 63, 1903. See also *Treatise on Photoelasticity* by Coker and Filon.

[5] See *Proc. of Congress for Intern. Math.*, Vol. 3, p. 12, Rome, 1909.

or

$$\left(1 - \frac{x}{c}\right)\frac{x}{c} = \frac{1}{3l\pi/8c - 1}. \tag{3.47}$$

Solving for x, we get

$$x = \frac{c}{2}\left(1 \pm \sqrt{1 - \frac{4}{3l\pi/8c - 1}}\right). \tag{3.48}$$

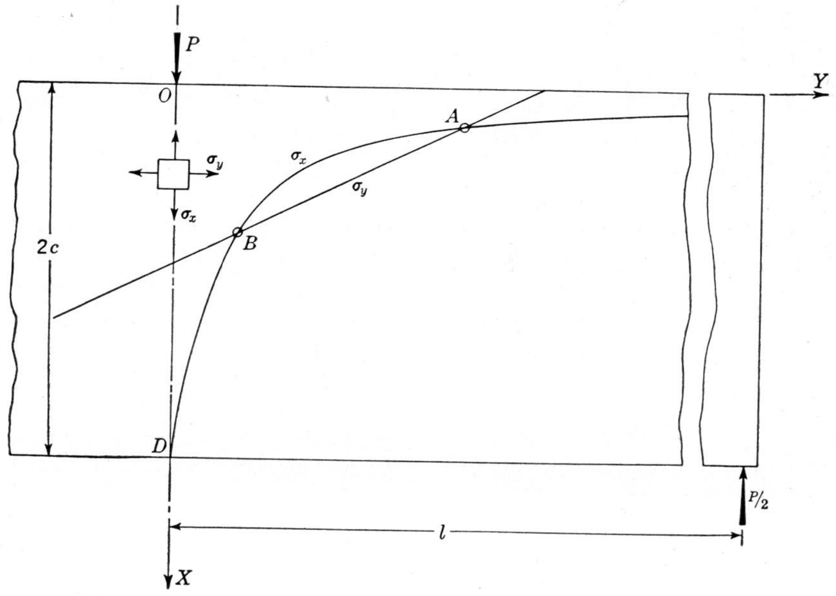

FIG. 3.25 Beam in Central Bending.

Curves of σ_y and σ_x at section of symmetry under concentrated load illustrating positions of isotropic points A and B.

The roots of eq. (3.48) are coincident when

$$\frac{3l\pi}{8c} - 1 = 4, \tag{3.49}$$

i.e., when

$$\frac{l}{c} = \frac{40}{3\pi} = 4.24.$$

The coincident values of x are

$$x = \frac{c}{2}. \tag{3.50}$$

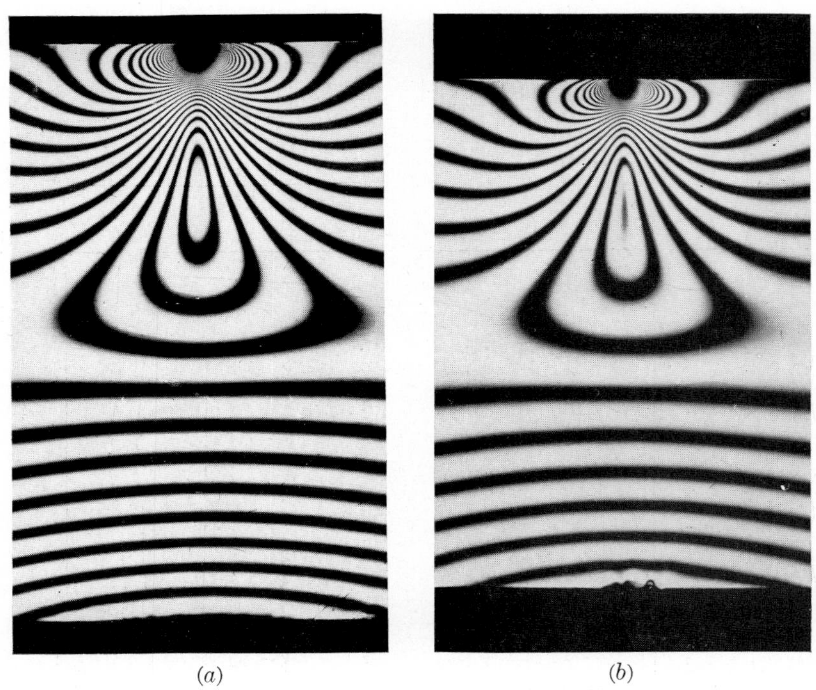

(a) (b)

FIG. 3.26 Stress Patterns of Beams with Concentrated Loads at the Center Illustrating Formation of First Isotropic Region.

(a) No isotropic region: $l/c = 4.02$; $2l = 4.00$ in.; $2c = 0.995$ in.; $t = 0.239$ in.; $P = 193.9$ lb.; $F = 180$ psi. shear.

(b) Isotropic region just forming: $l/c = 4.19$; $2l = 3.500$ in.; $2c = 0.836$ in.; $t = 0.232$ in.; $P = 116.5$ lb.; $F = 185$ psi. shear.

It follows that for l/c greater than 4.24 the radicand in eq. (3.48) is greater than zero and less than unity, so that there exist two distinct positive roots. Again for l/c less than 4.24 the above radicand is negative and the roots are imaginary.

In terms of isotropic points this means that ***in beams carrying a concentrated load at the center and supported at the ends a single isotropic point or region will be formed when the ratio of span to depth is 4.24, two isotropic points will be developed for all ratios greater than 4.24, and no isotropic zone will exist for shorter beams.***

The stress patterns shown in Figs. 3.26 and 3.27 provide experimental data for a verification of the above-mentioned theoretical conclusion. The figures show that for $l/c = 4.02$ no isotropic point exists, at $l/c = 4.19$ there is clear evidence of the formation of such a zone, at $l/c = 4.26$

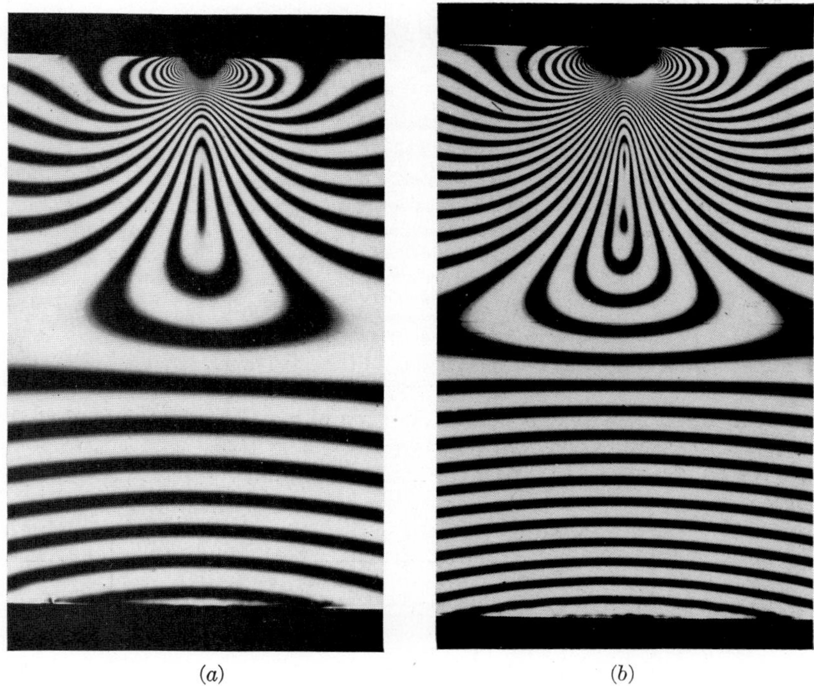

(*a*) (*b*)

Fig. 3.27 Stress Patterns of Beams with Concentrated Loads at the Centers Illustrating Formation of Isotropic Points.

(*a*) Shows one isotropic region which occurs when curves of σ_x and σ_y of Fig. 3.25 are tangent to each other: $l/c = 4.26$; $2l = 3.500$ in.; $2c = 0.822$ in.; $t = 0.237$ in.; $P = 116.5$ lb.; $F = 181.5$ psi. shear.

(*b*) Shows two isotropic points: $l/c = 4.47$; $2l = 3.00$ in.; $2c = 0.671$ in.; $t = 0.247$ in.; $P = 118$ lb.; $F = 174$ psi. shear.

the isotropic region is fully formed, and at $l/c = 4.47$ we see two distinct isotropic points, which remain a permanent part of the stress system for all longer beams. Furthermore, inspection of Fig. 3.27(*a*) shows the center of the isotropic zone to be approximately at one-fourth of the depth below the upper fibers of the beam, as given by eq. (3.50).

It is of interest to carry this verification a little further. From eq. (3.48) it is possible to calculate the roots for any ratio of l/c. Putting

FIG. 3.28 Stress Pattern of a Beam in Bending with a Concentrated Load at the Center Showing Two Isotropic Points.

$l/c = 5.22$; $2l = 3.00$ in.; $2c = 0.584$ in.; $t = 0.253$ in.; $P = 86$ lb.; $F = 170$ psi. shear.

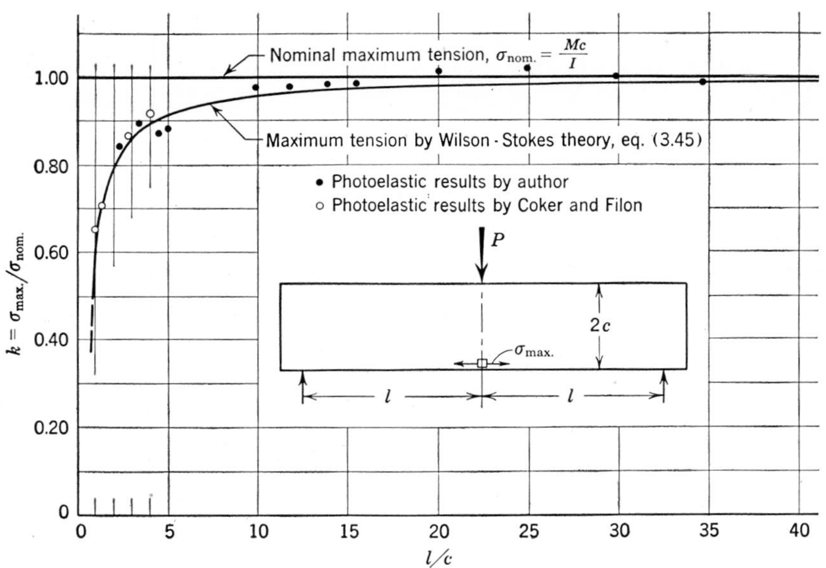

FIG. 3.29 Curves Showing Maximum Tensile Stresses in Centrally Loaded Beams.

$l/c = 5.22$, we find for the positions of the isotropic points

$$x_1 = 0.736c, \quad x_2 = 0.264c.$$

The corresponding experimental values taken from Fig. 3.28 are

$$x_1 = 0.72c, \quad x_2 = 0.28c.$$

Similarly putting $l/c = 6$ we obtain theoretically

$$x_1 = 0.792c, \quad x_2 = 0.208c,$$

and for the corresponding experimental values, Fig. 3.22(*b*), we have

$$x_1 = 0.78c \quad \text{and} \quad x_2 = 0.2c.$$

It may therefore be concluded that ***the experimental results completely substantiate the Wilson-Stokes theory.***

Attention is directed to Fig. 3.29, which shows the maximum tensile stresses obtained from eq. (3.45) and from the flexure formula. The adjacent points represent photoelastic results. It is seen that the flexure formula always gives safe values. However, in short beams these values may be considerably greater than the true stresses. Thus for l/c equal to 4 the difference is 20 per cent, and for l/c equal to 5 it is 9 per cent, approximately.

CHAPTER 4

THE CIRCULAR DISK

PART I STRESSES IN CIRCULAR DISKS

§4.1 Introduction. This chapter consists of two parts. Part I deals with a mathematical analysis of stresses in circular disks subjected to uniform radial pressures, uniform circumferential shear stresses, concentrated loads acting along a diameter, and concentrated loads acting along an arbitrary chord.

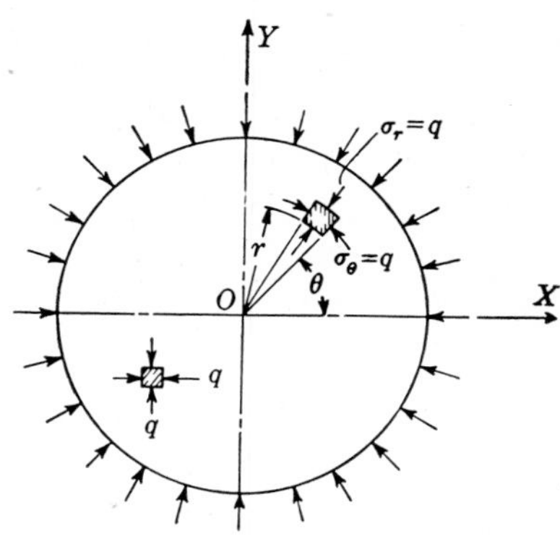

FIG. 4.1 Sketch Showing Notation for Stresses Caused by a Uniform Radial Pressure on a Circular Disk.

Part II is a mathematical treatment of the basic photoelastic phases of a disk subjected to concentrated diametral loads. Specifically, equations are derived for the isochromatics or fringes, the isoclinics, and stress trajectories. The theoretical curves are then compared with those obtained photoelastically. This comparison contributes much to the fuller appreciation of both methods.

§4.2 Elementary Stresses in Circular Disks. (*a*) *Radial Forces.* We first consider the simplest possible system of boundary forces — a system of uniform radial tractions of intensity q, Fig. 4.1. If r, θ be the polar coordinates of a point in the disk, then owing to symmetry the stresses will not depend on θ and will be functions of r only. Assuming as a stress function the expression

$$\phi = Cr^2, \tag{4.1}$$

which satisfies the compatibility eq. (1.42*a*), the stress components are found by means of eqs. (1.24). Thus

$$\sigma_r = 2C,$$

$$\sigma_\theta = 2C,$$

$$\tau_{r\theta} = 0.$$

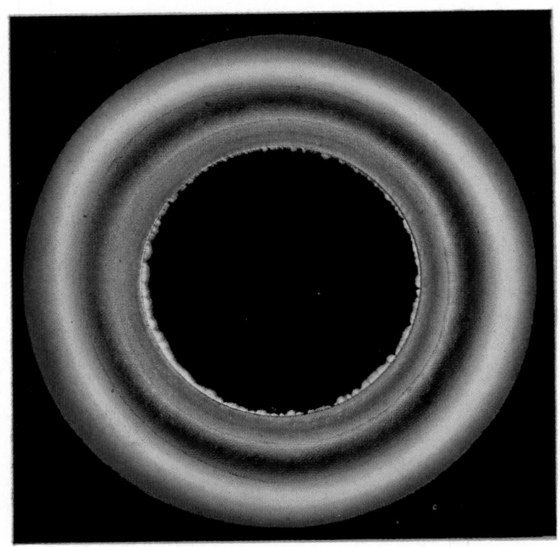

FIG. 4.2(b) Colored Stress Pattern of Model in Fig. 4.2(a) Showing that Disk is in a State of Isotropic Stress.

Letting

$$C = \frac{q}{2},$$

we obtain

$$\left.\begin{aligned} \boldsymbol{\sigma}_r &= \boldsymbol{q}, & (a)\\ \boldsymbol{\sigma}_\theta &= \boldsymbol{q}, & (b)\\ \boldsymbol{\tau}_{r\theta} &= \boldsymbol{0}, & (c) \end{aligned}\right\}(4.2)$$

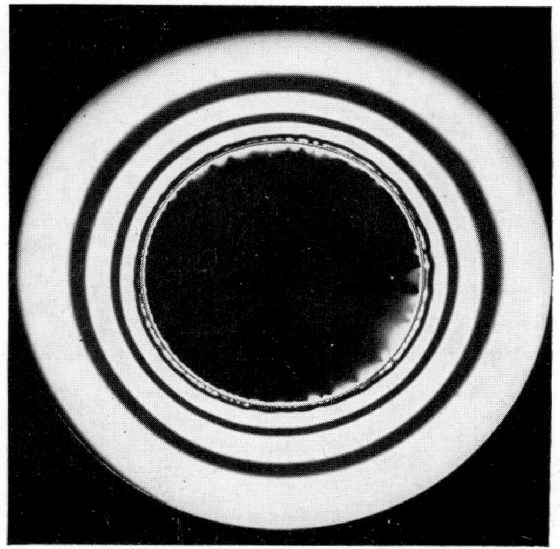

FIG. 4.2(a) Stress Pattern of a Circular Disk under Uniform Radial Pressures Produced by a Ring. Monochromatic Light Source.

Diameter of disk = 0.9295 in.; inside diameter of ring = 0.926 in.; outside diameter of ring = 1.7835 in.; thickness = 0.1375 in.; model fringe value, F = 313 psi. shear; material-Bakelite BT–61–893.

which satisfy all boundary conditions. It follows that ***the whole disk forms an isotropic region of the same stress intensity q that is acting on the boundary.*** Tensile tractions develop isotropic tensile stresses, and compressive tractions develop compressive stresses.

The stress pattern of Fig. 4.2 corroborates the theoretical conclusion regarding the state of stress produced by uniform compression. It shows a Bakelite disk uniformly compressed by a circular ring of the same material and thickness as the disk. The hole in the ring surrounding the disk was initially slightly smaller than the disk. The ring was expanded by heating, and the hole was lubricated until the disk could be inserted without pressure. The stress pattern shown was obtained after room temperature was established in both. The state of stress in the disk is seen to be isotropic. This is even more strikingly revealed by a colored stress pattern, in which the disk appears uniformly and permanently black and the ring shows multicolored isochromatics, Fig. 4.2(*b*).

It should be noted that the contact surfaces were not polished. The slight irregularities in the pattern in the region of contact are due to the roughness of the finish.

(*b*) *Pure Shear.* For the case of pure shear we assume a stress function

$$\phi = \frac{M\theta}{2\pi}, \tag{4.3}$$

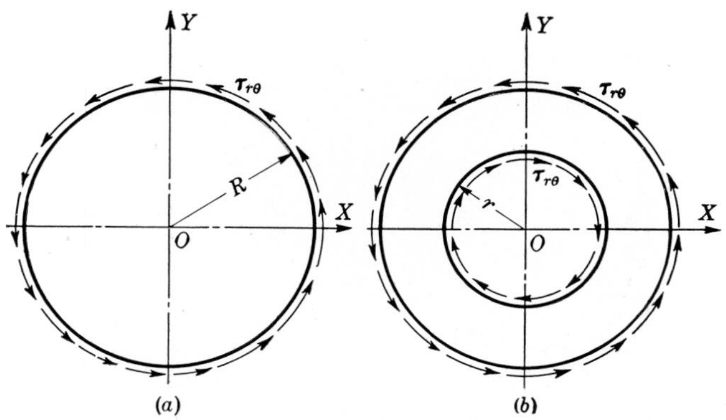

FIG. 4.3 Sketches Showing Stresses Produced by Pure Shear on a Disk.

in which M is the torque of the boundary forces, i.e., their resultant moment about the origin, Fig. 4.3. The stress components are found to be

$$\left.\begin{aligned} \sigma_r &= 0, && (a) \\ \sigma_\theta &= 0, && (b) \\ \tau_{r\theta} &= \frac{M}{2\pi r^2}. && (c) \end{aligned}\right\} \tag{4.4}$$

This also follows from simple considerations of statics since the moment of the shear stresses on any concentric circle, Fig. 4.3(*b*), must balance the applied torque M, or

$$\tau_{r\theta} 2\pi r^2 = M. \tag{4.5}$$

(*c*) *Radial Compression and Shear.* A case of some practical importance is represented by the combined action of uniform radial compression and uniform shear. The resulting stresses are found by superimposing the stresses from cases (*a*) and (*b*) above. Thus

$$\left.\begin{aligned} \sigma_r &= q, & (a)\\ \sigma_\theta &= q, & (b)\\ \tau_{r\theta} &= \frac{M}{2\pi r^2}\cdot & (c)\end{aligned}\right\}(4.6)$$

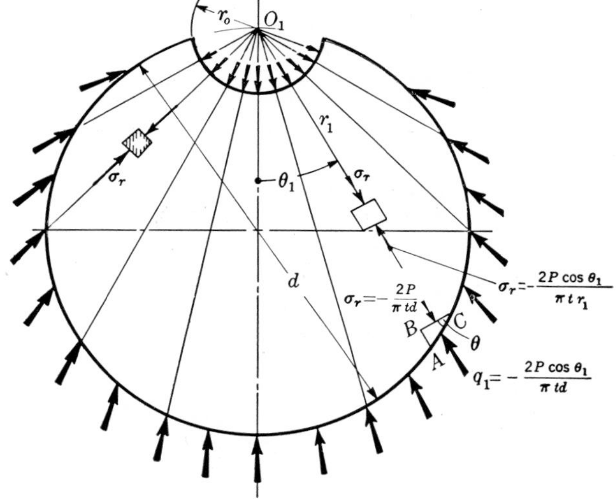

FIG. 4.4 Sketch of Free Body Diagram of a Circular Section (Disk) Tangent to the Edge of a Semi-Infinite Plate Acted on by the Statical Equivalent of a Normal Concentrated Load. Notation.

§4.3 Concentrated Diametral Loads on a Disk. (*a*) We next consider a circular disk, Fig. 4.4, from which a small semicircular groove of radius r_o has been removed. On this groove we assume variable compressive tractions q which follow the distribution

$$q = -q_o\frac{\cos\theta_1}{r_o} \qquad (2.2)$$

$$= -\frac{2P}{\pi t}\frac{\cos\theta_1}{r_o},$$

in which P is the concentrated load statically equivalent to the q forces on the groove, and t is the thickness of the disk. On the circular boundary of diameter d we assume compressive tractions q_1 of magnitude $2P \cos \theta_1/\pi td$ per unit length, all directed toward point O_1, the center of the small semicircle of radius r_o.

For such boundary forces the state of stress is, at all points in the disk, identically the same as in the semi-infinite plate subjected to a concentrated normal load P discussed in §2.2, i.e.,

$$\left.\begin{aligned} \sigma_r &= -\frac{2P}{\pi t}\frac{\cos \theta_1}{r_1}, && (a)\\ \sigma_\theta &= 0, && (b)\\ \tau_{r\theta} &= 0, && (c) \end{aligned}\right\} \quad (2.8)$$

which are derived from the stress function given by eq. (2.3). The boundary conditions are clearly satisfied. Thus for all points on the circle

$$\frac{\cos \theta_1}{r_1} = \frac{1}{d}, \quad \text{a constant,}$$

so that on the boundary

$$\sigma_r = -\frac{2P}{\pi td}.$$

For equilibrium, Fig. 4.4,

$$q_1(AC)t = \sigma_r(BC)t,$$

whence

$$\begin{aligned} q_1 &= \sigma_r \frac{BC}{AC} = \sigma_r \cos \theta_1 \\ &= -\frac{2P \cos \theta_1}{\pi td}. \end{aligned}$$

Furthermore, on the boundary of the small semicircular groove of radius r_o, $\sigma_r = q$. Hence all boundary conditions are met. The solution would obviously be the same if the disk were inverted, so that the groove would be at the bottom instead of at the top of the disk.

(b) Suppose now that two diametrically opposite grooves with centers at O_1 and O_2 are removed from the disk, Fig. 4.5, and that two sets of boundary forces of the type just considered are applied; one set,

$$q' = -\frac{2P}{\pi t}\frac{\cos \theta_1}{d},$$

converging at point O_1, the other set,

$$q'' = -\frac{2P}{\pi t}\frac{\cos\theta_2}{d},$$

converging at O_2. On the basis of superposition we conclude that we still have an exact solution for the state of stress in the disk, and, specifically,

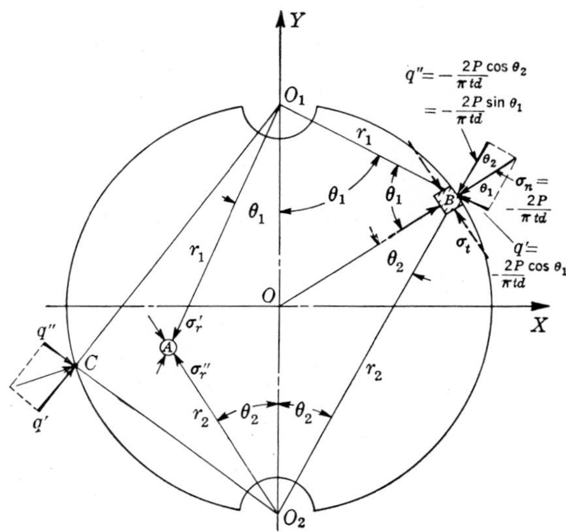

FIG. 4.5 Sketch Showing Boundary Forces on a Circular Disk Resulting from the Superposition of Equal and Opposite Systems of the Type Shown in Fig. 4.4. Notation.

that each point in the body, such as point A, Fig. 4.5, is subjected to two radial compressions σ_r' and σ_r'' directed toward the centers O_1 and O_2, respectively, where

$$\left.\begin{aligned}\sigma_r' &= -\frac{2P}{\pi t}\frac{\cos\theta_1}{r_1}, && (a)\\ \sigma_r'' &= -\frac{2P}{\pi t}\frac{\cos\theta_2}{r_2}. && (b)\end{aligned}\right\}(4.7)$$

We observe that on the circular boundary the radial lines r_1 and r_2, and therefore q' and q'', are everywhere perpendicular to each other.

Since, for points on the circular boundary, Fig. 4.5,

$$\theta_2 = 90° - \theta_1,$$

$$q'' = -\frac{2P \sin \theta_1}{\pi t d}.$$

The resultant traction σ_n on the circular boundary is therefore given by

$$\sigma_n = -\sqrt{(q')^2 + (q'')^2}$$

$$= -\frac{2P}{\pi t d}\sqrt{\cos^2 \theta_1 + \sin^2 \theta_1}$$

$$= -\frac{2P}{\pi t d}, \quad \text{a constant},$$

the minus sign indicating compression. It will also be noted that the direction of the resultant traction is toward the center of the disk,

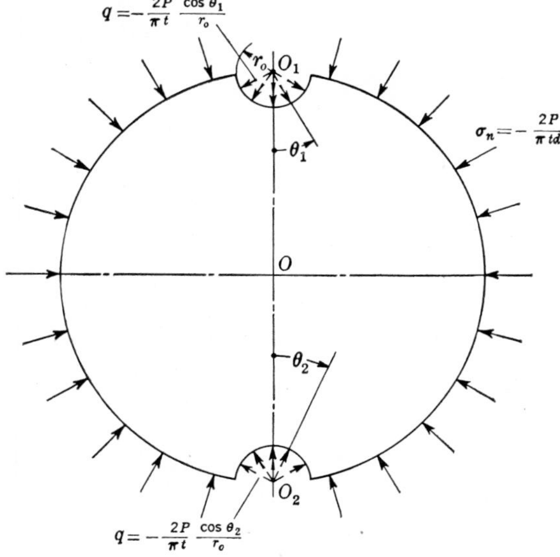

FIG. 4.6 Sketch Showing the Resulting Boundary Forces for Fig. 4.5.

point O, Fig. 4.5. The tractions on the circular boundary thus reduce to a constant radial compression of magnitude $2P/\pi td$ converging at the center of the disk. Hence eqs. (4.7) represent an exact solution for a grooved disk with boundary forces as shown in Fig. 4.6.

(*c*) Lastly, if to the external forces shown in Fig. 4.6 we add to the circular boundary a uniform normal tension of $2P/\pi td$, then this boundary would be completely freed from external forces, and the stress at each point within the disk would merely be increased by a uniform isotropic tension $2P/\pi td$, (§4.2). In this way we arrive at a solution for the exact state of stress in a disk carrying compressions along two opposite semicircular grooves. ***If now the grooves be small in comparison with the diameter of the disk, the solution obtained becomes also the solution for the stresses produced by the statically equivalent concentrated loads P which replace the distributed forces on the grooves.***

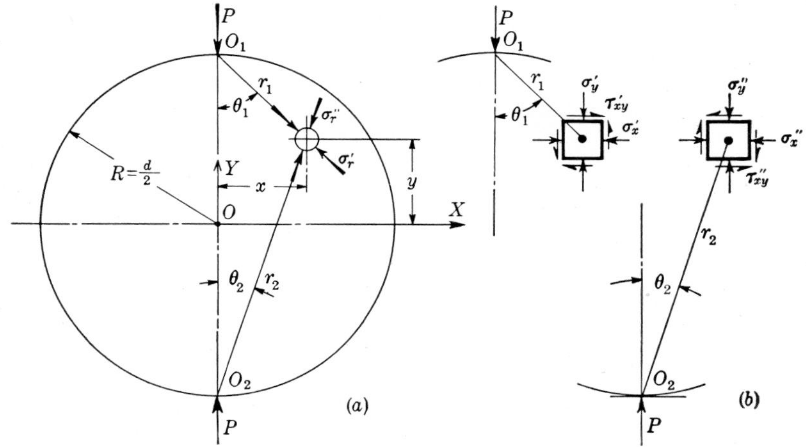

Fig. 4.7 Sketches Showing Notation for Rectangular Stress Components in a Disk under the Action of Two Diametrically Opposite Concentrated Loads.

§4.4 Rectangular Stress Components.

From the preceding section it follows that the state of stress in a disk subjected to concentrated diametral loads P, Fig. 4.7, is given by the following system of rectangular stress components

$$\left.\begin{aligned} \sigma_x &= \sigma_r' \sin^2 \theta_1 + \sigma_r'' \sin^2 \theta_2 + \frac{2P}{\pi td}, && (a) \\ \sigma_y &= \sigma_r' \cos^2 \theta_1 + \sigma_r'' \cos^2 \theta_2 + \frac{2P}{\pi td}, && (b) \\ \tau_{xy} &= \sigma_r' \sin \theta_1 \cos \theta_1 - \sigma_r'' \sin \theta_2 \cos \theta_2. && (c) \end{aligned}\right\} \quad (4.8)$$

Substituting for σ_r' and σ_r'' the expressions from eqs. (4.7), we have

$$\left.\begin{aligned} \sigma_x &= -\frac{2P}{\pi t}\left[\frac{\cos\theta_1 \sin^2\theta_1}{r_1} + \frac{\cos\theta_2 \sin^2\theta_2}{r_2} - \frac{1}{d}\right], && (a) \\ \sigma_y &= -\frac{2P}{\pi t}\left[\frac{\cos^3\theta_1}{r_1} + \frac{\cos^3\theta_2}{r_2} - \frac{1}{d}\right], && (b) \\ \tau_{xy} &= \frac{2P}{\pi t}\left[\frac{\cos^2\theta_1 \sin\theta_1}{r_1} - \frac{\cos^2\theta_2 \sin\theta_2}{r_2}\right], && (c) \end{aligned}\right\} \quad (4.9)$$

in which θ_1 and θ_2 are treated as positive for points to the right, and negative for points to the left, of the Y axis. The directions of the shear stresses are shown in Fig. 4.7(*b*).

Inspection of Fig. 4.7 shows that

$$\left.\begin{aligned} \sin\theta_1 &= \frac{x}{r_1}, \quad \cos\theta_1 = \frac{R-y}{r_1}, && (a) \\ \sin\theta_2 &= \frac{x}{r_2}, \quad \cos\theta_2 = \frac{R+y}{r_2}, && (b) \end{aligned}\right\} \quad (4.10)$$

where R is the radius of the disk. Substituting in eqs. (4.9) we obtain

$$\left.\begin{aligned} \sigma_x &= -\frac{2P}{\pi t}\left[\frac{(R-y)x^2}{r_1^4} + \frac{(R+y)x^2}{r_2^4} - \frac{1}{d}\right], && (a) \\ \sigma_y &= -\frac{2P}{\pi t}\left[\frac{(R-y)^3}{r_1^4} + \frac{(R+y)^3}{r_2^4} - \frac{1}{d}\right], && (b) \\ \tau_{xy} &= \frac{2P}{\pi t}\left[\frac{(R-y)^2 x}{r_1^4} - \frac{(R+y)^2 x}{r_2^4}\right], && (c) \end{aligned}\right\} \quad (4.11)$$

in which

$$\left.\begin{aligned} r_1^2 &= x^2 + (R-y)^2, && (a) \\ r_2^2 &= x^2 + (R+y)^2. && (b) \end{aligned}\right\} \quad (4.12)$$

For points on the diameter perpendicular to the loads, the X axis, Fig. 4.7,

$$\left.\begin{aligned} y &= 0, && (a) \\ r_1 &= r_2 = \sqrt{x^2 + R^2}. && (b) \end{aligned}\right\} \quad (4.13)$$

Substituting these in eqs. (4.11) and simplifying we obtain

$$\left.\begin{aligned}\sigma_x &= -\frac{2P}{\pi td}\left[\frac{16d^2x^2}{(d^2+4x^2)^2}-1\right]\\ &= \frac{2P}{\pi td}\left[\frac{d^2-4x^2}{d^2+4x^2}\right]^2, &&(a)\\ \sigma_y &= -\frac{2P}{\pi td}\left[\frac{4d^4}{(d^2+4x^2)^2}-1\right], &&(b)\\ \tau_{xy} &= 0 &&(c)\end{aligned}\right\}\quad(4.14)$$

Eq. (4.14a) shows that on the X axis σ_x is always positive or tensile. The accompanying vertical normal stress σ_y is negative or compressive. This follows from eq. (4.14b) if we observe that the maximum value of x is $d/2$. Both stresses vanish on the circumference, i.e., at the ends of the horizontal diameter, and their maximum values are developed at the center of the disk where $x = 0$. These maximum stresses are

$$\left.\begin{aligned}(\sigma_x)_{\substack{x=0\\y=0}} &= \frac{2P}{\pi td} &&(a)\\ \text{and}\qquad (\sigma_y)_{\substack{x=0\\y=0}} &= -\frac{6P}{\pi td}. &&(b)\end{aligned}\right\}\quad(4.15)$$

The last value of σ_y is approximately twice the value of the average compression P/td.

On the Y axis, where

$$x = 0,$$
$$r_1 = R - y,$$
$$r_2 = R + y,$$

we have, from eqs. (4.11),

$$\left.\begin{aligned}\sigma_x &= \frac{2P}{\pi td}, &&(a)\\ \sigma_y &= -\frac{2P}{\pi t}\left[\frac{2}{d-2y}+\frac{2}{d+2y}-\frac{1}{d}\right], &&(b)\\ \tau_{xy} &= 0. &&(c)\end{aligned}\right\}\quad(4.16)$$

We thus see that across the vertical central section, i.e., along the line of the loads, the horizontal tension is constant and the vertical compression

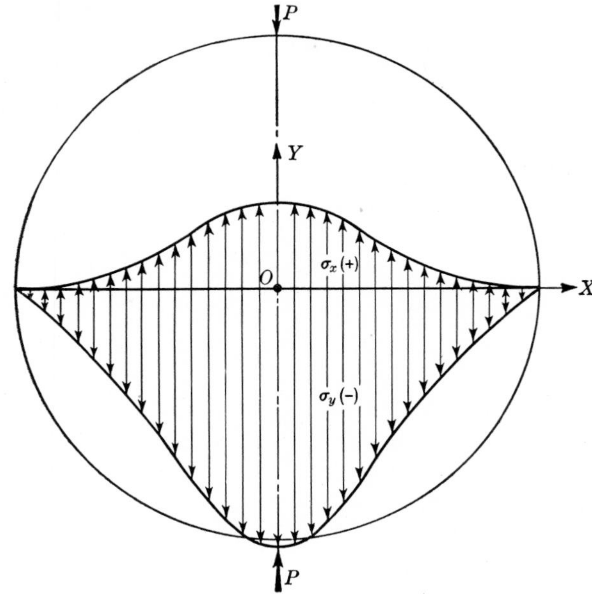

FIG. 4.8(a) Curves Showing the Stress Distribution along the Horizontal Section of Symmetry for a Disk under Diametral Compression.

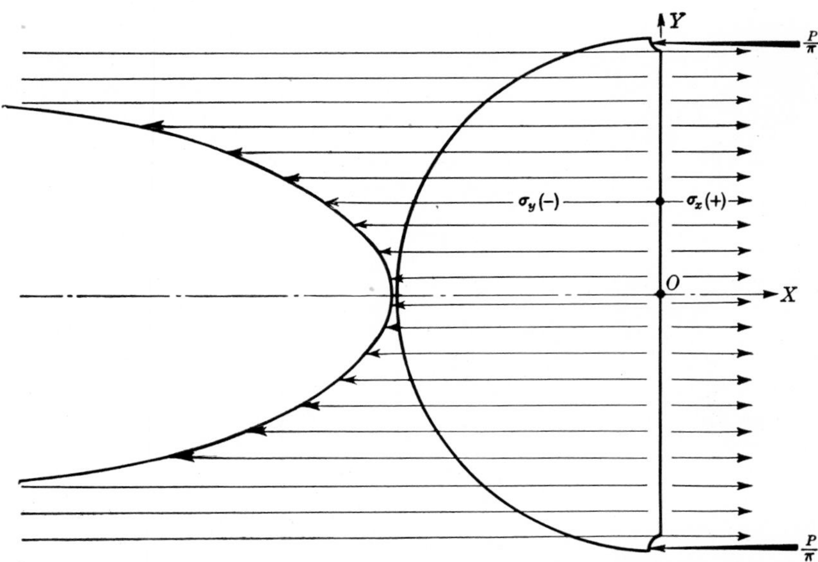

FIG. 4.8(b) Curves Showing the Stress Distribution along the Vertical Section of Symmetry.

is infinite when $r_1 = 0$ or when $r_2 = 0$. The minimum numerical value of the vertical compression is $\dfrac{6P}{\pi td}$ at the center of the disk. The distribution of the stresses across the X and Y axes is shown in Fig. 4.8.

Attention is called to Fig. 4.8(*b*), in which horizontal trusts P/π must be introduced for purposes of equilibrium (see §2.2, eq. 2.9).

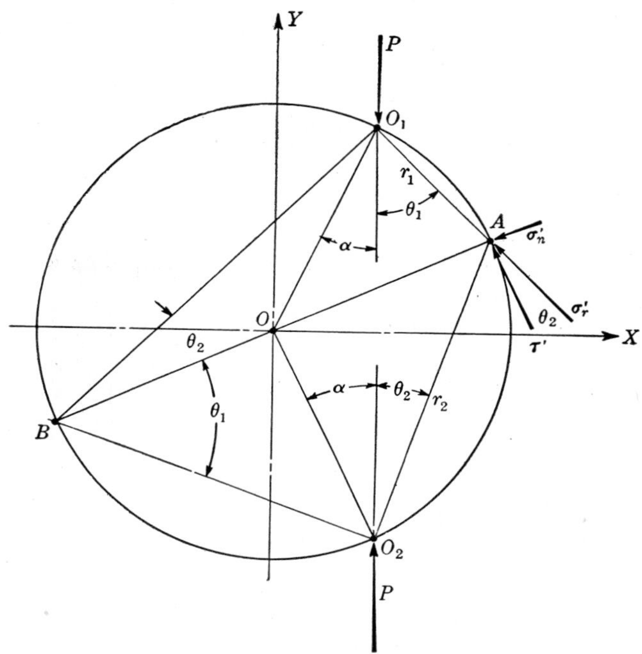

FIG. 4.9 Sketch Showing General Notation for Two Equal and Opposite Concentrated Loads Acting along an Arbitrary Chord O_1O_2 of a Circular Disk.

§4.5 Disk Subjected to Loads Acting along a Chord. We next consider two equal, collinear, and opposite loads P acting at the extremities of an arbitrary chord O_1 and O_2, Fig. 4.9, and again assume that each load produces a radial stress system defined by eqs. (2.8), i.e.,

$$\sigma_r = -\frac{2P\cos\theta}{\pi tr}$$

$$\sigma_\theta = 0,$$

$$\tau_{r\theta} = 0.$$

At any point A on the circumference of the circle we would thus have two radial stresses σ_r' and σ_r'' acting along the radii vectors r_1 and r_2 respectively. Since the acute angle which σ_r' makes with the tangent at A equals θ_2, Fig. 4.9, the normal and tangential components σ_n', τ' of this stress are given by

$$\left.\begin{aligned}\sigma_n' &= \sigma_r' \sin^2 \theta_2, \qquad &(a)\\ \tau' &= \frac{\sigma_r'}{2} \sin 2\theta_2. \qquad &(b)\end{aligned}\right\}(4.17)$$

Similarly, the components σ_n'', τ'' of the radial stress σ_r'' are given by

$$\left.\begin{aligned}\sigma_n'' &= \sigma_r'' \sin^2 \theta_1, \qquad &(a)\\ \tau'' &= \frac{\sigma_r''}{2} \sin 2\theta_1. \qquad &(b)\end{aligned}\right\}(4.18)$$

Substituting for σ_r' and σ_r'' the expressions corresponding to eqs. (2.8), i.e.,

$$\left.\begin{aligned}\sigma_r' &= -\frac{2P \cos \theta_1}{\pi t r_1}, \qquad &(a)\\ \sigma_r'' &= -\frac{2P \cos \theta_2}{\pi t r_2}, \qquad &(b)\end{aligned}\right\}(4.19)$$

and observing that

$$\left.\begin{aligned}r_1 &= d \sin \theta_2, \qquad &(a)\\ r_2 &= d \sin \theta_1, \qquad &(b)\end{aligned}\right\}(4.20)$$

where d is the diameter of the disk, we get for σ_n, the resultant normal stress,

$$\begin{aligned}\sigma_n &= \sigma_n' + \sigma_n''\\ &= -\frac{2P}{\pi t d}(\cos \theta_1 \sin \theta_2 + \cos \theta_2 \sin \theta_1)\\ &= -\frac{2P}{\pi t d} \sin (\theta_1 + \theta_2). \qquad (4.21)\end{aligned}$$

Inspection of Fig. 4.9 shows that on the circular boundary

$$\theta_1 + \theta_2 = \frac{\pi}{2} \pm \alpha,$$

depending on whether the point A is on the arc O_1O_2 which is less than a semicircle, or on the arc O_1O_2 which is greater than a semicircle. However, since

$$\sin\left(\frac{\pi}{2}+\alpha\right) = \sin\left(\frac{\pi}{2}-\alpha\right),$$

it follows that

$$\sigma_n = -\frac{2P}{\pi t d}\sin\left(\frac{\pi}{2}+\alpha\right), \tag{4.22}$$

where α is as shown in Fig. 4.9.

Inspection of the figure shows that the shear stresses τ' and τ'' go in opposite directions. The resultant shear stress is therefore given by

$$\begin{aligned}\tau &= \tau' - \tau'' \\ &= -\frac{2P}{\pi t d}(\cos\theta_1\cos\theta_2 - \cos\theta_2\cos\theta_1) = 0.\end{aligned} \tag{4.23}$$

The boundary stresses thus reduce to a radial compression of constant magnitude, which can be removed by the addition of a radial tension of equal magnitude. ***The stresses at any point in the disk produced by two concentrated collinear loads acting along an arbitrary chord are then obtained by combining two radial stresses σ_r' and σ_r'' with an isotropic tension of magnitude $\frac{2P}{\pi t d}\sin\left(\frac{\pi}{2}+\alpha\right)$.***

§4.6 Rectangular Stress Components for Loads along a Chord. The general expressions for the rectangular stress components for loads acting along an arbitrary chord are the same as those given by eqs. (4.9) for loads along a diameter, except for the isotropic tension, which in this case is $2P\sin(\pi/2+\alpha)/\pi t d$ instead of $2P/\pi t d$. Hence

$$\left.\begin{aligned}\sigma_x &= -\frac{2P}{\pi t}\left[\frac{\cos\theta_1\sin^2\theta_1}{r_1}+\frac{\cos\theta_2\sin^2\theta_2}{r_2}-\frac{\sin(\pi/2+\alpha)}{d}\right], && (a)\\ \sigma_y &= -\frac{2P}{\pi t}\left[\frac{\cos^3\theta_1}{r_1}+\frac{\cos^3\theta_2}{r_2}-\frac{\sin(\pi/2+\alpha)}{d}\right], && (b)\\ \tau_{xy} &= \frac{2P}{\pi t}\left(\frac{\cos^2\theta_1\sin\theta_1}{r_1}-\frac{\cos^2\theta_2\sin\theta_2}{r_2}\right). && (c)\end{aligned}\right\} \tag{4.24}$$

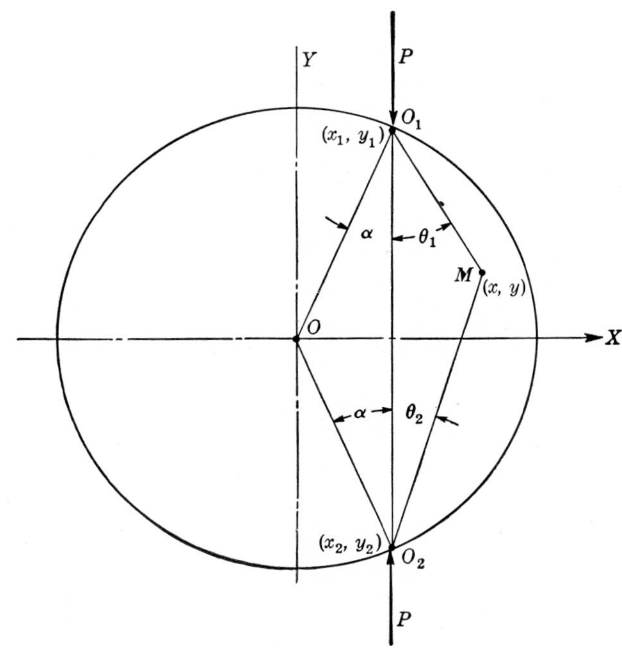

FIG. 4.10 Notation for Rectangular Stress Components for a Circular Disk with Two Equal and Opposite Loads along a Chord.

Referring to Fig. 4.10, let (x_1, y_1), (x_2, y_2) be the coordinates of points O_1 and O_2 respectively, and let (x, y) be the coordinates of any point M in the disk. Noting that $x_1 = x_2$ and $y_1 = -y_2$, we have

$$\left.\begin{aligned} \sin\theta_1 &= \frac{x - x_1}{r_1}, && (a)\\ \cos\theta_1 &= \frac{y_1 - y}{r_1}, && (b)\\ \sin\theta_2 &= \frac{x - x_1}{r_2}, && (c)\\ \cos\theta_2 &= \frac{y - y_2}{r_2} = \frac{y + y_1}{r_2}. && (d) \end{aligned}\right\} \quad (4.25)$$

Substituting in eq. (4.24), we get

$$
\left.
\begin{aligned}
\sigma_x &= -\frac{2P}{\pi t}\left[\frac{(y_1 - y)(x - x_1)^2}{r_1{}^4} + \frac{(y_1 + y)(x - x_1)^2}{r_2{}^4} \right. \\
&\qquad\qquad \left. - \frac{\sin\,(\pi/2 + \alpha)}{d}\right], \qquad (a) \\
\sigma_y &= -\frac{2P}{\pi t}\left[\frac{(y_1 - y)^3}{r_1{}^4} + \frac{(y_1 + y)^3}{r_2{}^4} - \frac{\sin\,(\pi/2 + \alpha)}{d}\right], \qquad (b) \\
\tau_{xy} &= \frac{2P}{\pi t}\left[\frac{(y_1 - y)^2(x - x_1)}{r_1{}^4} - \frac{(y_1 + y)^2(x - x_1)}{r_1{}^4}\right], \qquad (c)
\end{aligned}
\right\} (4.26)
$$

in which

$$r_1{}^2 = (x - x_1)^2 + (y_1 - y)^2$$

and

$$
\begin{aligned}
r_2{}^2 &= (x - x_1)^2 + (y - y_2)^2 \\
&= (x - x_1)^2 + (y + y_1)^2.
\end{aligned}
$$

These are general expressions which will hold for any pair of loads along an arbitrary chord. The results obtained in the preceding article for the case of loads acting along a diameter can also be found from the last set of equations. Along the X axis, $r_1 = r_2$, $y = 0$, and eqs. (4.26) reduce to

$$
\left.
\begin{aligned}
\sigma_x &= -\frac{2P}{\pi t}\left[\frac{2y_1(x - x_1)^2}{r^4} - \frac{\sin\,(\pi/2 + \alpha)}{d}\right], \qquad (a) \\
\sigma_y &= -\frac{2P}{\pi t}\left[\frac{2y_1{}^3}{r^4} - \frac{\sin\,(\pi/2 + \alpha)}{d}\right], \qquad (b) \\
\tau_{xy} &= 0. \qquad (c)
\end{aligned}
\right\} (4.27)
$$

A theoretical solution is also available for the stresses in a disk in equilibrium subjected to any number of concentrated loads on the boundary. It can be shown[1] that the stresses at any point in the disk produced by n concentrated loads are obtained by combining in the proper manner, all the radial stresses, i.e.,

$$\sigma_r = -\sum_{i=1}^{i=n} \frac{2P_i}{\pi t d}\frac{\cos\theta_i}{r_i}, \qquad (4.28)$$

[1] See *Theory of Elasticity*, by S. Timoshenko, p. 106. Original solutions by H. Hertz, *Z. Math. Physik*, Vol. 28, 1883, or *Gesammelte Werke*, Vol. I, p. 283; and by J. H. Michell, *Proc. London Math. Soc.*, Vol. 32 p. 44, 1900, and Vol. 34, p. 134, 1902.

and adding to it an isotropic tension given by

$$\sum_{i=1}^{i=n} \frac{2P_i}{\pi t d} \sin (\theta_1 + \theta_2)_i, \tag{4.29}$$

in which θ_1 and θ_2 are as shown in Fig. 4.9.

PART II PHOTOELASTIC ASPECTS OF THE DISK

THEORETICAL AND EXPERIMENTAL RESULTS[1]

§4.7 The Dipolar Equation of the Fringes or Isochromatics in a Disk Subjected to Concentrated Diametral Loads. The basic definition of a fringe or isochromatic curve is given by the simple expression

$$p - q = \Delta, \text{ a constant.}$$

In terms of the rectangular components σ_x, σ_y, τ_{xy} we have

$$\left.\begin{aligned} \Delta &= (p - q) = \sqrt{(\sigma_x - \sigma_y)^2 + 4\tau_{xy}^2} && (a) \\ \text{or} \quad \Delta^2 &= (\sigma_x - \sigma_y)^2 + 4\tau_{xy}^2. && (b) \end{aligned}\right\} \tag{4.30}$$

Substituting the values from eq. (4.9), multiplying both sides by $\pi^2 t^2 / 4P^2$, and squaring and collecting terms of like coefficients, we obtain

$$\frac{\pi^2 t^2 \Delta^2}{4P^2} = \frac{A}{r_1^2} + \frac{B}{r_2^2} + \frac{2C \cos \theta_1 \cos \theta_2}{r_1 r_2}, \tag{4.31}$$

where

$$\left.\begin{aligned} A &= \cos^2 \theta_1 (\sin^4 \theta_1 + 2 \sin^2 \theta_1 \cos^2 \theta_1 + \cos^4 \theta_1) && (a) \\ &= \cos^2 \theta_1, && (b) \end{aligned}\right\} \tag{4.32}$$

$$\left.\begin{aligned} B &= \cos^2 \theta_2 (\sin^4 \theta_2 + 2 \sin^2 \theta_2 \cos^2 \theta_2 + \cos^4 \theta_2) && (a) \\ &= \cos^2 \theta_2, && (b) \end{aligned}\right\} \tag{4.33}$$

and

$$\left.\begin{aligned} C &= (\sin^2 \theta_1 - \cos^2 \theta_1)(\sin^2 \theta_2 - \cos^2 \theta_2) - \sin 2\theta_1 \sin 2\theta_2 && (a) \\ &= \cos 2(\theta_1 + \theta_2). && (b) \end{aligned}\right\} \tag{4.34}$$

Adding and subtracting $(2 \cos \theta_1 \cos \theta_2)/r_1 r_2$ to the right side of eq. (4.31) and substituting the simplified expressions for A, B, and C,

[1] Except for detail and some notation the treatment in Part II is essentially the same as that of Professor F. W. Bubb. See his paper "Photoelastic Theory of the Roller Bearing," *Photoelastic Journal*, Vol. I, No. 6–12, June-December, 1938.

Eq. (4.43) provides a simple way to check a stress pattern. By inserting the coordinates (x, y) of an arbitrary point in the disk we can

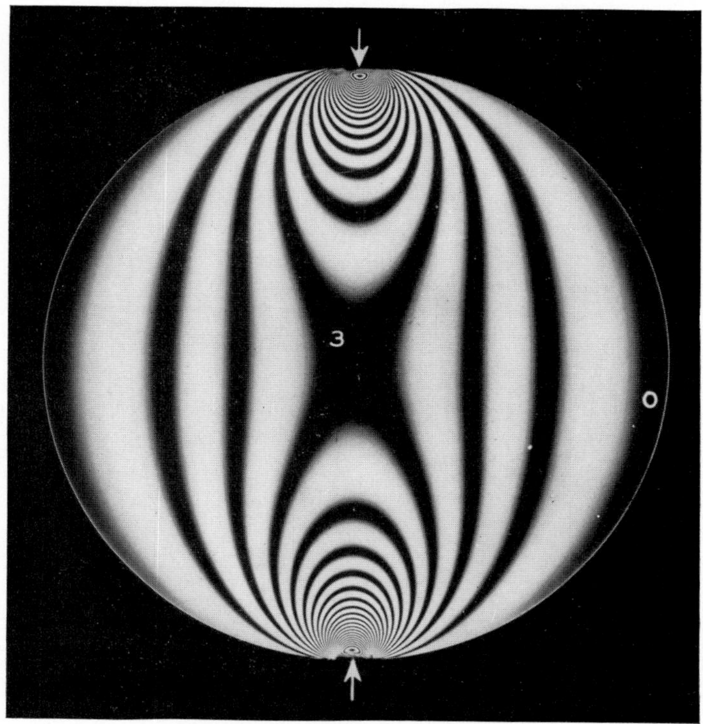

FIG. 4.11 Stress Pattern of a Disk Compressed by Two Diametrically Opposite Flat Steel Bars.

$P = 161.7$ lb.; diameter, $d = 1.600$ in.; $t = 0.200$ in.; $F = 215$ psi. shear.

readily calculate the fringe order passing through the corresponding point in the stress pattern, and this can then be compared with the experimental value.

Referring again to Fig. 4.11 (see legend for dimensions), let us calculate the fringe order n_c at the origin. Putting $x = y = 0$, we find, eq. (4.43),

$$\begin{aligned} n_c &= \frac{K}{R^2} \\ &= \frac{2P}{\pi t F R} = \frac{2 \times 161.7}{\pi \times 0.2 \times 215 \times 0.8} \\ &= 3. \end{aligned} \tag{4.43a}$$

Inspection of the stress pattern also gives a value of 3.

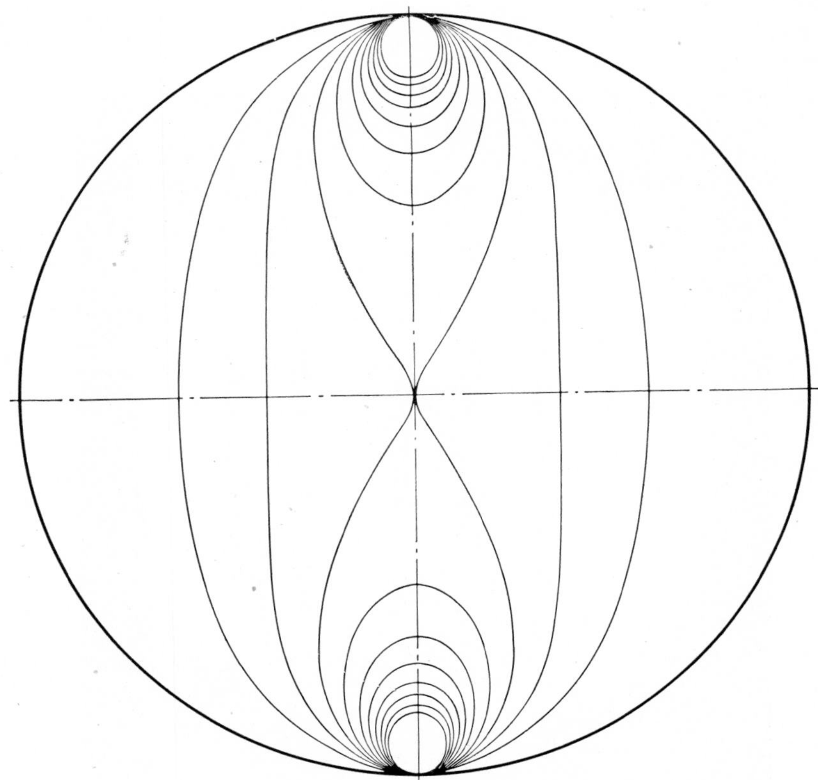

FIG. 4.12 Theoretical Stress Pattern Drawn by Plotting the Curves of Eqs. (4.44) and (4.45); Fringe Order at Center, $n_c = 3$.

For purposes of constructing a theoretical stress pattern we solve eq. (4.43) explicitly for x and y, and obtain after simplification

$$x^2 = -R^2 - y^2 - \frac{K}{2n} + \sqrt{\frac{K^2}{4n^2} + \frac{2R^2K}{n} + 4R^2y^2}, \qquad (4.44)$$

$$y^2 = R^2 - x^2 - \frac{K}{2n} \pm \sqrt{\frac{K^2}{4n^2} - 4R^2x^2}. \qquad (4.45)$$

The reason for choosing the positive root in eq. (4.44) is fairly obvious. Since the left side of this expression is positive, the right side must be positive. The first three terms on the right side all being negative, it follows that the positive root must be selected.

Eq. (4.44) is convenient to calculate the fringes which intersect the

X axis, whereas eq. (4.45) is more useful to determine the fringes or isochromatics which intersect the Y axis only, i.e., the ovals which lie above and below the X axis. The stress pattern shown in Fig. 4.12 was calculated by the above equation, and fringe 3 was made to pass through the origin.

Intercepts. In order to find the X and Y intercepts for a fringe of order n we put $y = 0$ in eq. (4.44) and $x = 0$ in eq. (4.45). This gives

$$x^2 = -R^2 - \frac{K}{2n} + \sqrt{\frac{K^2}{4n^2} + \frac{4R^2K}{2n}}, \tag{4.46}$$

$$y^2 = R^2 - \frac{K}{n}, \qquad (a)$$

or

$$y^2 = R^2. \qquad (b) \quad (4.47)$$

From the last equation we have

$$y = \pm R. \tag{4.48}$$

This reveals an important aspect of the fringes or isochromatics, namely, that they all pass through the points of application of the loads. The stress patterns shown in Figs. 4.11 and 4.12 corroborate this conclusion. In the experimental stress pattern, Fig. 4.11, some fringes do not pass through the points of application of the loads. This seeming discrepancy is easily explained if we observe that the actual loads are not concentrated but distributed over finite flattened portions of the disk. Another effect of this distribution of the load is to move the points of maximum shear stress away from the boundaries and to produce a local fringe formation similar to that encountered in the case of a distributed load on a semi-infinite plate, Figs. 2.27 and 2.30.

In addition to the constant intercepts $y = \pm R$, eq. (4.47a) shows that for sufficiently large values of n, i.e., when n is greater than K/R^2, there are two additional intercepts given by

$$y = \pm\sqrt{R^2 - \frac{K}{n}}. \tag{4.49}$$

For truly concentrated loads the fringes originate at the points of application of the loads, travel toward the center of the disk, where they momentarily merge, then separate and travel toward the outer circular boundary, which they never reach, since, as shown before, the stress at the boundary remains zero.

§4.9 General Method for Plotting Fringes. In the problem under consideration the analytical expression for $(p - q)$ was readily derived,

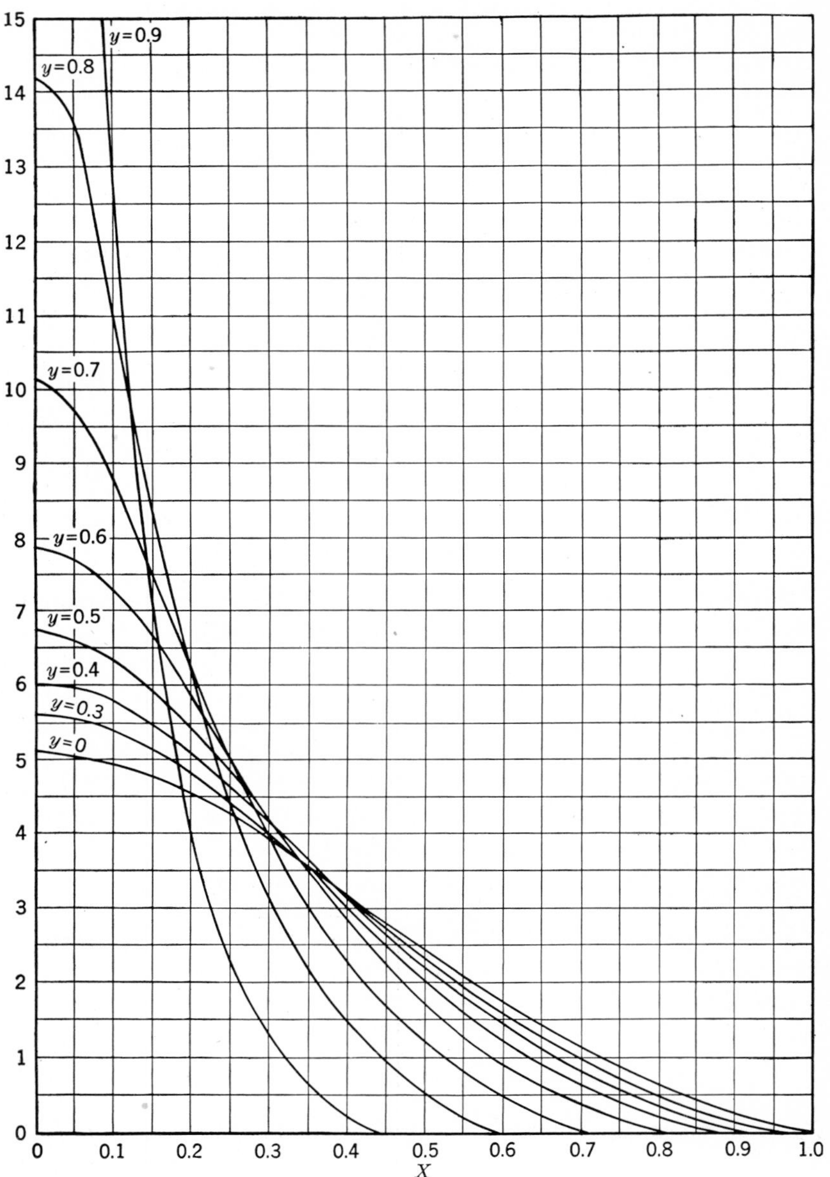

FIG. 4.13 Theoretical Influence Curves of $(p - q)$ for Horizontal Sections of a Disk Subjected to Vertical Diametral Loads.

Ordinates in fringes; abscissas represent distances from center of disk of unit radius. Note: These curves can be obtained from eq. (4.44) by arbitrarily taking $K = 2$, $R = 1$ and then adjusting the scale of the ordinates so that the fringe order at the origin, n_c, is equal to the desired value.

and there was no difficulty in obtaining explicit expressions for x as a function of y, or y as a function of x. Should mathematical difficulties arise the curves of $(p - q)$ can be obtained by a semigraphical process. An illustration of this procedure is given in Fig. 4.13, which shows curves

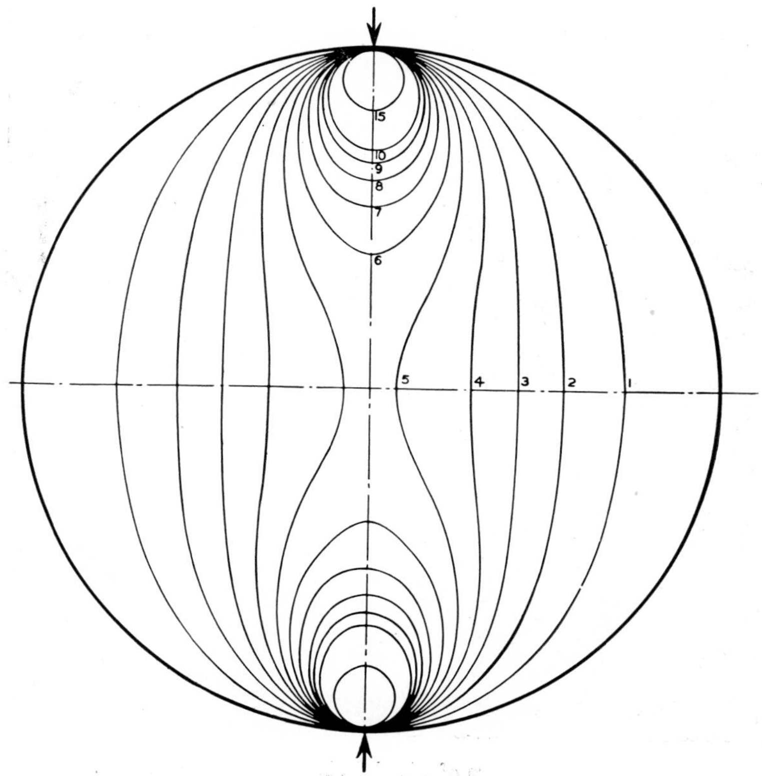

FIG. 4.14 Theoretical Stress Pattern Based on Curves in Fig. 4.13.

of $(p - q)$ for arbitrary constant values of y, i.e., curves showing the distribution of the shear stresses across sections transverse to the line of the loads. From such curves it is a simple matter to plot the loci of the constant $(p - q)$. The intersections of a horizontal line corresponding to a given shear stress with the curves of $(p - q)$ for constant values of y give the coordinates of the fringe or isochromatic corresponding to the given stress. The curves of Fig. 4.14 were constructed in this manner. The corresponding experimental pattern is shown in Fig. 4.15. ***The degree of agreement between the calculated and experimental curves***

can be clearly seen from Figs. 4.16 and 4.17, which show directly the two sets of intercepts. Inspection of these curves shows the corroboration to be well-nigh perfect.

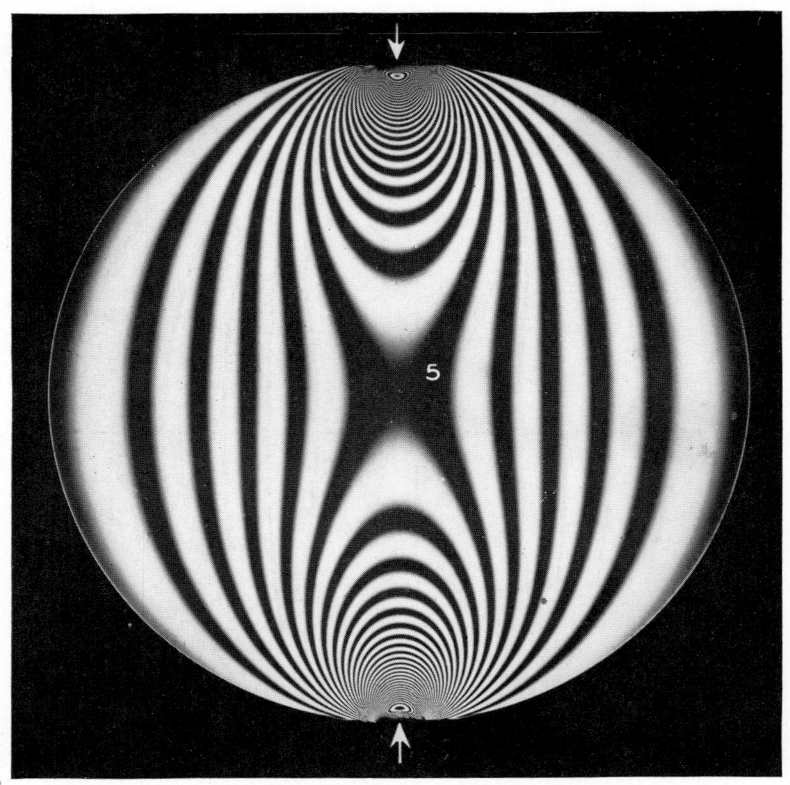

Fig. 4.15 Stress Pattern of a Disk in Diametral Compression. $P = 272.5$ lb. For dimensions see Fig. 4.11.

Fig. 4.18 gives the theoretical isopachic stress pattern, i.e., loci of constant $(p + q)$. This pattern is based upon the curves of Fig. 4.19, which were calculated from eqs. (4.11).

§4.10 Isoclinics. The angles which the principal stresses make with the X axis are given by the expression

$$\tan 2\theta = \frac{2\tau_{xy}}{\sigma_x - \sigma_y} \cdot \qquad [(1.13), \text{Vol. I}]$$

This is also the basic equation defining an isoclinic if we add the requirement that θ be constant. Substituting for σ_x, σ_y, τ_{xy} their values from eqs. (4.9) and simplifying, we obtain

$$\tan 2\theta = \frac{-r_1 \cos \theta_2 \sin 2\theta_2 + r_2 \cos \theta_1 \sin 2\theta_1}{r_1 \cos \theta_2 \cos 2\theta_2 + r_2 \cos \theta_1 \cos 2\theta_1}. \tag{4.50}$$

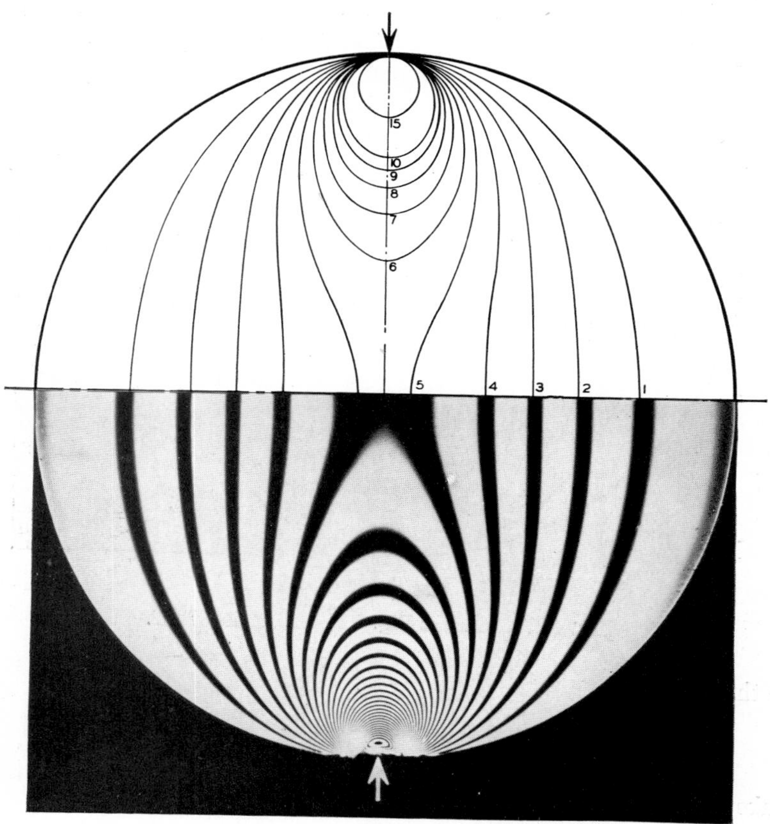

FIG. 4.16 Comparison of Theoretical and Photoelastic Stress Patterns for the Horizontal Half of a Disk in Diametral Compression, Obtained by Combining Figs. 4.14 and 4.15.

The radii vectors r_1 and r_2 can at once be eliminated by observing, Fig. 4.7, that

$$\frac{r_1}{r_2} = \frac{\sin \theta_2}{\sin \theta_1},$$

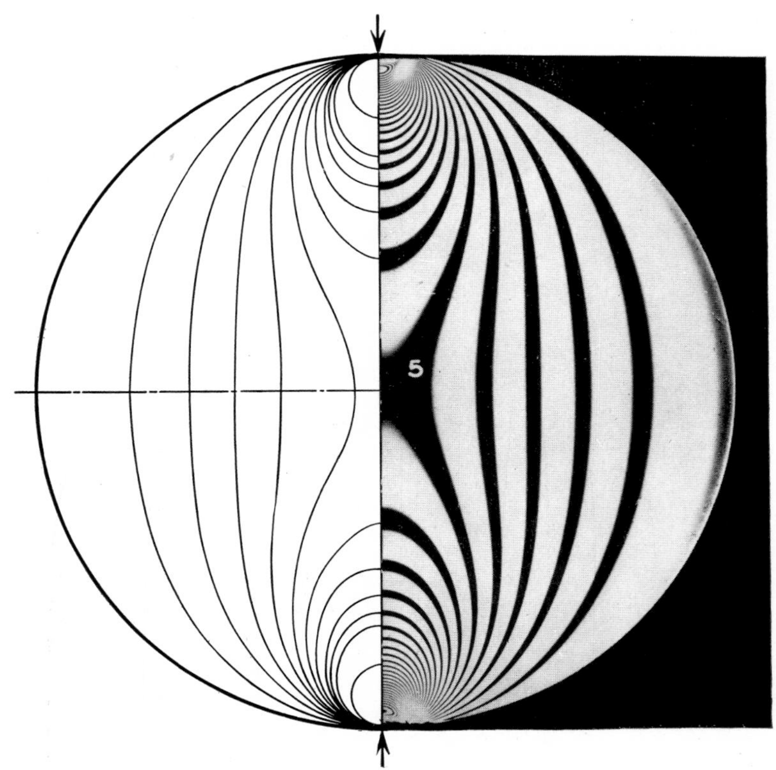

FIG. 4.17 Same as Fig. 4.16 for Vertical Half.

so that

$$r_1 = r_2 \frac{\sin \theta_2}{\sin \theta_1}.$$

Substituting the last expression for r_1, eq. (4.50) reduces to

$$\tan 2\theta = \frac{\sin^2 2\theta_1 - \sin^2 2\theta_2}{\sin 2\theta_1 \cos 2\theta_1 + \sin 2\theta_2 \cos 2\theta_2}$$

$$= -\frac{\cos 4\theta_1 - \cos 4\theta_2}{\sin 4\theta_1 + \sin 4\theta_2}. \tag{4.51}$$

From trigonometry we have

$$\cos \alpha - \cos \beta = -2 \sin \tfrac{1}{2}(\alpha + \beta) \sin \tfrac{1}{2}(\alpha - \beta),$$

$$\sin \alpha + \sin \beta = 2 \sin \tfrac{1}{2}(\alpha + \beta) \cos \tfrac{1}{2}(\alpha - \beta).$$

Eq. (4.51) may therefore be written as

$$\tan 2\theta = \frac{\sin \frac{1}{2}(4\theta_1 + 4\theta_2) \sin \frac{1}{2}(4\theta_1 - 4\theta_2)}{\sin \frac{1}{2}(4\theta_1 + 4\theta_2) \cos \frac{1}{2}(4\theta_1 - 4\theta_2)}$$

$$= \tan (2\theta_1 - 2\theta_2). \tag{4.52}$$

This gives two roots θ and θ' differing by 90°, i.e.,

$$2\theta = 2\theta_1 - 2\theta_2 \quad (a)$$

or

$$2\theta' = \pi + 2\theta_1 - 2\theta_2. \quad (b) \qquad (4.53)$$

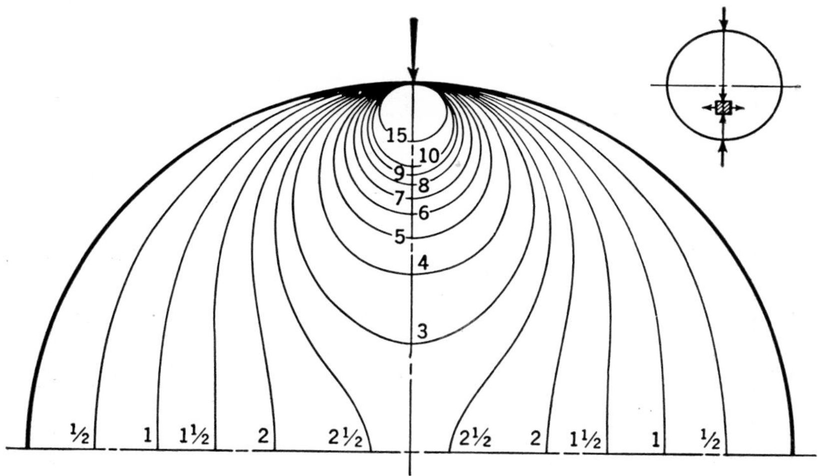

FIG. 4.18 Theoretical Isopachic Stress Pattern for a Disk in Diametral Compression, Based on Curves of Fig. 4.19.

From (4.53a) we have

$$\theta = \theta_1 - \theta_2$$

$$\tan \theta = \frac{\sin (\theta_1 - \theta_2)}{\cos (\theta_1 - \theta_2)}$$

$$= \frac{\sin \theta_1 \cos \theta_2 - \cos \theta_1 \sin \theta_2}{\cos \theta_1 \cos \theta_2 + \sin \theta_1 \sin \theta_2} \cdot \tag{4.54}$$

Using the expressions from eqs. (4.10), this becomes

$$\tan \theta = \frac{2xy}{R^2 - y^2 + x^2} \cdot \tag{4.55}$$

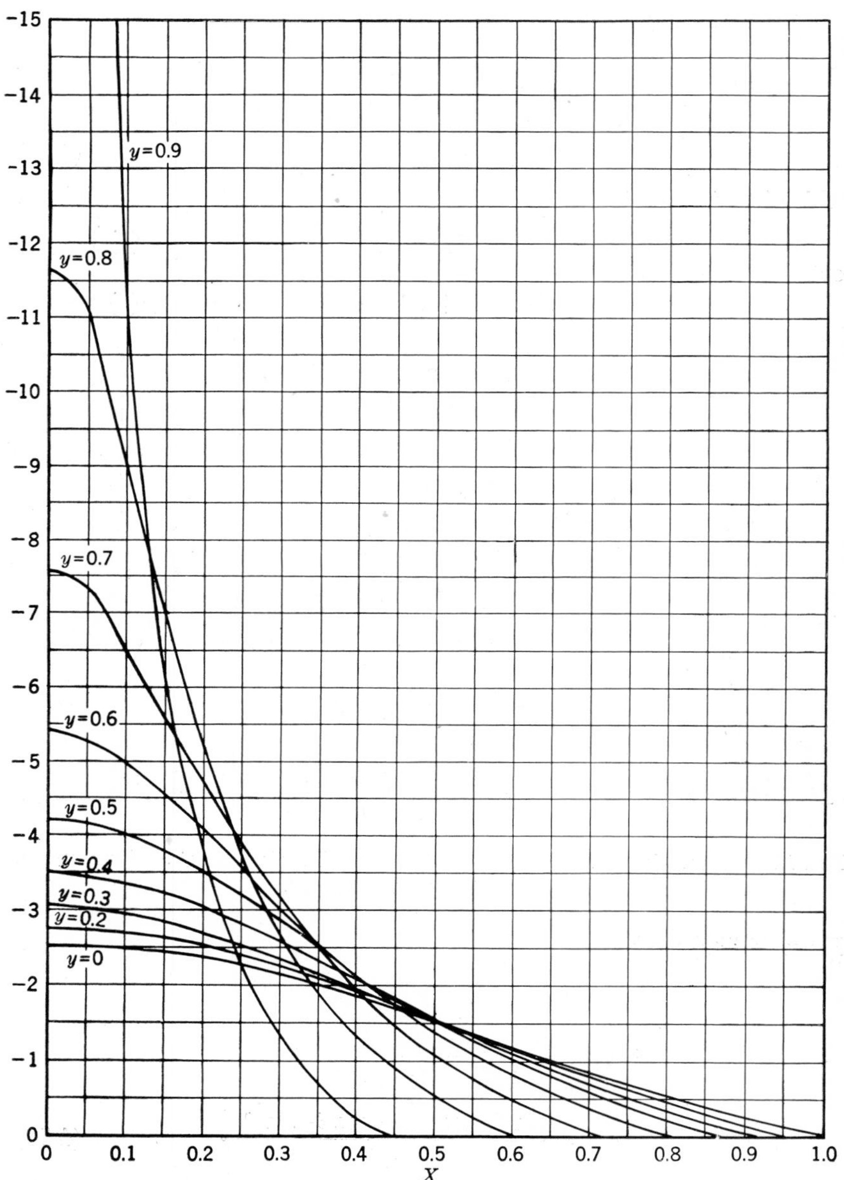

FIG. 4.19 Theoretical Curves of $(p - q)$ for Horizontal Sections of a Disk Subjected to Vertical Diametral Loads, Based on Eqs. (4.11).

Ordinates in fringes; abscissas represent distances from center of disk of unit radius. See note in Fig. 4.13.

Hence, the equation of the isoclinic of parameter θ is

$$x^2 - 2xy \cot \theta - y^2 + R^2 = 0, \tag{4.56}$$

in which $\cot \theta$ is a constant.

Since the second root θ' differs from θ by a constant value, and specifically

$$\theta' = \theta + \frac{\pi}{2},$$

it follows that eq. (4.56) is also the locus of points along which θ' is a constant. In other words, through a given point there exists only one isoclinic.

Eq. (4.56) is a second-degree equation of the general form

$$Ax^2 + 2Hxy + By^2 + C = 0, \tag{4.57}$$

representing a parabola, ellipse, or hyperbola depending on whether the discriminant $(H^2 - AB)$ equals zero, is less than zero, or is greater than zero.[1] In the case under consideration

$$A = 1, \quad H = -\cot \theta, \quad B = -1.$$

Hence

$$H^2 - AB = \cot^2 \theta + 1,$$

and this is clearly greater than zero. ***It follows that the isoclinics given by eq. (4.56) are hyperbolas.***

Furthermore, eq. (4.56) can be transformed by means of a rotation of axes so that the term in xy would vanish. When this is done it assumes the simple form

$$x'^2 - y'^2 = \frac{R^2}{C} \tag{4.58}$$

in which C is a constant. The last formula will be recognized as the standard form of a rectangular hyperbola, that is, one in which the asymptotes are perpendicular to one another.

Basic Property of Isoclinics. We observe that, if in eq. (4.56) we put $x = 0$, then

$$y^2 = R^2,$$

so that

$$y = \pm R, \tag{4.59}$$

showing that ***all isoclinics above the X axis pass through the point of***

[1] See textbooks on analytic geometry.

application of the downward load and those below the X axis pass through the point of application of the upward load.

§4.11 Equations of the Asymptotes. It is shown in analytic geometry that the asymptotes of the hyperbola

$$Ax^2 + 2Hxy + By^2 + C = 0 \tag{4.57}$$

are obtained by solving the equation

$$Ax^2 + 2Hxy + By^2 = 0$$

for y in terms of x. Hence, for the hyperbola represented by eq. (4.56), the asymptotes are obtained from

$$x^2 - 2xy \cot \theta - y^2 = 0, \tag{4.60}$$

and this yields for the equations of the asymptotes

$$\left.\begin{aligned} y &= x\ (\csc \theta - \cot \theta), && (a) \\ y &= -x\ (\csc \theta + \cot \theta). && (b) \end{aligned}\right\} \quad (4.61)$$

For a particular isoclinic, of parameter θ_o, intersecting the free circular boundary at a point (x_o, y_o), Fig. 4.20,

$$\left.\begin{aligned} \cot \theta_o &= \frac{x_o}{y_o}, && (a) \\ \csc \theta_o &= \sqrt{1 + \frac{{x_o}^2}{{y_o}^2}} = \frac{R}{y_o}, && (b) \\ \csc \theta_o - \cot \theta_o &= \frac{R - x_o}{y_o}, && (c) \\ \csc \theta_o + \cot \theta_o &= \frac{R + x_o}{y_o}; && (d) \end{aligned}\right\} \quad (4.62)$$

and the equations of the asymptotes are therefore given by

$$\left.\begin{aligned} y &= \frac{R - x_o}{y_o} \cdot x, && (a) \\ y &= -\frac{R + x_o}{y_o} \cdot x. && (b) \end{aligned}\right\} \quad (4.63)$$

The graphical construction of the asymptotes is shown in Fig. 4.20. The foci of the rectangular hyperbolas, eq. (4.56), lie on line OV which bisects the right angle between the asymptotes. The distance OV from

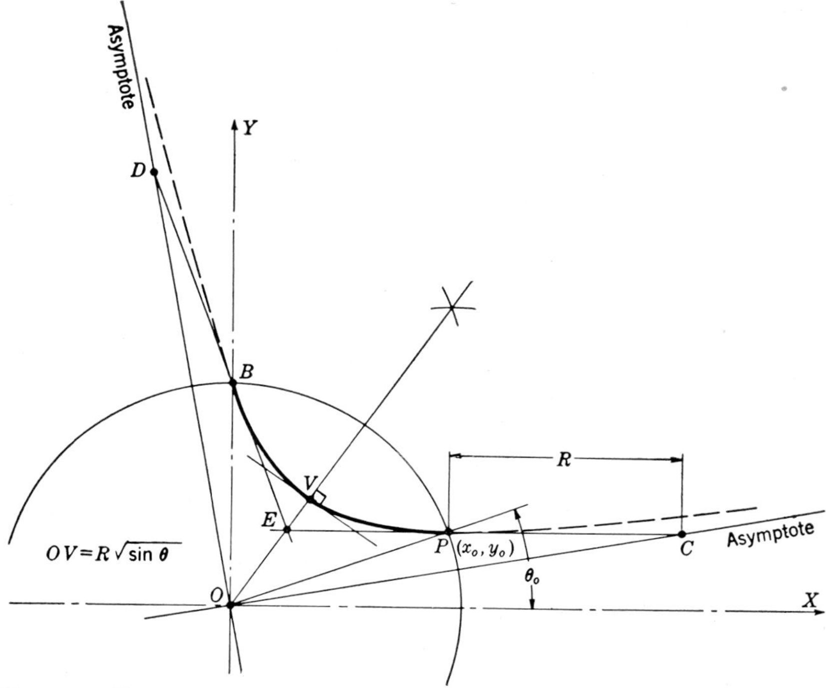

FIG. 4.20 Sketch Showing the Graphical Construction of an Isoclinic for a Disk in Diametral Compression.

the origin to the vertex is given by

$$\begin{aligned} OV &= \sqrt{Ry_o} \\ &= R\sqrt{\sin \theta_o}. \end{aligned} \tag{4.64}$$

Slopes of Isoclinics at Boundary. In order to determine the slope of the isoclinic of parameter θ_o at any point (x, y) we differentiate the expression

$$x^2 - 2 \cot \theta_o xy - y^2 + R^2 = 0$$

and obtain

$$\frac{dy}{dx} = \frac{x - y \cot \theta_o}{y + x \cot \theta_o}. \tag{4.65}$$

Let x_o, y_o represent the coordinates of the point of intersection of the isoclinic of parameter θ_o with the circular boundary; then, Fig. 4.20,

$$\tan \theta_o = \frac{y_o}{x_o},$$

and the slope of the isoclinic at the boundary vanishes, i.e.,

$$\left(\frac{dy}{dx}\right)_{\substack{x=x_o\\y=y_o}} = \frac{x_o - y_o \cot\theta_o}{x_o \cot\theta_o + y_o} = 0. \tag{4.66}$$

Hence ***the isoclinics are all horizontal where they intersect the boundary of the disk.***

Referring to Fig. 4.20 it is seen that the distance OV and the slopes at P, B and V are all known. This s sufficient to construct the isoclinic.

Photographs of several isoclinics are shown in Fig. 4.21. ***Comparison with the theoretical curves given in the same figure shows complete agreement with all the theoretical aspects.***

§4.12 Stress Trajectories. We have defined stress trajectories as curves the tangents to which represent the directions of one of the principal stresses at the points of tangency; see §1.29, Vol. I. The mathematical formulation of this definition is

$$\frac{dy}{dx} = \tan\theta. \tag{4.67}$$

Since through each point there are two mutually perpendicular trajectories we have, using eq. (4.55),

$$\left.\begin{aligned} \frac{dy}{dx} &= \frac{2xy}{R^2 + x^2 - y^2} && (a)\\ &\text{and}\\ \frac{dy}{dx} &= -\frac{R^2 + x^2 - y^2}{2xy}. && (b)\end{aligned}\right\} \tag{4.68}$$

The solution of eq. (4.68a) is

$$(y - C)^2 + x^2 = C^2 - R^2, \tag{4.69}$$

and the solution of eq. (4.68b) is

$$y^2 + (x + C_1)^2 = C_1{}^2 + R^2, \tag{4.70}$$

in which C and C_1 are constants. This can be readily verified by direct substitution. The stress trajectories thus consist of two families of orthogonal circles which can easily be constructed graphically. ***The centers of the first set lie on the Y axis, and those of the second on the X axis.*** We shall refer to these as *horizontal* and *vertical* trajectories, respectively.

Let it now be required to construct a stress trajectory through an arbitrary given point (x, y). It is evident that the coordinates of the given

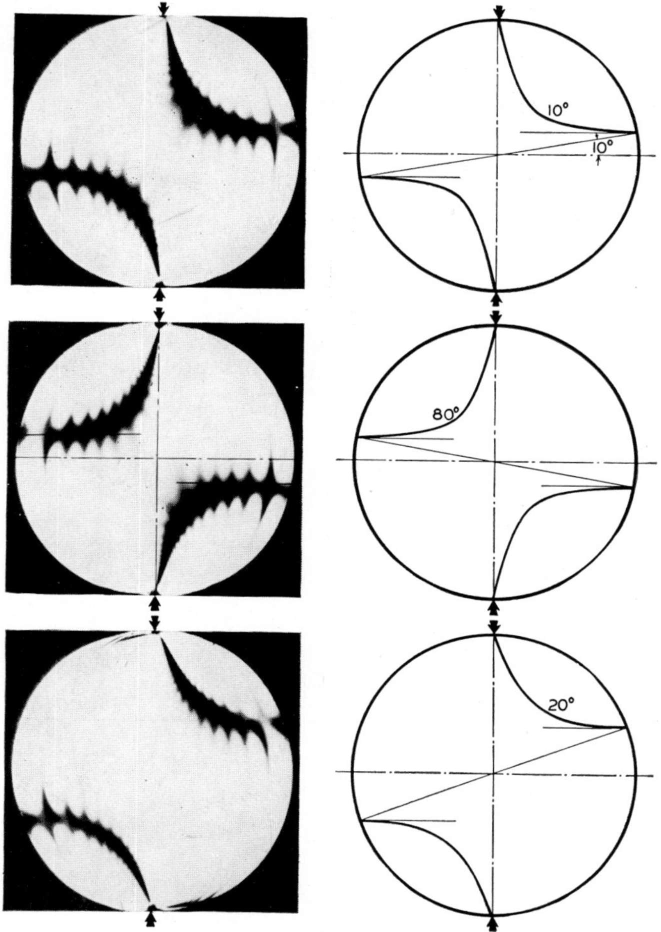

FIG. 4.21 Comparison of Three Theoretically Constructed Isoclinics and Photographs of Isoclinics of Corresponding Parameters in a Disk in Diametral Compression.

Diameter of model = 1.225 in.; t = 0.252 in.; P = 266 lb. Bakelite.

point determine the values of the constants C and C_1. Putting $C_1 = 0$ in eq. (4.70), we obtain

$$x^2 + y^2 = R^2,$$

showing that the boundary of the disk is itself a stress trajectory, a conclusion which completely agrees with the given condition that the boundary is free. We further observe that, regardless of the value of C_1 in eq. (4.70), $y = \pm R$ when $x = 0$. This means that ***all vertical trajectories must pass through the points of application of the loads, points B_1 and B_2, Fig. 4.22,*** and do not intersect the circumference elsewhere, except when the value of $C_1 = 0$, when the stress trajectory coincides with the boundary.

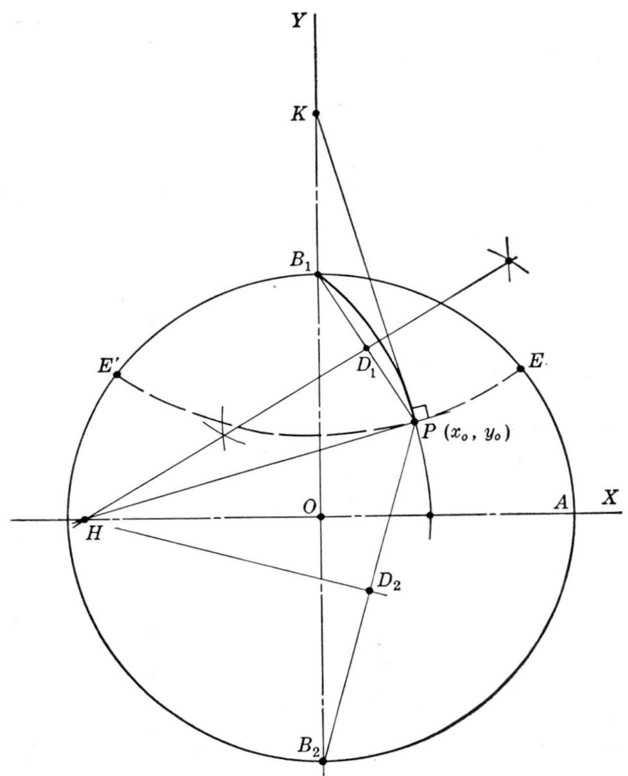

FIG. 4.22 Sketch Showing the Graphical Construction of a Principal Stress Trajectory for a Disk in Diametral Compression.

In order to draw the stress trajectories through an arbitrary point $P(x, y)$ we draw the lines PB_1 or PB_2 and construct perpendiculars through the midpoints D_1 or D_2 of these segments. The intersection of these midpoints with the X axis gives the center H of the vertical trajectory through point P, the radius of which is HP, Fig. 4.22.

We next draw a perpendicular PK to HP at point P. The intersec-

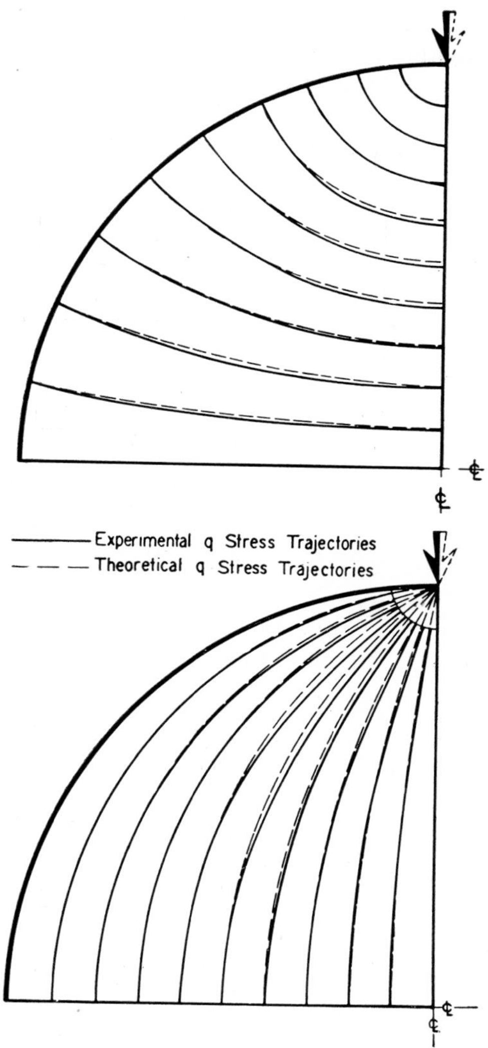

Fig. 4.23 Comparison of Experimental and Theoretical Stress Trajectories for a Disk in Diametral Compression.

Theoretical trajectories were constructed as shown in Fig. 4.22. Experimental trajectories were taken from Fig. 1.39, Vol. I.

tion of this perpendicular with the Y axis gives the center K of the horizontal trajectory through the same point.

The experimental and theoretical stress trajectories are compared in Fig. 4.23. The experimental curves are taken from Fig. 1.39, Vol. I.

§4.13 The Disk as a Photoelastic Dynamometer. ***The circular disk discussed in this chapter can be used as a photoelastic dynamometer to measure reactions and loads in statically indeterminate structures.***

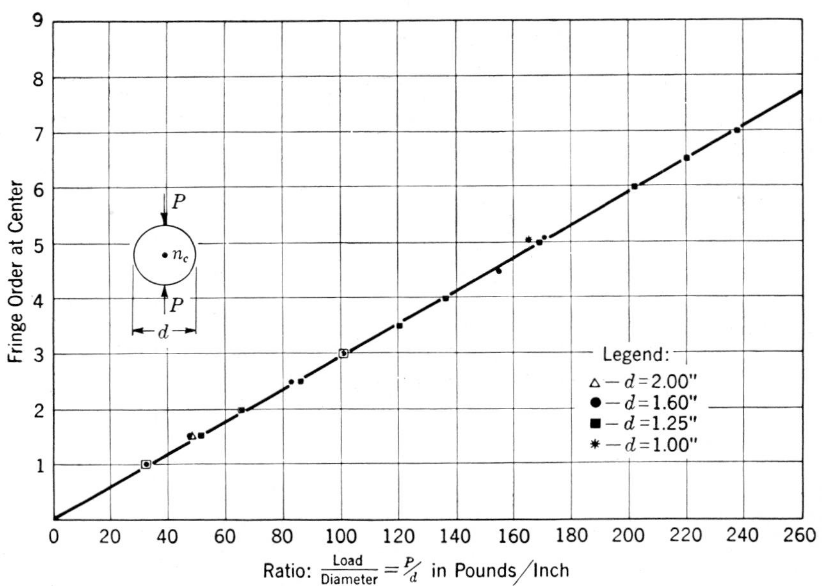

FIG. 4.24 Curve Showing Experimental and Theoretical Values of n_c as a Function of P/d, Eq. (4.72).

From eqs. (4.41) and (4.42) we have for the fringe order n_c at the center of the disk

$$n_c = \frac{4P}{\pi t F 2R}. \tag{4.71}$$

Since

$$Ft = f, \qquad [(5.10), \text{Vol. I}]$$

$$n_c = \frac{4}{\pi f}\frac{P}{d}. \tag{4.72}$$

Hence the fringe order n_c is a linear function of (P/d) and is independent of the thickness. The result is clearly substantiated by the experimental curve of Fig. 4.24. Some of the stress patterns on which this curve is based were shown in Figs. 4.11 and 4.15. It follows that the load P acting on a disk of diameter d is given by the expression

$$P = \frac{\pi f}{4} n_c d. \tag{4.73}$$

Since the fringe order n_c at the center of the disk can be determined with a high degree of precision and is not materially affected by initial stresses, the disk becomes a very practical photoelastic dynamometer, both for the application of loads and for the measurement of redundant reactions. It also provides a simple and accurate method for the determination of the fringe value.

CHAPTER 5

CONCENTRATED LOAD ON AN INFINITE PLATE

§5.1 Strains and Displacements from the Stress Function $\boldsymbol{\phi = Cr\theta \sin \theta}$. We have seen in §2.2 that the stress function

$$\phi = Cr\theta \sin \theta \tag{2.3}$$

satisfies the condition of continuity, eq. (1.42*a*), and that it leads to the stress components

$$\left.\begin{aligned} \sigma_r &= -\frac{2P}{\pi t}\frac{\cos\theta}{r}, && (a)\\ \sigma_\theta &= 0, && (b)\\ \tau_{r\theta} &= 0. && (c) \end{aligned}\right\} \tag{2.8}$$

The displacements u and v are determined from Hooke's Law, which in polar coordinates and for plane stress take on the form (see Chapter 1, Vol. I)

$$\left.\begin{aligned} \epsilon_r &= \frac{1}{E}(\sigma_r - \nu\sigma_\theta), && (a)\\ \epsilon_\theta &= \frac{1}{E}(\sigma_\theta - \nu\sigma_r), && (b)\\ \gamma_{r\theta} &= \frac{1}{G}\tau_{r\theta} = \frac{2(1+\nu)}{E}\tau_{r\theta}. && (c) \end{aligned}\right\} \tag{5.1}$$

Further, it has previously been shown that

$$\epsilon_r = \frac{\partial u}{\partial r}, \tag{1.3}$$

$$\epsilon_\theta = \frac{u}{r} + \frac{1}{r}\frac{\partial v}{\partial \theta}, \tag{1.4}$$

$$\gamma_{r\theta} = \frac{1}{r}\frac{\partial u}{\partial \theta} + \frac{\partial v}{\partial r} - \frac{v}{r}. \tag{1.7}$$

Substituting the stresses from eq. (2.8) in eq. (5.1) and replacing the strains in terms of the displacements, we obtain

$$\left.\begin{aligned} \frac{\partial u}{\partial r} &= -\frac{2P}{\pi t E}\frac{\cos\theta}{r}, &(a)\\ \frac{u}{r} + \frac{1}{r}\frac{\partial v}{\partial \theta} &= \frac{2\nu P}{\pi t E}\frac{\cos\theta}{r}, &(b)\\ \frac{1}{r}\frac{\partial u}{\partial \theta} + \frac{\partial v}{\partial r} - \frac{v}{r} &= 0. &(c) \end{aligned}\right\}\tag{5.2}$$

Integrating eq. (5.2*a*) we have

$$u = -\frac{2P}{\pi t E}\cos\theta \log r + f(\theta), \tag{5.3}$$

in which $f(\theta)$ is a function of θ only. Substituting the above value of u in eq. (5.2*b*) and multiplying by r, we obtain

$$-\frac{2P}{\pi t E}\cos\theta\log r + f(\theta) + \frac{\partial v}{\partial\theta} = \frac{2\nu P}{\pi t E}\cos\theta, \tag{5.4}$$

whence

$$\frac{\partial v}{\partial \theta} = \frac{2\nu P}{\pi t E}\cos\theta + \frac{2P}{\pi t E}\log r\cos\theta - f(\theta), \tag{5.5}$$

and

$$v = \frac{2\nu P}{\pi t E}\sin\theta + \frac{2P}{\pi t E}\log r \sin\theta - \int f(\theta)\,d\theta + F(r), \tag{5.6}$$

in which $F(r)$ is a function of r only. In order to find $f(\theta)$ and $F(r)$ we form $\partial u/\partial\theta$ and $\partial v/\partial r$ from the expressions for u and v just found and substitute in eq. (5.2*c*). Thus, from eq. (5.3)

$$\frac{\partial u}{\partial \theta} = \frac{2P}{\pi t E}\log r\sin\theta + \frac{d}{d\theta}f(\theta), \tag{5.7}$$

and from eq. (5.6)

$$\frac{\partial v}{\partial r} = \frac{2P}{\pi t E}\frac{\sin\theta}{r} + \frac{d}{dr}F(r). \tag{5.8}$$

Upon substitution in eq. (5.2*c*) and multiplication by r we obtain

$$\begin{aligned} \frac{d}{d\theta}f(\theta) + \frac{2P}{\pi t E}\sin\theta + r\frac{d}{dr}F(r) - \frac{2\nu P}{\pi t E}\sin\theta \\ + \int f(\theta)\,d\theta - F(r) = 0. \end{aligned}\tag{5.9}$$

This equation must be true for all values of r and θ. Since these are independent quantities it follows that we may put each of them separately equal to zero.

Letting $r = 0$ in eq. (5.9) we obtain

$$\frac{d}{d\theta} f(\theta) + \frac{2P}{\pi t E} (1 - \nu) \sin \theta + \int f(\theta) \, d\theta = 0, \tag{5.10}$$

where the constant of integration resulting from the last term contains also $F(0)$. It can be verified that

$$f(\theta) = -\frac{(1 - \nu)P}{\pi t E} \theta \sin \theta + A \sin \theta + B \cos \theta \tag{5.11}$$

is the general solution, in which A and B are arbitrary constants.

If next we let $\theta = 0$, and keep r different from zero, eq. (5.9) reduces to

$$r \frac{d}{dr} F(r) - F(r) = 0. \tag{5.12}$$

It can further be verified that the solution to this equation is

$$F(r) = Cr, \tag{5.13}$$

in which C is arbitrary. With these expressions for $f(\theta)$ and $F(r)$ the expressions for u and v, given respectively by eqs. (5.3) and (5.6), become

$$u = -\frac{2P}{\pi t E} \log r \cos \theta - \frac{(1 - \nu)P}{\pi t E} \theta \sin \theta + A \sin \theta + B \cos \theta \tag{5.14}$$

and

$$v = -\frac{(1 - \nu)}{\pi t E} P\theta \cos \theta + \frac{(1 + \nu)}{\pi t E} P \sin \theta + \frac{2P}{\pi t E} \log r \sin \theta + A \cos \theta - B \sin \theta + Cr, \tag{5.15}$$

in which the constants A, B, and C are determined from given conditions, such as symmetry or constraints.

Consider, for example, the semi-infinite grooved plate shown in Fig. 5.1, which is subjected to radial pressures on the groove, and in which the stresses are defined by eqs. (2.8). In order to evaluate the constants A, B, C, we assume that the points on the X axis, which is an axis of symmetry, have no displacement in the Y direction, i.e.,

$$v = 0 \quad \text{where} \quad \theta = 0.$$

This gives

$$A = -Cr.$$

Since this must be true for all values of r it means that

$$A = C = 0. \tag{5.16}$$

In order to determine the constant B we denote by u' and v' the component displacements represented by $B \cos \theta$ and $-B \sin \theta$, respectively, i.e.,

$$u' = B \cos \theta, \quad v' = -B \sin \theta. \tag{5.17}$$

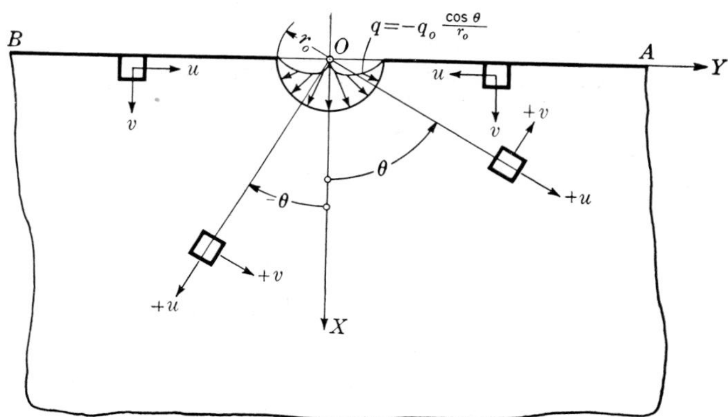

Fig. 5.1 Sketch Showing Notation Used for the Displacements in a Semi-Infinite Plate with a Semicircular Groove Subjected to the Statical Equivalent of a Normal Concentrated Load.

The resultant of u' and v' would clearly be equal to B, and its direction would at all points be parallel to the X axis. The constant B thus represents a rigid body displacement and may be ignored.[1] The final expressions for the displacements are

$$u = \frac{P}{\pi t E}\left[-(1 - \nu)\theta \sin \theta - 2 \cos \theta \log r\right] \tag{5.18}$$

and

$$v = \frac{P}{\pi t E}\left[-(1 - \nu)\theta \cos \theta + (1 + \nu) \sin \theta + 2 \sin \theta \log r\right]. \tag{5.19}$$

The displacements of the points on the free straight boundary, the Y axis, Fig. 5.1, are of special significance. To find the radial displacements u we put $\theta = \pm\pi/2$ in eq. (5.18) and obtain

$$(u)_{\theta = \pm\pi/2} = -\frac{(1 - \nu)P}{2tE}. \tag{5.20}$$

[1] This interpretation of the constant B is due to Professor E. Sternberg.

Since ν is less than unity it follows that the displacement u is always negative, i.e., toward the origin. ***All the points on the straight boundary OA and OB, Fig. 5.1, receive equal translations to the origin.***

The v or vertical displacements on the straight boundary are obtained from eq. (5.19). Thus on OA

$$(v)_{\theta=\pi/2} = \frac{P}{\pi tE}[(1+\nu) + 2\log r] \tag{5.21}$$

and on OB

$$(v)_{\theta=-\pi/2} = -\frac{P}{\pi tE}[(1+\nu) + 2\log r]. \tag{5.22}$$

Hence

$$(v)_{\theta=\pi/2} = -(v)_{\theta=-\pi/2}.$$

Since the sign of v for $\theta = \pi/2$ is opposite to that of v for $\theta = -\pi/2$ it follows that ***the vertical displacements of the straight edge on opposite sides of the origin go in the same direction.*** In interpreting these displacements we must remember that a positive direction for v means the direction in which θ increases, Fig. 5.1.

§5.2 Displacements in a Multiply Connected Body. We next consider an infinite plate, Fig. 5.2, from which a small circular hole of radius r_o has been removed and the circular boundary of which is subjected to a stress system defined by the expressions

$$\left.\begin{aligned} q = \sigma_r &= -q_o\frac{\cos\theta}{r_o}, && (a)\\ \sigma_\theta &= 0, && (b)\\ \tau_{r\theta} &= 0. && (c)\end{aligned}\right\} \tag{2.2}$$

and

This leads to radial compressive tractions on the lower half of the circle and to radial tensions on the upper half, Fig. 5.2.

Choosing again the stress function

$$\phi = Cr\theta\sin\theta, \tag{2.3}$$

we obtain the same stress components as those given by eq. (2.5), i.e.,

$$\left.\begin{aligned} \sigma_r &= 2C\frac{\cos\theta}{r}, && (a)\\ \sigma_\theta &= 0, && (b)\\ \tau_{r\theta} &= 0. && (c)\end{aligned}\right\} \tag{2.5}$$

Letting $C = -q_o/2$, it is clear that ***the above stresses satisfy the boundary*** *conditions: they vanish at infinity, and on the small circular hole of radius r_o they reduce to the assumed boundary tractions given by eq. (2.2.). Nevertheless, eqs. (2.5) are not the true solution to the problem. The reason for this lies in the fact that the displacements from this solution are not single valued, although the stresses are.* The displacements

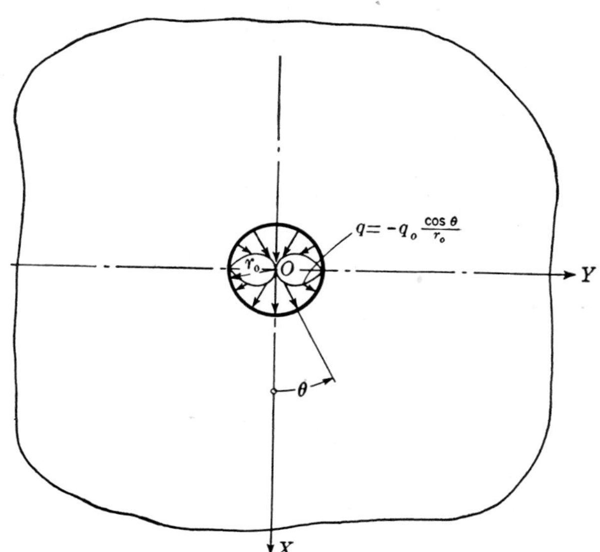

FIG. 5.2 Sketch Showing an Infinite Plate with an Interior Small Hole Subjected to Boundary Forces Equivalent to a Concentrated Load.

u and v are in this case identical with those given by eqs. (5.18) and (5.19) except for the coefficient $P/\pi t$ which is replaced by the constant C from the stress function (2.3); see eq. (2.7). But the first terms giving u and v, eqs. (5.18) and (5.19), contain the angle θ and clearly change their values as θ is increased by 2π. Consider for example points on the positive branch of the X axis. From symmetry it follows that the horizontal displacements v on the branch must vanish. This result is obtained from eq. (5.19) by putting $\theta = 0$. However, assume that we arrive at these points not by letting $\theta = 0$, but by going clear around the origin one complete revolution and making $\theta = 2\pi$. The value of the displacements would then be

$$(v)_{\theta=2\pi} = -\frac{C}{E}2\pi(1-\nu),$$

i.e., the displacements on the X axis are not single valued. This, of course, is impossible, and the solution must be rejected on that score. We thus see that ***a stress function may lead to single-valued stresses which satisfy the boundary conditions as far as the tractions are concerned but at the same time may give rise to many-valued displacements. It follows that the displacements as well as the stresses must be determined and analyzed before a solution can be said to have been found. This condition can occur only in multiply connected bodies. In simply connected bodies, such as the semi-infinite plate, the angle θ will always be less than 2π, and therefore the displacements will always be single valued.***

§5.3 The Stress Function $\phi = Ar \cos \theta \log r$. In connection with the problem of a concentrated load acting at an isolated point of an infinite plate it will be useful to have the stresses and deformations from the stress function

$$\phi = Ar \cos \theta \log r, \tag{5.23}$$

which can readily be shown to satisfy the condition of continuity, eq. (1.42*a*).

Stress Components. As in the preceding cases we find the stress components by means of the expression

$$\left.\begin{aligned} \sigma_r &= \frac{1}{r}\frac{\partial \phi}{\partial r} + \frac{1}{r^2}\frac{\partial^2 \phi}{\partial \theta^2}, && (a) \\ \sigma_\theta &= \frac{\partial^2 \phi}{\partial r^2}, && (b) \\ \tau_{r\theta} &= \frac{1}{r^2}\frac{\partial \phi}{\partial \theta} - \frac{1}{r}\frac{\partial^2 \phi}{\partial r\,\partial \theta}. && (c) \end{aligned}\right\} \tag{1.24}$$

The resulting stress components are

$$\left.\begin{aligned} \sigma_r &= A\frac{\cos \theta}{r}, && (a) \\ \sigma_\theta &= A\frac{\cos \theta}{r}, && (b) \\ \tau_{r\theta} &= A\frac{\sin \theta}{r}. && (c) \end{aligned}\right\} \tag{5.24}$$

Strain Components. The strain components are found from the expression

$$\left.\begin{aligned}\epsilon_r &= \frac{1}{E}(\sigma_r - \nu\sigma_\theta), &(a)\\ \epsilon_\theta &= \frac{1}{E}(\sigma_\theta - \nu\sigma_r), &(b)\\ \gamma_{r\theta} &= \frac{2(1+\nu)\tau_{r\theta}}{E}. &(c)\end{aligned}\right\}(5.1)$$

Substituting the expressions for the stresses from eqs. (5.24), we have

$$\left.\begin{aligned}\epsilon_r &= \frac{(1-\nu)}{E}A\frac{\cos\theta}{r}, &(a)\\ \epsilon_\theta &= \frac{(1-\nu)}{E}A\frac{\cos\theta}{r}, &(b)\\ \gamma_{r\theta} &= \frac{2(1+\nu)}{E}A\frac{\sin\theta}{r}. &(c)\end{aligned}\right\}(5.25)$$

Displacements u and v. The displacements are obtained from the relations

$$\epsilon_r = \frac{\partial u}{\partial r}, \tag{1.3}$$

$$\epsilon_\theta = \frac{u}{r} + \frac{1}{r}\frac{\partial v}{\partial \theta}, \tag{1.4}$$

$$\gamma_{r\theta} = \frac{1}{r}\frac{\partial u}{\partial \theta} + \frac{\partial v}{\partial r} - \frac{v}{r}. \tag{1.7}$$

From (1.3) and (5.25a) we obtain

$$u = \frac{(1-\nu)}{E}A\cos\theta\log r + f(\theta), \tag{5.26}$$

in which $f(\theta)$ is an arbitrary function of θ. From (1.4) and (5.25b) we obtain

$$\frac{\partial v}{\partial \theta} = \frac{(1-\nu)}{E}A\cos\theta - u. \tag{5.27}$$

Substituting u from eq. (5.26) in (5.27), we get

$$\frac{\partial v}{\partial \theta} = \frac{(1-\nu)}{E} A \cos\theta - \frac{(1-\nu)}{E} A \cos\theta \log r - f(\theta)$$

$$= \frac{(1-\nu)}{E} A \cos\theta\,(1 - \log r) - f(\theta), \qquad (5.28)$$

whence

$$v = \frac{(1-\nu)}{E}(1 - \log r) A \sin\theta - \int f(\theta)\, d\theta + F(r), \qquad (5.29)$$

in which $F(r)$ is a function of r only.

From (5.25c) and (1.7) we have

$$\frac{2(1+\nu)}{E} A \sin\theta = \frac{\partial u}{\partial \theta} + r\frac{\partial v}{\partial r} - v. \qquad (5.30)$$

From eqs. (5.26) and (5.29) we have

$$\frac{\partial u}{\partial \theta} = -\frac{(1-\nu)}{E} A \log r \sin\theta + \frac{d}{d\theta} f(\theta), \qquad (5.31)$$

$$\frac{\partial v}{\partial r} = -\frac{(1-\nu)}{E} A \frac{\sin\theta}{r} + \frac{d}{dr} F(r). \qquad (5.32)$$

Substituting in eq. (5.30) and collecting terms we have

$$\frac{2(1+\nu)}{E} A \sin\theta = -\frac{2(1-\nu)}{E} A \sin\theta + \frac{d}{d\theta} f(\theta) + r\frac{d}{dr} F(r)$$

$$+ \int f(\theta)\, d\theta - F(r). \qquad (5.33)$$

This equation is satisfied if

$$F(r) = 0 \qquad (a)$$

and

$$\frac{df(\theta)}{d\theta} + \int f(\theta)\, d\theta = \frac{4A \sin\theta}{E}. \qquad (b)$$

(5.34)

A particular solution of eq. (5.34b) is

$$f(\theta) = \frac{2A\theta \sin\theta}{E}. \qquad (5.35)$$

To verify we form

$$\frac{df(\theta)}{d\theta} = \frac{2A}{E}(\theta \cos\theta + \sin\theta),$$

and integrating by parts we get

$$\int f(\theta)\, d\theta = \frac{2A}{E} \int \theta \sin \theta \, d\theta$$

$$= \frac{2A}{E} (-\theta \cos \theta + \sin \theta),$$

so that

$$\frac{df(\theta)}{d\theta} + \int f(\theta)\, d\theta = \frac{4A}{E} \sin \theta. \tag{5.34b}$$

Substituting $f(\theta)$ from eq. (5.35) and $F(r)$ from eq. (5.34a) in eqs. (5.26) and (5.29), we obtain

$$u = \frac{(1 - \nu)}{E} A \cos \theta \log r + \frac{2A}{E} \theta \sin \theta \tag{5.36}$$

and

$$v = \frac{(1 - \nu)}{E} (1 - \log r) A \sin \theta + \frac{2A}{E} (\theta \cos \theta - \sin \theta). \tag{5.37}$$

§5.4 Concentrated Force Acting at a Point of an Infinite Plate. If a small circular hole be cut from the center of the infinite plate, Fig. 5.2, and if the forces acting upon the circular boundary be assumed to follow eq. (2.2), then all the boundary stress conditions would be met by the stress components given by eqs. (2.5), which are derived from the stress function (2.3). Furthermore, the forces acting on the circular boundary are clearly equivalent to a concentrated load parallel to the X axis, Fig. 5.3. From the point of view of boundary conditions expressed in terms of stresses, eqs. (2.5) represent a solution to the problem. Examination of the stress system given by eqs. (5.24), Fig. 5.4, derived from the stress function

$$\phi = Ar \cos \theta \log r, \tag{5.23}$$

shows, however, that these boundary forces are also equivalent to a concentrated load and that therefore eqs. (5.24) represent as satisfactory a solution as those derived from the function

$$\phi = Cr\theta \sin \theta. \tag{2.3}$$

Both functions lead, however, to many-valued displacements, as can be seen from eqs. (5.18), (5.19), (5.36), and (5.37). For this reason neither one represents the true solution for a concentrated load acting at a point of an infinite plate, Fig. 5.3.

The true solution can, however, be obtained by superimposing the stresses and the deformations resulting from the two stress functions, (2.3) and (5.23). In this superposition the coefficient A of the stress

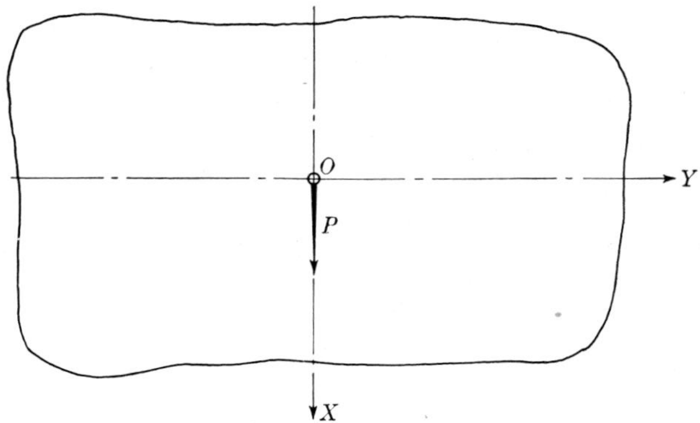

FIG. 5.3 Sketch Showing a Concentrated Force Which is Statically Equivalent to the Distributed Pressures Shown in Fig. 5.2.

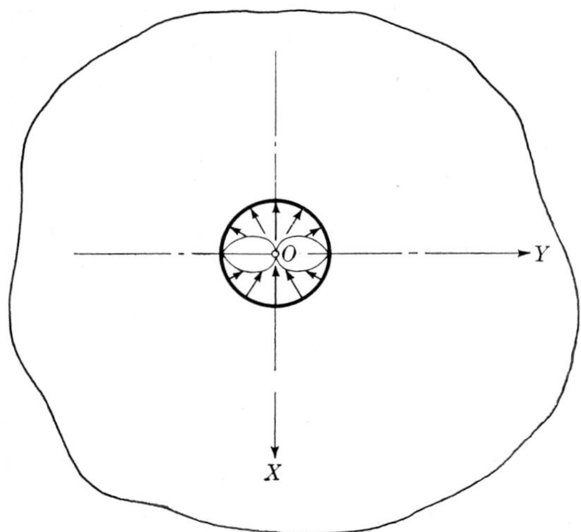

FIG. 5.4 Sketch Showing Boundary Stresses on a Circular Hole in an Infinite Plate as Obtained from Eqs. (5.24).

function (5.23) can be so adjusted that the many-valued terms entering into the displacements u and v will vanish. The multivalued terms in the u deformations are $2A\theta \sin \theta/E$ in eq. (5.36), and $-P(1 - \nu)\theta$

$\sin \theta / \pi t E$ in eq. (5.18). Equating their sum to zero we have

$$\frac{2A}{E}\theta \sin \theta - \frac{P}{\pi t E}(1 - \nu)\theta \sin \theta = 0,$$

from which

$$A = \frac{P(1 - \nu)}{2\pi t}. \tag{5.38}$$

The same result is obtained by equating to zero the sum of the multi-valued terms giving the v deformations.

Attention is called to the meaning of P in the last expressions for the coefficient A, eq. (5.38). This load P represents the load acting on a semi-infinite plate; see §2.2, eq. (2.7). When dealing with an infinite plate the total equivalent concentrated load corresponding to the distribution defined by eq. (2.5a) is twice as great as that acting on a semi-infinite plate. Designating this load by P', we have $P = P'/2$. In terms of P', eq. (5.38) becomes

$$A = \frac{P'(1 - \nu)}{4\pi t}. \tag{5.39}$$

It follows that ***by combining the stress functions given by eqs. (2.3) and (5.23) and choosing the coefficient A in accordance with eq. (5.39) the true solution for a concentrated load acting at a point of an infinite plate will be obtained.*** The stresses in the infinite plate thus consist of two systems. One system is derived from the stress function (2.3) and gives the components

$$\left.\begin{aligned} \sigma_r' &= -\frac{2P}{\pi t}\frac{\cos\theta}{r} = -\frac{P'}{\pi t}\frac{\cos\theta}{r}, && (a) \\ \sigma_\theta' &= 0, && (b) \\ \tau_{r\theta}' &= 0. && (c) \end{aligned}\right\} \tag{5.40}$$

The other stress system is derived from the stress function (5.23) and yields the components

$$\left.\begin{aligned} \sigma_r'' &= \frac{A\cos\theta}{r} = \frac{P'(1-\nu)}{4\pi t}\frac{\cos\theta}{r}, && (a) \\ \sigma_\theta'' &= \frac{A\cos\theta}{r} = \frac{P'(1-\nu)}{4\pi t}\frac{\cos\theta}{r}, && (b) \\ \tau_{r\theta}'' &= \frac{A\sin\theta}{r} = \frac{P'(1-\nu)}{4\pi t}\frac{\sin\theta}{r}. && (c) \end{aligned}\right\} \tag{5.41}$$

The resultant stresses are

$$\sigma_r = \sigma_r' + \sigma_r'',$$
$$\sigma_\theta = \sigma_\theta' + \sigma_\theta'',$$
$$\tau_{r\theta} = \tau_{r\theta}' + \tau_{r\theta}''.$$

This gives

$$\left.\begin{aligned} \sigma_r &= -\frac{P'}{4\pi t}(3+\nu)\frac{\cos\theta}{r}, & (a)\\ \sigma_\theta &= \frac{P'(1-\nu)}{4\pi t}\frac{\cos\theta}{r}, & (b)\\ \tau_{r\theta} &= \frac{P'(1-\nu)}{4\pi t}\frac{\sin\theta}{r}. & (c)\end{aligned}\right\} \quad (5.42)$$

Rectangular Stress Components. The rectangular stress components corresponding to eqs. (5.42) can be found by inspection and superposition using eqs. (1.3*a*), (1.4*a*), (1.5), and (1.6), Vol. I. Substituting the components from eqs. (5.42) we obtain

$$\sigma_x = \frac{P'}{4\pi t}\frac{\cos\theta}{r}[-(3+\nu)\cos^2\theta + (1-\nu)\sin^2\theta - 2(1-\nu)\sin^2\theta]$$

$$= \frac{P'}{4\pi t}\frac{\cos\theta}{r}[-(3+\nu)\cos^2\theta - (1-\nu)\sin^2\theta]$$

$$= \frac{P'}{4\pi t}\frac{\cos\theta}{r}[-(3+\nu) + 2(1+\nu)\sin^2\theta], \qquad (5.43a)$$

$$\sigma_y = \frac{P'}{4\pi t}\frac{\cos\theta}{r}[-(3+\nu)\sin^2\theta + (1-\nu)\cos^2\theta + 2(1-\nu)\sin^2\theta]$$

$$= \frac{P'}{4\pi t}\frac{\cos\theta}{r}[(1-\nu) - 2(1+\nu)\sin^2\theta], \qquad (5.43b)$$

and

$$\tau_{xy} = \frac{P'}{4\pi t}\frac{\cos\theta}{r}[(3+\nu) + (1-\nu)]\frac{\sin 2\theta}{2} - \frac{P'(1-\nu)}{4\pi t}\frac{\sin\theta\cos 2\theta}{r}$$

$$= \frac{P'}{4\pi t}\frac{\sin\theta}{r}[4\cos^2\theta - (1-\nu)\cos 2\theta]$$

$$= \frac{P'}{4\pi t}\frac{\sin\theta}{r}[(1-\nu) + 2(1+\nu)\cos^2\theta]. \qquad (5.43c)$$

The resultant displacements can be obtained by combining the components given by eqs. (5.18) and (5.19) with those from eqs. (5.36) and (5.37).

We see that eqs. (5.42) contain Poisson's ratio ν, so that the stresses are a function of the material used. It has already been pointed out that this can happen only in multiply connected bodies. It will be shown later that even in such bodies the influence of the material upon the stresses is small and may for all practical purposes be neglected.

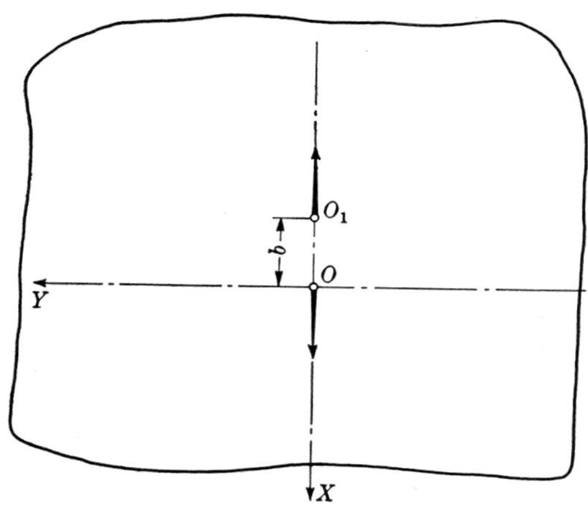

FIG. 5.5 Sketch Showing Two Equal and Opposite Loads on an Infinite Plate.

§5.5 Combinations of Concentrated Loads Acting on a Small Region of an Infinite Plate. From the solution for a single concentrated load obtained in §5.4 and from the principle of superposition, solutions for combinations of concentrated loads can be obtained. For example, the stresses produced by two collinear, equal, and opposite loads acting at points O and O_1, separated by a small distance b, Fig. 5.5, can be obtained by writing

$$\left.\begin{aligned} \sigma_x' &= \sigma_x - \left(\sigma_x + b\frac{\partial \sigma_x}{\partial x}\right) = -b\frac{\partial \sigma_x}{\partial x}, &\quad (a)\\ \sigma_y' &= \sigma_y - \left(\sigma_y + b\frac{\partial \sigma_y}{\partial x}\right) = -b\frac{\partial \sigma_y}{\partial x}, &\quad (b)\\ \tau_{xy}' &= \tau_{xy} - \left(\tau_{xy} + b\frac{\partial \tau_{xy}}{\partial x}\right) = -b\frac{\partial \tau_{xy}}{\partial x}, &\quad (c) \end{aligned}\right\}(5.44)$$

in which σ_x', σ_y', and τ_{xy}' are the resultant stress components. But

$$\left.\begin{aligned}\frac{\partial \sigma_x}{\partial x} &= \frac{\partial \sigma_x}{\partial r}\frac{\partial r}{\partial x} + \frac{\partial \sigma_x}{\partial \theta}\frac{\partial \theta}{\partial x} \\ &= \frac{\partial \sigma_x}{\partial r}\cos\theta - \frac{\partial \sigma_x}{\partial \theta}\frac{\sin\theta}{r}, \qquad &(a) \\ \frac{\partial \sigma_y}{\partial x} &= \frac{\partial \sigma_y}{\partial r}\cos\theta - \frac{\partial \sigma_y}{\partial \theta}\frac{\sin\theta}{r}, \qquad &(b)\end{aligned}\right\}(5.45)$$

and

$$\frac{\partial \tau_{xy}}{\partial x} = \frac{\partial \tau_{xy}}{\partial r}\cos\theta - \frac{\partial \tau_{xy}}{\partial \theta}\frac{\sin\theta}{r}. \qquad (c)$$

Substituting the derivatives obtained from eqs. (5.43), we find

$$\left.\begin{aligned}\sigma_x' &= \frac{bP}{4\pi t r^2}[-(3+\nu)\cos^2\theta + (1-\nu)\sin^2\theta \\ &\qquad + 8(1+\nu)\sin^2\theta\cos^2\theta], \qquad &(a) \\ \sigma_y' &= \frac{bP}{4\pi t r^2}[(1-\nu)\cos^2\theta + (1+3\nu)\sin^2\theta \\ &\qquad - 8(1+\nu)\sin^2\theta\cos^2\theta], \qquad &(b) \\ \tau_{xy}' &= \frac{bP}{4\pi t r^2}[-(\sigma+2\nu) \\ &\qquad + 8(1+\nu)\sin^2\theta]\sin\theta\cos\theta. \qquad &(c)\end{aligned}\right\}(5.46)$$

These stresses rapidly diminish as r/b gets large. Since the resultant of the applied system is zero it follows from Saint Venant's principle that the stresses at an appreciable distance from the loads must vanish.

By superimposing two stress systems such as those given by eq. (5.46) we obtain the solution for four loads applied in the manner shown in Fig. 5.6(a), or the equivalent three forces shown in Fig. 5.6(b). The stress components for these forces in polar coordinates are

$$\left.\begin{aligned}\sigma_r &= -2(1-\nu)\frac{bP}{4\pi r^2 t}, \qquad &(a) \\ \sigma_\theta &= 2(1-\nu)\frac{bP}{4\pi r^2 t}, \qquad &(b) \\ \tau_{r\theta} &= 0. \qquad &(c)\end{aligned}\right\}(5.47)$$

The corresponding rectangular components are

$$\left.\begin{aligned}\sigma_x &= -2(1-\nu)\frac{bP}{4\pi r^2 t}(1-2\sin^2\theta) && (a)\\ \sigma_y &= 2(1-\nu)\frac{bP}{4\pi r^2 t}(1-2\sin^2\theta), && (b)\\ \tau_{xy} &= -2(1-\nu)\frac{bP}{4\pi r^2 t}\sin 2\theta && (c)\end{aligned}\right\}(5.48)$$

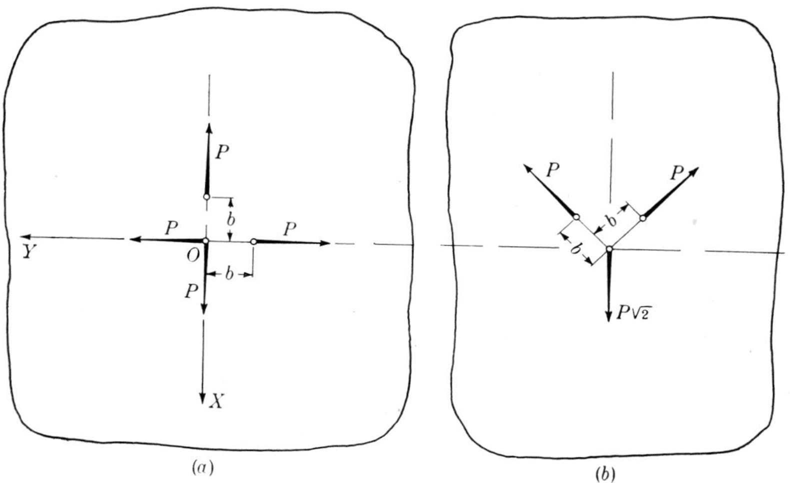

FIG. 5.6 Sketches Showing Four Concentrated Loads and Their Equivalent Three Loads on an Infinite Plate for Which Eqs. (5.46) are the Solution.

Inspection of eqs. (5.47) shows that the resulting stresses do not depend on θ; they depend on r only. The maximum shear stresses are therefore constant on circles having their centers at point O, Fig. 5.6.

By the same reasoning as in deriving eqs. (5.46), a solution can be obtained for the stresses produced by a couple M, Fig. 5.7. The resulting stress components are

$$\left.\begin{aligned}\sigma_r &= 0, && (a)\\ \sigma_\theta &= 0, && (b)\\ \tau_{r\theta} &= -\frac{M}{2\pi r^2}\cdot && (c)\end{aligned}\right\}(5.49)$$

§5.6 Concentrated Load on a Bar of Finite Width. Starting with the solution for a concentrated load on an infinite plate, R. C. J. Howland obtained the stresses in a bar of finite width and infinite length, subjected

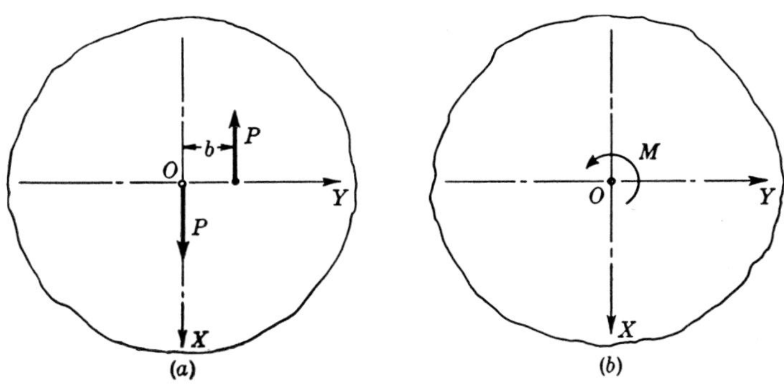

FIG. 5.7.

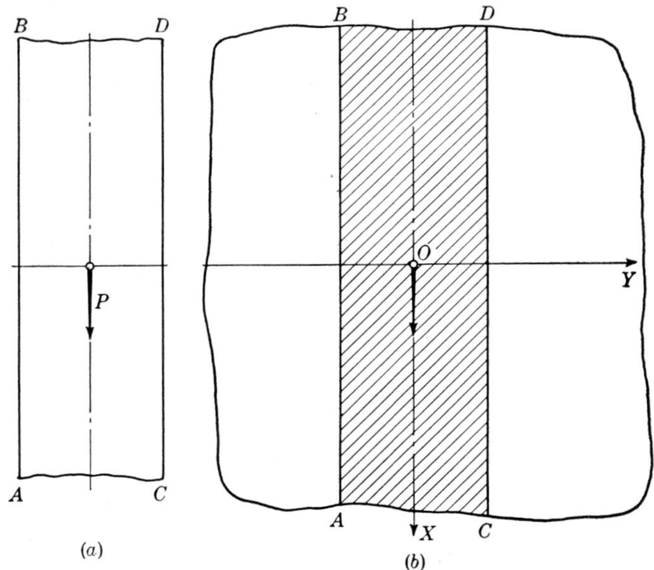

FIG. 5.8.

to a concentrated load parallel to the long edge and acting along the plane of symmetry, Fig. 5.8(a). The general procedure was to determine the boundary forces along the edges AB and CD in the infinite plate,

Fig. 5.8(*b*), and then to determine the stresses which result from the removal of these boundary tractions. These stresses were calculated by means of infinite series, which is a rather long and difficult procedure.[1] Howland's calculations show that at distances from the origin greater than the width of the bar the stress distribution is practically uniform.

[1] See R. C. J. Howland, *Proc. Roy. Soc., London,* Vol. 124, p. 89, 1929.

CHAPTER 6

THE INFLUENCE OF THE MATERIAL ON STRESS DISTRIBUTION

PART I

§6.1 Introduction. It has been shown that, in plane problems dealing with simply connected bodies subjected only to known boundary forces, the stress distribution is independent of the constants of the materials; i.e., for the same loads and geometry the stresses are the same in all homogeneous and isotropic bodies. Convincing corroboration of this conclusion is provided by the large number of comparative theoretical and photoelastic results which are shown in the preceding chapters. We refer, for example, to the comparative stress patterns obtained from the semi-infinite plate acted upon by concentrated loads of uniform pressures, from wedges with concentrated loads, and to the patterns from disks under diametral compression, to mention but a few cases.

It has further been shown that in multiply connected bodies the stress distribution depends, in general, on Poisson's ratio ν, as for example when a concentrated load acts on an infinite plate, eqs. (5.42). We will now show that the effect of the material on the stresses is small and that it may be neglected for all practical purposes. In this chapter we present direct evidence from steel, aluminum, Bakelite, and Celluloid which proves the last statement.

§6.2 Special Cases and Numerical Examples. Before presenting the comparative results from metals and transparent specimens attention is called to the fact that ***even in multiply connected bodies there are cases in which the stress distribution is independent of the material. This is true when the resultant of the forces applied to the boundary of any hole reduces to zero or to a couple,*** as for example when a ring or cylinder is under uniform pressure, or when there is a uniform shear around the hole, Fig. 6.1.[1]

It is instructive to examine the numerical effect produced by different values of Poisson's ratio. For this purpose we consider the stresses in an infinite plate under the action of a concentrated load. We have previ-

[1] For a proof see *Treatise on Photoelasticity*, by Coker and Filon, pp. 128–130 and 501–524.

experimental results obtained from the stresses in nitrocellulose or glass models can be accepted as giving valid results for similar members or structures of steel, since the effect of the difference of Poisson's ratio is probably less than the order of the possible experimental error. The general effect of increasing ν is seen to be in the direction of easing the stresses."[1]

Bickley's conclusions also agree with those of Filon for a circular ring in which the outer radius is infinite.[2]

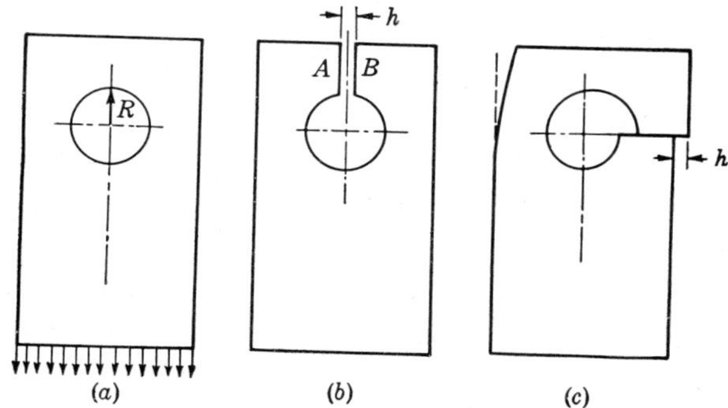

FIG. 6.3 Sketches Showing Manner of Making Cuts for a Dislocation Corresponding to Force R Acting as Shown.

§6.3 The Photoelastic Determination of the Effect of Poisson's Ratio on the State of Stress. So far we have shown that the effect of Poisson's ratio on the state or value of the stress is small. It is significant, however, to add that this effect, whatever its magnitude, can be determined photoelastically, so that ***the optical method is self-sufficient and provides the complete mechanism for the transition from model to prototype.***

Consider, for example, a multiply connected plate of material M and Poisson's ratio ν. For concreteness let us assume this to be a steel eyebar. Let the boundary of the hole in the bar be subjected to arbitrarily distributed tractions having a resultant R, Fig. 6.3(a). The stress components in the steel plate we denote by σ_x, σ_y, and τ_{xy}. Assume now a photoelastic model, of, say, Bakelite, for which Poisson's ratio is ν' with corresponding stress components σ_x', σ_y', and τ_{xy}'.

After obtaining all the basic photoelastic data from the Bakelite model, let us remove the external loads, and introduce a cut AB of width h extending from the hole to the outside boundary of the plate, the cut being made in such a way that the gap h is transverse to the direction

[1] *Ibid.*

[2] L. N. G. Filon, *British Assoc. Rept.*, 1921.

of the force R, Fig. 6.3(b). Suppose we next force the faces of the cut together, seal the gap with a suitable cement, and, when the cement hardens, remove the external pressures used to force the faces of the cut together. This operation of closing the gap will produce a system of strains and stresses known as a dislocation. The stress components in such a dislocation we designate by σ_x'', σ_y'', and τ_{xy}''. It can be shown[1] that the three sets of stresses are related in the following manner

$$\left.\begin{aligned} \sigma_x &= \sigma_x' + \alpha\sigma_x'', & (a) \\ \sigma_y &= \sigma_y' + \alpha\sigma_y'', & (b) \\ \tau_{xy} &= \tau_{xy}' + \alpha\tau_{xy}'', & (c) \end{aligned}\right\} \quad (6.1)$$

in which the coefficient α is given by

$$\alpha = -\frac{R(\nu - \nu')}{E'ht}, \tag{6.2}$$

E' being the modulus of elasticity of the photoelastic model and t its thickness.

The terms $\alpha\sigma_x''$, $\alpha\sigma_y''$, $\alpha\tau_{xy}''$ represent the corrections to the stresses σ_x', σ_y', and τ_{xy}' which are necessary in order to pass from the photoelastic model to the metal prototype. In order to obtain an idea of the magnitude of the correction involved it is only necessary to calculate these at several critical points where the stresses are a maximum.

If there is more than one hole in the body a dislocation can be constructed for each hole and the corresponding correction obtained. The resultant stress components are

$$\sigma_x = \sigma_x' + \alpha_1\sigma_{x1}'' + \alpha_2\sigma_{x2}'' + \cdots + \alpha_n\sigma_{xn}'', \text{ etc.} \tag{6.3}$$

in which σ_{xn}'' denotes the stress component due to the dislocation at the nth hole.

This procedure necessitates n photoelastic models, one for each dislocation. The problem can be much simplified if it is observed that eq. (6.3) can be written in the form

$$\begin{aligned} \sigma_x = \sigma_x' &+ (\alpha_1 - \alpha_2)\sigma_{x1}'' + (\alpha_2 - \alpha_3)(\sigma_{x1}'' + \sigma_{x2}'') \\ &+ (\alpha_3 - \alpha_4)(\sigma_{x1}'' + \sigma_{x2}'' + \sigma_{x3}'') \\ &+ \cdots + \alpha_n(\sigma_{x1}'' + \sigma_{x2}'' + \cdots \sigma_{xn}''), \end{aligned} \tag{6.4}$$

This equation shows that ***one model is sufficient for the determination of all corrections even when there are n holes.*** If the dislocations are introduced one at a time and the stresses (σ_{x1}''), $(\sigma_{x1}'' + \sigma_{x2}'')$,

[1] See Coker and Filon, §6.15, p. 518; also Filon's *Manual of Photoelasticity*, p. 76.

$(\sigma_{x1}'' + \sigma_{x2}'' + \sigma_{x3}'')$, etc., are successively determined, we have the necessary data for the transition from a multiply connected body with n holes to its prototype.

With several holes it may also happen that the external boundary cannot be reached with straight cuts. Theory shows,[1] however, that the cuts need not be straight. They may be curved or zigzag. The only condition is that the faces of the cut can be brought together by means of a displacement h transverse to the force R on the hole, Figs. 6.3(*b*) and 6.3(*c*).

The theory of dislocation has been verified for a circular ring by Rolla,[2] Corbino,[3] and Trabacchi.[4]

The conclusion regarding the influence of the materials on the state of stress is borne out by comparing the results from photoelastic investigations with corresponding stresses obtained directly from metals. This we now proceed to show.

PART II ALUMINUM AND BAKELITE

Stress Concentration Factors around a Central Circular Hole in a Plate Loaded through a Pin in the Hole

§6.4 Plate Loaded through a Pin in a Hole. Further light on the influence of the material on the state of stress is thrown by comparing the results from a recent strain-gage investigation of factors of stress concentration in large Duraluminum plates in tension pulled by means of a single axial pin, Fig. 6.4, and an independent study of the same problem by the photoelastic method.[5]

The strain gage measurements on the aluminum plates were made in the Research Laboratories of the Aluminum Company of America, and

[1] The theory for dislocations was originally given by J. H. Michell, G. Weingarten, and V. Volterra. See respectively: "On the Direct Determination of Stress in an Elastic Solid, with Application to the Theory of Plates," *London Math. Soc. Proc.*, Vol. XXXI, pp. 100–124, 1899; *Rend. accad. Lincei*, Ser. v, Vol. X (1st sem.), 1901, p. 57 and "Sur l'équilibre des corps élastiques multiplement connexes," *Ann. l'école normale*, Ser. III, Vol. XXIV, pp. 401–517, 1907.

[2] *Rend. accad. Lincei*, Vol. XVI (1st sem.), 1907.

[3] *Ibid.*, Ser. v, Vol. XVIII, pp. 437–444, 1909; *Nuovo cimento*, Ser. v, Vol. XVII, pp. 361–370, 1909.

[4] "I fenomeni di doppia rifrazione accidentale prodotti dalle tensioni create in an corpo elastico dalle distorsioni di Volterra," *Rend. accad. Lincei*, Ser. v, Vol. XVIII, pp. 444–449, 1909; see also *Nuovo cimento*, Pisa, Ser. v, Vol. XVII, pp. 371–377, 1909.

[5] "Stress Concentration Factors around a Central Circular Hole in a Plate Loaded through Pin in the Hole," by M. M. Frocht and H. N. Hill, *Journal of Applied Mechanics, Trans. A.S.M.E.*, March, 1940.

FIG. 6.4 Photograph Showing Large Plate in Testing Machine and Attached Tensometers as Used by the Aluminum Company of America to Measure the Strains in Plates under the Action of a Single Axial Pin.

the optical studies in the Photoelastic Laboratory of the Carnegie Institute of Technology. Although this work was carried on at approximately the same time, ***the problems were independently conceived and executed, and the results were compared only after the investigations had been completed.***

The problem studied represents a multiply connected body, in which the boundary of the hole is subjected to a resultant concentrated load. We have seen that it is precisely under such conditions that Poisson's ratio influences the state of stress. A comparison of the results will show the magnitude of the influence.

The problem of the determination of the stress distribution in a plate loaded through a pin in a hole in the plate has been treated mathematically, notably by Bickley[1] and Knight.[2] Bickley confined his treatment to a plate of infinite width, assuming various expressions for the nature of the distribution of forces between pin and plate. Knight considered only one set of boundary forces on the hole but extended his solution to cover plates of finite width, giving specific results for a plate having a width twice as great as the diameter of the hole. Published results of experimental studies of this problem seem to be very meager. Coker[3] reports the results of a photoelastic investigation on one specimen 18 in. by 6 in. by 0.157 in. in which the load was applied through a neat-fitting pin of 0.766-in. diameter. The results of an investigation of a specimen of different proportions is credited to Stoltenberg.[4]

Most of the tests involved plates loaded through a single pin in a hole on the longitudinal center line of the plate, but several tests were made on plates loaded through two pins symmetrically situated about the center line of the plate. Numerical values for the stress concentration factor (k) are given for ratios of hole diameter to width of plate ($2r/D$) ranging from 0.086 to 0.76.

§6.5 Tests Involving Strain-Gage Measurements. The tests made using the strain-gage method employed a 1-in.-thick plate of high-strength aluminum alloy of the Duralumin type and an 8-in.-diameter pin. To obtain different ratios of pin diameter to plate width, the plate was decreased in width in successive steps from its original value of 55 in.

[1] See reference 1, p. 176.

[2] R. C. Knight, "Action of a Rivet in a Plate of Finite Breadth," *Phil. Mag.*, Vol. 19 (7), pp. 517–540, March, 1935.

[3] *A Treatise on Photoelasticity*, by E. G. Coker and L. N. G. Filon, Cambridge University Press, 1931, p. 525.

[4] See: "On the Fatigue Strength of Riveted and Welded Joints and the Design of Dynamically Stressed Structural Members Based on Conclusions Drawn from Fatigue Tests," by K. Schaechterle in *Proc. International Association for Bridge and Structural Engineering*, Vol. 2, pp. 312–379, 1934.

to a final width of 12 in. Fig. 6.4 is a photograph of the test set-up when the plate was 55 in. wide. The original head distance H of 20 in. Fig. 6.5, was maintained until the final test, in which it was reduced to 12 in.

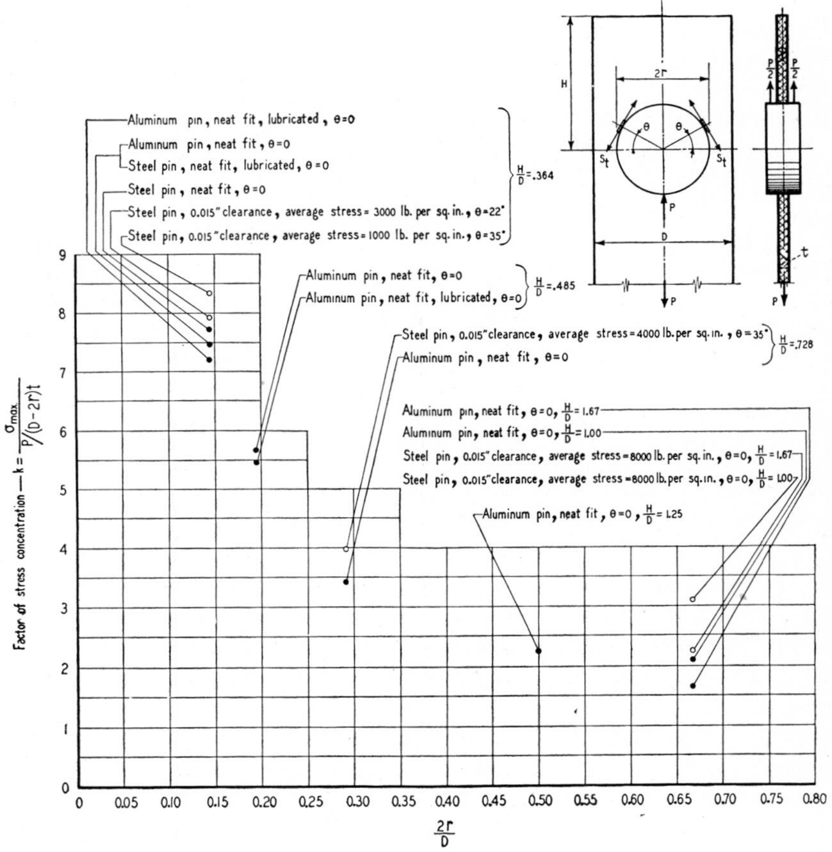

FIG. 6.5 Factors of Stress Concentration in Large Steel and Aluminum Plates Pulled by Single Pins, Fig. 6.4, Showing Effect of Clearance.

Strains in the immediate vicinity of the hole were measured with Huggenberger tensometers of ½-in. gage length. Strains at other locations in the plate were measured with tensometers of 1-in. gage length. In the vicinity of free boundaries, strains were measured in directions parallel to and normal to the boundary. Elsewhere strains were measured on three or more intersecting gage lines forming a rosette.[1] Because of the finite gage length and width of knife edges of the instruments, it was impossible to obtain a direct measure of the maximum unit strains occurring at the edge of the hole. These values were obtained by extrapolation of curves constructed from measured values.

In most of these tests the pin was a neat fit in the hole, the diameters of the pin and hole being the same within 0.0005 in. In other tests the pin had a clearance of 0.015 in. on the diameter. Several tests were made

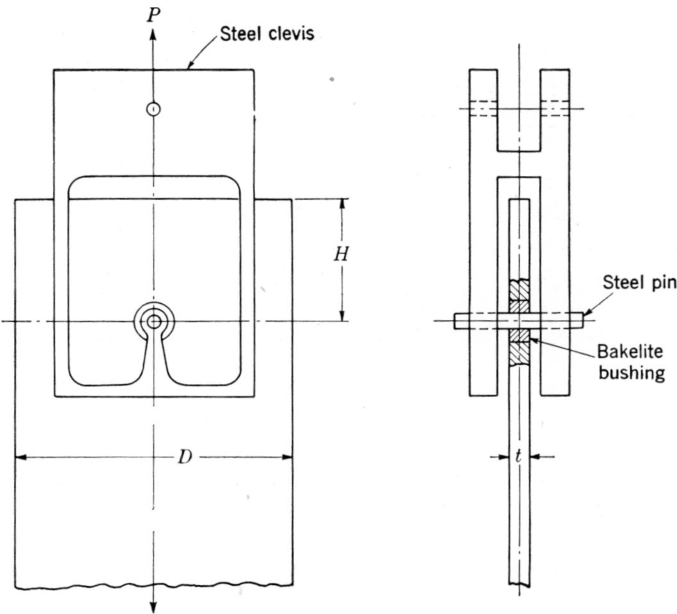

FIG. 6.6 Drawing of Clevis Used to Apply Tensile Loads to Photoelastic Models without Obscuring the Region around the Pin.

The Bakelite bushing has a $\frac{1}{4}$-in. steel core.

with close-fitting pins to study the effect of lubrication of the pin on the factor of stress concentration. A colloidal graphite grease was used as the lubricant. In some tests the pin was of steel; in others, the pin and the plate were both of aluminum.

Stress concentration factors have been determined for each test as the ratio of the maximum tensile stress at the edge of the hole to the average stress on the minimum net section of the plate. These factors are shown in Fig. 6.5.

[1] For the interpretation of strain rosette data see *Photoelasticity*, Vol. I, Chapter 1.

§6.6 Photoelastic Results. In the photoelastic investigations the models, both plate and bushing, were of Bakelite BT-61-893. The load was applied by means of a steel pin passing through the bushing and a clevis which made it possible to obtain a clear stress pattern of the highly stressed regions around the hole, Fig. 6.6. Typical stress patterns are shown in Figs. 6.7, 6.8, and 6.9.

Fig. 6.10 is a photograph of the test set-up showing the clevis for the tests involving two pins.

The specimens in the photoelastic investigation had a nominal thickness of ¼ in. Dimensions of the specimens were chosen so that the influence of the following factors on the stress concentration factor could be studied:

1. The ratio of the diameter of the hole to the width of the plate ($2r/D$).
2. The clearance between the pin and the hole.
3. The ratio of the head distance to the width of the plate (H/D).
4. Application of the axial load through two symmetrically placed pins of equal diameters.

Factors of stress concentration have been calculated directly from the data furnished by the stress pattern in the usual manner, i.e.,

$$k = \frac{\sigma_{\text{max.}}}{\sigma_{\text{nominal}}} = \frac{n_{\text{max.}}\, 2F}{(P/A)}$$

in which k = the factor of stress concentration.
$n_{\text{max.}}$ = maximum fringe order.
$2F$ = model fringe value in pounds per square inch tension.
P = the applied load.
A = the minimum net area through the hole or holes.

Stress-concentration factors thus determined for each of the cases photoelastically investigated are plotted in Fig. 6.11.

In the tests in which the plate was loaded through two pins, the head distances H were great enough so that they did not influence the stress-concentration factors. The diameters of the pins in the double-pin tests were taken equal to the radius of the single pin used for a plate of the same dimensions. The results thus obtained, Fig. 6.11, provide a comparison between the factors of stress concentration for the single-pin and the double-pin tests under conditions of constant ratio of bearing to mean tensile stresses. The factors shown in Fig. 6.11 for the double-pin tests have been plotted against ratios of $2r/D$, in which r is the radius of

FIG. 6.7 Stress Pattern of the Head of a Bar Pulled by a Pin.

Width of bar, $D = 2.140$ in.; diameter of hole, $2r = 0.990$ in.; diameter of pin = 0.975 in.; thickness of each = 0.270 in.; $P = 389$ lb.; $F = 159$ psi. shear.

FIG. 6.8 Stress Pattern of the Head of a Bar in Tension Loaded through Pin with Clearance.

Width of bar, $D = 5.937$ in.; diameter of hole, $2r = 0.750$ in.; diameter of pin = 0.732 in.; thickness of bar = 0.259 in.; thickness of pin = 0.338 in.; $P = 426$ lb.

the equivalent single pin for the same ratio of bearing to mean tensile stress.

§6.7 Discussion of Results. ***Both investigations show that the main factors influencing the state of stress are: (a) the ratio 2r/D, (b) the clearance between the pin and the hole, and (c) the ratio H/D.***

1. *Effect of* $2r/D$ *Ratio.* As can be seen in Figs. 6.5 and 6.11, there is a definite relationship between the stress concentration factor and the ratio of hole diameter to width of plate. For a $2r/D$ ratio of 0.7, the

FIG. 6.9 Stress Pattern of the Head of a Bar With Two Pins.

Width of bar, $D = 2.250$ in.; diameter of holes, $2r = 0.501$ in.; diameter of pins = 0.501 in.; thickness of each = 0.249 in.; $P = 507$ lb.

values of the stress-concentration factors are in the neighborhood of 2. The factors increase as the ratios $2r/D$ decrease, being in the region of 6 to 8 when that ratio is 0.15. The spread in the stress-concentration factors shown for a given ratio of $2r/D$ is largely caused by the effects of the clearance between the pin and the hole, and the head distance H.

2. *Effect of Clearance between Pin and Hole.* ***Both investigations show that the factors of stress concentration are increased by the presence of clearance between the pin and the hole.*** This effect was evidenced throughout the whole range of $2r/D$ ratios from 0.086 to 0.76 and is

FIG. 6.10 Photograph of Double Clevis Used in Loading the Bar of Fig. 6.9.

particularly pronounced at small ratios of $2r/D$. In the aluminum tests, Fig. 6.5, at $2r/D = 0.145$, a clearance of 0.015 in. raised the factor from 7.2 to 8.4 approximately. In the photoelastic tests, Fig. 6.11, at $2r/D = 0.085$, a clearance of 0.002 in. raised the factor from 10.6 to 12.1, and a clearance of 0.03 in. raised the same factor to 13.6 approximately.

The effect of the clearance is associated with the head size H, being greater for the smaller ratios of H/D. For instance, in the investigation involving the oversize aluminum specimens, Fig. 6.5, at $2r/D$ ratio of 0.67, the introduction of clearance increased the stress concentration factor about 35 per cent when the H/D ratio was 1.67, while, for H/D ratio of 1.00, the increase was about 50 per cent. Similar effects can be observed in the photoelastic tests. Thus at $2r/D = 0.63$ the influence of 0.018-in. clearance for $H/D = 0.66$ is to raise the value of k from 2.15 to 2.7 approximately, whereas the same clearance at $H/D = 1.23$ scarcely changes the value of k. This can further be seen at $2r/D = 0.76$. The same influence of clearance on the maximum stresses has also been observed on previous occasions.[1] This increase in stress can be ex-

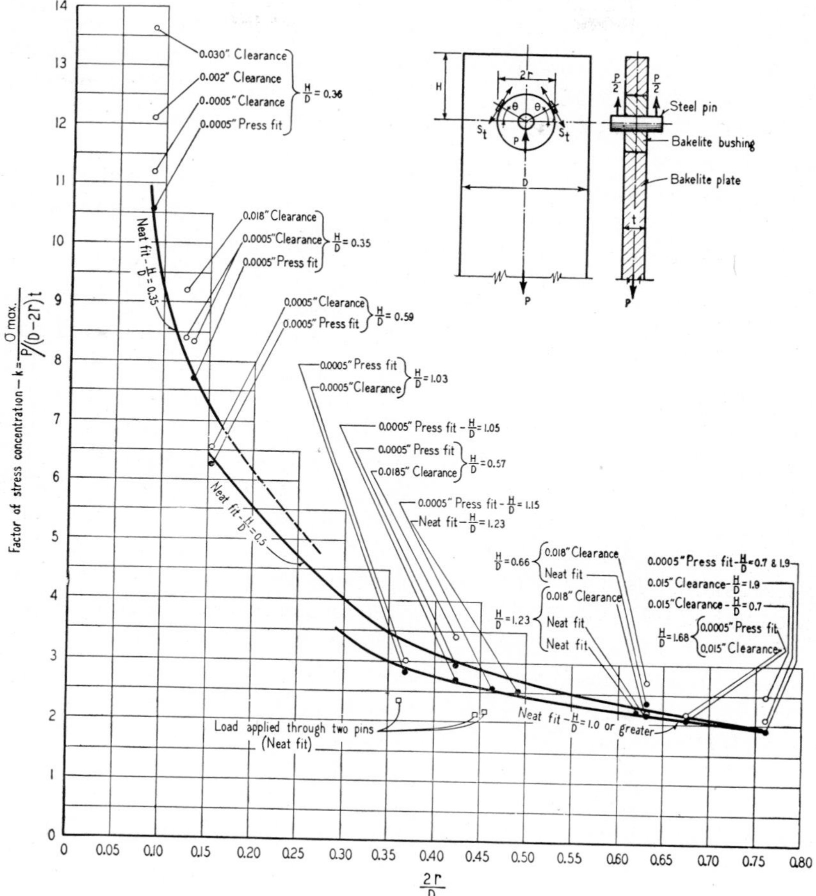

FIG. 6.11 Photoelastically Determined Stress Concentration Factors for Bakelite Bars Strained by Single Pins Showing Effect of Clearance and of H/D.

plained on the theory that it permits sharp local changes in the curvature of the circular boundary of the hole.

[1] See "The Behavior of a Brittle Material at Failure," by M. M. Frocht, *Journal of Applied Mechanics*, September, 1936; also "An Investigation of the Stress Distribution in Aluminum Connecting Rods," by R. L. Templin, *Mechanical Engineering*, March, 1936; and "Spannungsverteilung in einem Querhaupt," by E. Lehr, *Zeitschrift angew. Math. Mech.*, Vol. 79, 1935, Figs. 16 and 17.

From the noted description of the points plotted in Fig. 6.5, it can be seen that, in the aluminum plates in which there was clearance between pin and hole, the maximum stresses did not always occur at the ends of the horizontal diameter. However, in every test involving close-fitting pins, the maximum stresses did occur at the ends of the horizontal diameter. ***The same effect of the clearance on the location of the maximum tensile stress at the edge of the hole was found in the photoelastic investigation.***

As might be expected, while the relation between maximum stress and load was practically linear for the cases involving close-fitting pins, for the tests in which the pin was smaller than the hole the stress concentration factor was somewhat higher for the smaller loads. This is demonstrated by the two values shown in Fig. 6.5 for a $2r/D$ ratio of 0.145 and the steel pin with 0.015-in. clearance. The same relation between load and maximum stress was encountered in the photoelastic tests. The variations in stress-concentration factors with the load for the tests involving clearance on the pin were small compared to the differences between the factors for the loose pin and the close-fitting pin.

3. *Effect of Head Distance* (*Ratio of H/D*). Fig. 6.12 shows a composite of the values of k for close-fitting pins obtained from both investigations, as well as the results of other investigators, both theoretical and experimental. In this figure the effects of clearance have been eliminated but the effect of the head distance on the factors of stress concentration has been emphasized. As the ratio of H/D decreases, the maximum stress and consequently the stress-concentration factor increases. Thus, at $2r/D = 0.15$, k equals 6.5 when $H/D = 0.5$ and k equals 7.3 when $H/D = 0.35$. The results of the photoelastic investigation indicate that the effect of the head distance decreases with increasing ratios of $2r/D$. Beyond a certain value of H/D, an increase in head distance has no effect. For a $2r/D$ ratio of 0.76, two specimens were found to have the same factor of stress concentration (for the case of a close-fitting pin) for an H/D ratio of 1.9, as for an H/D ratio of 0.7. ***This behavior is not entirely substantiated by the results of the strain-gage measurements on the oversize aluminum specimens.*** In this investigation (see Fig. 6.5) for a close-fitting pin and a $2r/D$ ratio of 0.667, a stress-concentration factor of 1.65 was determined for an H/D ratio of 1.67, while the corresponding value for an H/D ratio of 1.00 was 2.1.

4. *Effect of Number of Pins.* The results of the photoelastic investigation, Fig. 6.11, show that the stress-concentration factors are smaller when the load is equally distributed between two symmetrically situated pins than when the plate is loaded through a single central pin of a diameter equal to the sum of the diameters of the two pins. The few

tests of this type made indicated decreases in the factor of stress concentration of about 20 per cent as compared with corresponding values for plates loaded through a single pin.

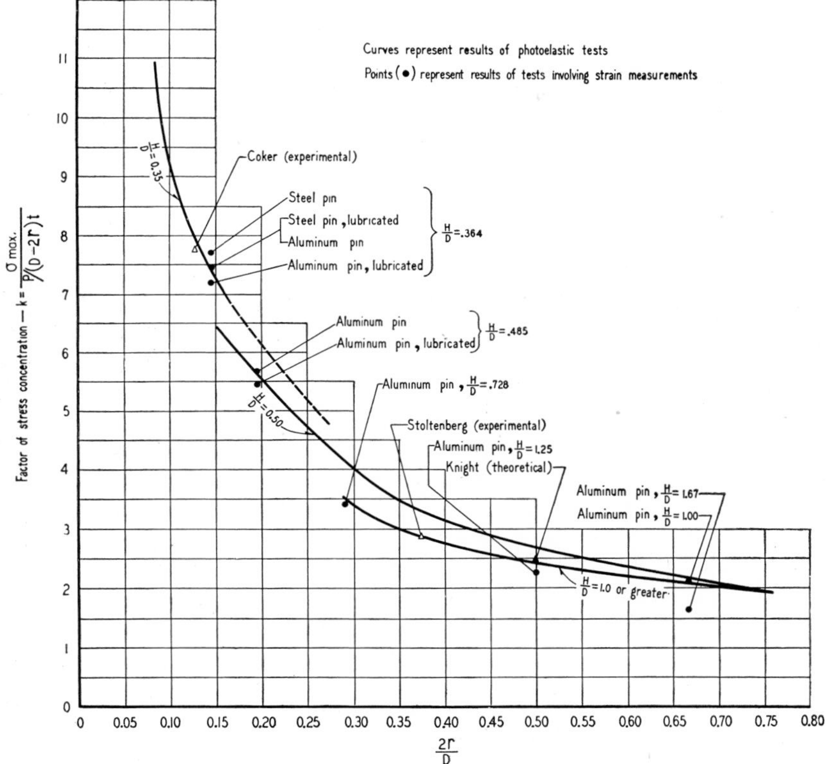

FIG. 6.12 Curves of Stress Concentration Factors for Plates Strained by Single Pins Showing Effect of H/D.

Results from theory, photoelasticity, and strain measurements are given.

5. *Effects of Material of Pin and Lubrication.* The tests made on the aluminum specimens (see Fig. 6.5) indicated a very slight increase in the maximum stress when the close-fitting aluminum pin was replaced by a steel pin having the same fit. Lubrication of the pin produced a small but measurable decrease in the values of k.

6. *Factors of Stress Concentration Based on Average Bearing Stresses.* In Fig. 6.13 are shown values for a stress-concentration factor (k_b) defined as the ratio of the maximum tensile stress at the edge of the hole to the average bearing stress on the pin. The data given in Fig. 6.12

have been replotted in this manner in Fig. 6.13. In addition, two points are shown representing the values determined by Bickley[1] and Knight[2] for a hole in an infinite plate. The curve shown in Fig. 6.13 falls slightly below the experimental points in the region where the values of $2r/D$ are small, because these points represent the result of tests in which the

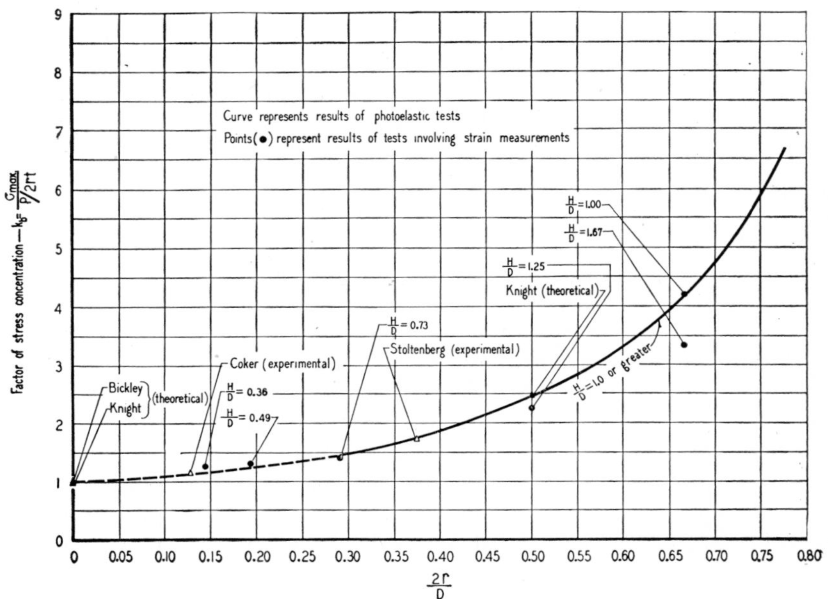

FIG. 6.13 Factors of Stress Concentration in Plates Strained by Single Pins Expressed as the Ratio of the Maximum Tensile Stress in the Plate Divided by the Average Bearing Stress on the Pin.

Results are from photoelastic tests, strain-gage measurements, and theoretical calculations.

maximum stresses were influenced by the head distance (see Fig. 6.5). The curve of Fig. 6.13 indicates that, for a plate loaded through a close-fitting or loose pin in a hole in the plate, the maximum tensile stresses at the edge of the hole will be greater than the average bearing stress on the pin.[3]

[1] W. G. Bickley, "Distribution of Stress Round a Circular Hole in a Plate," *Phil. Trans. Royal Society, London,* Vol. 227, A, pp. 383–415, 1928.

[2] R. C. Knight, "Action of a Rivet in a Plate of Finite Breadth," *Phil. Mag.,* Vol. 19 (7), pp. 517–540, March, 1935.

[3] It will be found that as a first approximation, for closely fitting pins and H/D greater than unity, the maximum tension equals the sum of the average bearing stress plus 1.5 times the nominal tension.

It is seen that ***there exists good quantitative agreement between all phases of the problem which were investigated by the two methods. The two materials and methods yield essentially the same factors of stress concentration.*** For values of $2r/D$ less than 0.5 the agreement is excellent. For values of $2r/D$ greater than 0.5 the values obtained from the aluminum plate are slightly lower than the corresponding values obtained photoelastically.

Both investigations show the same quantitative effect of clearance on the factors of stress concentrations, and on the position of the maximum stresses. For small values of $2r/D$ the influence of the ratio H/D is also the same, although for large values of $2r/D$ there is some divergence. Lastly there is also agreement in the effect of the magnitude of the load on the values of k.

PART III STEEL AND BAKELITE

§6.8 Isopachic Stress Patterns. The photoelastic stress patterns give the loci of constant $(p - q)$. It is also possible to obtain optically patterns giving the loci of constant $(p + q)$. Patterns which give the loci of equal sums of principal stresses are known as isopachic patterns. The term isopachic is due to Coker and Filon and is derived from the two Greek words *iso*, meaning same, and *pachic*, meaning thickness.

Unlike photoelastic models, which must be transparent, those used for isopachic patterns may be made of opaque materials, including metals, provided the materials are homogeneous and isotropic and can be polished to a good optical flat. Fig. 6.14 shows an isopachic pattern obtained from a steel ring 0.243 in. thick, 0.751 in. in outside diameter, 0.375 in. in inside diameter, and subjected to concentrated diametral loads.

We shall here omit a description of the theory on which isopachic patterns are based or the technique employed in obtaining them. These topics are discussed in the next chapter. For our present purpose it will be sufficient to state that the fringes in these patterns are interference fringes similar to the well-known Newton's rings, and that the interpretation of these patterns is similar to that of the photoelastic images. ***Each fringe is, however, the locus of a constant sum of principal stresses, instead of the difference, and these sums are proportional to the order of the isopachic fringe.***

§6.9 Boundary Stresses from Steel and Bakelite. The pattern of the steel ring shown in Fig. 6.14 provides another important source of data bearing on the influence of the material on the stress distribution. ***Since at free boundaries one principal stress is zero it follows that at such***

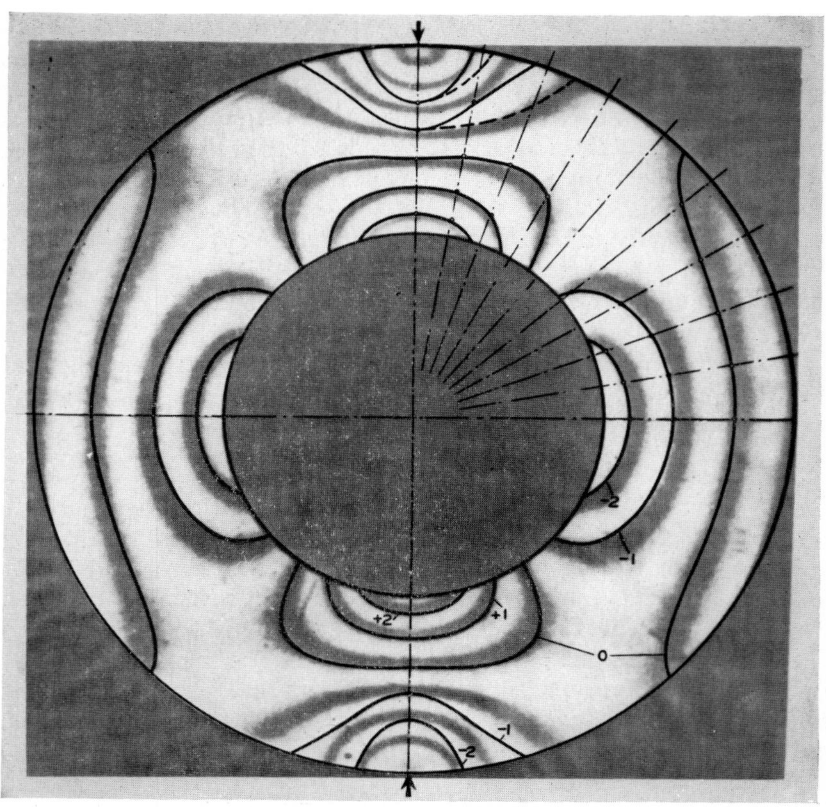

FIG. 6.14 Composite Photograph of a Theoretical Isopachic Stress Pattern and One Obtained from a Stainless Steel Ring.

Inner diameter = 0.376 in.; outer diameter = 0.751 in.; t = 0.243 in.

boundaries the stresses can be determined from either the isopachic or the photoelastic pattern. Furthermore, since the hole in the ring under consideration is free from external forces, the theory of elasticity tells us that the induced stresses are independent of Poisson's ratio, even though the ring constitutes a multiply connected body. The first test of the theory is provided by a comparison of the free-boundary stresses obtained from the steel and the Bakelite models, Figs. 6.14 and 6.15. If the theory is sound, the distribution of the boundary stresses should be the same in both models. On the other hand, deviations in these stresses would indicate that the physical constants of the material influence the stress distribution.

FIG. 6.15 Photoelastic Stress Pattern from a Bakelite Ring under Concentrated Diametral Loads of 202.6 Lb.

Inner diameter = 0.766 in.; outer diameter = 1.532 in.; t = 0.1795 in.; F = 480 psi. in tension or compression.

It should be noted that this comparison can be made without measuring the loads on the steel ring. Inspection of the isopachic and photoelastic patterns shows that the singular or zero points on the circular boundary of the hole coincide. In both patterns they lie on lines inclined at 36° approximately with the line of the loads. The photographs further show that the points of maximum stress also coincide. This establishes a quantitative relation between the isopachic and photoelastic fringes. For example, the maximum compressive fringe order in the Bakelite model around the hole is 16.75. At the corresponding point of the isopachic pattern the fringe order is 2.75. The ratio of 6.06 represents the number of photoelastic fringes per isopachic interference fringe. We can now plot the complete curve of boundary stresses in the isopachic pattern since these stresses are directly proportional to the order of the fringes.

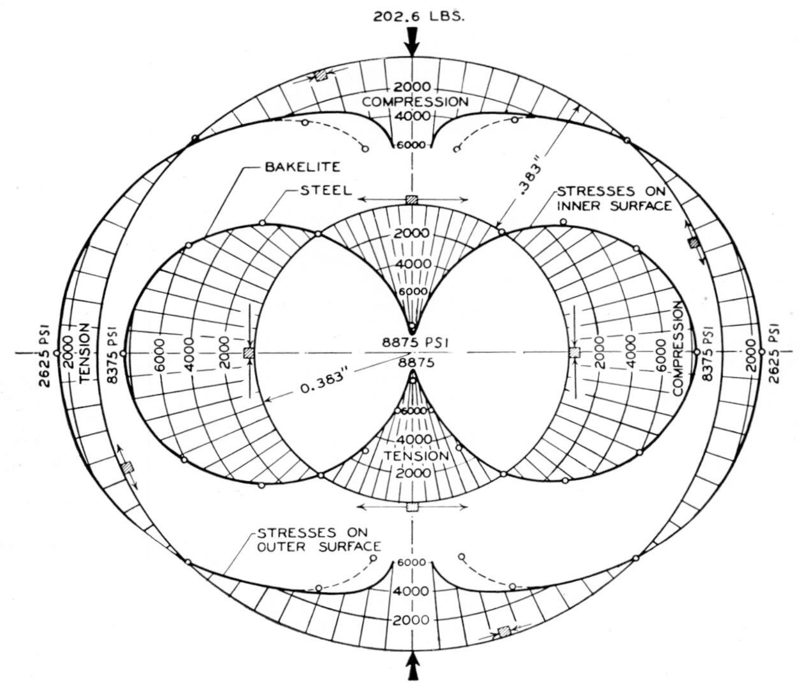

FIG. 6.16 Comparative Curves of Boundary Stresses from Bakelite and Steel Models Obtained from Photoelastic and Isopachic Patterns.

Full curve from Bakelite model, Fig. 6.15. Open circles from steel model, Fig. 6.14 or 7.16. The results show that in the elastic state the physical constants do not influence the stress distribution.

The final results are shown in Fig. 6.16. The full curve represents the photoelastic values, and the open circles are the corresponding values from the steel model. ***It should be emphasized that the full curve has not been drawn through the open circles.*** The relative positions of the curve and the circles shows, therefore, the influence of the material on the stress distribution. Inspection of Fig. 6.16 shows the agreement to be nearly perfect. The only discrepancies occur in the vicinity of the concentrated loads, where the stresses from the steel specimen are greater than those from the Bakelite model. These discrepancies do not invalidate the theoretical conclusions, since in those regions the stresses are no longer elastic, as considerable yielding has taken place, especially in the Bakelite ring. The agreement of the boundary stresses obtained from steel and Bakelite rings especially around the hole thus corroborates the theoretical conclusion that the stress distribution is independent of the physical constants of the material.

§6.10 Comparison of Experimental and Theoretical Isopachic Patterns. As already stated the photoelastic pattern provides values of $(p - q)$ at every point in the model, and on free boundaries, where one principal stress vanishes, it gives also the values of $(p + q)$. It will be shown later (see Chapter 8), that when the boundary values of $(p + q)$ are known the values of this sum can be calculated at all interior points. From the computed values of $(p + q)$ isopachic curves can be plotted for the whole model. In other words from the boundary values furnished by the photoelastic pattern it is also possible to construct a complete theoretical isopachic pattern.

Fig. 6.14 is a composite photograph of the isopachic stress patterns obtained optically from the steel ring and the calculated theoretical contours. The composite photograph shows good agreement between the two solutions in all regions except in the immediate vicinity of the concentrated loads. It must be remembered that the calculated pattern rests on boundary values from the Bakelite ring in which, as stated before, the state of stress near the loads is somewhat different from that in the steel model, owing to local plastic flow. The assumption that the applied loads were strictly concentrated is probably another factor contributing to the local discrepancies. The two patterns show good agreement and add further strength to the theoretical conclusions regarding the relation between the state of stress and the material of the stressed body.

The correctness of the isopachic pattern from the steel ring can be further tested by combining the curves of $(p + q)$ which it provides with the photoelastic values of $(p - q)$ to determine the actual principal stresses p and q and to examine these from the standpoint of equilibrium.

§6.11 Stresses across Sections of Symmetry. Figs. 6.17 and 6.18 show the principal stresses across the sections of symmetry determined by combining the $(p - q)$ values from the Bakelite model with the $(p + q)$ values from the steel ring. Fig. 6.17 shows comparative curves of the normal stresses across the horizontal section of symmetry $B'B$. The results from three methods are compared: the one under discussion involving the isopachic curves from the steel ring, the slope-equilibrium method,[1] and the results from the mathematical theory of elasticity.[2] ***Again the agreement is seen to be completely satisfactory.***

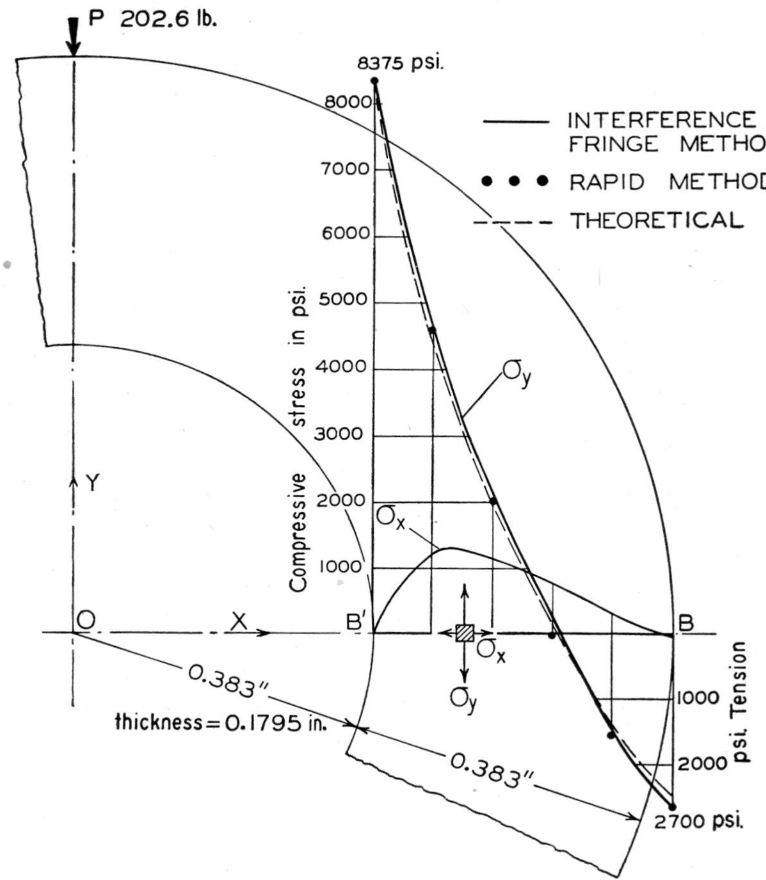

FIG. 6.17 Comparative Curves of Principal Stresses across Horizontal Section of Symmetry of Ring in Diametral Compression.

Results combine data from Bakelite and steel and show different methods.

[1] See Chapter VII, Vol. I, or author's paper "A Rapid Method for the Determination of Principal Stresses across Sections of Symmetry from Photoelastic Data," *Journal of Applied Mechanics, Trans. A.S.M.E.*, March, 1938.

[2] See S. Timoshenko, *Theory of Elasticity,* McGraw-Hill Book Co., New York, 1934, p. 119.

The results across the sections of symmetry are further checked from the point of view of equilibrium, Fig. 6.18. In checking the forces across section $D'D$, Fig. 6.18, a small semicircular section was removed and the original load replaced by a horizontal thrust of $P/\pi = 64.5$ lb. and a vertical load of $P/2 = 101.3$ lb. which enter into the theoretical solution of this problem [see eq. (2.9)]. As shown in Fig. 6.18 the error in the summation of moments is 6.4 per cent and in the summation of X and Y forces 2.7 per cent and 2.6 per cent, respectively.

Another case in point is provided by a study of comparative stresses in steel and Celluloid models made by the late Y. Satake at University College, London, and reported by Coker and Filon in their *Treatise on Photoelasticity*.[1] Satake measured the sums of the principal stresses $(p + q)$ in a steel tension bar with a central circular hole by means of a lateral extensometer. Comparison with the stresses in a similar Celluloid bar showed substantial agreement. Other comparative studies can be found in the literature.

§6.12 Summary. The theory shows that in plane problems dealing with simply connected bodies subjected only to known boundary forces the stresses are independent of the physical constants of the material. The same is true in multiply connected bodies in which the traction on the holes reduces to a zero resultant or to a couple. We have seen that experiments completely substantiate these conclusions.

Theory further shows that even where the stresses are affected by Poisson's ratio this effect can be determined photoelastically, by means of a dislocation. Experiment as well as theory, however, shows that the effect is small, and that for all practical purposes it is negligible.

It is, perhaps, relevant to add that none of the elementary formulas of strength of materials used by engineers contain the elastic constants. Consider, for instance, the basic and familiar formulas

$$\sigma = \frac{P}{A},$$

$$\sigma = \frac{My}{I},$$

$$\tau = \frac{Tr}{J}.$$

These contain neither Poisson's ratio nor the modulus of elasticity and

[1] See §6.03.

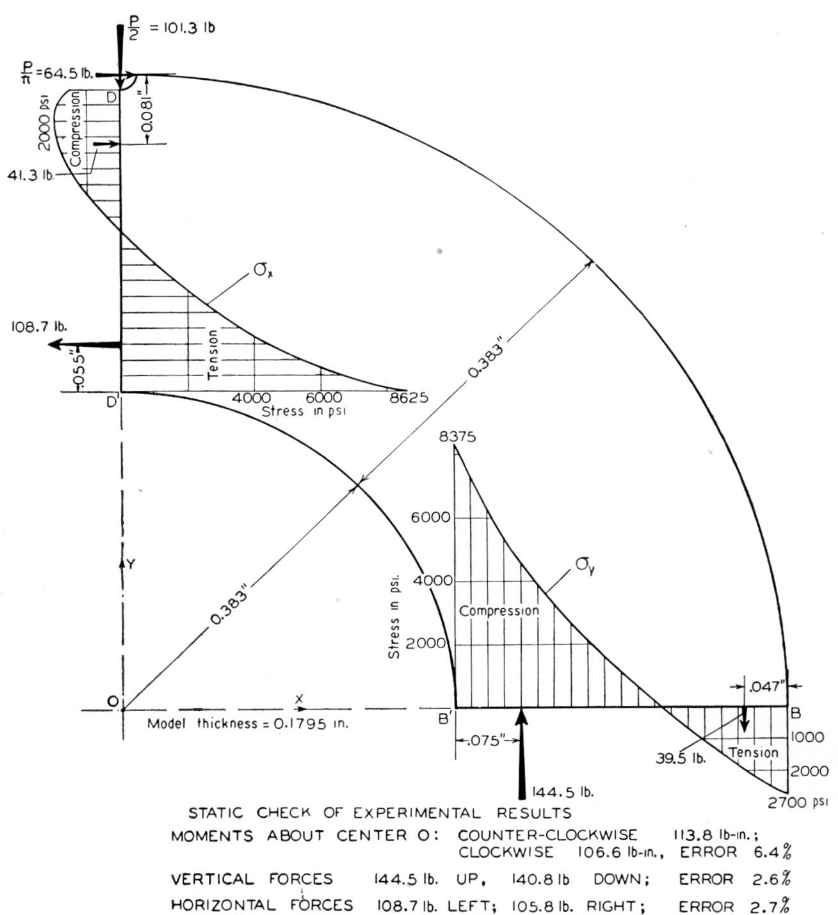

FIG. 6.18 Principal Normal Stresses across Sections of Symmetry of Ring in Diametral Compression.

Results again combine data from photoelastic and isopachic stress patterns. Note static check.

therefore say in effect that the state of stress does not depend on the properties of the stressed material.

It should also be noted that the employment of models as such in stress analysis is no new procedure. In fact, engineers show no reluctance to accept data even from non-homogeneous models, such as cardboard, as, for example, in structural analysis by means of deformeters.

CHAPTER 7

LATERAL EXTENSOMETERS AND ISOPACHIC CURVES

§7.1 Introduction. In Vol. I we discussed several methods for the determination of the principal stresses p and q. Those methods were dependent on photoelastic data. By means of the equations of equilibrium the values of $(p - q)$ from the stress patterns were combined with the data from the isoclinics to give p and q separately.

In the present chapter methods for the determination of $(p + q)$ are described, which, with the exception of Neuber's equations, are independent of the photoelastic data. These methods yield the full sums of the principal stresses, which in combination with the photoelastic values of the differences give the principal stresses p and q.

The chapter consists of three parts. In Part I experimental methods employing extensometers are described. In Parts II and III experimental and graphical methods respectively are discussed for the determination of complete isopachic patterns, i.e., patterns giving the loci of constant values of $(p + q)$. Several miscellaneous methods are briefly touched upon.

PART I LATERAL EXTENSOMETERS

§7.2 Theory of Lateral Extensometers. Among the first experimental methods used to determine the sum of the principal stresses $(p + q)$ in two-dimensional problems are the methods that utilize the lateral deformations δ, which always accompany the main strains in the plane of the loads. This lateral deformation is given by

$$\delta = -\frac{\nu t(p + q)}{E}.$$

This equation may be written

$$\delta = -K(p + q),$$

in which

$$K = \frac{\nu t}{E};$$

i.e., K is a constant for all points in a homogeneous isotropic model of uniform thickness obeying Hooke's Law. The value of K can be determined from a tension bar cut from the same sheet as the model itself, and the lateral deformations δ can be calculated without the specific evaluations of Poisson's ratio ν, the modulus of elasticity E, or the thickness t.

The instruments used to measure δ are known as *lateral extensometers.* There are three general types of such extensometers: optical or interferometers, mechanical, and electrical. The interferometers are among the oldest and most sensitive. Electrical extensometers have only recently been introduced.

§7.3 Brief Theory of Interference Fringes. We review briefly the theory of the simplest case of interference fringes. In Fig. 7.1, let a ray R from a monochromatic source O be incident normally on the half mirror A–A, which for concreteness we can take as the polished surface of a glass plate. Upon reaching the surface A–A, part of the light is reflected upwards and is represented in our figure by vector a, and a part is transmitted. The transmitted ray upon reaching the lower surface B–B is also partially reflected, and this component is designated by vector b. Upon reaching surface A–A this vector b is again resolved, a part of it, denoted by c, being transmitted. The rays a and c meet and combine to form a new ray d, the nature of which depends on the thickness h of the air film. Taking the difference in optical path as $2h$, and remembering that upon reflection from a denser to a rarer medium the ray is retarded by $\lambda/2$, we get for the condition of interference the familiar equation

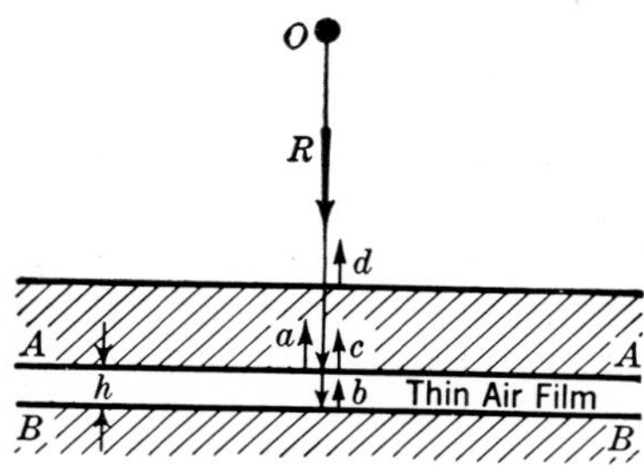

FIG. 7.1 Sketch Showing Formation of Interference Fringes.

$$\left(2h + \frac{\lambda}{2}\right) = (2n + 1)\frac{\lambda}{2}, \tag{7.1}$$

where n is any integer and λ the wave length of the light, since interference takes place if the rays meet with a phase difference equal to an odd number of half wave lengths.

Solving for h, we get

$$h = \frac{n\lambda}{2}, \tag{7.2}$$

which means that for a beam of parallel rays interference fringes will appear for h equal 0, ½, 2/2, 3/2, etc., wave lengths.

It also means that no two fringes could cross and that along any one interference fringe the depth or thickness of the film is constant. If one surface, say A–A, be considered perfectly flat and taken as a datum plane then the interference fringes would represent contours or isopachic curves of the surface B–B.

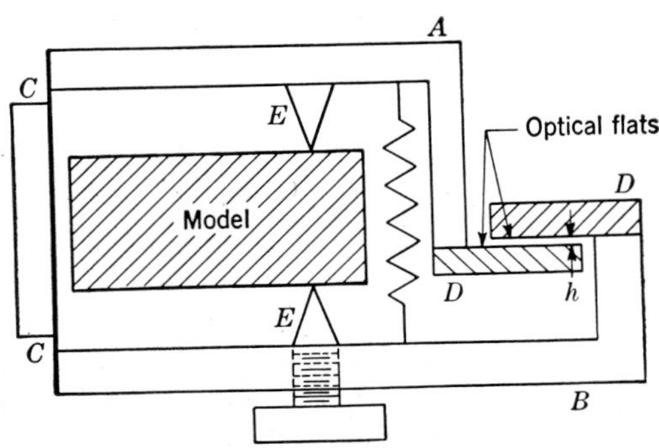

FIG. 7.2 Sketch Showing Mesnager's Interferometer.

§7.4 Interferometers. The design of the first interferometer for photoelastic research is generally credited to A. Mesnager, Fig. 7.2. The mechanism consists of two angular bars A and B attached to a flexible steel plate C–C. At the right end the bars are equipped with optical flats D–D separated by a small air gap h. The needle points E–E which move integrally with the bars are brought in contact with the model, and they transmit the deformation of the model to the optical flats in a somewhat magnified form. This deformation is measured by observing the movement of the interference fringes between the optical flats. With green light (5461 Å), a displacement of 0.000001 in. can be readily measured.

A recent improvement over Mesnager's interferometer was made by Vose, Fig. 7.3. This interferometer is simple and rugged. The cone-tipped screws can be adjusted to fit models of different sizes. Pressure on the contact points is provided by the wire spring. Fig. 7.4 shows the instrument in use. It is suspended by means of a string attached to the center of gravity. This arrangement relieves the contact points of load. As in Mesnager's interferometer, the deformation is measured by observing the movement of the fringes between the optical flats and counting their number.

Fig. 7.3 Photograph of Vose's Interferometer.

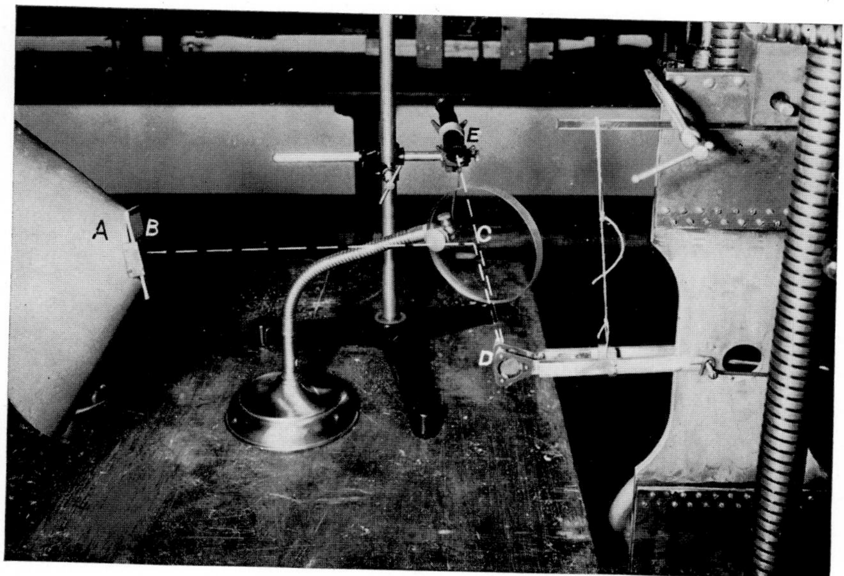

Fig. 7.4 Photograph Showing Vose's Interferometer Attached to a Tension Bar; also Source of Light A, Half Mirror C, and Telescope E. (From Vose.)

Two other interferometer methods have been devised and used: one by Favre and the other by Fabry. They are mainly of scientific and historic significance. In both, the surfaces of the model must be optically flat

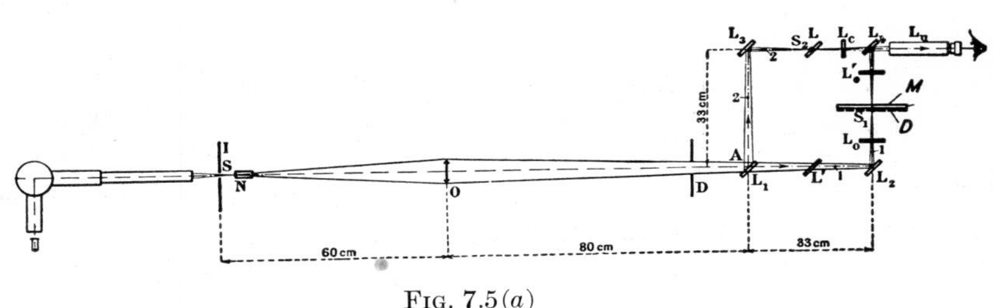

FIG. 7.5(a)

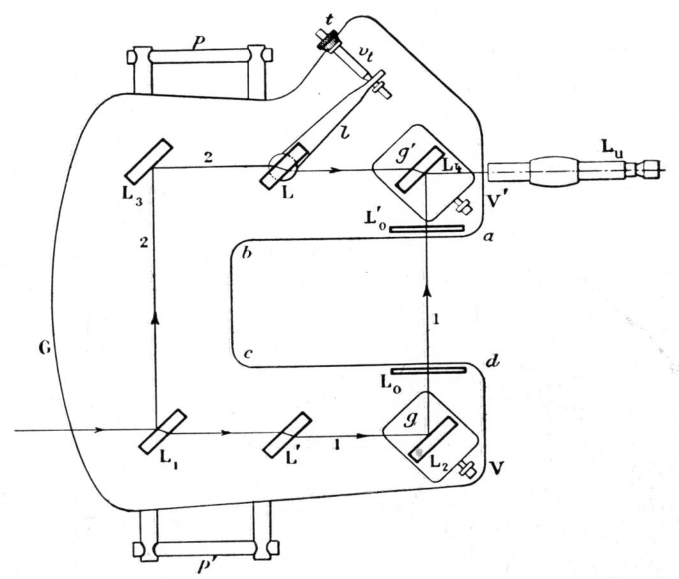

FIG. 7.5(b)

and parallel. Precautions must also be taken to maintain constant temperature. The models are generally of glass. Favre's interferometer follows the Mach-Zehnder type, Fig. 7.5. In Fabry's method the two faces of the model are half silvered and are used as interferometer surfaces. A third type was used by Maris. He determined δ by observ-

FIG. 7.5(*c*)

FIG. 7.5 Favre's Interferometer.

(*a*) Schematic diagram of elements: S = source of light (mercury lamp); I, D = diaphragms; N = prism polarizer; O = lens; L_1, L_3, L_c = half-silvered mirrors; L_2, L_4 = full-silvered mirrors; L, L' = glass plates; L_o, L_o' = half-wave plates; M = model; L_u = eyepiece. (*b*) Detailed arrangement of plates and mirrors. (*c*) Photograph of actual interferometer.

ing interference fringes in a thin air film formed between one silvered surface of the model and an auxiliary optical flat or datum plane.[1,2,3,4]

§7.5 Mechanical Lateral Extensometers. These instruments mechanically magnify the required deformations, either by means of levers only, or by combining a mechanical lever with a reflected beam of light.

Fig. 7.6 shows a photograph of Coker's lateral extensometer which utilizes the combined mechanical-optical lever. In this instrument one of the contact needles is fixed and the other transmits the lateral displacement to a lever which in turn rotates a small concave mirror. A beam of light carrying with it an image of a fine cross falls on the mirror and is reflected from it to a screen. As the measuring needle moves the mirror

[1] *Mesures des efforts intérieurs dans les solides et applications*, by A. Mesnager, Buda-Pesth, International Association for Testing of Materials, 1901. See also "Contribution à l'étude de la déformation élastique," *Ann. des Ponts et Chaussées*, Vol. 4, pp. 128–190, 1901.

[2] "Sur une nouvelle méthode optique de détermination des tensions intérieures," by H. Favre, *Rev. d'Optique*, Vol. 8, pp. 193–213, 241–261, 289–307, 1929.

[3] "Sur une nouvelle méthode pour l'étude expérimentale des tensions élastiques," by C. Fabry, *Comptes rendus*, Vol. 190, pp. 457–460, 1930.

[4] "Photoelastic Investigations of the Tensile Test Specimen, the Notched Bar, the Ship Propeller Strut, and the Roller Path Ring," by H. B. Maris, *J. Opt. Soc. Am.*, Vol. 15, pp. 194–200, 1927.

rotates and the reflected image of the cross moves along the screen. This movement is the measure of the deformations. Vast magnifications of almost any size can be obtained by placing the screen at a suitable distance from the mirror. With this instrument it is readily possible to

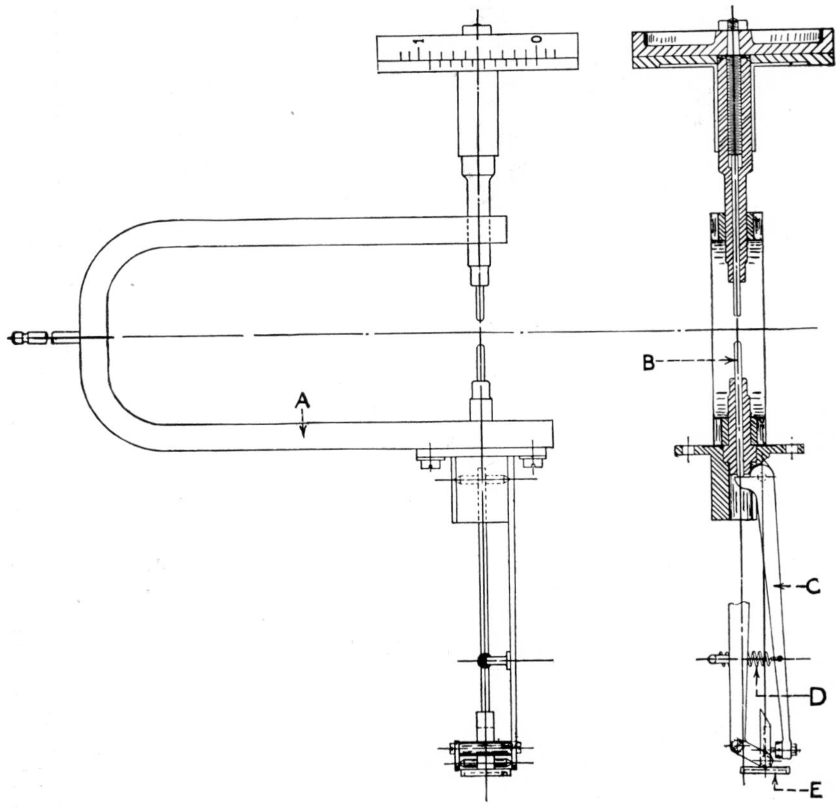

FIG. 7.6(a) Coker's Lateral Extensometer.

Line drawing of structural elements: A = main frame; B = movable needle; C = bell crank lever; D = spring; E = pivoted mirror.

measure deformations of 1×10^{-5} in. or even 1×10^{-6} in. In his numerous researches, Coker determined $(p + q)$ almost exclusively with this instrument. The extensometer can be moved by means of micrometers along two mutually perpendicular directions, making it possible to measure the thickness of the model along a given line both before and after loading.

The only objection to the Coker-type extensometer arises from the fact that the measuring needles can move only in the lateral direction, i.e., along the line determined by the points of contact. The needles are con-

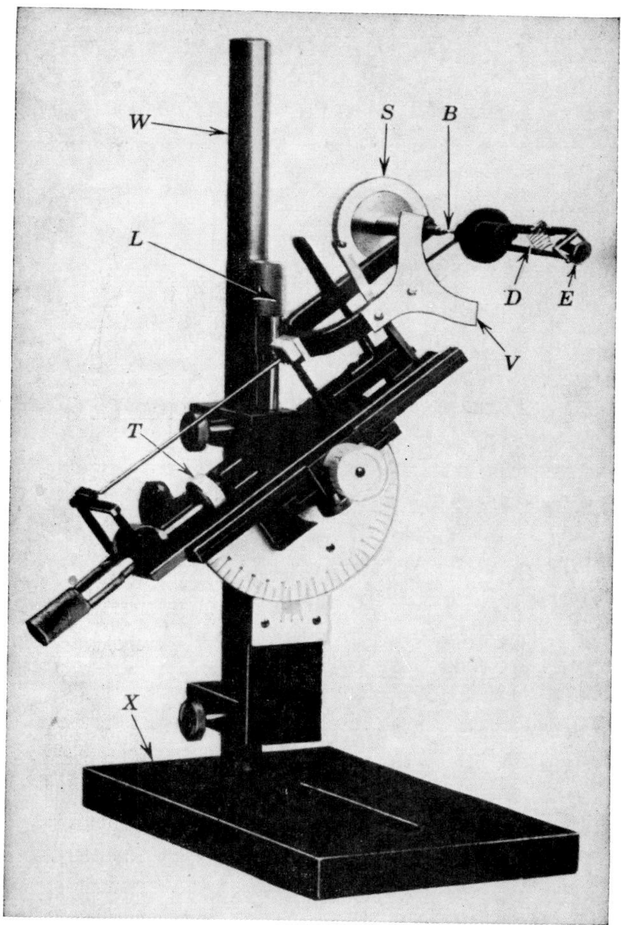

FIG. 7.6(*b*) Photograph of Coker's Extensometer.

L = vertical micrometer adjustment; S = calibrating screw and drum; T = micrometer screw stop; V = orientation scale of mirror; W = vertical pillar; X = base.

strained in every other direction. Since the needles are fixed and the points in the model in contact with the needles undergo relative displacements under load, ***the measured lateral deformation δ does not corre-***

spond to the initial set of points on the model. This tends to displace the curve of $(p + q)$ from its true position in the manner shown in Fig. 7.7. Furthermore, ***even in smoothly polished, well-prepared models there are variations in the thickness from point to point of the same order of magnitude as the required deformation,*** so that an additional error may originate in this source.

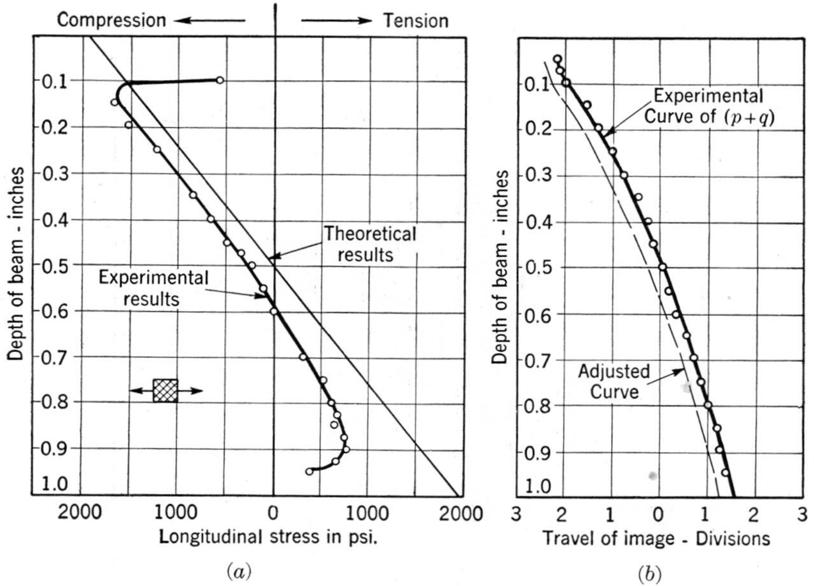

FIG. 7.7 Curves of $(p + q)$ Determined by Coker's Lateral Extensometer. (a) Pure bending; (b) section in centrally loaded beam ⅛ in. from center.

Several extensometers have been designed in recent years in which one main objective was to allow the extensometer and needles complete freedom of movement, and thereby to eliminate the error in the Coker extensometer. Vose's interferometer,[1] and the adaptation of the Huggenberger tensometers[2] shown in Fig. 7.8, tend to accomplish this end. Here the measuring needles are clamped, rather tightly, to the model by means of stiff springs, and the extensometer as a whole is free to move

[1] See "An Application of the Interferometer Strain Gage in Photoelasticity," by R. W. Vose, *Journal of Applied Mechanics*, September, 1935, p. A-99 to p. A-102.

[2] See "Fatigue of Shafts at Fitted Members with a Related Photoelastic Analysis," by R. E. Peterson and A. M. Wahl, *Journal of Applied Mechanics*, March, 1935.

with the points to which the needles are attached. However, the very pressure needed to eliminate the slipping of the contact needles may in itself introduce a disturbance into the required deformation.

§7.6 Electrical Extensometers. Fig. 7.9 shows a rather recent type of lateral extensometer developed by Anderson and the late A. V.

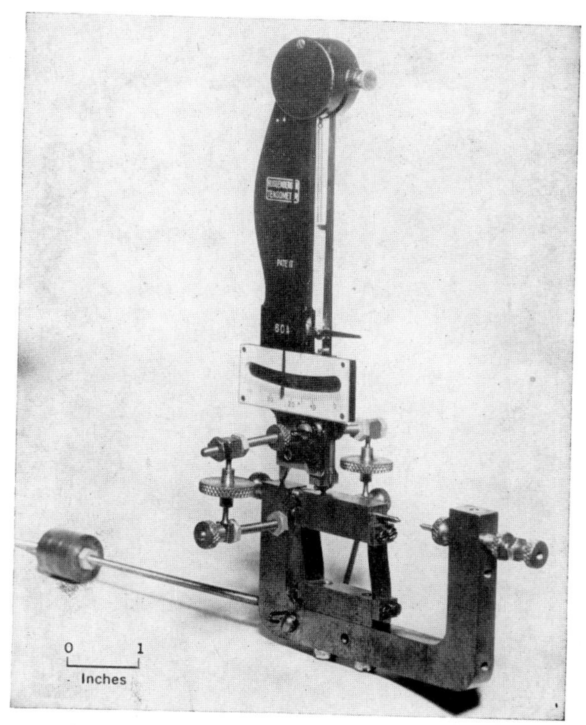

FIG. 7.8(*a*) Photograph of Lateral Extensometer Employing Huggenberger Tensometer.

de Forest.[1] This instrument utilizes the great sensitivity of the electrical strain gages developed by de Forest and Ruge (SR-4 gages), which respond to the changes in electrical resistance in wires under strain.

The instrument consists of three parts: the U-shaped frame, Fig 7.9(*a*), which is clamped to the model, a portable galvanometer, and a compensator element, Fig. 7.9(*b*). Four strain-sensitive elements are

[1] See "A New Lateral Extensometer," by A. V. de Forest and A. R. Anderson, *Proceedings of Tenth Semi-Annual Eastern Photoelasticity Conference*, December, 1939, pp. 31–34.

glued to the curved sections of the frame as shown in Fig. 7.9(*a*). When the frame is clamped to the model with a light initial pressure, it can follow the changes in the thickness of the model caused by the appilcation of the loads. Gages 1–2 and 3–4 take strains of opposite sign to those taken by gages 1–4 and 2–3.

FIG. 7.8(*b*) Extensometer in Position on Test Specimen. (From Peterson and Wahl.)

The strain-sensitive gages on the extensometer, Fig. 7.9(*a*), act as arms of a Wheatstone bridge, and the strains introduced into them are measured in the bridge as changes in resistance.

The instrument is calibrated by means of a simple tension test exactly like Coker's extensometer. Fig. 7.10 shows a curve of $\sigma_1 + \sigma_2 = (p + q)$ across the transverse section of symmetry in a tension bar with a central circular hole as determined by de Forest and Anderson with this extensometer.

§7.7 General Observations on Lateral Extensometers. The value of $(p + q)$ determined from lateral deformations is independent of all photoelastic data such as fringe order at a point or the isoclinic through it. It is also independent of the values of δ at any other point in the model. This eliminates the cumulative errors inherent in most, if not

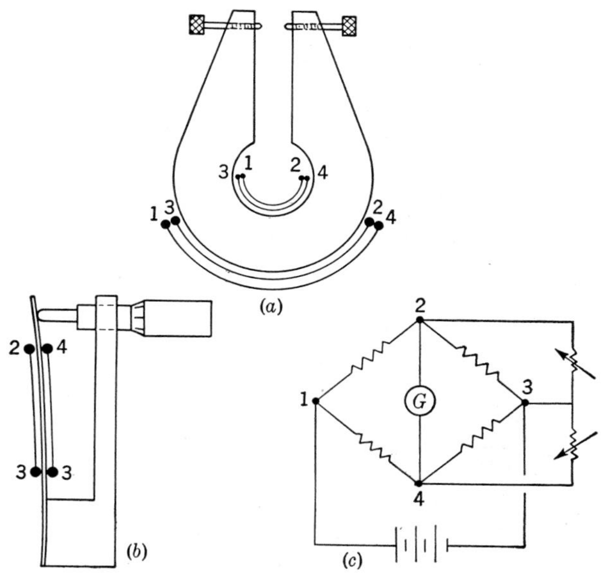

Fig. 7.9 Sketches Showing Elements of the de Forest Anderson Electronic Extensometer.

(a) Arrangement of wire-resistance gages on U-frame; (b) compensator unit; (c) wiring diagram.

all, of the processes requiring integration. A good lateral extensometer is probably the quickest means of determining $(p + q)$ at an isolated point. The method, however, is lengthy when a large region is to be explored. In such cases the method of harmonization or iteration is to be preferred. See the next chapter.

In addition, it is important to remember that eq. (1.37c), Vol. I, on which the lateral extensometer rests, is applicable only to thin bars in which the stresses may be assumed to be two-dimensional.

As already pointed out (see §1.9), in thick bars the state of stress around a discontinuity is generally three-dimensional even when the utmost precautions are taken to develop a sensibly uniform stress in the regions surrounding the discontinuity.

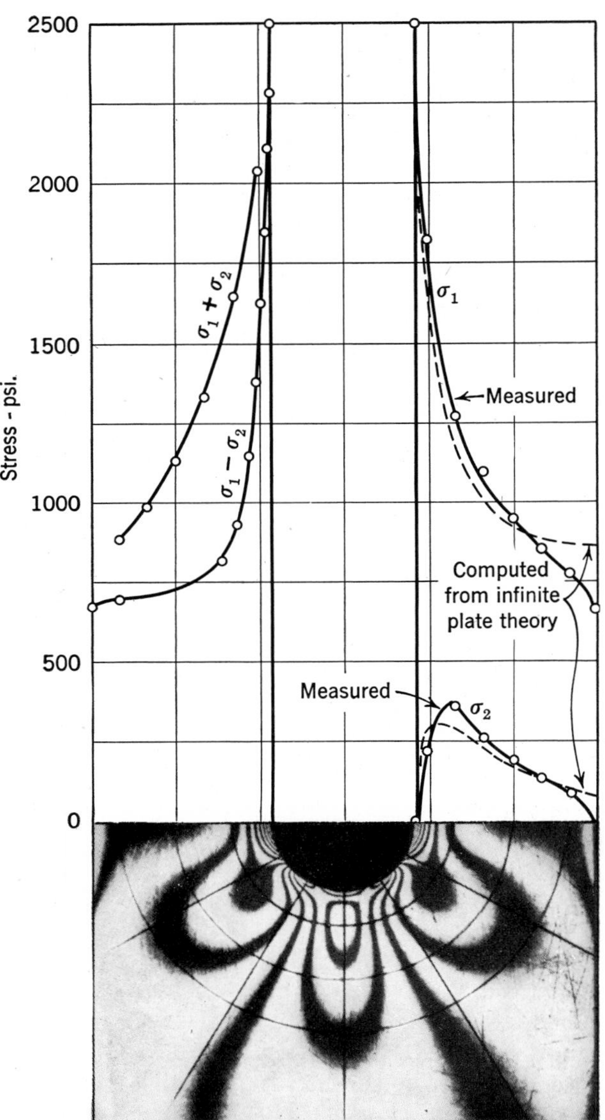

FIG. 7.10 Principal Stresses in a Tensile Bar with a Circular Hole as Determined by de Forest and Anderson with an Electronic Extensometer.

In such plates there are developed not only the usual two-dimensional stresses σ_x and σ_y but also an appreciable transverse stress σ_z in the direction of the thickness. For example, in a tension bar, 3 in. by 1 in. in cross section, containing a central slot 0.5 in. long with radii at the roots of 0.04 in., the transverse stress σ_z is equal to the average tension approximately.

From eq. (1.43) we have

$$\sigma_x + \sigma_y = \frac{-\delta_z E + t(\sigma_z)_{\text{ave.}}}{\nu t}.$$

It follows that, when $t(\sigma_z)_{\text{ave.}}$ is an appreciable quantity, the effect of dropping that term and of calculating $(\sigma_x + \sigma_y)$ as in a thin plate may lead to a serious error. It should be emphasized that this error is independent of the accuracy with which the deformation is determined.

Failure to take this three-dimensional effect into consideration has led some investigators to the erroneous conclusion that factors of stress concentrations in thick plates are much smaller than in thin bars, whereas reliable photoelastic measurements show that these factors are substantially the same. ***The essential point is that the lateral extensometer is inherently an instrument suitable for thin plates and unsuitable for thick plates.***

§7.8 Approximate Values of $(p + q)$. Approximate values of $(p + q)$ can be obtained from models deformed at 260° F. ***At that temperature the deformations are so great that they can be measured with an ordinary micrometer.*** Thus, taking E for Bakelite as 600,000 psi. at room temperature and as 1000 psi. at 260° F., it is seen from the expression

$$\delta = -\frac{\nu}{E} t(p + q)$$

that at 260° F. the deformation per unit stress is at least 600 times as great as at room temperature. Assuming a conservative value of 50 psi. for $(p + q)$, $t = \frac{1}{4}$, $\nu = \frac{1}{2}$, and $E = 1000$, we have $\delta = 0.006$ in. approximately. Deformations of such magnitudes can be easily measured. To facilitate the work we draw a square network on the model and measure the thickness at the center of each square before and after loading.

Fig. 7.11(a) shows a set of isopachic curves determined by means of a Federal Ames Dial for a bar strained at 260° F by a snugly fitting rivet. Fig. 7.12 shows the principal stresses p and q as well as the shear and normal stresses determined by combining $(p - q)$ from a photoelastic

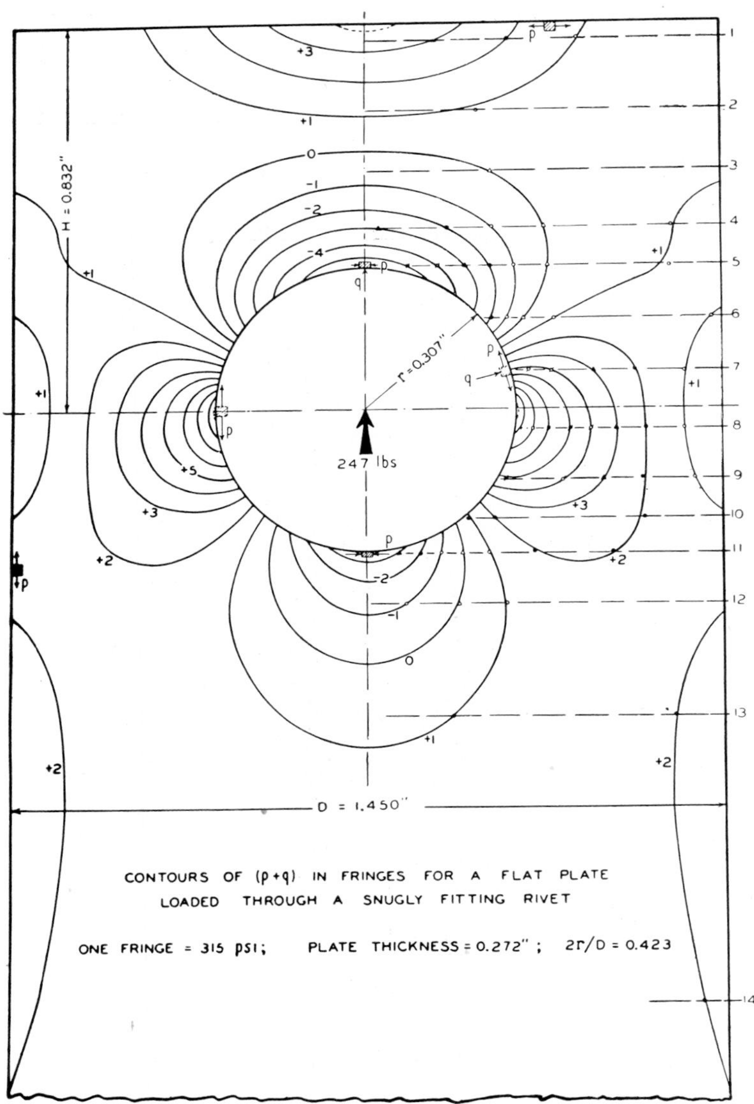

FIG. 7.11 (*a*) Isopachic Curves for the Head of Bar Strained by a Pin Determined by Means of an Ordinary Micrometer by Measuring the Lateral Deformations Produced by Frozen Stresses.

pattern, Fig. 7.11(*b*), with $(p + q)$ from the frozen model. It is seen that the normal stresses across section A–A form a system substantially in equilibrium.

FIG. 7.11(*b*) The Frozen Stress Pattern of the Model Shown in (*a*).

The method described above can be used as an approximate self-inclusive method to determine first approximations to factors of stress concentrations. The only equipment needed is a Bakelite or other plastic model, a small furnace, and a good micrometer.

PART II ISOPACHIC STRESS PATTERNS BY EXPERIMENTAL METHODS

§7.9 Isopachic Patterns by Reflection. (*a*) *Inherent Plane of Symmetry.* In a two-dimensionally stressed body there is always one plane of symmetry. This plane bisects the body and has no lateral displacements. It is the only plane which in thin plates remains a plane under all loads giving two-dimensional stresses. This plane we will call the *inherent plane of symmetry*. It is obvious that there may be one or two more planes of symmetry perpendicular to the plane just discussed. A

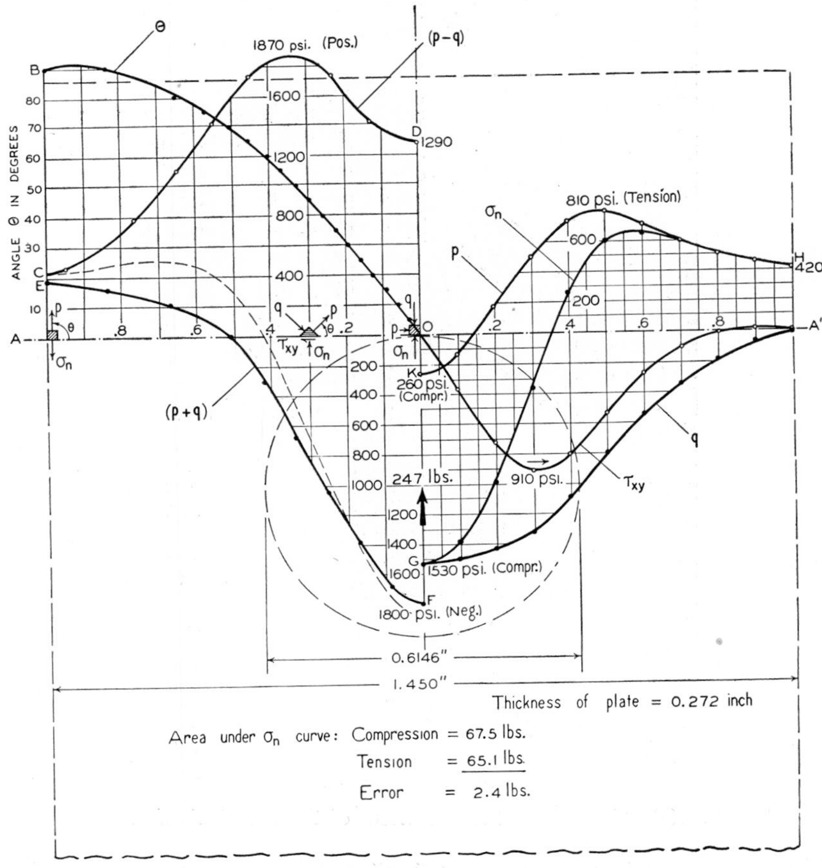

FIG. 7.12 Curves of Normal and Shear Stresses Determined from Fig. 7.11 (*a*) and (*b*). Note static check.

two-dimensionally stressed body which has no plane of symmetry other than the inherent plane will be spoken of as a non-symmetrical two-dimensional body.

(*b*) *Deformation of a Flat Surface in a Two-Dimensional Stress System.* If a plate which is subjected to a two-dimensional stress system has initially flat surfaces, these surfaces, after the application of the loads, will no longer be flat. They will be deformed. If one of these surfaces is polished and a plate of glass with a good optical surface, a datum plane, is brought close to it so that the two planes are separated by a thin film of air, and if now the model is strained and its polished face illuminated by a normal beam of monochromatic light, then the interference fringes obtained by reflection would be paths of constant thickness of the air film between the datum plane and the face of the model.

(c) *Isopachic Patterns.* If we assume that during the application of the loads to the model the inherent plane of symmetry in the model and the datum plane remain parallel relative to one another so that the changes in the thickness of the air film could be attributed to the stresses alone, then ***each interference fringe would directly represent a path of constant*** $(p + q)$. The resulting pattern will be referred to as an *isopachic pattern.*

§7.10 Equipment and Procedure. The main equipment needed to obtain an isopachic pattern by reflection consists of: (1) a monochromatic source of light, (2) a collimating lens, (3) a straining frame, (4) an interferometer or datum plane, (5) a balancing or adjusting head, and (6) a camera, Fig. 7.13.

The optical path is as shown in the sketch of Fig. 7.14. A beam of monochromatic light originates at the source G, is collimated by lens H, and is partially reflected by the glass plate I. The reflecting surface of this plate is set vertically and at 45° to the direction of the collimated beam HI. The reflected beam IK meets the inclined plane of the interferometer prism K and is again reflected vertically downward, passes through the air gap between the prism K and model L, and retraces its path to the plate I carrying with it the image of the isopachic stress pattern, which can be observed and recorded by the camera J.

The interferometer prism was placed directly on the polished surface of the model and rested on the high points developed in it by the loads. Since the weight of the prism is not uniformly distributed, and since there may be small differences in the elevations of the high spots in the model itself, the interferometer surface may not be parallel to the inherent plane of symmetry. In order to assure that the planes in question are parallel, the interferometer prism was set in a light Bakelite disk about 5 in. in diameter which we call a balancing or adjusting head, Fig. 7.15.

This head was fixed to the glass prism by means of two small horizontal screws as shown in Fig. 7.15. The balancing or adjusting of the prism for parallelism and symmetry was attained by means of small weights placed on the horizontal disk at suitable points.

§7.11 Isopachic Pattern of a Steel Ring. ***Fig. 7.16 shows an isopachic stress pattern obtained from a steel ring*** using the apparatus of Fig. 7.13. This is the same pattern which is shown in Fig. 6.14 in combination with the corresponding theoretical pattern. The reliability of

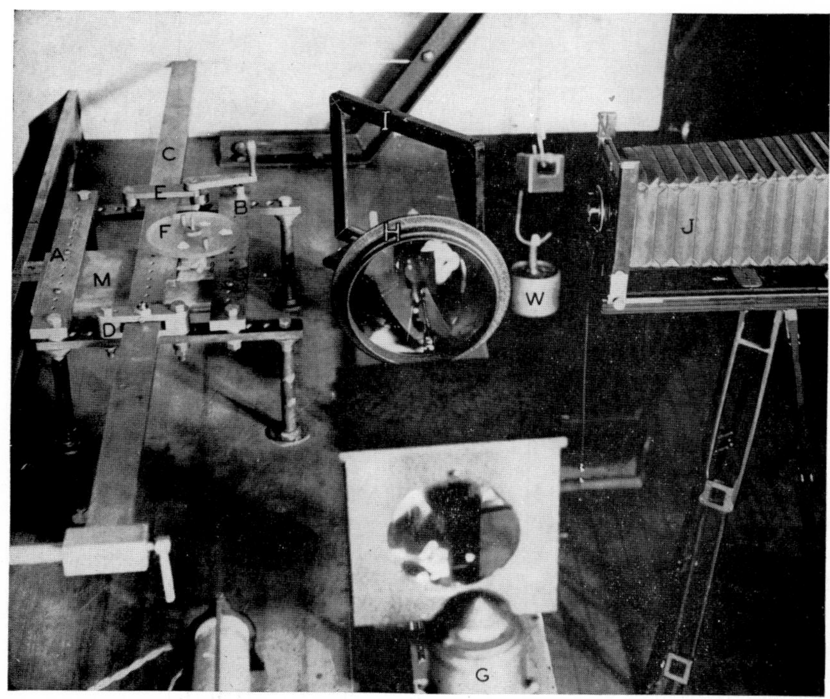

FIG. 7.13 Photograph of Equipment Used to Obtain Isopachic Stress Patterns. A, B = cross bars; C = loading lever; D, E = lever bearing and guide; F = balancing head of prism; G = mercury-vapor lamp; H = collimating lens; I = reflecting glass plate; J = camera, M = supporting plate; W = weights for loading.

the results has already been discussed in the preceding chapter, where it was shown that by combining the values of $(p + q)$ from the steel ring with the values of $(p - q)$ from a Bakelite ring stresses are obtained which satisfy the boundary conditions as well as the laws of equilibrium. This is true not only on the sections of symmetry but also across arbitrary radial sections.[1]

[1] See author's paper, " On the Optical Determination of Isopachic Stress Patterns," *Proceedings Fifth International Congress for Applied Mechanics*, pp. 221–227, held in 1938 at Cambridge, Mass., John Wiley & Sons, New York.

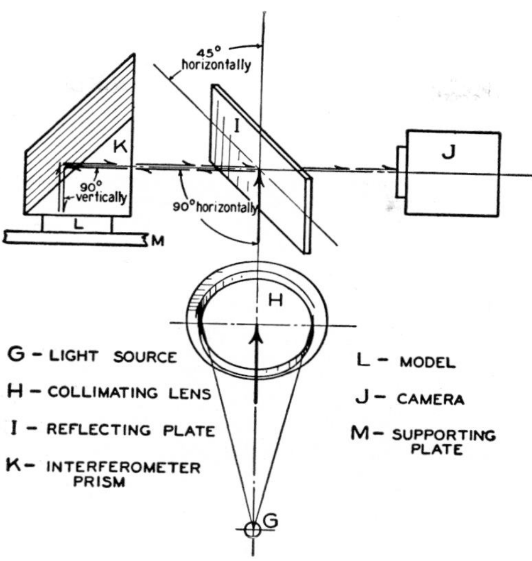

FIG. 7.14 Schematic Diagram of Optical Path.

All axes shown through lens *H* and reflecting glass plate *I* lie in one horizontal plane.

FIG. 7.15 Photograph Showing Adjusting Head in Place on Interferometer, and Small Weights Used for Balancing.

Image of steel ring can be clearly seen through prism.

§7.12 Significance and Extension of Isopachic Patterns. Thus far we have emphasized only that aspect of isopachic patterns which bears on the influence of the material on the stress distribution. There is, however, another angle to it which, although not of great practical importance, is of decided scientific interest. ***These patterns complete***

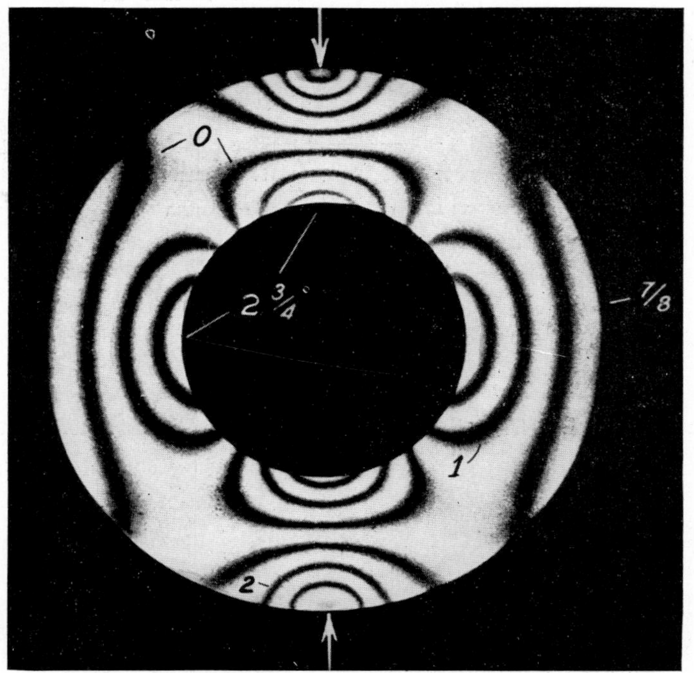

FIG. 7.16 Isopachic Stress Pattern from a Stainless-Steel Ring Subjected to Concentrated Diametral Loads.

Dimensions of model: inner diameter = 0.375 in.; outer diameter = 0.751 in.; thickness = 0.243 in.

the optical solution of a two-dimensional problem by providing loci of constant sums of principal stresses analogous to the photoelastic stress patterns which give constant differences.

The optical method discussed here can be extended to non-symmetrical bodies. In such cases a positive means must be provided to keep the datum plane of the interferometer parallel to the inherent plane of symmetry of the model. Such a result can be obtained by equipping the model with one or two projecting wings or arms, attached at points sufficiently distant from the stressed region under observation so as not

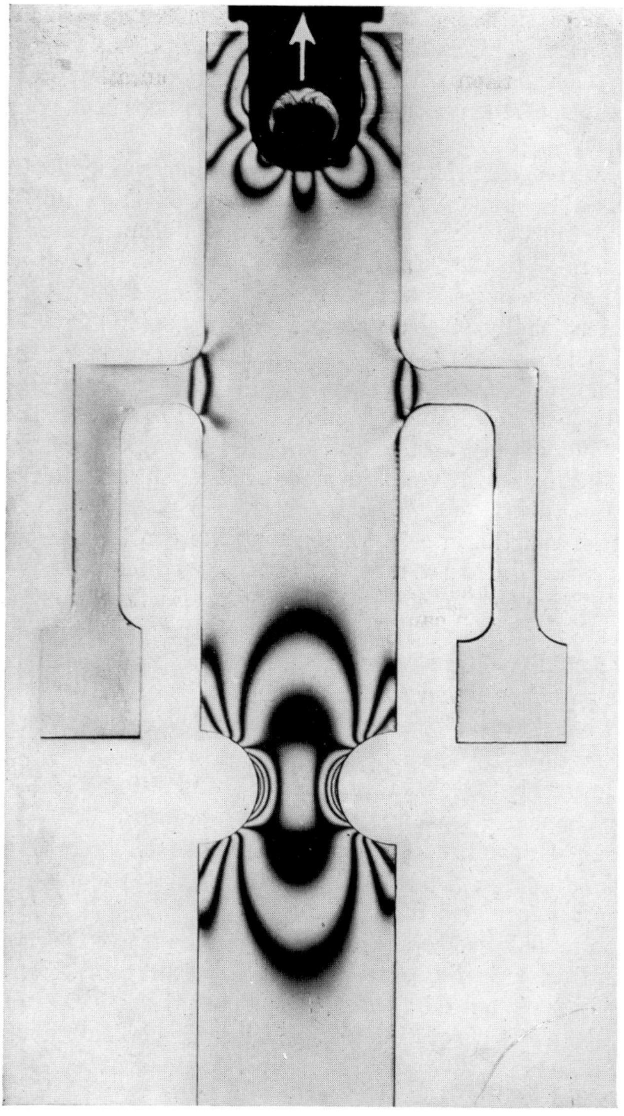

FIG. 7.17 Photoelastic Stress Pattern of a Model with Strain-Free Arms Showing that the Arms Do Not Affect the Stress Distribution at Regions Far from the Points of Attachment.

to affect its state of stress. It follows from Saint Venant's principle that such arms, if attached through a single small area, remain free from strain or stress. This is clearly shown in the photoelastic pattern of Fig. 7.17. Comparison with a stress pattern from a bar without arms shows that the attached arms do not alter the stresses in the region under investigation.

The interferometer prism can be set in a casing equipped with a three-point adjustable support, which in turn rests on the strain-free arms. Before applying the loads the interferometer datum plane is adjusted until it is parallel to the polished face of the model. Since the supports on which the adjusting screws rest remain free from strain, it follows that in two-dimensionally stressed systems the datum plane must remain parallel to the inherent plane of symmetry during and after the application of the loads.

It may be found desirable to make attachable arms with flat polished surfaces, which may be utilized to verify the assumption that the datum plane remains fixed relative to the model, and at the same time furnish a level for adjustment.

The model and the interferometer supports can be tied together by means of a spring to act as a unit, and in this way difficulties due to vibrations and relative motion can be eliminated. Further, the interferometer can be adjusted so that it does not rest on the model but is separated from it by a thin layer of air in order to provide space for possible expansion of the specimen under strain.

A somewhat different procedure for isopachic stress patterns by reflection was suggested by Tesar.[1]

§7.13 Isopachic Stress Patterns from Transmitted Light. (*a*) Very interesting isopachic patterns have been obtained by Sinclair and Bucky, using transmitted light and a Mach-Zehnder or Jamin interferometer.

In this procedure two identical models, identically loaded must be used. The models are separated by a quartz plate 0.139 inches thick cut perpendicular to the optic axis. After emergence from the first model, the beam is passed at normal incidence through the quartz plate, which has the effect of rotating all directions of polarization through 90°. The rotated image is then passed through the second model. The basic equation in this method is

$$n = t(p + q)\left(-2\frac{\mu\nu}{E} + C_1 + C_2\right),$$

[1] See "Photoélasticité méthode purement optique pour déterminer les déformations d'épaisseurs des modèles, etc.," by V. Tesar, *Rev. d'optique,* Vol. 11, pp. 97–104, 1932.

where μ is the index of refraction, C_1 and C_2, the direct and transverse stress optic coefficients. An isopachic pattern from a Bakelite model is shown in Fig. 7.19.[1]

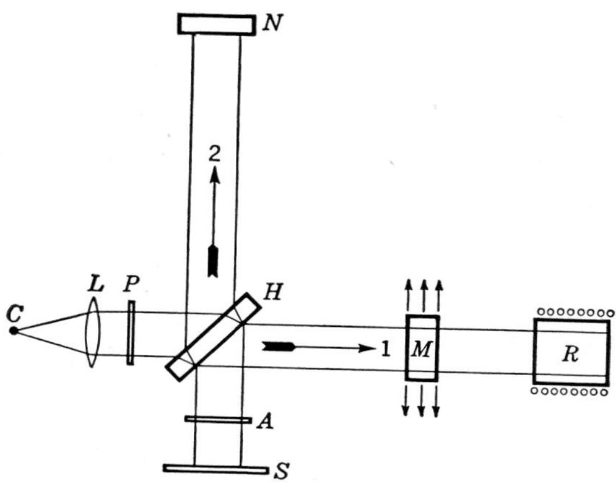

FIG. 7.18 Sketch Showing Bubb's Interferometer for Isopachic Patterns.

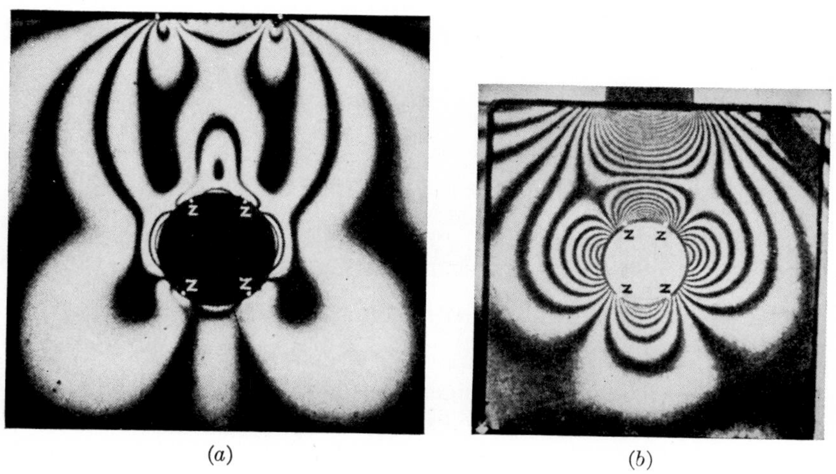

(a) (b)

FIG. 7.19 State of Stress around a Tunnel Directly below a Pier.

(a) Photoelastic stress pattern; (b) corresponding isopachic pattern. (From Sinclair and Bucky.)

(b) Another set-up giving isopachic patterns by transmitted light

[1] See "A New Optical Method for the Determination of the Principal Stress Sum," by D. Sinclair, *Proceedings of the Tenth Semi-Annual Eastern Photoelasticity Conference*, held in December, 1939, at Cambridge, Mass.

has been proposed by Bubb, Fig. 7.18. ***In this arrangement only one transparent model is employed.***[1]

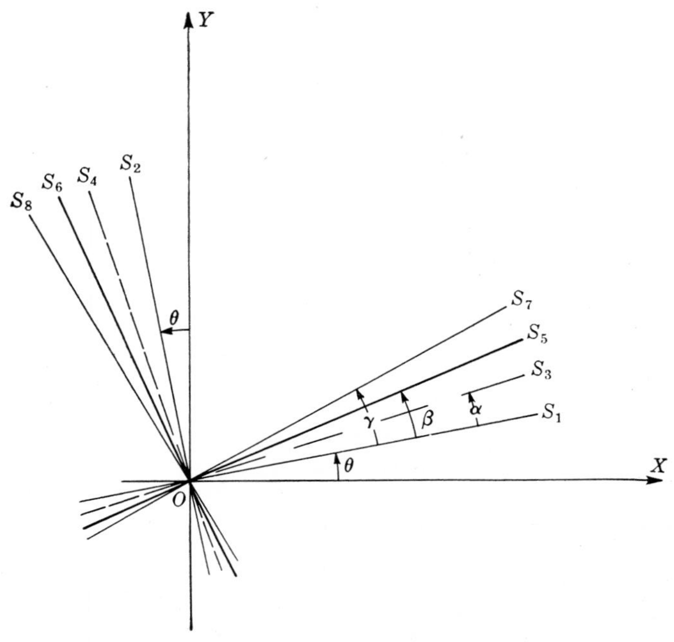

FIG. 7.20 Notation for Neuber's Equations: S_1, S_3, S_5, and S_7 = tangents to stress trajectory, isopachic, isochromatic, and isoclinic, respectively; S_2, S_4, S_6, and S_8 = corresponding normals.

PART III ISOPACHIC PATTERNS — NEUBER'S GRAPHICAL METHOD

§7.14 Notation and Statement of Problem. Referring to Fig. 7.20,

$\Sigma = (p + q)$, Σ_n — isopachic curves of order n.
$\Delta = (p - q)$, Δ_n — fringe or isochromatic of order n.
S_1, S_2 — directions of principal stress trajectories.
S_3 — direction of isopachic curve Σ_n.
S_5 — direction of fringe or isochromatic Δ_n.
S_7 — direction of isoclinic.
S_4, S_6, S_8 — normals to S_3, S_5, S_7 respectively; positive direction of S_4 obtained by a counterclockwise rotation of S_3, etc.
O — arbitrary point on fringe Δ_n.

[1] For further details see "A Complete Photoelastic Instrument," by Frank W. Bubb, *Journal of the Optical Society of America*, Vol. 30, No. 7, pp. 297–298. July, 1940.

X, Y — arbitrary rectangular reference axis through O.
θ — angle between S_1 and X axis.
α — angle between S_1 and S_3.
β — angle between S_1 and S_5.
γ — angle between S_1 and S_7.

All angles are measured from S_1, and the counterclockwise direction is taken as positive.

The problem is to determine the direction S_3 of the isopachic curve Σ_n through point O. This reduces itself to a problem of determining the angle α from the angles β and γ which can be found from the photoelastic data.

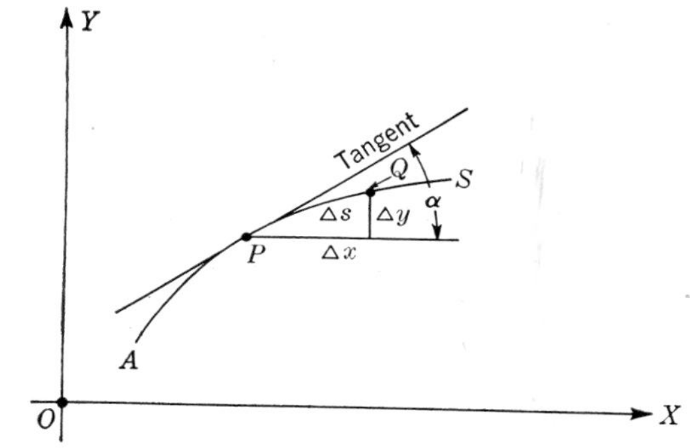

FIG. 7.21.

§7.15 The Directional Derivative. In Fig. 7.21 let A–S be a curve in the XY plane, and let P and Q be two points on this curve separated by the increment Δs, with corresponding projections of Δx and Δy. Now consider a function $u = f(x, y)$ defined at every point in a region S containing the curve A–S.

If Δf denotes the change in the value of $f(x, y)$ in going from P to Q, then the directional derivative is defined as the

$$\operatorname*{limit}_{\Delta s \to 0} \frac{\Delta f}{\Delta s}$$

and represents the rate of change of $f(x, y)$ along the curve A–S. Also

$$\operatorname*{limit}_{\Delta s \to 0} \frac{\Delta x}{\Delta s} = \frac{dx}{ds} = \cos \alpha$$

and

$$\operatorname*{limit}_{\Delta s \to 0} \frac{\Delta y}{\Delta s} = \frac{dy}{ds} = \sin \alpha,$$

where α is the angle which the tangent to A–S at P makes with the X axis. Now from the theory of partial derivatives we have

$$\frac{\partial f}{\partial s} = \frac{\partial f}{\partial x}\frac{dx}{ds} + \frac{\partial f}{\partial y}\frac{dy}{ds}\cdot$$

Hence

$$\frac{\partial f}{\partial s} = \frac{\partial f}{\partial x}\cos\alpha + \frac{\partial f}{\partial y}\sin\alpha. \tag{7.3}$$

§7.16 Neuber's Equations of Isopachic Curves. In §2.8, Vol. I, we derived the equations

$$\left.\begin{aligned} &\frac{\partial \Sigma}{\partial s_1} + \frac{\partial \Delta}{\partial s_1} + 2\Delta\frac{\partial \theta}{\partial s_2} = 0, && (a)\\ \text{and}\qquad &\frac{\partial \Sigma}{\partial s_2} - \frac{\partial \Delta}{\partial s_2} + 2\Delta\frac{\partial \theta}{\partial s_1} = 0. && (b)\end{aligned}\right\} \tag{7.4}$$

These equations will now be transformed to give the directions of the isopachic curves Σ_n. From the general equation for the directional derivative, eq. (7.3), it follows that

$$\left.\begin{aligned} \frac{\partial \Sigma}{\partial s_1} &= \frac{\partial \Sigma}{\partial s_3}\cos\alpha - \frac{\partial \Sigma}{\partial s_4}\sin\alpha, && (a)\\ \frac{\partial \Sigma}{\partial s_2} &= \frac{\partial \Sigma}{\partial s_3}\sin\alpha + \frac{\partial \Sigma}{\partial s_4}\cos\alpha, && (b)\\ \frac{\partial \Delta}{\partial s_1} &= \frac{\partial \Delta}{\partial s_5}\cos\beta - \frac{\partial \Delta}{\partial s_6}\sin\beta, && (c)\\ \frac{\partial \Delta}{\partial s_2} &= \frac{\partial \Delta}{\partial s_5}\sin\beta + \frac{\partial \Delta}{\partial s_6}\cos\beta, && (d)\\ \frac{\partial \theta}{\partial s_1} &= \frac{\partial \theta}{\partial s_7}\cos\gamma - \frac{\partial \theta}{\partial s_8}\sin\gamma, && (e)\\ \frac{\partial \theta}{\partial s_2} &= \frac{\partial \theta}{\partial s_7}\sin\gamma + \frac{\partial \theta}{\partial s_8}\cos\gamma. && (f)\end{aligned}\right\} \tag{7.5}$$

But from the definition of S_3, S_5, and S_7 it follows that

$$\left.\begin{aligned} \frac{\partial \Sigma}{\partial s_3} &= 0, && (a) \\ \frac{\partial \Delta}{\partial s_5} &= 0, && (b) \\ \frac{\partial \theta}{\partial s_7} &= 0. && (c) \end{aligned}\right\} \quad (7.6)$$

and

With these in mind, eqs. (7.5) reduce to

$$\left.\begin{aligned} \frac{\partial \Sigma}{\partial s_1} &= -\frac{\partial \Sigma}{\partial s_4} \sin \alpha, && (a) \\ \frac{\partial \Sigma}{\partial s_2} &= \frac{\partial \Sigma}{\partial s_4} \cos \alpha, && (b) \\ \frac{\partial \Delta}{\partial s_1} &= -\frac{\partial \Delta}{\partial s_6} \sin \beta, && (c) \\ \frac{\partial \Delta}{\partial s_2} &= \frac{\partial \Delta}{\partial s_6} \cos \beta, && (d) \\ \frac{\partial \theta}{\partial s_1} &= -\frac{\partial \theta}{\partial s_8} \sin \gamma, && (e) \\ \frac{\partial \theta}{\partial s_2} &= \frac{\partial \theta}{\partial s_8} \cos \gamma. && (f) \end{aligned}\right\} \quad (7.7)$$

The minus signs in eqs. (7.7) are due to the fact that the angles α, β, and γ, which locate S_1 with respect to S_3, S_5, and S_7, are negative angles for purposes of the directional derivative.

Substituting these expressions in eqs. (7.4) and transposing, we obtain

$$\left.\begin{aligned} \frac{\partial \Sigma}{\partial s_4} \sin \alpha &= -\frac{\partial \Delta}{\partial s_6} \sin \beta + 2\Delta \frac{\partial \theta}{\partial s_8} \cos \gamma, && (a) \\ \frac{\partial \Sigma}{\partial s_4} \cos \alpha &= \frac{\partial \Delta}{\partial s_6} \cos \beta + 2\Delta \frac{\partial \theta}{\partial s_8} \sin \gamma. && (b) \end{aligned}\right\} \quad (7.8)$$

If we now denote the distances between successive isopachics, successive fringes, and successive isoclinics by a, b, and c respectively, so that a, b, c are measured along S_4, S_6, and S_8 respectively, as shown in

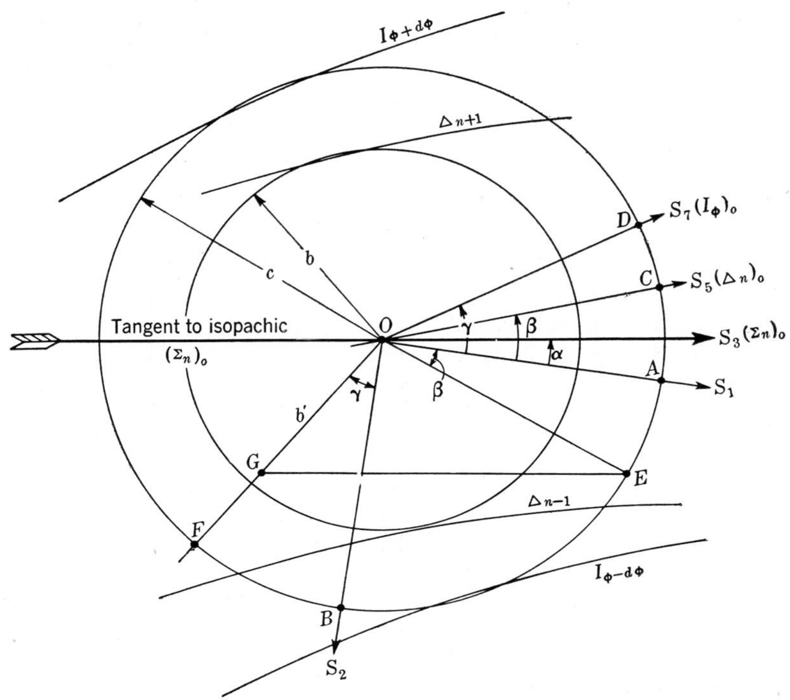

FIG. 7.22 Sketch Showing Neuber's Method for the Construction of a Tangent to an Isopachic Curve at Any Point.

Fig. 7.22, we can write eqs. (7.8) approximately as follows:

$$\frac{d\Sigma}{a}\sin\alpha = -\frac{d\Delta}{b}\sin\beta + 2\Delta\frac{d\theta}{c}\cos\gamma \qquad (a)$$

and

$$\frac{d\Sigma}{a}\cos\alpha = \frac{d\Delta}{b}\cos\beta + 2\Delta\frac{d\theta}{c}\sin\gamma. \qquad (b) \qquad (7.9)$$

For simplicity we choose

$$d\Sigma = d\Delta.$$

Multiplying each term by $bc/d\Delta$, we can write eqs. (7.9) thus:

$$\frac{bc}{a}\sin\alpha = -c\sin\beta + 2\Delta\frac{d\theta}{d\Delta}b\cos\gamma, \qquad (a)$$

$$\frac{bc}{a}\cos\alpha = c\cos\beta + 2\Delta\frac{d\theta}{d\Delta}b\sin\gamma. \qquad (b) \qquad (7.10)$$

If we now introduce the symbols a', b', where

$$a' = \frac{bc}{a} \quad \text{and} \quad b' = 2\Delta \frac{d\theta}{d\Delta} b = 2b\left(\frac{\Delta}{d\Delta}\right) d\theta, \tag{7.11}$$

and solve for the angle α, we get from eqs. (7.10)

$$a' \sin \alpha = b' \cos \gamma - c \sin \beta \quad (a)$$

and

$$a' \cos \alpha = b' \sin \gamma + c \cos \beta. \quad (b) \tag{7.12}$$

These equations, first developed by Neuber, form the basis for his graphical method for the determination of α and isopachic curves. From the above equations we obtain by division

$$\tan \alpha = \frac{b' \cos \gamma - c \sin \beta}{b' \sin \gamma + c \cos \beta} \cdot \tag{7.13}$$

Four quantities are thus required to find α: the angles β and γ, the length c, and the quantity b'. The first three are readily measured.

In order to simplify the evaluation of b', eq. (7.11), we take $d\Delta$ as unity. Then, letting n denote the order of the fringe through O,

$$\left(\frac{\Delta_n}{d\Delta}\right)_o = n = 1, 2, 3 \cdots.$$

If $d\theta$ is taken as $5° = 0.0873$ radian, then

$$2\left(\frac{\Delta_n}{d\Delta}\right)_o d\theta = 0.1746n.$$

Hence, for $d\theta = 5°$,

$$b' = 0.1746nb. \tag{7.14}$$

Eq. (7.14) defines a family of straight lines as shown in Fig. 7.23, from which the value of b' corresponding to b can easily be found.

§7.17 Graphical Method for Isopachic Curves. The graphical evaluation of α as given by eq. (7.13) is carried out in the following manner, Fig. 7.22:

1. Prepare a large composite drawing of the isochromatics, isostatics, and isoclinics.

2. Select a point of intersection of a fringe with an isoclinic, point O, and determine S_3 and S_7 at that point.

3. From O as a center draw two circles of radii b and c, approximately tangent to the nearest fringes and to the nearest isoclinics.

4. On the circle of radius c, denote by A and B the intersections with

S_1 and S_2, and by C and D the intersection with the tangents to the isochromatic S_5 and isoclinic S_7 respectively.

5. Lay off an arc $AE = AC$ so that the stress trajectory S_1 bisects angle EOC, and angle $AOE = \beta$.

6. Lay off arc $BF = AD$, so that angle $BOF = \gamma$.

7. On OF lay off $OG = b'$, and draw GE.

8. The straight line through O parallel to GE is the direction of the isopachic $(\Sigma_n)_o$ through point O.

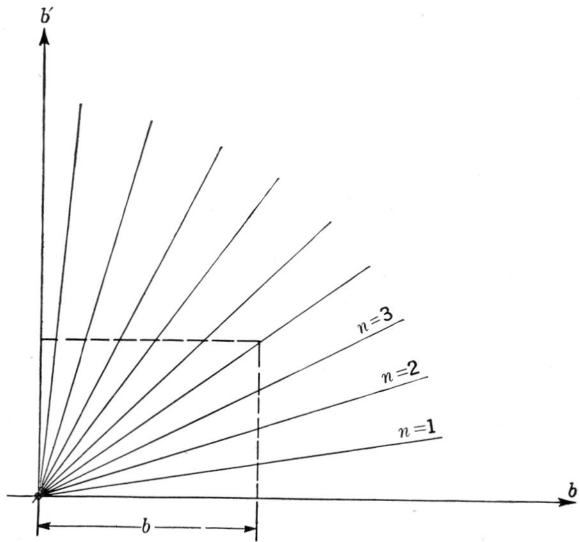

FIG. 7.23 Neuber's Nomograph for the Evaluation of b' in Eq. (7.13); $d\theta = 5°$; $n = \dfrac{\Delta n}{d\Delta}$.

Proof: In Fig. 7.24 lay off $EN = b$, and draw the straight line NP parallel to GO. Let PE be taken as the distance a. From similar triangles it then follows that

$$\frac{GE}{OE} = \frac{b}{a}$$

or

$$GE = \frac{bc}{a} = a'.$$

From E we drop a perpendicular EM to S_1, and from G we draw GL

perpendicular to EM. We see that

$$ML = OK = b' \cos \gamma,$$

$$ME = c \sin \beta,$$

and

$$EL = b' \cos \gamma - c \sin \beta.$$

Hence

$$\frac{EL}{GE} = \frac{b' \cos \gamma - c \sin \beta}{a'} = \sin \alpha,$$

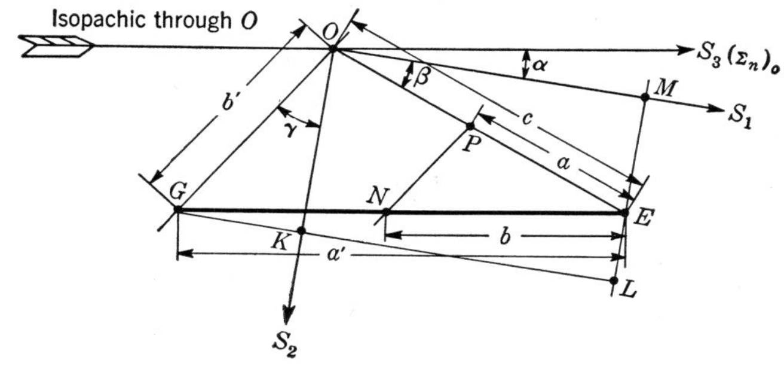

FIG. 7.24 Sketch Showing Method of Finding Distance a from Point O to Next Isopachic.

which obviously defines the angle α given by eq. (7.13). Fig. 7.24 gives the value of a, which represents the distance from O to the next isopachic.

§7.18 Free Boundaries and Order of Isopachics. A free boundary is a stress trajectory where one of the principal stresses vanishes. It can be shown that at such boundaries

$$\left.\begin{aligned} \tan \alpha &= \tan \beta + 2 \cot \gamma \quad \text{for} \quad p = 0 \qquad (a)\\ \text{and} \qquad \cot \alpha &= \cot \beta + 2 \tan \gamma \quad \text{for} \quad q = 0. \qquad (b) \end{aligned}\right\} (7.15)$$

These equations show that at free boundaries the evaluation of α is much simpler than at interior points. The starting points in the graphical evaluation of the isopachic curves are naturally points on free boundaries from which the order of some isochromatics is determined.

Angles α are then determined at a larger number of interior points, and the isopachic curves are drawn as in constructing isostatics from isoclinics. The values of $(p + q)$ along isopachic curves which do not intersect the boundaries are determined from a set of orthogonal curves.

For further details and special cases the reader is referred to Neuber's

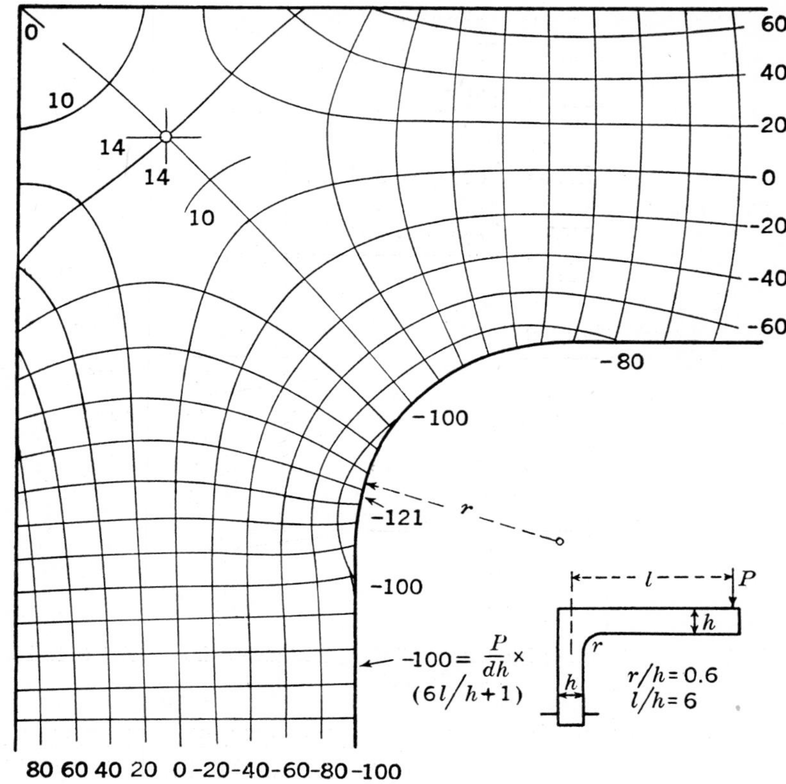

FIG. 7.25 Isopachic Curves and Orthogonal Lines from Neuber.

paper.[1] Another method for deriving Neuber's equations is given by Knoll and Schneider.[2] Fig. 7.25 shows a set of isopachic curves determined by Neuber.

In conclusion, with Neuber's graphical method to determine isopachic curves it may be useful to determine the isoclinics by coating the model with a brittle lacquer as was done by Durelli. Figs. 7.26 show typical results from this procedure.[3]

[1] See "Exact Construction of the $(\sigma_1 + \sigma_2)$—Network from Photoelastic Observations," by H. P. Neuber, *Trans. A.S.M.E.*, Vol. 56, pp. 733–737, 1934.

[2] See *Experimental Methods of Stress Analysis* (Russian), pp. 78–80, publication of the Photoelastic Laboratory of the Bubnov University, Leningrad, U.S.S.R., 1935.

[3] "Experimental Determination of Isostatic Lines," A. J. Durelli, *J. Applied Mechanics, Trans. A.S.M.E.*, December, 1942, pp. A155–A160.

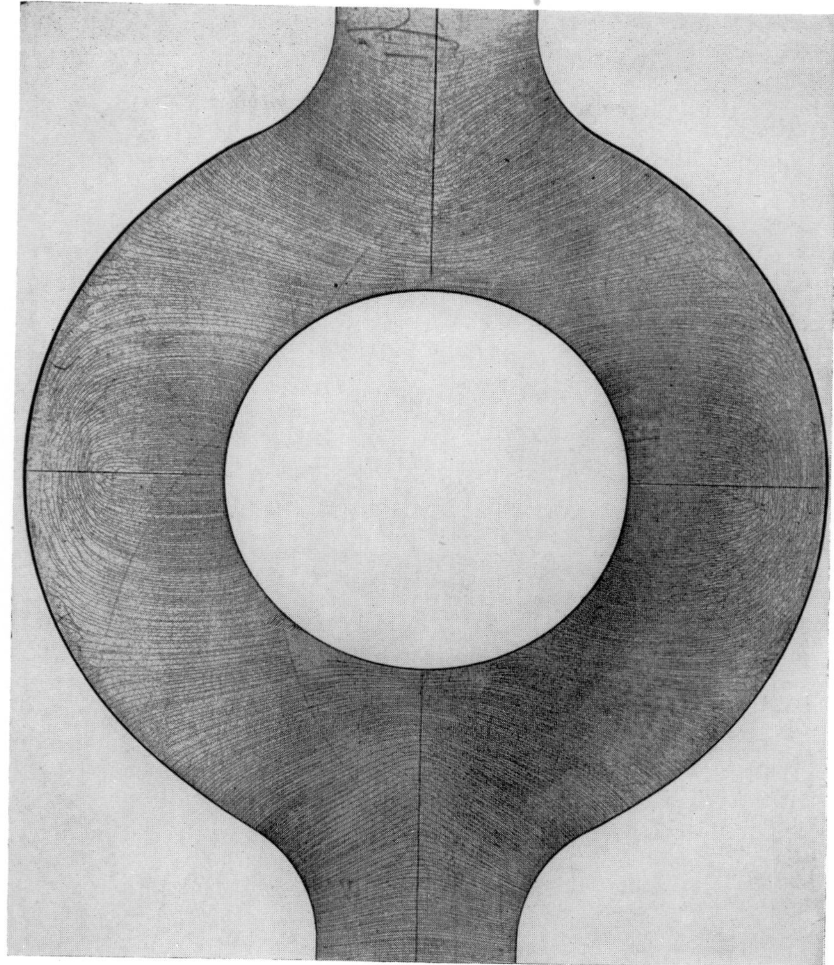

FIG. 7.26(*a*) Photograph of Stress Trajectories as Determined by Durelli Using Brittle Lacquer.

Model was first sprayed and coating allowed to dry. Tensile loads were then applied.

§7.19 Miscellaneous Methods. (*a*) *Membrane Methods.* It has already been shown (§1.15) that the sums of the principal stresses satisfy Laplace's equation, i.e.,

$$\frac{\partial^2 \Sigma}{\partial x^2} + \frac{\partial^2 \Sigma}{\partial y} = 0. \qquad (1.14b)$$

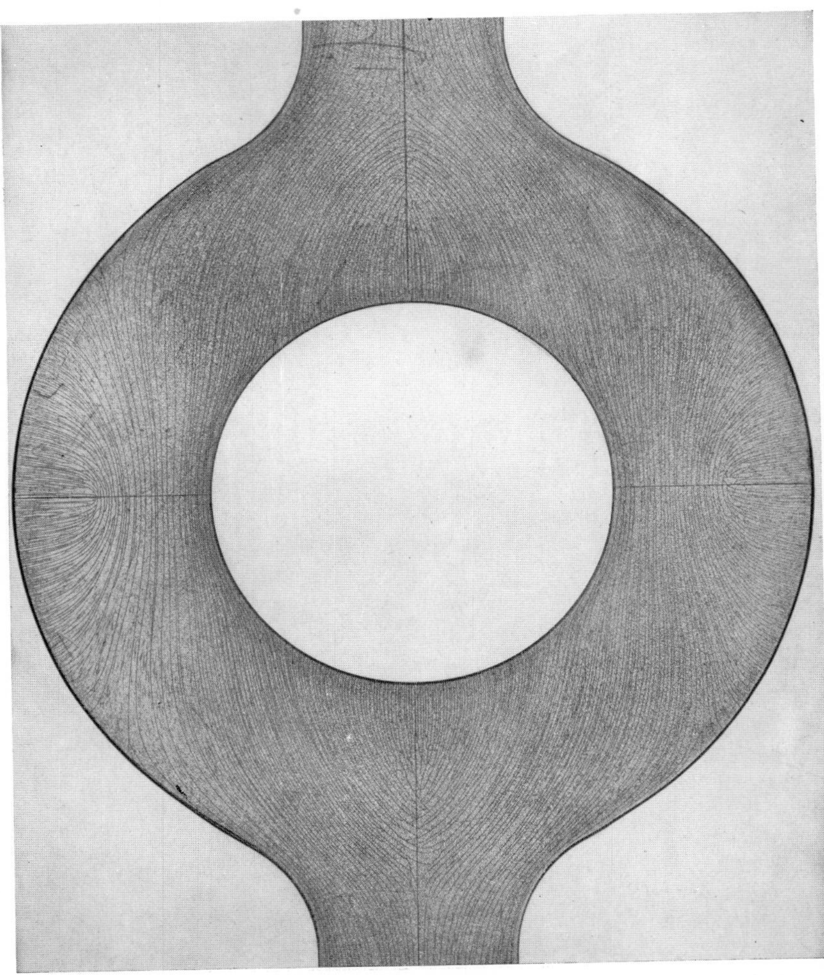

FIG. 7.26(b) Photograph of Stress Trajectories Orthogonal to Those Shown in (a), as Determined by Durelli Using Brittle Lacquer.

Here tensile loads were applied first and the lacquer next. When coating was dry loads were removed.

It can be shown that eq. (1.14b) is also the equation of the surface of a stretched membrane acted upon by forces applied only at its boundaries.

Accordingly if the boundary ordinates of this surface be made proportional to the boundary values of $(p + q)$ in a stressed two-dimensional plate, then the interior ordinates under the membrane would directly represent the values of $(p + q)$ at the corresponding points in the model.

These observations were made by den Hartog,[1] Biot,[2] Biezeno,[3] and Koch.

In the experimental procedure a thin wall is erected around a boundary having the same shape as the model itself, and the height of the wall is at each point made proportional to the value of $(p + q)$ at the corresponding point on the boundary of the model. A membrane is then formed over the wall. Two types of membranes have been successfully used: a soap film similar to that used in torsion problems,[4] and rubber membranes.[5,6].

(b) *Electrical Methods.* It has been also suggested that eq. (1.14b) can be solved by measuring the potential in a metal plate having the same shape as the model, on the boundary of which an electrical potential proportional to $(p + q)$ is impressed.[7] It can be shown that the potential at each point in the plate is proportional to $(p + q)$ at the corresponding point in the model.

(c) *Numerical Methods.* ***The most powerful and practical methods for the solution of Laplace's equation and the determination of isopachic patterns are the numerical methods, which were first introduced into photoelasticity by Weller and Shortley.*** Starting with the boundary values of $(p + q)$ obtainable from good photoelastic patterns, the values of $(p + q)$ can be calculated at all interior points.

The numerical methods are of great importance in many branches of engineering and physics. They are treated in detail in the next chapters.

[1] J. P. den Hartog, "Experimentelle Lösung des ebenen Spannungsproblems," *Zeitschrift. angew. Math. Mech.*, Vol. 11, p. 156, 1931.

[2] M. A. Biot, "Contribution à la technique photoélastique," *Annales soc. scientifique Bruxelles*, Vol. B53, pp. 13–15, 1933.

[3] C. B. Biezeno and J. J. Koch, "Über einige Beispiele zur elektrischen Spannungsbestimmung," *Ingenieur Archiv*, Vol. 4, pp. 384–393, 1933.

[4] E. E. Weibel, "Application of Soap-Film-Studies to Photoelastic Stress Determination," *Assoc int. des ponts et charpentes — Mémoires*, Vol. 3, pp. 421–438, 1935.

[5] J. G. McGivern and H. L. Supper, "A Membrane Analogy Supplementing Photoelasticity," *Trans. A.S.M.E.*, Vol. 56, pp. 601–604, 1934.

[6] M. A. Biot and H. Smits, "Étude photo-élastique des tensions de contraction dans un barrage," *Bull. tech. de l'Union des ingénieurs sortis des écoles spéciales de Louvain*, No. 4, p. 10, 1933.

[7] See references 2 and 3, above; see also L. Malavard, "L'analogie électrique comme méthode auxiliaire de la photo-élasticité," *Compt. rend.*, Paris, Vol. 206, pp. 38–39, 1938; and H. Meyer and F. Tank, "Über ein verbessertes elektrisches Verfahren zur Auswertung der Gleichung $\Delta\phi = 0$ und seine Anwendung bei photoelastischen Untersuchung," *Helv. Phys. Acta*, Vol. 8, pp. 315–317, 1935.

CHAPTER 8

THE NUMERICAL SOLUTION OF LAPLACE'S EQUATION

PART I ALGEBRAIC HARMONIZATION — ELEMENTARY CASES

§8.1 Introduction. Harmonic Functions. Dirichlet's Theorem. Any function $U(x, y)$ which satisfies the relation

$$\frac{\partial^2 U}{\partial x^2} + \frac{\partial^2 U}{\partial y^2} = 0 \tag{8.1}$$

is said to be *a harmonic function*, and eq. (8.1) is known as *Laplace's differential equation*, or briefly as *Laplace's equation.*

All harmonic functions possess one fundamental property which is formulated in Dirichlet's theorem. This theorem states that ***for a given boundary* Γ *surrounding a region R to which the function applies, and for specified boundary values on* Γ*, there exists only one solution of Laplace's equation for all points within the region R.***[1]

In §1.5 it was shown that the sums of the principal stresses $(p + q) = \Sigma$ form a harmonic function, i.e.,

$$\frac{\partial^2 \Sigma}{\partial x^2} + \frac{\partial^2 \Sigma}{\partial y^2} = 0. \tag{1.14b}$$

It follows that ***the sum of the principal stresses* Σ *is uniquely determined at every point within a given region of a two-dimensionally stressed body provided that the boundary stresses are known.*** It may be assumed that it is possible to obtain photoelastic stress patterns which yield boundary values of Σ of high accuracy. One effective method for the determination of the sums of principal stresses throughout the whole interior region of a two-dimensional problem rests on the utilization of these boundary values in accordance with Dirichlet's theorem. In this procedure it is necessary to solve eq. (1.14*b*) for a specified boundary and boundary values. The rigorous mathematical solution of Laplace's equation is possible only in cases where the boundaries are relatively simple. When the boundaries are complicated, it is generally difficult or

[1] For a proof of this theorem see textbooks on advanced calculus.

impossible to find an analytical solution. ***However, it is always feasible to obtain approximations by means of numerical solutions which are quite sufficient for all practical purposes.***

Although our main concern is with Laplace's equation as it affects photoelastic stress analysis, this problem transcends our immediate objectives. Harmonic functions enter into many branches of engineering. For example, the same necessity for an approximate solution of Laplace's equation arises in the calculation of electrostatic fields in regions enclosed by boundaries at known potentials, and in heat-conduction problems in connection with temperature distributions of the steady state. Laplace's equation also appears in certain problems of hydromechanics and gravitation, and in the calculations of the shapes of films and membranes.

In this and in the succeeding chapter we develop basic equations and methods which have been found effective in the numerical solution of Laplace's equation. These methods are also applicable to the solution of Poisson's equation

$$\frac{\partial^2 U}{\partial x^2} + \frac{\partial^2 U}{\partial y^2} = C, \text{ a constant,} \tag{8.2}$$

which arises in elasticity in the problem of torsion as well as in other branches of technology.

§8.2 Some Additional Properties of Harmonic Functions without Singularities.[1]

I. The value of a harmonic function at the center of a circle is equal to the mean value on the circumference.

II. A harmonic function in a given region cannot have a maximum value or a minimum value in the region except on the boundaries. The surface which the function defines can have no peaks or troughs. Hence, isopachic curves, i.e., loci of points along which the function is constant, cannot form closed curves.

III. If a harmonic function has a constant value on the boundary of a region it is constant throughout the region.

IV. The line integral

$$\int_c \frac{\partial U}{\partial N}\, ds = 0, \tag{8.3}$$

in which (c) is a closed boundary containing no singularities, and $\partial U/\partial N$ is the normal derivative.

[1] For proofs of these propositions see textbooks on advanced calculus.

§8.3 Basic Equations. Numerical or approximate solutions of Laplace's equation

$$\frac{\partial^2 U}{\partial x^2} + \frac{\partial^2 U}{\partial y^2} = 0 \tag{8.1}$$

are generally based on the fact that the value of the function U at an arbitrary point O of the region R to which the function U applies, Fig. 10.1, must satisfy the general equation:[1]

$$\left(\frac{1}{ac} + \frac{1}{bd}\right) u_o = \frac{1}{a(a + c)} u_a + \frac{1}{b(b + d)} u_b + \frac{1}{c(c + a)} u_c + \frac{1}{d(d + b)} u_d, \tag{8.4}$$

in which u_a, u_b, u_c, and u_d are the values of the harmonic function U at four neighboring points, A, B, C, and D respectively, with coordinates as shown in Fig. 8.1. Eq. (8.4) will be referred to as the *four-point influence equation*, or more briefly as the *four-point equation*.

The most common procedure in numerical solutions generally consists of drawing a square network distant h apart over the region R and adjusting the values at each point of intersection of the network lines (network points) until they satisfy the four-point equation. When that is attained, an approximate or numerical solution is said to have been found. The distance h between the network lines is called the lattice unit. The points A, B, C, and D may be located on the network lines, or on lines inclined 45° to them. In the first case we speak of normal neighbors; in the second case, of diagonal neighbors. In the treatment which follows both types are used.

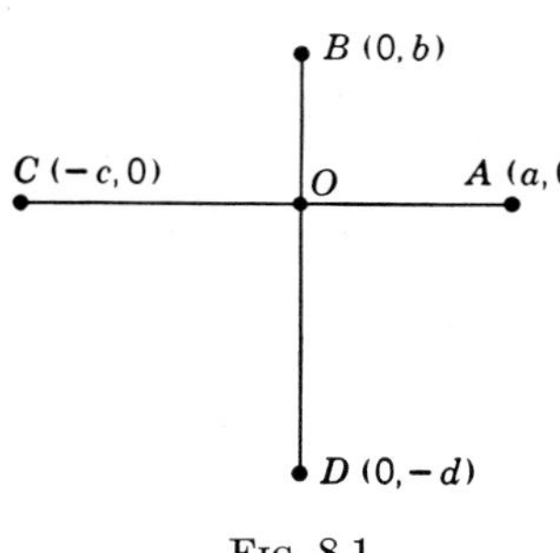

FIG. 8.1.

Most of the interior network points will have equally spaced neighbors. For such points eq. (8.4) reduces to

$$4u_o = u_a + u_b + u_c + u_d. \tag{8.5}$$

Eq. (8.5) is generally called *the Liebmann formula*.[2] Another case of

[1] For a derivation see Appendix A in this chapter.

[2] The derivation of this formula is generally credited to Liebmann. See *Sitzungsberichte der math.-phys. Klasse der Bayer. Akad.*, München, p. 385, 1918.

special interest is that in which $a = b$ and $c = d$, Fig. 8.1. Then eq. (8.4) reduces to

$$u_o = \frac{c(u_a + u_b)}{2(a + c)} + \frac{a(u_c + u_d)}{2(a + c)}. \tag{8.6}$$

Assuming $a < c$, and $a/c = \delta$, this may be written

$$u_o = \frac{(u_a + u_b)}{2(\delta + 1)} + \frac{\delta(u_c + u_d)}{2(\delta + 1)}, \tag{8.7}$$

where δ is a fraction less than unity, or

$$u_o = K_1(u_a + u_b) + K_2(u_c + u_d), \tag{8.8}$$

where the coefficients K_1 and K_2 are given by

$$\left.\begin{aligned} K_1 &= \frac{1}{2(\delta + 1)}, &&(a)\\ K_2 &= \frac{\delta}{2(\delta + 1)}. &&(b)\end{aligned}\right\}(8.9)$$

When $b = c = d$, $a < b$ and $a/b = \delta$, we have

$$u_o = \frac{u_a}{(1 + \delta)^2} + \frac{\delta u_c}{(1 + \delta)^2} + \frac{\delta(u_b + u_d)}{2(1 + \delta)}. \tag{8.10}$$

The process of adjustment which makes the values of a harmonic function agree with the four-point influence equation at each network point will for brevity be called a process of harmonization.

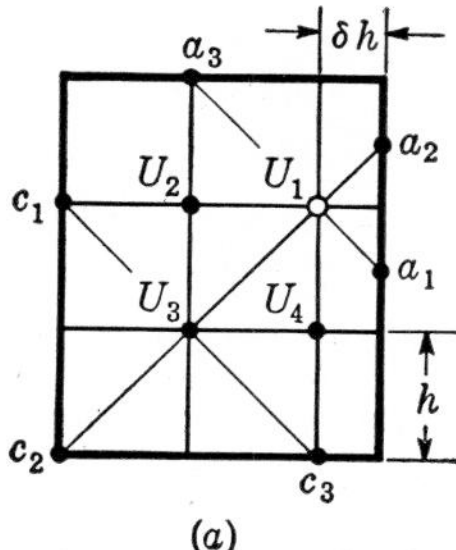

(a)

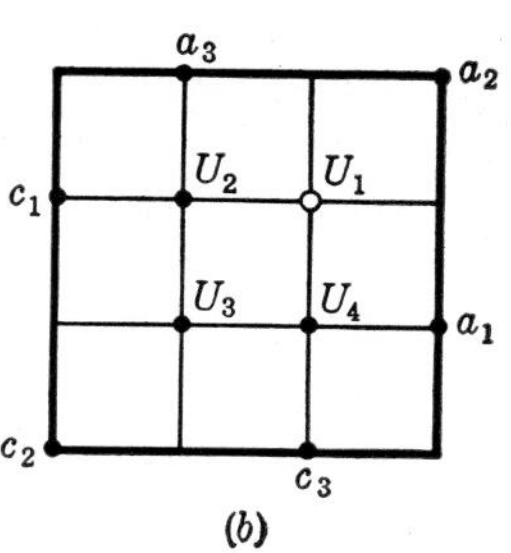

(b)

FIG. 8.2.

§8.4 Key Values. Definition. A set of interior values of U, so located in the region R to which the function U applies that, from these values, the values of U at all other network points can be calculated by the Liebmann or four-point formulas applied either normally or diagonally, is defined as a set of *key values.* In a square (3 × 3), Fig. 8.2(*b*), any one of the four interior values u_1, u_2, u_3, or u_4 is a key value for the whole region. Thus, if u_1 be known, u_3 can be found from the diagonal neighbors, and u_2, u_4 from the normal neighbors.

Similarly in a rectangle (4×3), Fig. 8.3(b), either u_1 or u_4 is a key value for the whole region. Thus, if u_1 be known, u_3 and u_5 can be found from diagonal neighbors, and u_2, u_4, u_6 from normal neighbors.

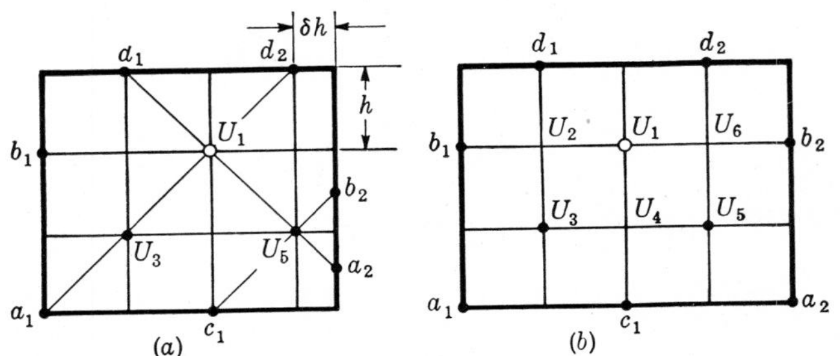

FIG. 8.3

A similar condition exists in a (4×4) square, Fig. 8.5(b), in which u_1, the value at the center of the square, defines the remaining eight interior values. Four of these values, u_2, u_3, u_4, u_5, are found from diagonal neighbors and the remaining four from normal neighbors. In all three cases, one key value is sufficient to obtain a complete numerical solution of Laplace's equation.

An interior, or unknown, value will always be denoted by u with a suitable subscript relating it to a given point. Known boundary values will be denoted by a, b, c, $\cdots$, etc.

§8.5 Key Values for Incomplete and Full (3×3) Rectangles, Fig. 8.2(a). (a) A rectangle $3(2 + \delta)$, in which δ is a fraction less than unity, will be spoken of as a incomplete (3×3) square, Fig. 8.2(a). In order to find the value u_1 we use eqs. (8.8) and (8.5). Thus,

$$\left.\begin{aligned} u_1 &= K_1(a_1 + a_2) + K_2(a_3 + u_3), && (a) \\ 4u_3 &= u_1 + c_1 + c_2 + c_3. && (b) \end{aligned}\right\} \quad (8.11)$$

Upon solving, eliminating K_1 and K_2 by eqs. (8.9), we have

$$(8 + 7\delta)u_1 = 4(a_1 + a_2) + \delta(4a_3 + c_1 + c_2 + c_3). \quad (8.12)$$

Putting δ equal to unity we obtain

$$15u_1 = 4\sum_{i=1}^{3} a_i + \sum_{i=1}^{3} c_i. \quad (8.13)$$

Eq. (8.13) gives the key value for a full (3×3) square, Fig. 8.2(b).

§8.6 Key Values for Incomplete and Full (3 × 4) Rectangles, Fig. 8.3. (*a*) A rectangle $3(3 + \delta)$, Fig. 8.3(*a*), will be spoken of as an incomplete (3 × 4) rectangle. Eqs. (8.5) and (8.8) give also the key value u_1 for this case. Thus,

$$\left.\begin{aligned} 4u_1 &= u_3 + u_5 + d_1 + d_2, & (a)\\ 4u_3 &= u_1 + a_1 + b_1 + c_1, & (b)\\ u_5 &= K_1(a_2 + b_2) + K_2(u_1 + c_1). & (c) \end{aligned}\right\} \quad (8.14)$$

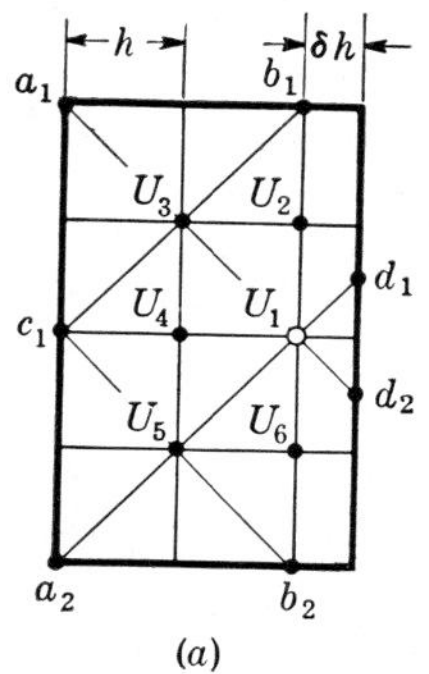

(*a*)

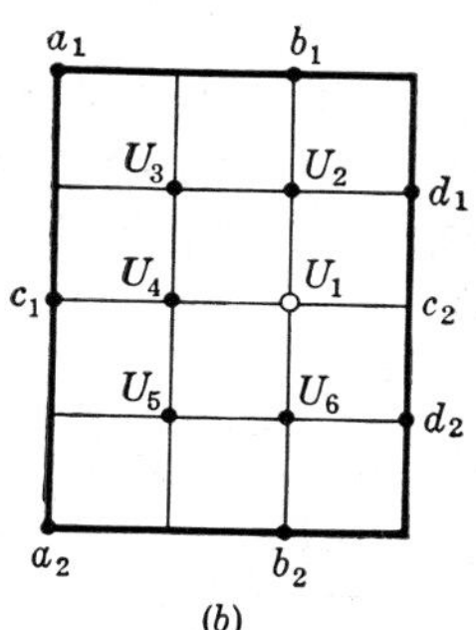

(*b*)

FIG. 8.4

Solving, and eliminating K_1 and K_2, we obtain

$$\left(\frac{15 + 13\delta}{1 + \delta}\right) u_1 = (a_1 + b_1 + c_1 + 4d_1 + 4d_2) + \left(\frac{2}{1 + \delta}\right)(a_2 + b_2 + \delta c_1). \quad (8.15)$$

(*b*) Putting δ equal to unity, we obtain the key value for a full rectangle (3 × 4), Fig. 8.3(*b*). Thus,

$$14u_1 = a_1 + a_2 + 2c_1 + 4(d_1 + d_2) + b_1 + b_2. \quad (8.16)$$

(*c*) By putting δ equal to zero, changing the notation of the boundary values to agree with that of Fig. 8.2(*b*), and observing that when δ becomes zero $a_2 = b_2 = a_1$, we obtain eq. (8.13), i.e., the key value for a full (3 × 3) square.

§8.7 Key Values for Incomplete and Full (4 × 3) Rectangles, Fig. 8.4. (*a*) A rectangle $4(2 + \delta)$, Fig. 8.4(*a*), will be spoken of as an incomplete (4 × 3) rectangle. In order to find the key value u_1 we again use eqs. (8.8) and (8.5) and obtain the following three equations:

$$\left.\begin{aligned} u_1 &= K_1(d_1 + d_2) + K_2(u_3 + u_5), & (a)\\ 4u_3 &= u_1 + a_1 + b_1 + c_1, & (b)\\ 4u_5 &= u_1 + a_2 + b_2 + c_1. & (c)\end{aligned}\right\} (8.17)$$

Upon solving we have

$$\left(\frac{4 + 3\delta}{\delta}\right) u_1 = \frac{2}{\delta}(d_1 + d_2) + \frac{1}{2}(a_1 + a_2 + b_1 + b_2) + c_1. \quad (8.18)$$

(b) Putting δ equal to unity in eq. (8.18) we obtain

$$7u_1 = \tfrac{1}{2}(a_1 + a_2 + b_1 + b_2) + 2(d_1 + d_2) + c_1. \quad (8.19)$$

This is the key value for a full (4 × 3) rectangle, Fig. 8.4(b), which agrees with eq. (8.16) giving the key value for a full (3 × 4) rectangle at the same point.

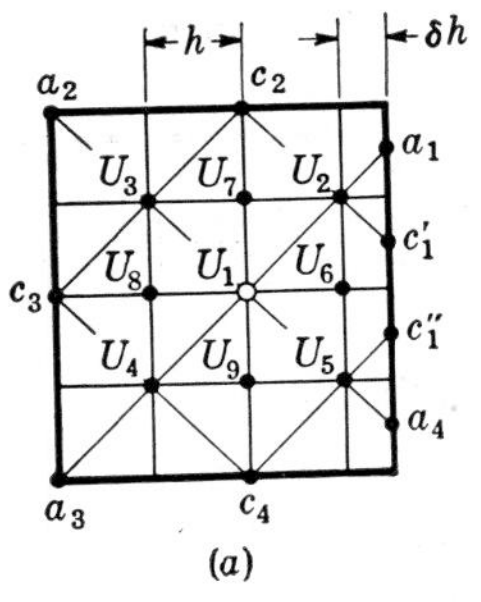

(a)

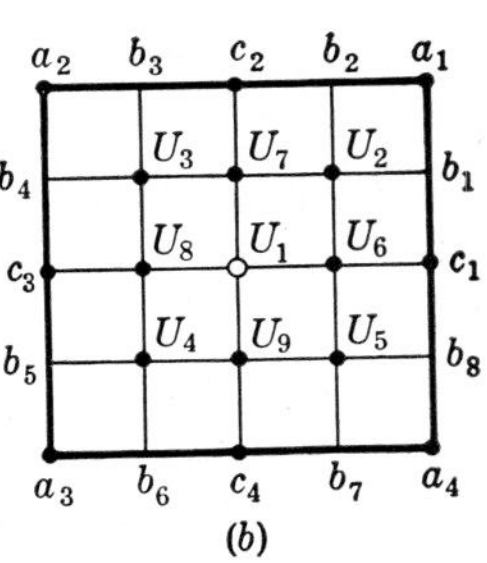

(b)

FIG. 8.5

§8.8 Key Values for Incomplete and Full (4 × 4) Squares, Fig. 8.5. (a) A rectangle $4(3 + \delta)$ will be spoken of as an incomplete (4 × 4) square, Fig. 8.5(a). There are three ways to obtain an expression for the key value u_1. The simplest procedure is to express u_1 in terms of u_2, u_3, u_4, and u_5 and then to express these quantities in terms of u_1. Using eqs. (8.5) and (8.8) we obtain the following five expressions:

$$\left.\begin{aligned} 4u_1 &= u_2 + u_3 + u_4 + u_5, & (a)\\ 4u_3 &= u_1 + a_2 + c_2 + c_3, & (b)\\ 4u_4 &= u_1 + a_3 + c_3 + c_4, & (c)\\ u_2 &= K_1(a_1 + c_1') + K_2(u_1 + c_2), & (d)\\ u_5 &= K_1(a_4 + c_1'') + K_2(u_1 + c_4). & (e)\end{aligned}\right\} (8.20)$$

Upon solving we have

$$\left(\frac{7+5\delta}{1+\delta}\right)u_1 = \tfrac{1}{2}(a_2+a_3+c_2+2c_3+c_4)+\frac{a_1+a_4+c_1'+c_1''}{1+\delta}$$
$$+\frac{\delta(c_2+c_4)}{1+\delta}. \qquad (8.21)$$

(*b*) Putting δ equal unity and observing that then $c_1' = c_1'' = c_1$, we obtain

$$6u_1 = \tfrac{1}{2}\sum_{i=1}^{4} a_i + \sum_{i=1}^{4} c_i. \qquad (8.22)$$

This gives the key value for a full (4×4) square.

(*c*) Eq. (8.21) also yields the key value for a rectangle (4×3). Putting δ equal to zero, changing the notation of the boundary values to agree with that of Fig. 8.4(*b*), and observing that, when $\delta = 0$, $c' = a_1 = d_1$, and $c_1'' = a_4 = d_2$, we obtain eq. (8.19) for a full (4×3) rectangle. The equations developed in sections 5, 6, 7, and 8 will be found useful in harmonization of rectangular figures as well as in figures of general boundaries.

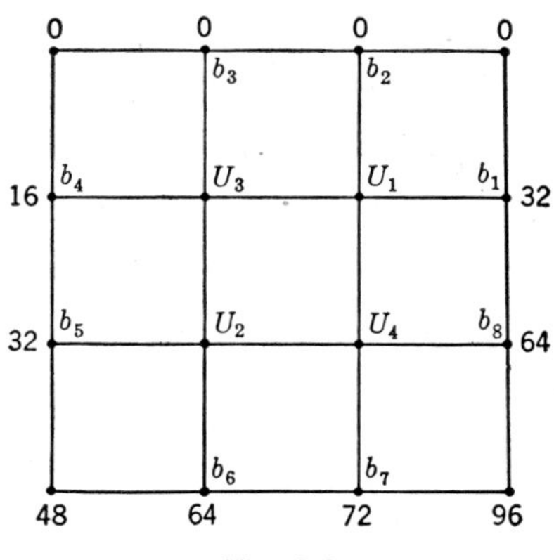

FIG. 8.6

PROBLEMS

1. Derive an expression for u_1 for the (3×3) square shown in Fig. 8.6, using normal neighbors only.

Ans. $24u_1 = 7(b_1 + b_2) + 2(b_3 + b_4 + b_7 + b_8) + b_5 + b_6.$ (8.23)

2. In Fig. 8.6 find u_1, u_2, u_3 and u_4 by eq. (8.23); and also by eq. (8.13) following the procedure outlined in §8.4. Assume boundary values as shown. Explain the slight differences in the results.

3. Derive an expression for u_1 for the (4×3) rectangle of Fig. 8.4(*b*), using normal neighbors only.

$$\textit{Ans.}\quad \tfrac{1}{24}\,[a_1 + a_2 + 3(b_1 + b_2) + 2(d_1 + d_2) + 4c_1 + 8c_2]. \qquad (8.24)$$

4. Derive an expression for the key value u_1 at the center of the (4×4) square, Fig. 8.5, using normal neighbors only.

$$\textit{Ans.}\quad 16u_1 = \sum_{i=1}^{8} b_i + 2\sum_{i=1}^{4} c_i. \qquad (8.25)$$

In the proceeding problem find u_1 in the following manner: use normal neighbors for u_1, u_6, u_7, u_8, u_9 and diagonal neighbors for u_2, u_3, u_4, u_5.

$$\textit{Ans.}\quad 20u_1 = 4\sum_{i=1}^{4} c_i + \sum_{i=1}^{4} a_i. \qquad (8.26)$$

6. In the (4×4) square of Fig. 8.5, find all nine interior values in three ways: eqs. (8.22), (8.25), and (8.26) respectively. Assume $a_1 = 2235$, $a_2 = 1118$, $a_3 = 3185$, $a_4 = 6370$, $b_1 = 2910$, $b_2 = 2160$, $b_3 = 1580$, $b_4 = 1455$, $b_5 = 2450$, $b_6 = 4500$, $b_7 = 6150$, $b_8 = 4900$, $c_1 = 3770$, $c_2 = 1935$, $c_3 = 1885$, $c_4 = 5520$. *Ans.* $u_1 = 3266$ approximately.

7. In the incomplete (4×3) rectangle of Fig. 8.4(*a*) assume $\delta = 0.5$, $a_1 = 3.69$, $a_2 = 2.08$, $b_1 = 3.95$, $b_2 = 3.00$, $c_1 = 3.00$, $d_1 = 3.70$, and $d_2 = 3.48$. Find all six interior values. *Ans.* $u_1 = 3.46$

8. In the incomplete (4×4) square of Fig. 8.5(*a*) assume $\delta = 0.5$, $a_1 = 4.10$, $a_2 = 3.69$, $a_3 = 2.08$, $a_4 = 3.60$, $c_1' = 3.92$, $c_1'' = 3.75$, $c_2 = 3.95$, $c_3 = 3.00$, $c_4 = 3.00$. Find all nine interior values. *Ans.* $u_1 = 3.46$.

§8.9 Laplacian Perimeters. In the application of the formulas for the elementary areas to long rectangles or composite rectangles, it will be found convenient to simplify the expressions of the key values already derived; specifically, we shall write the formula for each key value u for an elementary area in the form

$$\alpha u = P + u' \qquad (a)$$

or

$$\alpha u = P + u' + u'', \qquad (b) \qquad (8.27)$$

in which α is a constant coefficient, P is a quantity determined by the known boundary values, and u', u'' are unknown boundary values. The constant P in eqs. (8.27) will be referred to as a *Laplacian perimeter.* Since we have eight elementary areas — four complete and four incomplete rectangles — we shall need eight Laplacian perimeters. These will be denoted by P and p, for the complete and incomplete areas respectively, with suitable subscripts. Thus $P_{4\times4}$ will refer to a full (4×4) square, and $p_{4\times4}$ to an incomplete (4×4).

It will be seen later that, in long rectangles, the elementary formulas will be used so that one or at most two boundary values will be characteristically missing. Thus the formula for a full (4×4) square will always be used in such a manner that c_1 or c_3 or both will be unknown. In the definitions of the eight Laplacian perimeters that follow we are entirely guided by such considerations.

§8.10 Summary of Formulas for Elementary Figures in Terms of *P* and *p*.

(1) 3 × 3, Fig. 8.2(*b*), eq. (8.13).

$$\left.\begin{aligned} 15u_1 &= P_{3\times 3} + c_1, & (a)\\ P_{3\times 3} &= 4\sum_{i=1}^{3} a_i + c_2 + c_3. & (b)\end{aligned}\right\}(8.28)$$

(2) 3 × 4, Fig. 8.3(*b*), eq. (8.16).

$$\left.\begin{aligned} 14u_1 &= P_{3\times 4} + \sum \text{unknown } b\text{'s}, & (a)\\ P_{3\times 4} &= (a_1 + a_2 + 2c_1) + 4(d_1 + d_2) + \sum \text{known } b\text{'s}. & (b)\end{aligned}\right\}(8.29)$$

(3) 4 × 3, Fig. 8.4(*b*), eq. (8.19).

$$\left.\begin{aligned} 7u_1 &= P_{4\times 3} + c_1, & (a)\\ P_{4\times 3} &= 0.5(a_1 + a_2 + b_1 + b_2) + 2(d_1 + d_2). & (b)\end{aligned}\right\}(8.30)$$

(4) 4 × 4, Fig. 8.5(*b*), eq. (8.22).

$$\left.\begin{aligned} 6u_1 &= P_{4\times 4} + \sum \text{unknown } c\text{'s}, & (a)\\ P_{4\times 4} &= 0.5\sum_{i=1}^{4} a_i + \sum \text{known } c\text{'s}. & (b)\end{aligned}\right\}(8.31)$$

(5) 3 × 3, Fig. 8.2(*a*), eq. (8.12).

$$\left.\begin{aligned} \alpha_{3\times 3}u_1 &= p_{3\times 3} + c_1, & (a)\\ \alpha_{3\times 3} &= \frac{8 + 7\delta}{\delta}, & (b)\\ p_{3\times 3} &= \frac{4(a_1 + a_2)}{\delta} + 4a_3 + c_2 + c_3. & (c)\end{aligned}\right\}(8.32)$$

(6) 3 × 4, Fig. 8.3(*a*), eq. (8.15).

$$\left.\begin{aligned} \alpha_{3\times 4}u_1 &= p_{3\times 4} + b_1, & (a)\\ \alpha_{3\times 4} &= \frac{15 + 13\delta}{1 + \delta}, & (b)\\ p_{3\times 4} &= a_1 + c_1 + 4(d_1 + d_2) + \frac{2(a_2 + b_2 + \delta c_1)}{1 + \delta}. & (c)\end{aligned}\right\}(8.33)$$

(7) 4 × 3, Fig. 8.4(*a*), eq. (8.18).

$$\left.\begin{aligned}\alpha_{4\times 3}u_1 &= p_{4\times 3} + c_1, && (a)\\ \alpha_{4\times 3} &= \frac{4+3\delta}{\delta}, && (b)\\ p_{4\times 3} &= 0.5(a_1 + a_2 + b_1 + b_2) + \frac{2(d_1+d_2)}{\delta}\cdot && (c)\end{aligned}\right\}(8.34)$$

(8) 4 × 4, Fig. 8.5(*a*), eq. (8.21),

$$\left.\begin{aligned}\alpha_{4\times 4}u_1 &= p_{4\times 4} + c_3, && (a)\\ \alpha_{4\times 4} &= \frac{7+5\delta}{1+\delta}, && (b)\\ p_{4\times 4} &= 0.5(a_2 + a_3 + c_2 + c_4) + \frac{a_1 + a_4 + c_1' + c_1''}{1+\delta}\\ &\quad + \frac{\delta(c_2+c_4)}{1+\delta}\cdot && (c)\end{aligned}\right\}(8.35)$$

PART II THE ITERATIVE PROCESS

§8.11 The Iterative Process. Introduction. From the examples treated in the preceding part it is apparent that a set of simultaneous equations could be written down for a network of arbitrary size and shape which would express the basic requirement of a numerical solution of Laplace's equation given by the general four-point influence formula, eq. (8.4). However, when the number of interior points, and therefore the number of equations, becomes great, the exact simultaneous solution of the resulting set of equations is too laborious to be of practical value. Fortunately, ***it is always possible to obtain approximations to any set of linear equations, and therefore an approximation to the numerical solution of Laplace's equation, to any desired degree of accuracy.*** In this procedure it is possible to assume a set of arbitrary values at the network points and to improve them in successive steps until they satisfy eq. (8.4). This process of adjustment or harmonization is known as *the iterative process.*

§8.12 The Solution of a Set of Linear Equations by the Iterative Process. As an illustration of the iterative process we solve the set of four equations below:

$$\left.\begin{aligned}u_1 &= 8 + \tfrac{1}{4}(u_3 + u_4), && (a)\\ u_2 &= 24 + \tfrac{1}{4}(u_3 + u_4), && (b)\\ u_3 &= 4 + \tfrac{1}{4}(u_1 + u_2), && (c)\\ u_4 &= 34 + \tfrac{1}{4}(u_1 + u_2), && (d)\end{aligned}\right\}(8.36)$$

Inspection of these equations shows that u_1 and u_2 determine u_3 and u_4, and similarly, that u_3 and u_4 determine u_1 and u_2. We therefore begin by assigning arbitrary values, say zero to u_3 and u_4.

Substituting $u_3 = u_4 = 0$ in eqs. (8.36*a*) and (8.36*b*), we obtain

$$u_1 = 8 + \tfrac{1}{4}(0 + 0) = 8,$$

$$u_2 = 24 + \tfrac{1}{4}(0 + 0) = 24.$$

With the above values of u_1 and u_2 we calculate new values of u_3 and u_4. Thus,

$$u_3 = 4 + \tfrac{1}{4}(8 + 24) = 12,$$

$$u_4 = 34 + \tfrac{1}{4}(8 + 24) = 42.$$

The first set of values, $u_1 = 8$, $u_2 = 24$, $u_3 = u_4 = 0$, satisfies the first two of eqs. (8.36) but not the last two. On the other hand, the second set $u_1 = 8$, $u_2 = 24$, $u_3 = 12$ and $u_4 = 42$ satisfies the last two equations but not the first two. The process is then repeated until one set of four values satisfies all four equations.

TABLE 8.1

Approximation	Row	u_1	u_2	u_3	u_4
First	1			0	0
	2	8	24		
Second	3			12	42
	4	21.5	37.5		
Third	5			18.75	48.75
	6	24.9	40.9		
Fourth	7			20.45	50.45
	8	25.7	41.7		
Fifth	9			20.85	50.85
	10	25.92	41.92		
Sixth	11			20.96	50.96
	12	25.98	41.98		
Seventh	13			20.99	50.99
	14	26	42		

It can be shown[1] that upon repeating the process a sufficient number of times a state of convergence will be reached at which the roots will equal or approach the true values given by an exact solution. In the case under consideration convergence is, for all practical purposes, attained after seven approximations. The results are given in Table 8.1.

[1] See *Differential und integral Gleichungen der Mechanik und Physik*, by P. Frank and R. von Mises, F. Vieweg und Sohn, Berlin, 1930, part 1, p. 735.

This table shows the successive values as well as the manner in which they were obtained: each pair of values in one row determined the pair in the next row. Thus from the assumed values $u_3 = u_4 = 0$ we found $u_1 = 8$, $u_2 = 12$. From these values we calculated $u_3 = 12$, $u_4 = 42$, which in turn determined the values of $u_1 = 21.5$ and $u_2 = 37.5$, etc.

The values in the rows 1 and 2, 3 and 4, 5 and 6, etc., satisfy the first two of eqs. (8.36). The values in the rows 2 and 3, 4 and 5, 6 and 7, etc., satisfy the last two of eqs. (8.36). Inspection of Table 8.1 shows that after seven approximations the values converge to $u_1 = 26$, $u_2 = 42$, $u_3 = 21$, and $u_4 = 51$. It can be readily verified that these values represent the exact solution to eqs. (8.36).

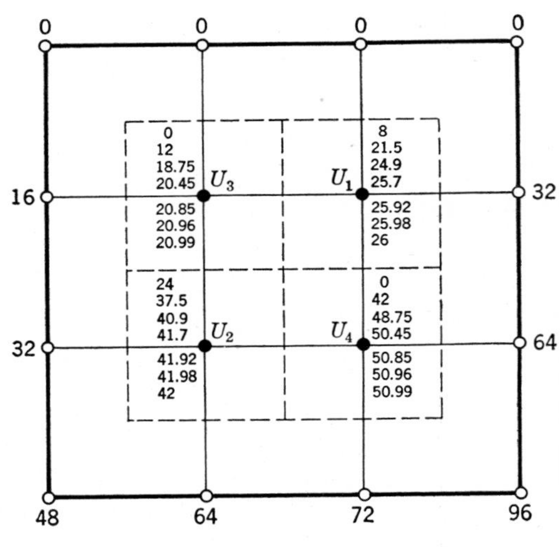

FIG. 8.7

§8.13 Procedure in Harmonization by Iteration. Order of Improvement. Inspection of Fig. 8.7 shows that the four equations solved in the preceding section by iteration, eqs. (8.36), represent the numerical solution for the (3×3) square in terms of the normal neighbors and given boundary values. The results in Table 8.1 are therefore the numerical solution for the square of Fig. 8.7.

In the method of iteration we do not always write down the necessary set of equations although the expressions are always implied. The results of the calculations are sometimes arranged as in Fig. 8.7, in which the columns near each interior point are identically the same as in Table 8.1.

Order of Improvement. In the example under consideration the order in which the points were improved was u_1, u_2, u_3, and u_4. However, the final results are independent of this order, although the intermediate values do depend on it. This can be clearly seen from Fig. 8.8, in which

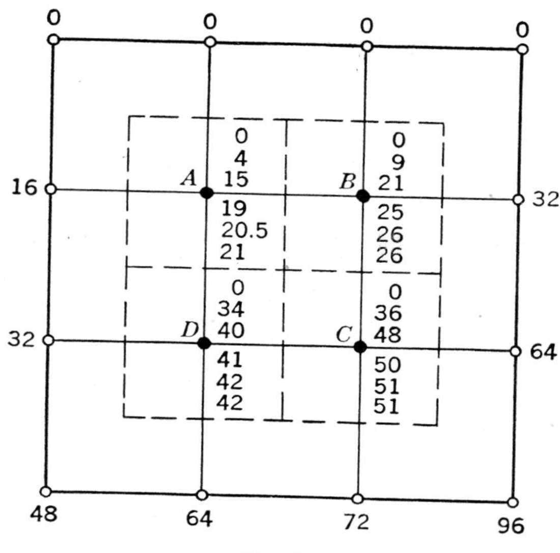

FIG. 8.8

the order of improvement is $u_a = u_3$, $u_b = u_1$, $u_c = u_4$, and $u_d = u_2$. The final results are the same as in Fig. 8.7. It is important, however, not to change the order of improvement during the solution, but to adhere to the same sequence in all traverses. In this case the equations are

$$u_a = 4 + \frac{u_b + u_d}{4},$$

$$u_b = 8 + \frac{u_a + u_c}{4}, \quad \text{etc.}$$

PART III INITIAL VALUES BY THE LINEAR ROSETTE METHOD

§8.14 Initial Values. The Linear Rosette Method. Instead of beginning with zeros, as was done in the preceding example, ***it will be found that much time and labor can be saved by starting the solution with a more reasonable set of first approximations.*** The method used to determine the initial values must, of course, be simple and rapid.

The values of u define a surface which may be roughly approximated by assuming threads or strings to pass over the given point in different directions to the terminal values of u. These threads may be thought of as fixed at one end and under suitable tension at the other. Each thread

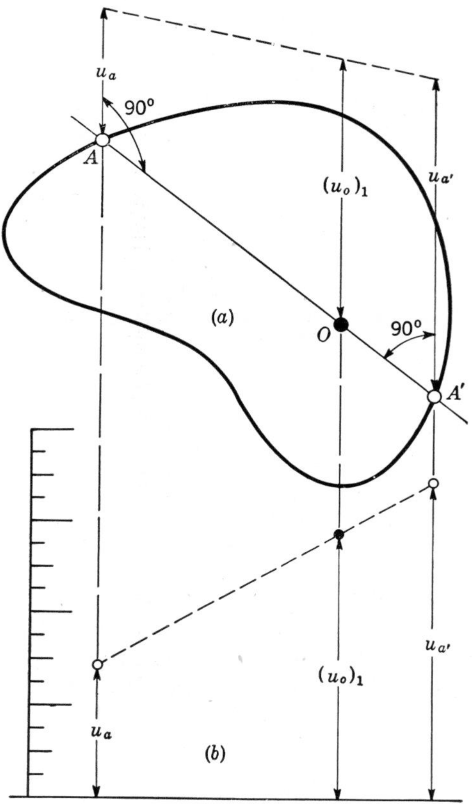

FIG. 8.9 Sketches Showing a Rapid Graphical Method for the Evaluation of an Initial Value for $(u_o)_1$.

is in general raised or lowered by an intersecting one. Ultimately they concur at one point, the height of which above the datum plane is, to a first approximation, equal to the arithmetic mean of the heights of all the strings passing over that point. Referring to Fig. 8.9(a), $(u_o)_1$ is the linear approximation to u_o from the string A–A', corresponding to the boundary values u_a and u_a', at points A and A' respectively. Such linear values can be found graphically in a few minutes, and they will always be of great help. The graphical evaluation of initial values is somewhat facilitated by laying off the end values from a fixed base line on a piece of transparent graph paper, Fig. 8.9(*b*).

At points near the boundary, and in particular near sources of stress concentration, the accuracy is notably good. This method of determining initial values will be referred to as the *Linear Rosette Method.* The number of lines in the rosette will depend on the manner in which the boundary stresses vary. The sharper this variation the greater should be the number of lines or strings.

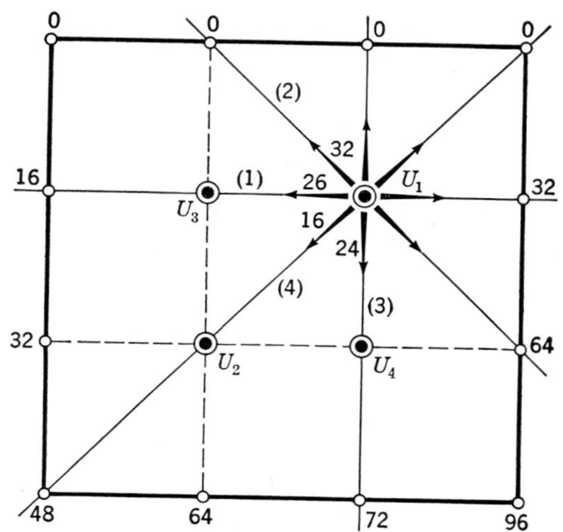

FIG. 8.10 Sketch of an Equiangular Linear Rosette for the Evaluation of u_1.

Example 8.1. As an illustration of the significance of initial values and the rosette method we solve again the problem in §8.12. Using an equiangular rosette, Fig. 8.10, we find $(u_1)_0 = 24.5$, or roughly 24. From diagonal values we obtain

$$(u_2)_0 = \tfrac{1}{4}(16 + 48 + 72 + 24) = 40.$$

Using normal points we have

$$(u_3)_0 = \tfrac{1}{4}(16 + 24 + 40) = 20,$$

$$(u_4)_0 = \tfrac{1}{4}(40 + 72 + 64 + 24) = 50.$$

These are our initial values.

It is apparent that without any further improvement we have obtained a good approximation to the true values. One traverse gives

$$u_1 = 25.5, \quad u_2 = 41.5, \quad u_3 = 20.75, \quad u_4 = 50.75,$$

and the next improvement gives

$$u_1 = 25.9, \quad u_2 = 41.9, \quad u_3 = 20.95, \quad u_4 = 50.95.$$

We have thus accomplished in two traverses essentially the same results which were previously accomplished in six.

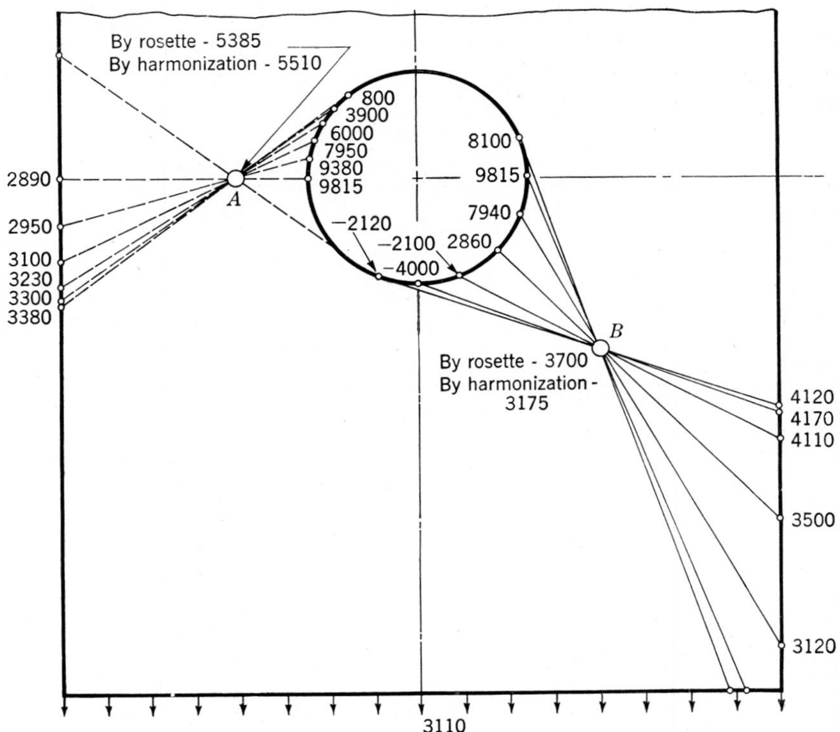

FIG. 8.11 Linear Rosettes for u_a and u_b.
Note simplicity of operations and quality of results.

§8.15 Linear Rosette as a Lateral Extensometer. ***When a good lateral extensometer is not readily available, the linear rosette may be used as a substitute.*** Experience shows that it generally yields good approximations, as can be seen from Fig. 8.11. The true values of $(p + q)$ obtained by harmonization are 5510 and 3175 at A and B respectively. The corresponding values from the rosettes are 5385 and 3700. Fig. 8.12 shows the stress pattern from which the boundary values were taken. Near a source of stress concentration the type of rosette shown, in which the limiting strings in the rosette are tangent to

FIG. 8.12 Photoelastic Stress Pattern of a Bar with a Central Circular Hole Subjected to Pure Tension Giving Boundary Values of $(p + q)$ for Fig. 8.10.

Width of bar = 1.042 in.; diameter of hole = 0.316 in.; fringe value of model = 333 psi. tension or compression; uniform stress in bar = 3.11 fringes; maximum tensile stress at hole = 9.81 fringes; maximum compressive stress at hole = 4.00 fringes.

the discontinuity, has been found to be quite sufficient. The accuracy seems to increase as the point gets closer to the discontinuity.

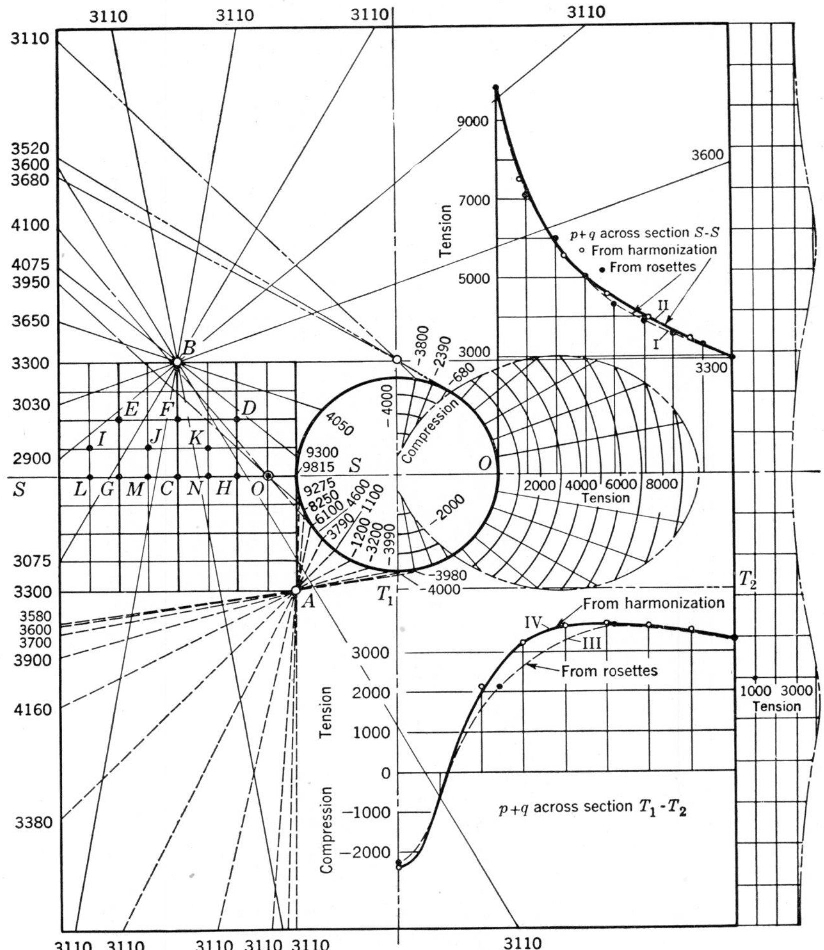

FIG. 8.13 Drawing Showing the Application of the Linear Rosette in Combination with Eq. (8.22) for a (4 × 4) Square to the Rapid Evaluation of Approximate Principal Stresses in a Bar with a Hole in Tension.

Results for the section of Symmetry S–S are given by curve I, and for section T_1–T_2 by curve III.

§8.16 Further Applications of the Linear Rosette. ***The linear rosette can be combined with eq. (8.22) for a (4 × 4) square to give a good approximation to the true distribution of $(p + q)$ across sections of***

symmetry. Thus in Fig. 8.13 we can find the complete distribution across the horizontal section of symmetry by determining $(p + q)$ at A and B from rosettes and then calculating the value at the center of the

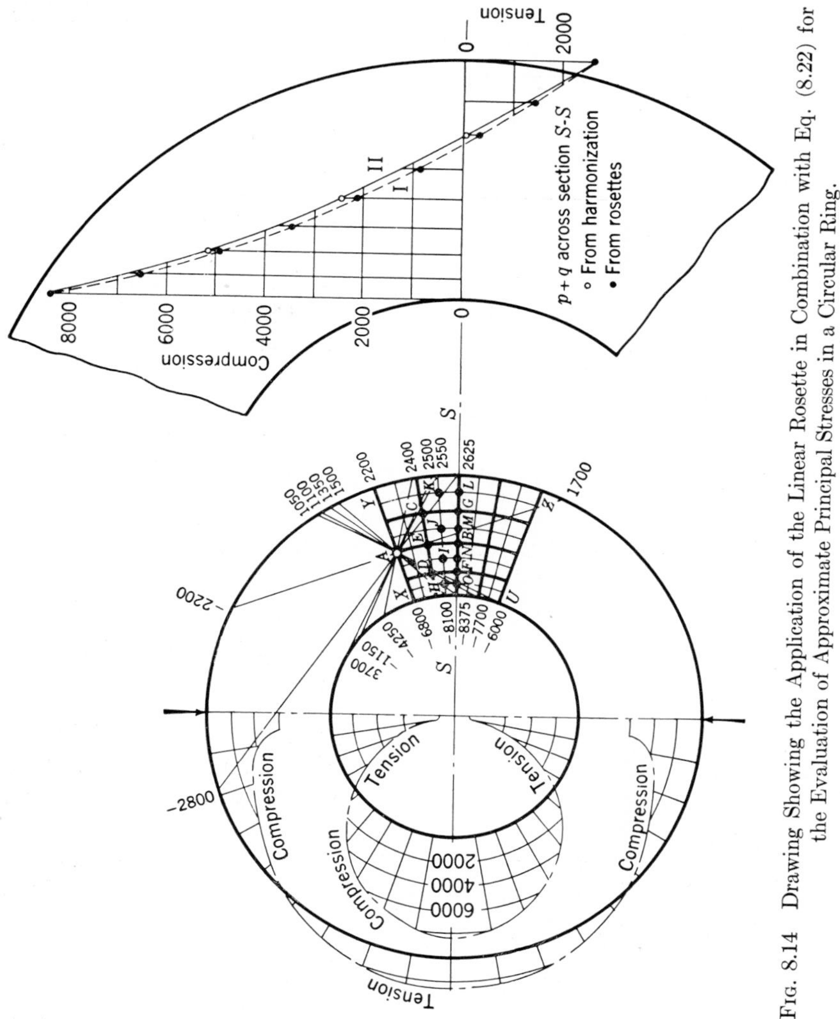

FIG. 8.14 Drawing Showing the Application of the Linear Rosette in Combination with Eq. (8.22) for the Evaluation of Approximate Principal Stresses in a Circular Ring.

square by eq. (8.22). The results are shown by curve I, Fig. 8.13. Curve II shows corresponding values from harmonization.

Curve III gives the values of $(p + q)$ across section $T_1 - T_2$. It is seen that even along this section the results are satisfactory. Attention is called to the maximum value which was determined from a rosette, showing again that near sources of stress concentrations the accuracy of the rosette is particularly good.

Another example is shown in Fig. 8.14. It is proved in §9.6 that the polar rectangle $XYZU$ transforms into a (4×4) square. In this

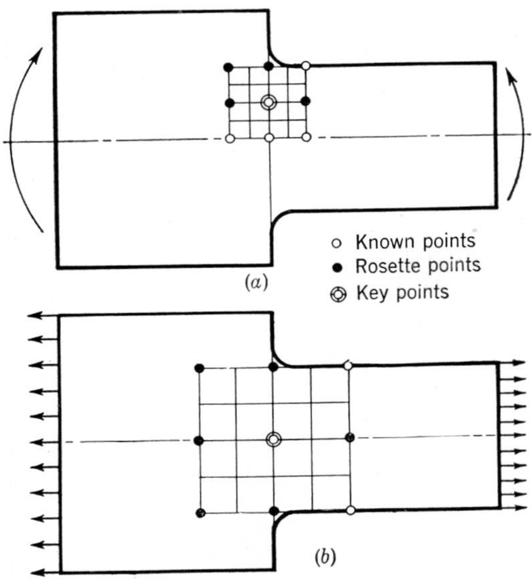

FIG. 8.15 Sketches Showing Possible Application of Linear Rosette and Eq. (8.22) to Bars with Fillets.

case only $(p + q)$ at A has to be found by a rosette. The remaining six values which enter into eq. (8.22) are known boundary values. The results may therefore be expected to be particularly good, and curves I and II show that they are.

Fig. 8.15 shows how the same idea can be applied to a bar with fillets in tension or bending. The method also gives excellent results in a tension bar with deep grooves.

PART IV METHOD OF BLOCK ITERATION

§8.17 Rectangular Areas. We consider next rectangular areas of arbitrary dimensions $(m \times n)$ and show how the key values in such figures can be found by combining the iterative process with the basic formulas for elementary rectangles, i.e., by the *block iteration.*

In rectangles $(m \times n)$, where $m = 3, 4$, and n is an integer, the number of key points k is given by

$$k = \frac{n-2}{2}, \quad \text{for } n \text{ odd},$$

$$k = \frac{n-1}{2}, \quad \text{for } n \text{ even}.$$

In rectangles $(m \times n')$, $n' = n + \delta$, where δ is a fraction less than unity,

$$k = \frac{n-1}{2}, \quad \text{for } n \text{ odd},$$

$$k = \frac{n}{2}, \quad \text{for } n \text{ even}.$$

The key points are numbered 1, 2, 3 $\cdots$ k, and the corresponding key values are denoted by u_1, u_2, u_3 $\cdots$ u_k, respectively, Fig. 8.16.

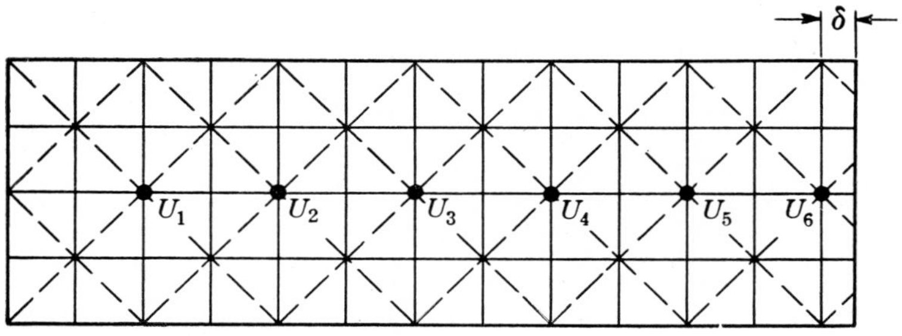

FIG. 8.16

To begin with, we divide the short side of the rectangle into three or four equal units. This determines the unit for the longer side and the value of n', which, in general, will not be an integer. Next we determine the required boundary values and calculate the Laplacian perimeters for the elementary figures surrounding each key point. We then calculate initial key values from diagonal points, using the Liebmann formula. Last, we write down explicitly the necessary equations and improve all key values in numerical order.

It is evident that ***the use of the basic formulas for elementary areas or blocks must result in a great saving of labor over the straight averaging process which employs the Liebmann formula only.*** Clearly, the number of equations to be solved is sharply reduced. For example, in a rectangle (4×16) there are 45 interior points necessitating 45 Liebmann equations. However, if we work only with key values in (4 × 4) squares the number of equations is reduced to 7. There is a vast difference in the time required to solve 7 equations as compared with 45. The saving in time is great even when one adds the additional time required to find the remaining 38 values, all of which are calculated by the direct use of the Liebmann formula. A numerical example will demonstrate this point.

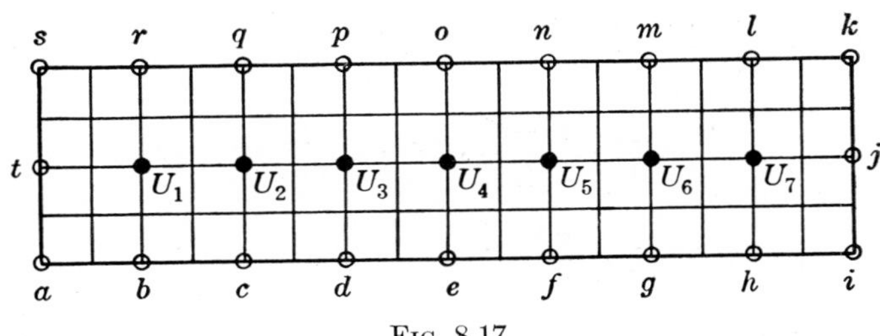

FIG. 8.17

Example 8.2. Find the key values in the (4 × 16) rectangle of Fig. 8.17 with boundary values as given in Table 8.2.

TABLE 8.2

a	b	c	d	e	f	g
2079	2996	3689	4220	4664	4997	5298
h	i	j	k	l	m	n
5561	5793	5829	5886	5677	5447	5193
o	p	q	r	s	t	
4913	4605	4277	3951	3689	2996	

Solution. (*a*) *Laplacian Perimeters to the Nearest Integer*, eq. (8.31*b*):

P_1	P_2	P_3	P_4	P_5	P_6	P_7
16,810	15,851	17,586	19,064	20,341	21,459	28,278

(*b*) *Initial Values from Diagonal Points:*

u_1	u_2	u_3	u_4	u_5	u_6	u_7
3433	3943	4381	4754	5076	5357	5606

(*c*) *Harmonization*, eq. (8.31*a*):

$$6u_1 = P_1 + u_2 = 16{,}810 + 3943,$$

$$u_1 = 3459.$$

$$6u_2 = P_2 + u_1 + u_3 = 15{,}851 + 3459 + 4381,$$

$$u_2 = 3949.$$

$$6u_3 = P_3 + u_2 + u_4 = 17{,}586 + 3949 + 4754,$$

$$u_3 = 4381.$$

$$6u_4 = P_4 + u_3 + u_5 = 19{,}064 + 4381 + 5076,$$

$$u_4 = 4754.$$

$$6u_5 = P_5 + u_4 + u_6 = 20{,}341 + 4754 + 5357,$$

$$u_5 = 5075.$$

$$6u_6 = P_6 + u_5 + u_7 = 21{,}459 + 5075 + 5606,$$

$$u_6 = 5357.$$

$$6u_7 = P_7 + u_6 = 28{,}278 + 5357,$$

$$u_7 = 5606.$$

This ends the traverse. In the case under consideration it will be found that the values obtained above differ only by a fraction of 1 per cent from those in the next traverse. The above values, or those in the second traverse, represent therefore the solution to the problem. The procedure remains the same when n is not an integer. In such cases the last perimeter is either for an incomplete (4×4), eq. (8.35c), or for an incomplete (4×3), eq. (8.34c).

The method is equally effective in composite rectangular areas, such as angles, channels, T shapes, Z shapes, etc.

PART V GENERAL BOUNDARIES

§8.18 Irregular and Curved Boundaries.

Harmonization by iteration is especially useful when the boundaries of the figure are curved or irregular. Consider point O, Fig. 8.18. The distances a and b from point O to points A and B respectively are clearly less than the lattice unit h. Such points on the boundary will generally be referred to as irregular points. They will be denoted by A and B, and their respective distances from O by a and b, with a always less than b.

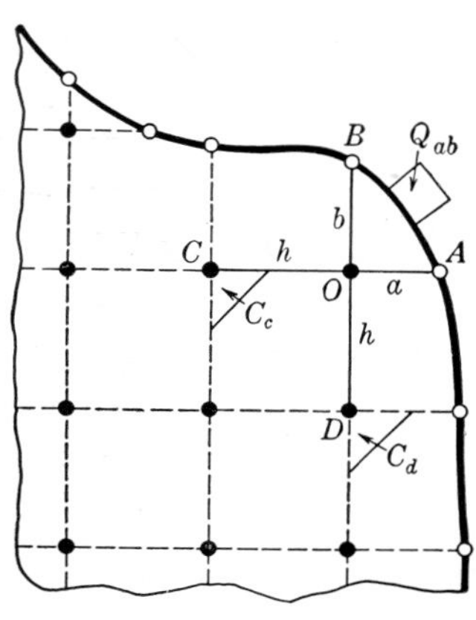

FIG. 8.18

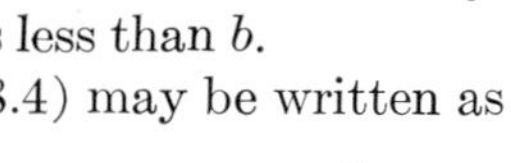

Eq. (8.4) may be written as

$$u_o = C_a u_a + C_b u_b + C_c u_c + C_d u_d. \tag{8.37}$$

After calculating the coefficients C_a, C_b, C_c, and C_d in the general four-point formula, it is desirable to simplify the expression to the form

$$\left.\begin{aligned} u_o &= Q + C_c u_c + C_d u_d, & (a)\\ Q &= C_a u_a + C_b u_b, \quad \text{a constant.} & (b) \end{aligned}\right\} \tag{8.38}$$

in which

It is convenient to write the value of Q on the boundary between points A and B and to write the values of C_c and C_d near points C and D respectively. Points A and C are always taken on one line, Fig. 8.18.

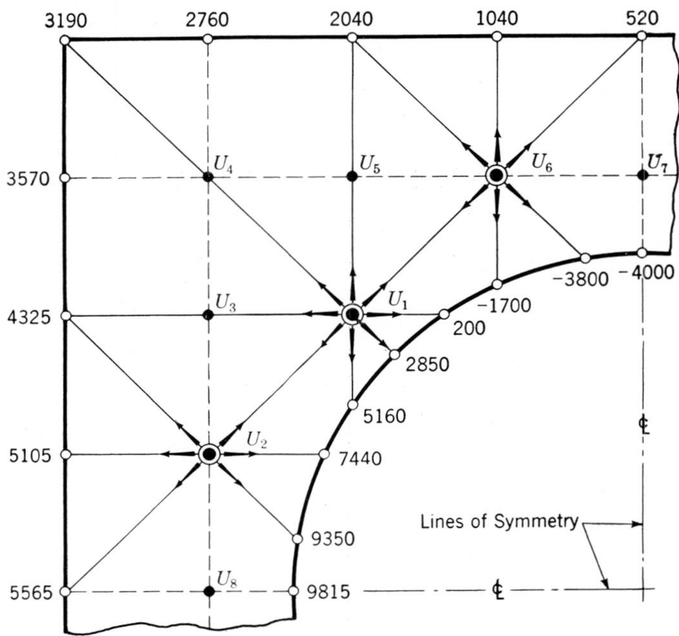

FIG. 8.19 Boundary Values and Notation Showing Order of Improvement; also Rosettes for u_1, u_2, and u_6.

Example 8.3. Curved Boundaries. As a next illustration of the iterative process we find a numerical solution for Laplace's equation for the configuration shown in Fig. 8.19.

Solution. (*a*) *Preliminary Steps.* After determining the boundary values we choose a convenient order of improvement, calculate the necessary irregular coefficients, and write down the basic equations. Since the stresses along the curved boundary vary appreciably it is desirable to bring in as many points as possible from that boundary. This suggests the use of normal neighboring points for the calculation of u_1. For simplicity we use the same system for all other points. The order of improvement is $u_1, u_2 \cdots u_8$.

There are minor reasons for this choice. It is desirable to improve u_1 first since it directly affects u_3 and u_5 and indirectly u_4, u_6, and u_7. Also, u_8 cannot be improved before u_2 is improved. However, different orders may be taken with equal effectiveness. We next measure the necessary distances a and b and calculate the irregular coefficients and the constants Q. The results are shown in Table 8.3.

TABLE 8.3

Irregular Coefficients

Point	u_1	u_2	u_6	u_7	u_8
a	0.630	0.792	0.792	0.576	0.576
b	0.630	1.00	1.00	1.00	1.00
C_a	0.307	0.311	0.311	0.402	0.402
C_b	0.307	0.221	0.221	0.183	0.183
C_c	0.193	0.247	0.247	0.232	0.232
C_d	0.193	0.221	0.221	0.183	0.183
$C_a u_a$	62	2314	−529	−1608	3946
$C_b u_b$	1584				
$C_c u_c$		1261	257	121	1291
Q	1646	3575	−272	−1487	5237

All coefficients for u_3, u_4, and u_5 are 0.25.

We now write down the explicit simplified expressions corresponding to Table 8.3 and the agreed-upon order of improvement. Thus

$$\left.\begin{aligned} u_1 &= 1646 + 0.193(u_3 + u_5), && (a) \\ u_2 &= 3575 + 0.221(u_3 + u_8), && (b) \\ u_3 &= 1081 + 0.25(u_1 + u_2 + u_4), && (c) \\ u_4 &= 1582 + 0.25(u_3 + u_5), && (d) \\ u_5 &= 510 + 0.25(u_1 + u_4 + u_6), && (e) \\ u_6 &= -272 + 0.221(u_5 + u_7), && (f) \\ u_7 &= -1487 + 0.183 \times 2u_6 = -1487 + 0.366u_6, && (g) \\ u_8 &= 5237 + 0.183 \times 2u_2 = 5237 + 0.366u_2. && (h) \end{aligned}\right\} \quad (8.39)$$

We note that u_7 and u_8 are on lines of symmetry, and therefore u_6 enters twice into u_7 and u_2 enters twice into u_8.

(*b*) *Initial Values.* In order to reduce the number of traverses or iterations we determine initial values. First we find $(u_1)_0$ from a four-line equiangular rosette. Using this value of $(u_1)_0$ and three-line rosettes we find $(u_2)_0$ and $(u_6)_0$, Fig. 8.19. The results are $(u_1)_0 = 2625$, $(u_2)_0 = 5975$, and $(u_6)_0 = -120$. The remaining five values are found by the Liebmann or four-point formula. Thus

$$(u_4)_0 = \tfrac{1}{4}(4325 + 3190 + 2040 + 2625) = 3045,$$
$$(u_3)_0 = \tfrac{1}{4}(4325 + 2625 + 5975 + 3045) = 3992,$$
$$(u_5)_0 = \tfrac{1}{4}(2040 + 2625 + 3045 - 120) = 1900.$$

Also by eq. (8.39*g*) and (8.39*h*)

$$(u_7)_0 = -1487 + 0.366(-120) = -1530,$$
$$(u_8)_0 = 5237 + 0.366 \times 5975 = 7427.$$

We now have a complete set of initial values. The irregular coefficients entering into $(u_7)_0$ and $(u_8)_0$ are those given in Table 8.3.

It will be seen later that the small effort involved in getting good initial values is more than offset by the resulting speed of convergence.

(c) *Harmonization.* We next solve eqs. (8.39) by iteration. Thus

$$
\begin{aligned}
(u_1)_1 &= 1646 + 0.193(3992 + 1900) = 2783,\\
(u_2)_1 &= 3575 + 0.221(3992 + 7427) = 6100,\\
(u_3)_1 &= 1081 + 0.25(2783 + 6100 + 3045) = 4063,\\
(u_4)_1 &= 1582 + 0.15(4063 + 1900) = 3073,\\
(u_5)_1 &= 510 + 0.25(2783 + 3073 - 120) = 1944,\\
(u_6)_1 &= -272 + 0.221(1944 - 1530) = -180,\\
(u_7)_1 &= -1487 + 0.366(-180) = -1553,\\
(u_8)_1 &= 5237 + 0.366 \times 6100 = 7472.
\end{aligned}
$$

This completes the first traverse or improvement. The cycle is now repeated, using always the last available values. The results from the next traverse are:

$$
\begin{aligned}
(u_1)_2 &= 1646 + 0.193(4063 + 1944) = 2806,\\
(u_2)_2 &= 3575 + 0.220(4063 + 7472) = 6125,\\
(u_3)_2 &= 1081 + 0.25(2806 + 6125 + 3073) = 4082,\\
(u_4)_2 &= 1582 + 0.25(4082 + 1944) = 3089,\\
(u_5)_2 &= 510 + 0.25(2806 + 3089 - 180) = 1939,\\
(u_6)_2 &= -272 + 0.221(1939 - 1553) = -187,\\
(u_7)_2 &= -1487 + 0.366(-187) = -1555,\\
(u_8)_2 &= 5237 + 0.366 \times 6125 = 7477
\end{aligned}
$$

For all practical purposes convergence has been obtained and the problem is solved.

Fig. 8.20 shows the same problem solved with zero initial values and a different order of improvement. It is seen that the results are essentially the same, but that it took four traverses to arrive at approximately the same degree of convergence as before. In large networks this may mean a great difference in labor and time.

PROBLEMS

1. Harmonize Fig. 8.20, using zero initial values and the same order of improvement as in Fig. 8.19.

2. Harmonize Fig. 8.20 using the given order of improvement and the initial values of Fig. 8.19.

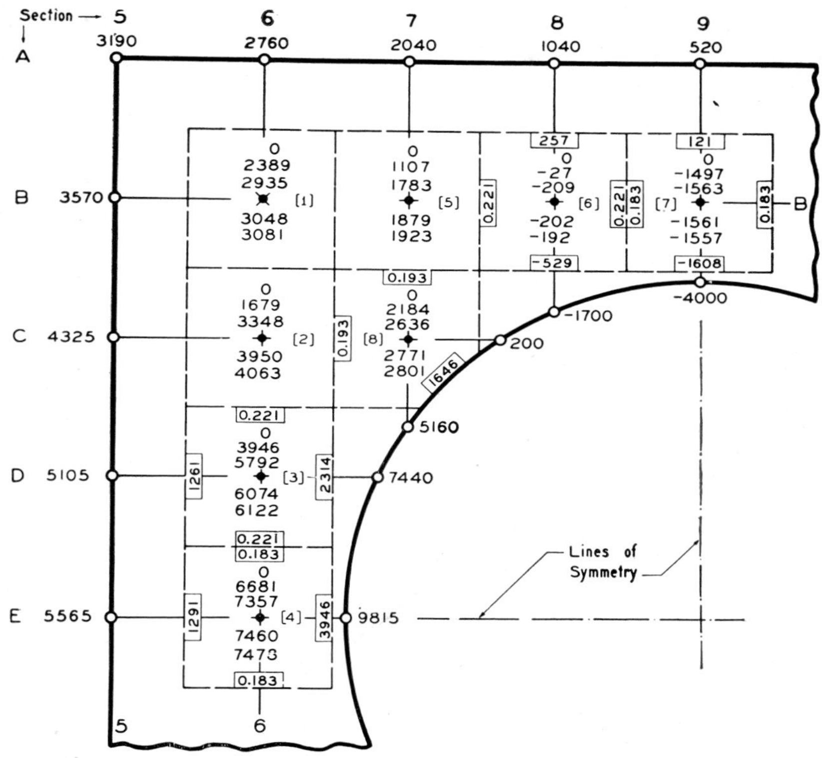

FIG. 8.20 Same Problem as in Fig. 8.19 Solved with Zero Initial Values and Using a Different Order.

§8.19 The Use of Fundamental Rectangles in Harmonization. Referring to Fig. 8.21 let us assume that we have a set of initial diagonal values u_1, u_2, etc., which have to be adjusted or harmonized. For simplicity we number the points in the finer network in the manner indicated, placing u_1 and u_2 on the line closest to the outside boundary. The consecutive points then fall on an accordionlike curve. The simplest (although not the shortest) way to harmonize the finer network is to improve the points in numerical order 1, 2, 3 · · ·, and to repeat the cycles until convergence is obtained. In this manner all points are improved the same number of times.

Considerable labor in harmonization can be saved if a regular rectangle

$(4 \times n)$ or $(3 \times n)$ can be inscribed in the figure under consideration. For example, in Fig. 8.21, we can inscribe a rectangle (4×10). ***In such cases we improve first all the points lying outside the regular figure and those on its boundary. We next adjust or harmonize the key values x, y, z, u in the regular rectangle to agree with the improved values on its boundaries, as in the preceding section. The key values are then***

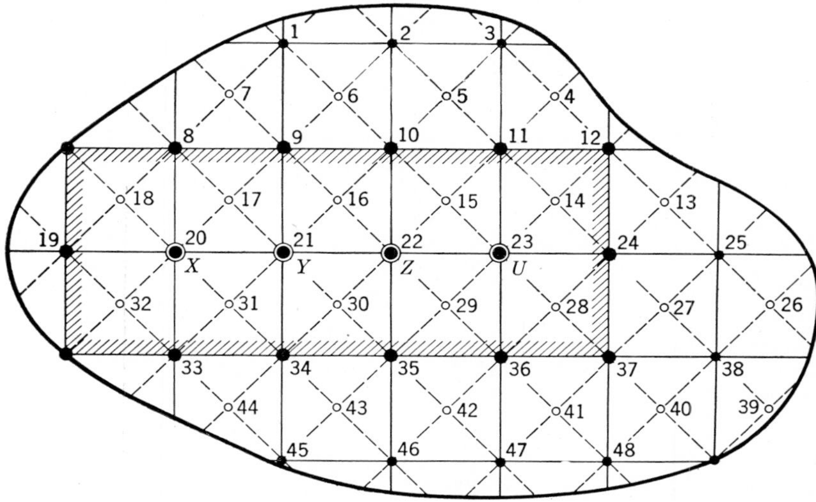

FIG. 8.21 Sketch Showing the Use of Regular Rectangles in the Harmonization of a Figure with an Irregular Boundary.

resolved to obtain the interior diagonal values. All points have now been improved once. This ends the traverse and the cycle is repeated. When satisfactory convergence has been attained the remaining values in the finer network are calculated from normal neighbors.

Sometimes it is possible to inscribe some combination of rectangles as in Fig. 8.22. Here again we first improve all points outside the regular figure and those on its boundary, points 1 to 21 inclusive. We then harmonize the key values x, y, z, u, v inside the regular figure, until they agree substantially with the values on the regular boundary, as in the preceding section. Finally we resolve the key values $x, \cdots v$ to obtain the diagonal values inside the regular figure, points 27 to 36 inclusive. The cycle is then repeated, until convergence is attained. We note that points A and B are not needed in the harmonization.

§8.20. Coarse and Mixed Networks. (*a*) *Coarse Network.* ***The process of harmonization can be expedited by reducing the number of***

network points, and therewith the number of unknowns. Much labor can be saved by using a preliminary coarse network. The effect of doubling the size of the lattice unit on the number of interior points N can be judged from the expression

$$N = (N_x - 1)(N_y - 1),$$

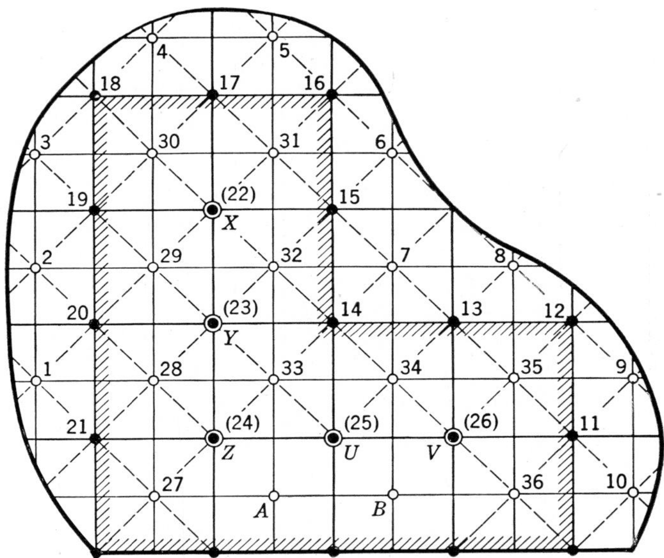

FIG. 8.22 Sketch Showing the Use of Composite Rectangles in the Harmonization of a Figure with a General Boundary.

which gives the value of N for a rectangular boundary with sides N_x and N_y. Thus in an (8×8) square $N_x = N_y = 8$ and $N = 49$. If we double the size of the lattice unit, $N_x = N_y = 4$ and $N = 9$. The number of unknowns is thus reduced from forty-nine to nine. Moreover, it can be shown that the rate of convergence increases rapidly as the number of equations is reduced. The net result is a drastic reduction in the time and labor necessary to effect the harmonization of the coarse network as compared with a finer one in which the lattice unit is half the size.

When the harmonization of the coarse network is completed it is a simple matter to resolve the coarse values, i.e., to calculate all the values of the next finer network.

Referring to Fig. 8.23(*b*), and assuming the boundary values as well as the six interior points in the coarse network to be known, it can be readily seen that all points marked d can be found from adjacent diagonal values and all points marked n can be found from adjacent normal values.

It is important to observe that *the new set of values obtained in the finer network must be readjusted or harmonized,* since the initial values from the coarse network will not be consistent with the final values in the finer network.

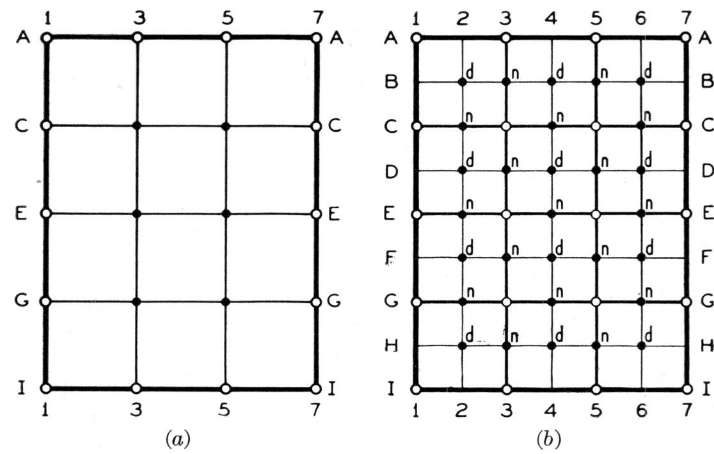

FIG. 8.23 Sketches Showing Transition from a Coarse to a Finer Network.

(*b*) *Mixed Networks.* ***Considerable labor can sometimes be saved by the use of a mixed network, in which the spacings in one region are twice the size of those in another.*** Mixed networks are especially desirable when there are sources of stress concentration and the region for exploration is relatively large.

In order to facilitate the transition from a finer network to a coarser one it is useful to introduce the transition points S_1, S_2, S_3, S_4 located on the boundary of the finer network, Fig. 8.24. Such an arrangement makes it possible to pass from one network to another by means of the Liebmann equation only.

§8.21 Initial Values in Coarse Network. The preliminary coarse network is basically a method for determining initial values for the finer network. These ***initial values in the coarse network can be determined rapidly by a combination of:*** (*1*) ***the linear rosette,*** (*2*) ***the assumption that near the boundary the values of u can be approximated by*** $(p - q)$, ***and*** (*3*) ***the use of the fundamental rectangles and the formulas for their key values.***

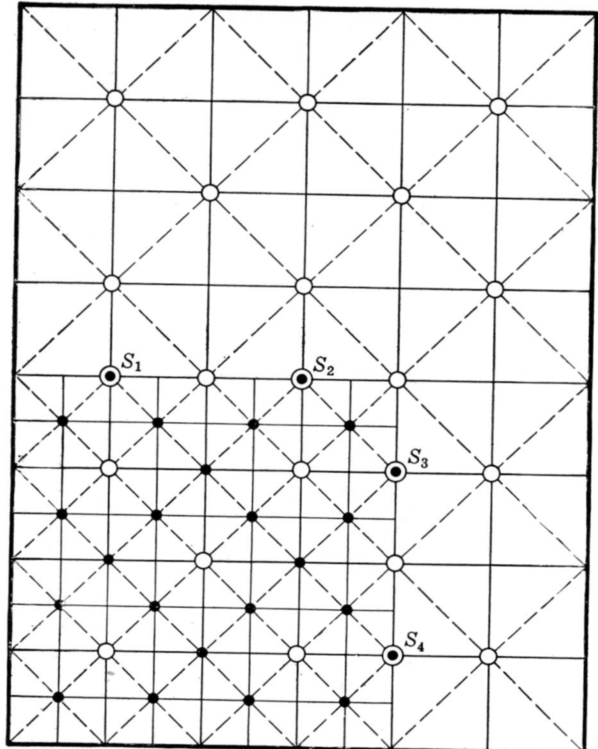

FIG. 8.24 Sketch Showing a Mixed Network and Method of Transition.

It will be useful to bear in mind that in general

$$\frac{\partial(p+q)}{\partial s_2} = \frac{\partial(p-q)}{\partial s_2} + \frac{2\partial q}{\partial s_2}$$

and that

$$\frac{\partial q}{\partial s_2} = -\frac{p-q}{\rho_1}. \qquad [(2.23), \text{Vol. I}]$$

Now at straight boundaries $\rho_1 = \infty$, $(p-q)/\rho_1 = 0$, and

$$\frac{\partial(p+q)}{\partial s_2} = \frac{\partial(p-q)}{\partial s_2}. \qquad (8.40)$$

Hence at boundaries which are fairly straight $(p+q)$ ***is of the same magnitude as*** $(p-q)$.

Consider for example the configuration in Fig. 8.25, in which there are twenty-six network points. We observe that we can inscribe a full (4×4) square in which the key value u_{13} is given by eq. (8.22) in terms

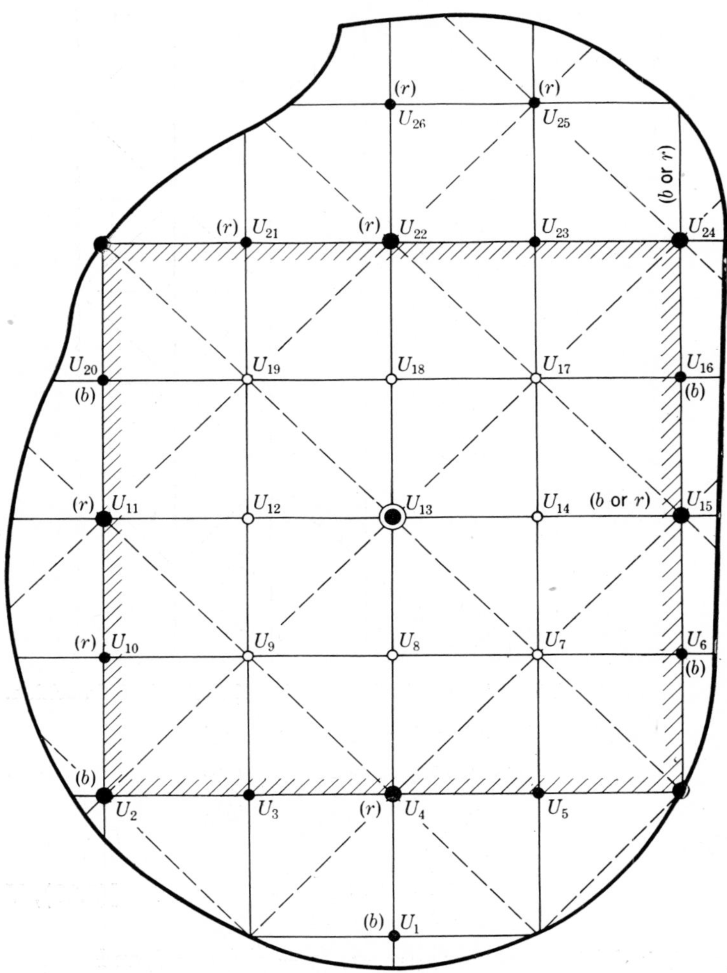

FIG. 8.25 Initial Values in a Coarse Network; r Indicates the Use of a Rosette; b Means the Nearest Boundary Value.

of u_2, u_4, u_{15}, u_{24}, u_{22}, and u_{11}. If these six values were known we could find all nine values inside the square.

The necessary six values can be approximated either by equating them to the nearest $(p - q)$, or by linear rosettes, depending on the distance from the point to the boundary. Thus u_4 and u_{22} will be found from rosettes and u_2, u_{15}, u_{24}, and u_{11} from the nearest $(p - q)$.

We then calculate u_{13} by eq. (8.22) and resolve it to obtain u_7, u_9, u_{17}, and u_{19}. The value of u_{25} is found from the nearest diagonal neighbors.

From the coarse values on the diagonals the remaining values such as u_3 and u_5 can be readily calculated. If the initial values, such as u_4 and u_{22}, have been determined with some degree of care, it is possible and even desirable to dispense with the harmonization of the coarse network and to resolve it directly into a finer network.

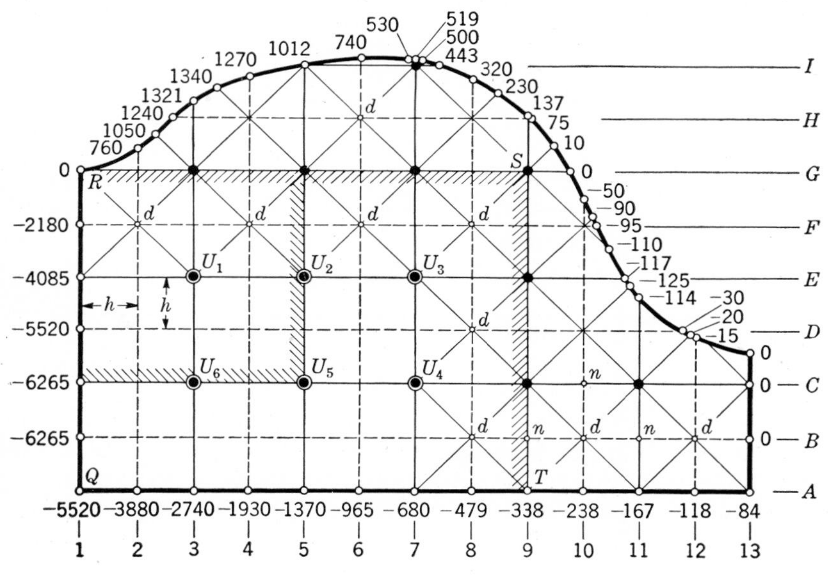

FIG. 8.26 Drawing for Example 8.4.

Example 8.4. Referring to Fig. 8.26 the problem is to determine by iteration all the values at the interior points of lattice unit h.

Solution: (*a*) We begin by taking a coarse network in which the lattice unit is $2h$, Fig. 8.27. We observe that the figure contains a rectangle (3×4) whose key value K could be found if the three values $G3$, $G7$, and $E9$ were known. These we find from four-line equiangular rosettes and obtain $G3 = G7 = 7$ and $E9 = -200$. Using the four nearest neighbors and a two-line rosette we next find $G9 = -4$. Lastly we find $C11$ using a three-line local rosette terminating at $E9$, $A9$, and $A11$ and obtain $C11 = -132$. The remaining coarse values can be calculated by the Liebmann formula. The complete set of fourteen coarse values is given in column 2, Table 8.4, and are marked (*c*). The time necessary to determine the complete set of coarse values was less than 1½ hours.

(*b*) The above coarse values are then resolved without improvement to give all the diagonal values (*d*) in the finer network of Fig. 8.26. The results of this resolution are shown in column 2, Table 8.4. For example, $F2 = -1600$,

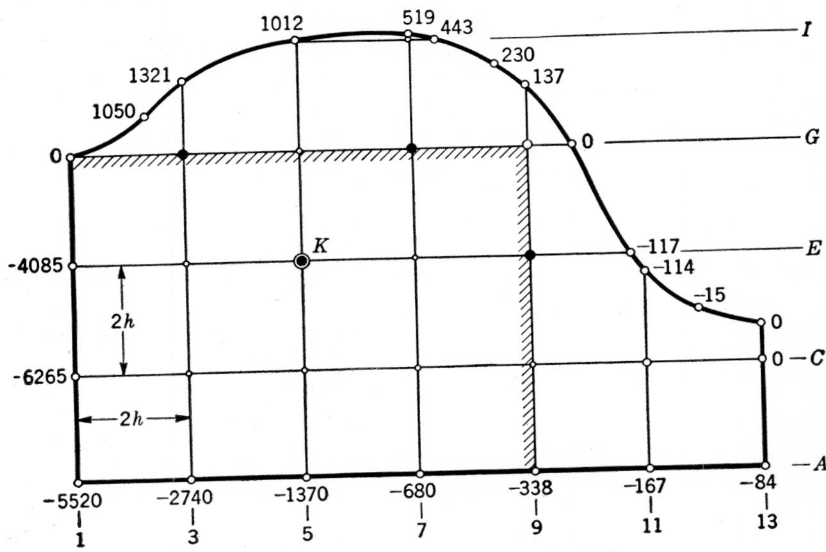

FIG. 8.27 Coarse Network for Fig. 8.26.

$H4 = 705$, etc. We now have a set of necessary initial diagonal values for the network of Fig. 8.26. It will be found later that the diagonal values around u_5 and u_6 are not needed.

(*c*) We next harmonize the initial values given in column 2, Table 8.4, in the order listed. In this process we proceed as in §8.19, harmonizing first all the values outside the (6 × 8) rectangle *RSTQ*, and those on its boundaries, making use of eqs. (8.41), which are all based on the general four-point influence formula:

$$\left.\begin{aligned}
I7 &= 470 + 0.0418u_c + 0.0406u_d, && (a)\\
H8 &= 102 + 0.167(u_b + u_d) + 0.222u_c, && (b)\\
H4 &= 767 + 0.166u_b + 0.222u_c, && (c)\\
G3 &= 343 + 0.214(u_b + u_d) + 0.244u_c, && (d)\\
G9 &= 4 + 0.167(u_b + u_d) + 0.222u_c, && (e)\\
F10 &= -78 + 0.101u_c + 0.0824u_d, && (f)\\
D10 &= -37 + 0.227(u_b + u_d) + 0.248u_c, && (g)\\
C11 &= -5 + 0.24(u_b + u_d) + 0.25u_c. && (h)
\end{aligned}\right\} \quad (8.41)$$

TABLE 8.4

1	2	3	4	5	6
		Improved Values			
Points*	Initial Values	Traverse 1	Traverse 2	Traverse 3	True Values
*I*7	519 (*c*)†	494	494	494	504
*H*8	207	186	186	184	189
*H*6	392	386	387	387	381
*H*4	705	774	770	772	765
*G*3	7 (*c*)	−14	4	3	0
*G*5	28 (*c*)	23	20	17	0
*G*7	7 (*c*)	20	14	9	0
*G*9	−4 (*c*)	−16	−19	−23	0
*F*10	−90	−99	−103	−104	−87
*E*9	−200 (*c*)	−227	−236	−238	−232
*D*10	−211	−221	−213	−213	−238
*C*9	−344 (*c*)	−358	−360	−363	−384
*C*11	−132 (*c*)	−147	−143	−142	−160
*B*12	−100	−100	−96	−98	−103
*B*10	−245	−251	−252	−253	−270
*E*3	−1992 (*c*)	−1976	−1997	−2003	−2032
*E*5	−916 (*c*)	−956	−973	−982	−1012
*E*7	−454 (*c*)	−465	−477	−483	−504
*C*7	−706 (*c*)	−739	−745	−751	−773
*C*5	−1491 (*c*)	−1495	−1518	−1523	−1555
*C*3	−2973 (*c*)	−3074	−3082	−3085	−3120
*F*2	−1600	−1519	−1520	−1521	−1535
*F*4	−736	−731	−737	−741	−765
*F*6	−331	−345	−354	−360	−381
*F*8	−162	−172	−180	−184	−189
*D*8	−435	−447	−455	−459	−479
*B*8	−526	−529	−531	−533	−544

* Points in column 1 are listed in the order of improvement.
† (c) in column 2 denotes coarse values.

We then improve the six values $u_1, u_2 \cdots u_6$ using eq. (8.22) for the (4×4) square. Columns 3, 4, 5, Table 8.4, show the successive values after three improvements. The last column gives the known true values. From the diagonal values in column 5 the remaining values (n) in the finer network can be readily calculated.

Figs. 8.28 and 8.29 show isopachic curves and contours of principal stresses for a grooved bar in tension as determined by block iteration.[1] For additional solutions see next chapter.

[1] "Calculation of Stresses within the Boundary of Photoelastic Models," by R. Weller and G. H. Shortley, *Journal of Applied Mechanics*, *Trans. A.S.M.E.*, June, 1939, Vol. 6, No. 2.

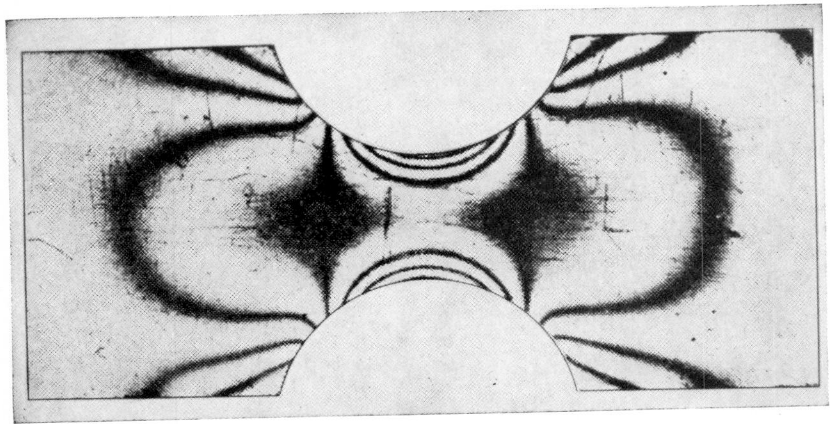

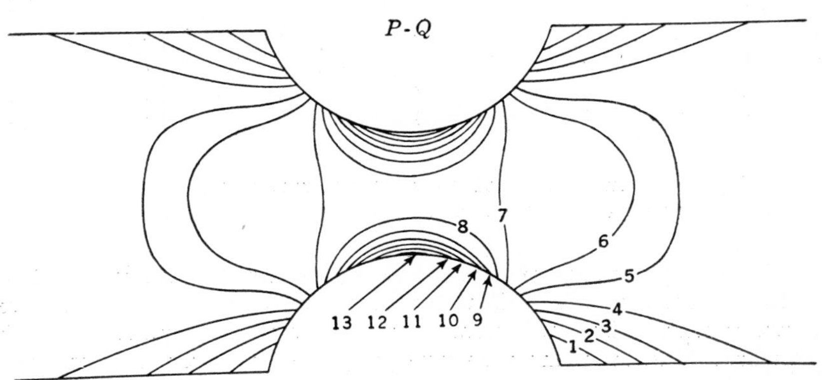

FIG. 8.28 Stress Pattern (*above*) and Drawing of Isochromatics (*below*) in a Grooved Bakelite Bar in Tension. (From Weller and Shortley.)

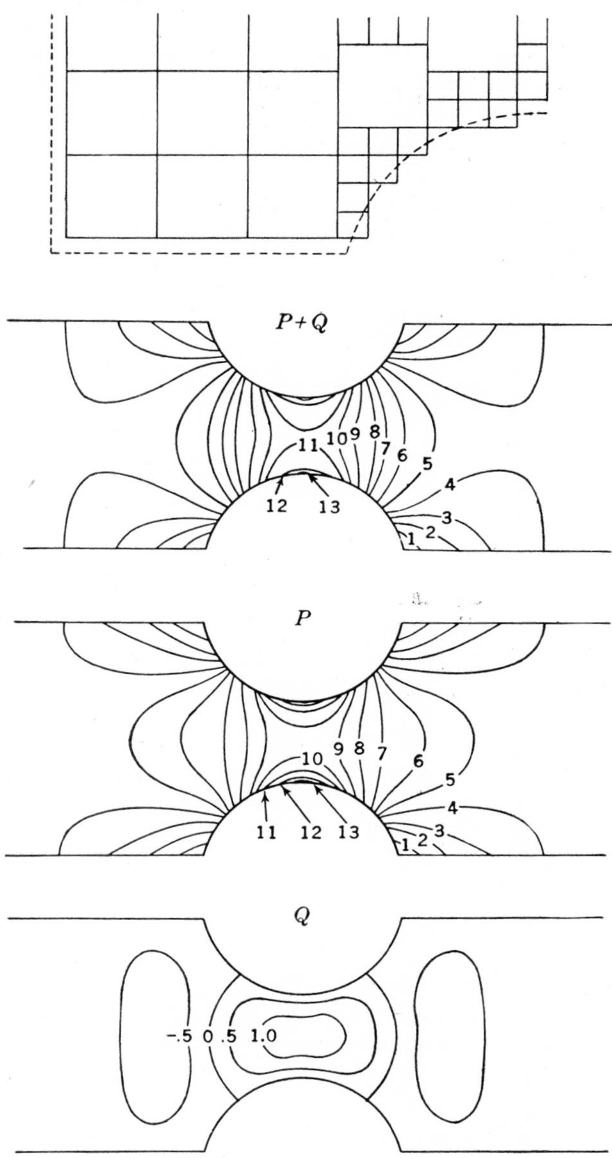

FIG. 8.29 Isopachic Curves and Contours of Principal Stresses for Grooved Bar in Fig. 8.28 Determined by Harmonization. (From Weller and Shortley.)

PART VI THE METHOD OF DIFFERENCES

§8.22 The Method of Differences. ***The number of traverses and the amount of arithmetic involved in the solution of a set of equations by iteration can be further reduced by harmonizing the differences between the values of two successive traverses rather than the actual values themselves.***

Letting $(u_i)_0$ denote the initial value at point (i) and $(u_i)_1$, $(u_i)_2$ the values after the first and second improvement, we may write

$$(u_i)_1 - (u_i)_0 = (\Delta u_i)_1,$$

$$(u_i)_2 - (u_i)_1 = (\Delta u_i)_2, \text{ etc.},$$

so that

$$(u_i)_1 = (u_i)_0 + (\Delta u_i)_1,$$

$$(u_i)_2 = (u_i)_0 + (\Delta u_i)_1 + (\Delta u_i)_2.$$

In general, after n traverses or improvements,

$$(u_i)_n = (u_i)_0 + \sum_{r=1}^{n} (\Delta u_i)_r. \tag{8.42}$$

The equations giving the increments Δu at the different points can be readily obtained from the basic equations for u_1, u_2, u_3, etc.

For example, referring to Fig. 8.18 and assuming u_c and u_o to be improved before u_d we have in any traverse k

$$(u_o)_k = Q + C_c(u_c)_k + C_d(u_d)_{k-1}. \tag{8.43}$$

By definition

$$\begin{aligned}(\Delta u_o)_k &= (u_o)_k - (u_o)_{k-1} \\ &= Q + C_c(u_c)_k + C_d(u_d)_{k-1} - Q - C_c(u_c)_{k-1} - C_d(u_d)_{k-2},\end{aligned}$$

or

$$(\Delta u_o)_k = C_c(\Delta u_c)_k + C_d(\Delta u_d)_{k-1}. \tag{8.44}$$

The equation for the increment $(\Delta u_i)_k$ differs from the equation giving $(u_i)_k$ itself in two respects: it does not contain the constant Q, and each u is replaced by its corresponding Δu.

As u_i approaches its limiting value, Δu_i approaches zero. The method of differences thus consists of replacing the boundary values by zeros and harmonizing the differences $(\Delta u_1)_k$, $(\Delta u_2)_k \cdots (\Delta u_n)_k$, at any stage k, by means of the increment equations until they vanish, and of adding the sum of all the increments to the last value of $(u_i)_0$, eq. (8.42). The value of k may be taken as unity.

It will be found that after a number of traverses each successive increment begins to bear a fixed ratio to the preceding one, i.e.,

$$\frac{(\Delta u_i)_k}{(\Delta u_i)_{k-1}} = \lambda, \quad \text{a constant.}$$

Assuming that this stage is reached at the end of m traverses, we can then write

$$\begin{aligned}\lim_{p\to\infty} \sum_{r=1}^{p} (\Delta u_i)_r &= (\Delta u_i)_m + \lambda(\Delta u_i)_m + \lambda^2(\Delta u_i)_m + \cdots + \lambda^\infty(\Delta u_i)_m \\ &= (\Delta u_i)_m(1 + \lambda + \lambda^2 + \cdots \lambda^\infty) \\ &= (\Delta u_i)_m \left(\frac{1}{1-\lambda}\right). \end{aligned} \tag{8.45}$$

Hence as soon as the stage m is reached at which λ is sensibly constant (technically this is known as the eigenvalue stage), it is possible to calculate the sum of all the differences, $\sum_{p=m}^{\infty} (\Delta u_i)_p$, without further iteration. Hence, by eqs. (8.42) and (8.45) the final value of u_i is

$$u_i = (u_i)_0 + (\Delta u_i)_1 + \cdots + (\Delta u_i)_{m-1} + (\Delta u_i)_m \left(\frac{1}{1-\lambda}\right). \tag{8.46}$$

This method is particularly useful when the set of equations is such that only one value need be assumed in order to calculate all others, as for example in the cases shown in Fig. 8.30, where u_1 determines all other u's. In such cases λ is a constant in all traverses, and it can be calculated directly from the equations of the increments. The final value of u_1 can then be determined after one traverse.

Consider, for example, the five unknowns in Fig. 8.30(e) in which the key value u_1 is related to the remaining four quantities by the following equations:

$$\left.\begin{aligned} (u_1)_m &= 0.25(u_2 + u_3 + u_4 + u_5)_{m-1}, && (a) \\ (u_2)_m &= Q_2 + C_2(u_1)_m, && (b) \\ (u_3)_m &= Q_3 + C_3(u_1)_m, && (c) \\ (u_4)_m &= Q_4 + C_4(u_1)_m, && (d) \\ (u_5)_m &= Q_5 + C_5(u_1)_m, && (e) \end{aligned}\right\} \tag{8.47}$$

in which m denotes the number of the traverses or improvements.

The corresponding equations for the increments in any traverse m are

$$\left.\begin{aligned}(\Delta u_1)_m &= 0.25\Delta(u_2 + u_3 + u_4 + u_5)_{m-1}, &(a)\\ (\Delta u_2)_m &= C_2(\Delta u_1)_m, &(b)\\ (\Delta u_3)_m &= C_3(\Delta u_1)_m, &(c)\\ (\Delta u_4)_m &= C_4(\Delta u_1)_m, &(d)\\ (\Delta u_5)_m &= C_5(\Delta u_1)_m. &(e)\end{aligned}\right\}(8.48)$$

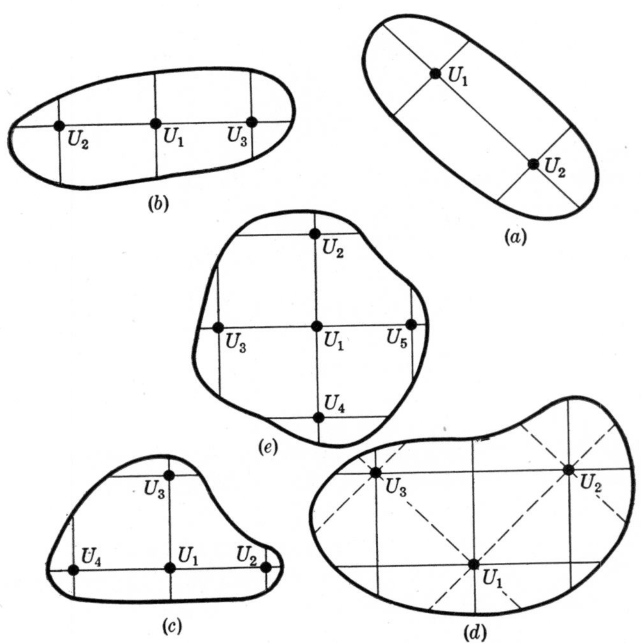

FIG. 8.30 Sketches Showing Special Cases in Which Difference Method is Particularly Effective.

Hence

$$\left.\begin{aligned}(\Delta u_1)_m &= 0.25[C_2(\Delta u_1)_{m-1} + C_3(\Delta u_1)_{m-1} + C_4(\Delta u_1)_{m-1} \\ &\qquad + C_5(\Delta u_1)_{m-1}] &(a)\\ &= 0.25(C_2 + C_3 + C_4 + C_5)(\Delta u_1)_{m-1} &(b)\end{aligned}\right\}(8.49)$$

and

$$\frac{(\Delta u_1)_m}{(\Delta u_1)_{m-1}} = 0.25(C_2 + C_3 + C_4 + C_5) = \lambda. \tag{8.50}$$

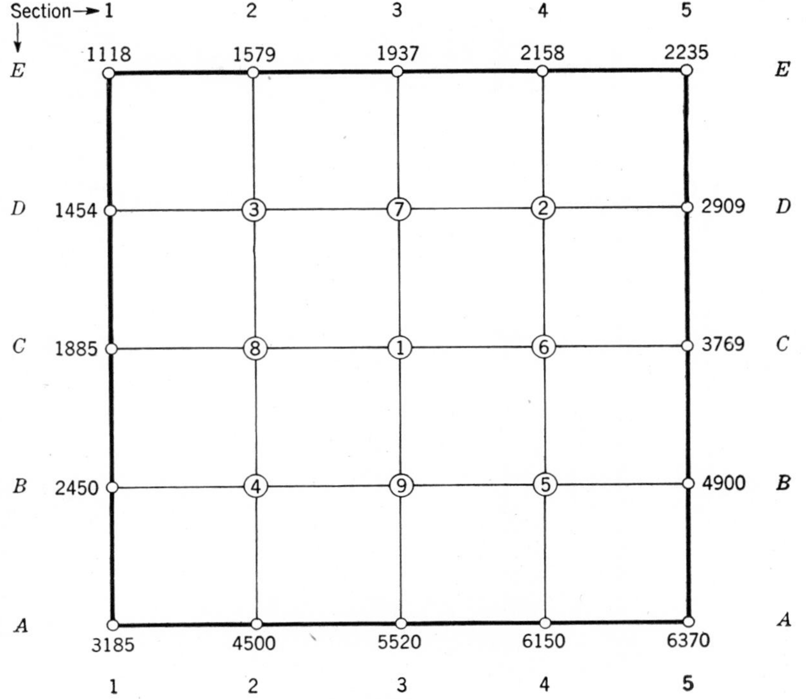

FIG. 8.31 Drawing for Example 8.5.

Example 8.5. Determine by the difference method the value of u_1 in the (4×4) square of Fig. 8.31.

Solution. The necessary equations are

$$\left.\begin{aligned} u_1 &= 0.25(u_2 + u_3 + u_4 + u_5), && (a)\\ u_2 &= 1985 + 0.25u_1, && (b)\\ u_3 &= 1235 + 0.25u_1, && (c)\\ u_4 &= 2648 + 0.25u_1, && (d)\\ u_5 &= 3915 + 0.25u_1. && (e) \end{aligned}\right\}(8.51)$$

Hence

$$C_2 = C_3 = C_4 = C_5 = 0.25,$$

and by eq. (8.50),

$$\lambda = 0.25(C_2 + C_3 + C_4 + C_5) = 0.25.$$

Assuming $(u_1)_0 = 0$, we find

$$(u_2)_0 = 1985, \quad (u_3)_0 = 1245, \quad (u_4)_0 = 2648, \quad (u_5)_0 = 3915$$

and

$$(u_1)_1 = 0.25(1985 + 1235 + 2648 + 3915) = 2446.$$

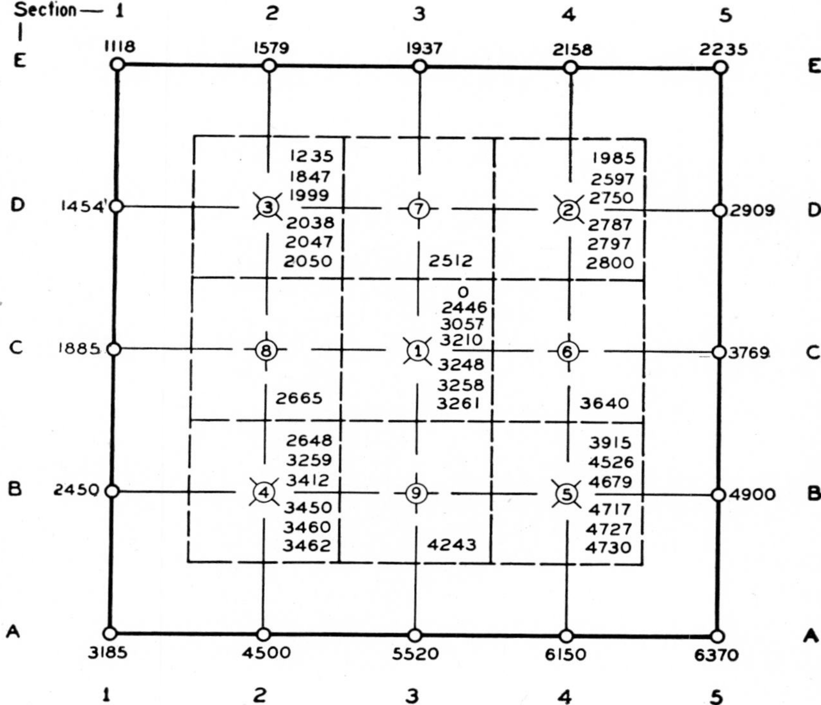

FIG. 8.32 Solution of Example 8.5 by Straight Harmonization Using the Liebmann Formula Only, and Assuming $(u_1)_0 = 0$.

By eq. (8.46) the final value of u_1 is given by

$$\begin{aligned} u_1 &= (\Delta u_1)_1 \left(\frac{1}{1-\lambda}\right) \\ &= [(u_1)_1 - (u_1)_0] \left(\frac{1}{1-\lambda}\right) \\ &= (2446 - 0) \times \left(\frac{1}{1-0.25}\right) = 3261. \end{aligned}$$

Check. By eq. (8.22),

$$u_1 = \tfrac{1}{12}(1118 + 2335 + 6370 + 3185) + \tfrac{1}{6}(1937 + 1885 + 5520 + 3769)$$
$$= 3269.$$

In areas surrounded by irregular boundaries the method is exactly the same, except for the coefficients C_2, C_3, etc., which will in general be different from each other.

Fig. 8.32 shows the same problem solved by straight harmonization with $(u_1)_0 = 0$. The difference in labor is obvious.

PART VII METHOD OF RELAXATION

§8.23 Method of Relaxation. A numerical method known as the *method of relaxation* has been developed in England by Professor Southwell.[1]

(*a*) *Residuals and Relaxation.* In this method the Liebmann formula is written as

$$u_1 + u_2 + u_3 + u_4 - 4u_o = Q. \tag{8.52}$$

Clearly, if the values $u_1, u_2 \cdots u_o$ are harmonized, Q equals zero. Conversely, if the values are not harmonized, Q does not vanish.

The quantity Q is spoken of as a *residual.* In terms of the residuals the numerical solution of Laplace's equation may be said to consist of such adjustments in the initial values of u as would make the residuals vanish. When the residual Q vanishes the point is said to be *relaxed.* The term *relaxed* would thus seem to be synonymous with *harmonized.*

(*b*) *Relaxation Pattern.* In the method of relaxation it is important to keep in mind a simple relation between the change Δu_o at any point O and the resulting changes in the residuals $Q_o, Q_1, \cdots$. Thus let $(Q_o)_0$ and $(Q_o)_1$ denote the residuals at O corresponding to values of u_o and $(u_o + \Delta u_o)$ respectively. Then

$$\left.\begin{aligned} (Q_o)_0 &= u_1 + u_2 + u_3 + u_4 - 4u_o, && (a)\\ \text{and}\quad (Q_o)_1 &= u_1 + u_2 + u_3 + u_4 - 4(u_o + \Delta u_o). && (b)\end{aligned}\right\} \tag{8.53}$$

The change in the residual at O, i.e., ΔQ_o, is then given by the expression

$$\Delta Q_o = (Q_o)_1 - (Q_o)_0 = -4\,\Delta u_o. \tag{8.54}$$

Similarly, Fig. 8.33,

$$\left.\begin{aligned} (Q_1)_0 &= (u_o + u_5 + u_6 + u_7 - 4u_1), && (a)\\ (Q_1)_1 &= (u_o + \Delta u_o) + u_5 + u_6 + u_7 - 4u_1, && (b)\\ \text{and}\quad \Delta Q_1 &= (Q_1)_1 - (Q_1)_0 = \Delta u_o. && (c)\end{aligned}\right\} \tag{8.55}$$

[1] See R. V. Southwell, *Relaxation Methods in Engineering Science*, Oxford University Press, 1940, Chapters VII and VIII; and *Relaxation Methods in Theoretical Physics*, Oxford, Clarendon Press, 1946. See also D. G. Christopherson and R. V. Southwell, "Relaxation Methods Applied to Engineering Problems," *Proc. Roy. Soc. London*, Vol. A168, pp. 317–350, 1938.

By analogy

$$\left.\begin{aligned} \Delta Q_1 = \Delta Q_2 = \Delta Q_3 = \Delta Q_4 &= \Delta u_o \qquad (a) \\ &= -\frac{\Delta Q_o}{4}. \qquad (b) \end{aligned}\right\} \quad (8.56)$$

There are thus three significant facts to remember:

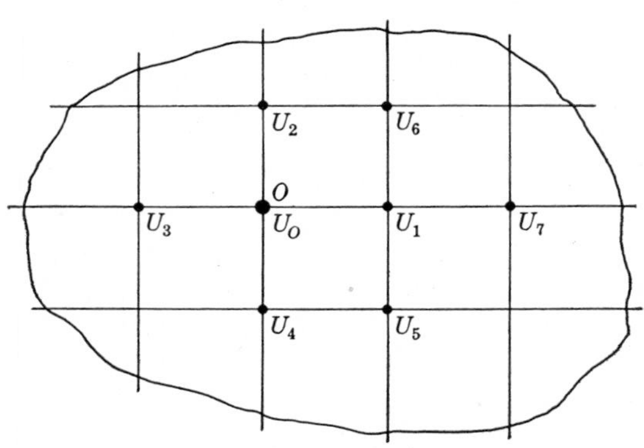

FIG. 8.33

1. ***A change in u_o affects all five residuals Q_o, Q_1, Q_2, Q_3, and Q_4 but does not affect any other residuals.***
2. ***The change in Q_o equals four times the change Δu_o and is of opposite sign,*** eq. (8.54).
3. ***The effect on Q_1, Q_2, Q_3, Q_4 equals the change Δu_o,*** eq. (8.56). These facts are shown graphically in Fig. 8.34, which is referred to as the *relaxation pattern.*

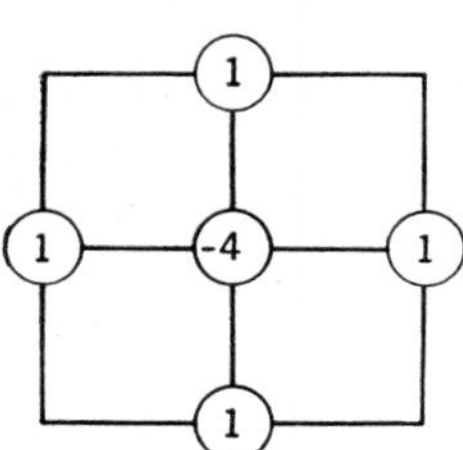

FIG. 8.34 Relaxation Pattern for the Liebmann Formula.

(c) *Vanishing Residuals.* A set of five residuals at a point O which satisfies the expression

$$Q_1 = Q_2 = Q_3 = Q_4 = \frac{Q_o}{4} \qquad (8.57)$$

will be spoken of as a vanishing set. Thus, the set $Q_o = -40$, $Q_1 = Q_2 = Q_3 = Q_4 = 10$ is a vanishing set. It is clear that by making $\Delta u_o = -10$ all residuals would vanish at once. For then, by eq. (8.54),

$$\begin{aligned} \Delta Q_o &= -4\ \Delta u_o \\ &= -4(-10) = 40, \end{aligned}$$

and by eq. (8.56a)

$$\Delta Q_1 = \Delta Q_2 = \Delta Q_3 = \Delta Q_4 = \Delta u_o = -10.$$

Hence, the point O can be completely relaxed by introducing a change of $\Delta u_o = -10$. This idea of creating a vanishing set at a point is an important guide in the method of relaxation.

Generally several changes in the value of u_o must be made before a vanishing set is obtained. In some cases it is desirable to introduce a value of Δu_o which is greater than that necessary to make Q_o vanish. In other cases the opposite choice is made. This is often referred to as *overshooting* and *undershooting*, respectively.

(d) *Operating Instructions.* The operating instructions are then as follows:

1. Calculate and record all residuals in the network.
2. Select the point at which the residual is numerically the greatest, and relax it approximately, overshooting or undershooting as may be indicated.
3. Calculate all the resulting changes in the residuals, as well as their final values, resulting from the relaxation of the largest residual.
4. Proceed to the point of the next greatest residual and repeat the process.

These instructions, which are admittedly vague, become clearer in the actual numerical solution of concrete problems. The method is rather flexible and highly subjective. To experts in the use of this method its flexibility is a great advantage in that it permits the computer to expedite a solution by exercising individual judgment and ingenuity. As in iteration good initial values are of great help.

Example 8.6. Consider the triangular area of Fig. 8.35 in which all boundary values are zero, and let it be required to find the three interior values u_1, u_2, u_3. The solution to this problem is obviously $u_1 = u_2 = u_3 = 0$. However, in order to illustrate the method, we deliberately assume a set of poor initial values: $u_1 = 40$, $u_2 = 60$, $u_3 = 120$.

Solution. 1. From the known boundary values and the assumed quantities for u_1, u_2, and u_3 we calculate the residuals $(Q_1)_0$, $(Q_2)_0$, and $(Q_3)_0$. Thus

$$\left.\begin{aligned} (Q_1)_0 &= 0 + 0 + 0 + 60 - 4 \times 40 = -100, \\ (Q_2)_0 &= 0 + 0 + 40 + 120 - 4 \times 60 = -80, \\ (Q_3)_0 &= 0 + 0 + 60 + 0 - 4 \times 120 = -420. \end{aligned}\right\} \quad (8.58)$$

2. The largest residual is $(Q_3)_0 = -420$, and therefore this point is relaxed first. A change of -105 in u_3 would eliminate $(Q_3)_0$ entirely. However, since all residuals are negative, we choose Δu_3 somewhat greater numeri-

cally, say -110; i.e., we overshoot 5. With this change in u_3 we have

$$(Q_3)_1 = -420 + 4(110) = +20,$$

$$(Q_2)_1 = -80 - 110 = -190,$$

$$(Q_1)_1 = -100.$$

These values are shown in the second row of Table 8.5.

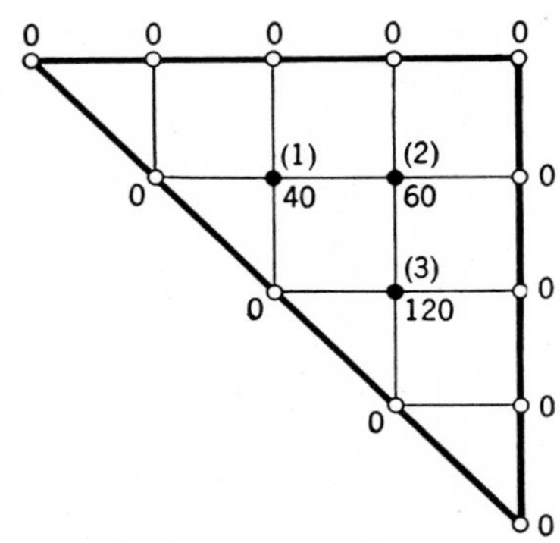

FIG. 8.35

3. We next relax u_2 and overshoot by $2\frac{1}{2}$ in order for the residuals to have opposite signs. Then choosing -50 for Δu_2 we obtain

$$(Q_1)_2 = -150, \quad (Q_2)_2 = 10, \quad (Q_3)_2 = -30$$

as shown in the third row of Table 8.5.

4. Next we relax u_1, letting $\Delta u_1 = -40$, i.e., overshooting again by $2\frac{1}{2}$. We then obtain

$$(Q_1)_3 = 10, \quad (Q_2)_3 = -30, \quad (Q_3)_3 = -30.$$

5. We now return to u_3 and choose $\Delta u_3 = -10$. This gives

$$(Q_1)_4 = 10, \quad (Q_2)_4 = -40, \quad (Q_3)_4 = 10,$$

which is a vanishing set of residuals for $\Delta u_2 = -10$.

Two other solutions which begin by overshooting u_3 are shown in Tables 8.6 and 8.7. Table 8.8 shows a solution in which u_3 is undershot. In the solution shown in Table 8.7 use was made of the known fact that the values must vanish everywhere.[1] The point is merely to show that available information can be utilized to shorten the process.

[1] Solutions in Tables 8.7 and 8.8 are by Professor Emmons. See his paper, "The Numerical Solution of Partial Differential Equations," *Quarterly of Applied Mathematics*, Vol. II, No. 2, pp. 173–195, October, 1944.

TABLES ILLUSTRATING METHOD OF RELAXATION

	POINT 1			POINT 2			POINT 3		
TABLE	Q	u	Δu	Q	u	Δu	Q	u	Δu
	−100	40		−80	60		−420	120	
	−100			−190			20		−110
8.5	−150			10		−50	−30		
	10		−40	−30			−30		
	10			−40			10		−10
	0			0		−10			
RESULTS	$Q_1 = 0$	$u_1 = 0$		$Q_2 = 0$	$u_2 = 0$		$Q_3 = 0$	$u_3 = 0$	
	−100	40		−80	60		−420	120	
	−100			−205			80		−125
8.6	−150			−5		−50	30		
	10		−40	−45			30		
	0			−5		−10	20		
	0			0			0		+5
RESULTS	$Q_1 = 0$	$u_1 = 0$		$Q_2 = 0$	$u_2 = 0$		$Q_3 = 0$	$u_3 = 0$	
	−100	40		−80	60		−420	120	
	−100			−200			60		−120
8.7	−160			40		−60	0		
	0		−40	0			0		
RESULTS	$Q_1 = 0$	$u_1 = 0$		$Q_2 = 0$	$u_2 = 0$		$Q_3 = 0$	$u_3 = 0$	
	−100	40		−80	60		−420	120	
	−100			−180			−20		−100
8.8	−150			20		−50	−70		
	10		−40	−20			−70		
	10			−40			10		−20
	0			0		−10	0		
RESULTS	$Q_1 = 0$	$u_1 = 0$		$Q_2 = 0$	$u_2 = 0$		$Q_3 = 0$	$u_3 = 0$	

Example 8.7. A somewhat more difficult problem is illustrated in Fig. 8.36, which represents the cross section of a furnace with an inside temperature of 500° F. and an outside constant temperature of 100° F. It can be shown that in the steady state the temperatures at each point satisfy Laplace's equation.[1] A solution by the method of relaxation is shown in Fig. 8.37. Professor Emmons gives the time required to obtain this solution as 1¾ hours and contrasts it with the 11 hours required by the averaging process.

It is no doubt true that the elementary iterative or averaging process is extremely slow if one limits himself to the Liebmann formula only and makes no effort to obtain good initial values. As already pointed out, tremendous savings in time can be made in the iterative process by utilizing the formulas for larger blocks. To be specific, the problem under consideration can be solved by block iteration in fifteen to twenty minutes without a calculating machine.

Thus, Fig. 8.38, the initial or first key values are found by the Liebmann formula and diagonal boundary values. This gives

$$(u_1)_0 = 200, \quad (u_2)_0 = 235, \quad (u_3)_0 = 300, \quad (u_4)_0 = 300.$$

These values are all improved by the formula for a (4×4) square

$$6u = 0.5 \sum_{i=1}^{4} a_i + \sum_{i=1}^{4} c_i. \tag{8.22}$$

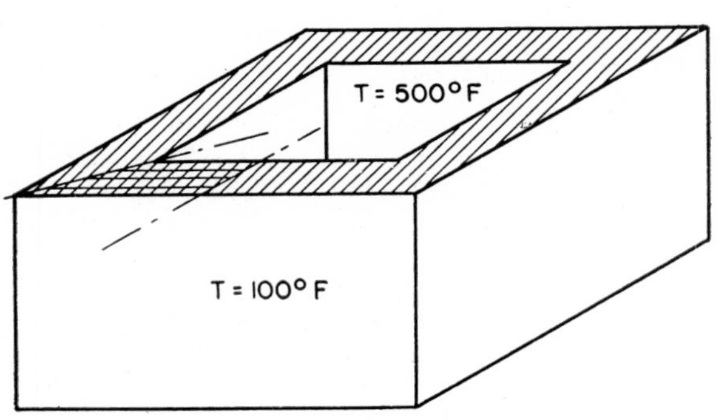

FIG. 8.36 Sketch of Furnace for Example 8.7.

Thus

$$6(u_1)_1 = 0.5(500 + 100 + 100 + 100) + 2 \times 235 + 200,$$

$$(u_1)_1 = 178.$$

$$6(u_2)_1 = 0.5(500 + u_2 + 200) + 300 + 500 + 178 + 100,$$

$$(u_2)_1 = 259.$$

$$6(u_3)_1 = 0.5(500 + 500 + 100 + 100) + 300 + 500 + 259 + 100,$$

$$(u_3)_1 = 293.$$

$$6(u_4)_1 = 0.5 \times 1200 + 300 + 500 + 293 + 100,$$

$$(u_4)_1 = 299.$$

The next traverse gives

$$(u_1)_2 = 186, \quad (u_2)_2 = 260, \quad (u_3)_2 = 293, \quad (u_4)_2 = 299.$$

The remaining eight values are found by the direct use of the Liebmann formula. The final answers are shown in Fig. 8.38.

As far as Laplace's equation is concerned, the author has a decided preference for the block iterative process. It is definite and teachable. We have found it relatively rapid not only in simple rectangular areas but also where the boundaries are quite irregular.

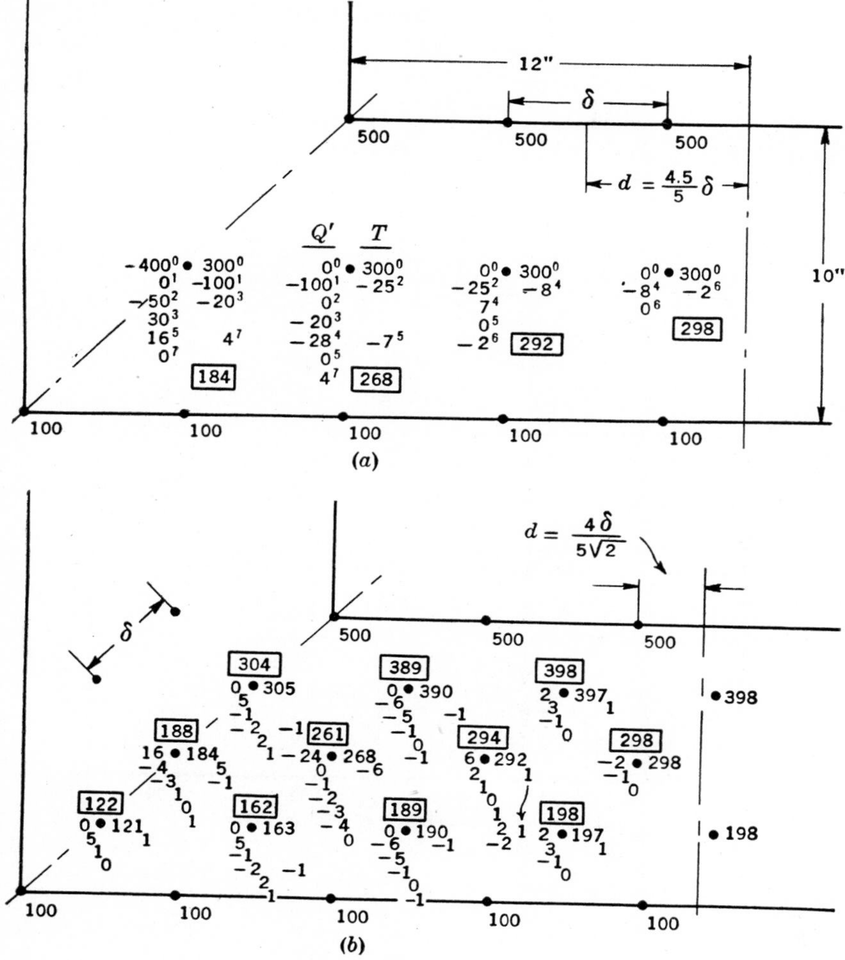

FIG. 8.37 Solution of Furnace Problem of Fig. 8.36 by Relaxation. (From Emmons. See footnote 1, p. 284.)

The real power and advantage of the method of relaxation becomes evident only in partial differential equations which are more complicated than Laplace's. In photoelasticity, our chief interest is in Laplace's equation, and, therefore, the iterative process has here found preference.

§8.24 Poisson's Equation. The methods of iteration developed in this chapter can be extended with slight modifications to apply to the numerical solution of the more general Poisson's equation

$$\frac{\partial^2 U}{\partial x^2} + \frac{\partial^2 U}{\partial y^2} = F(x, y), \tag{8.59}$$

in which $F(x, y)$ is defined in the interior region.

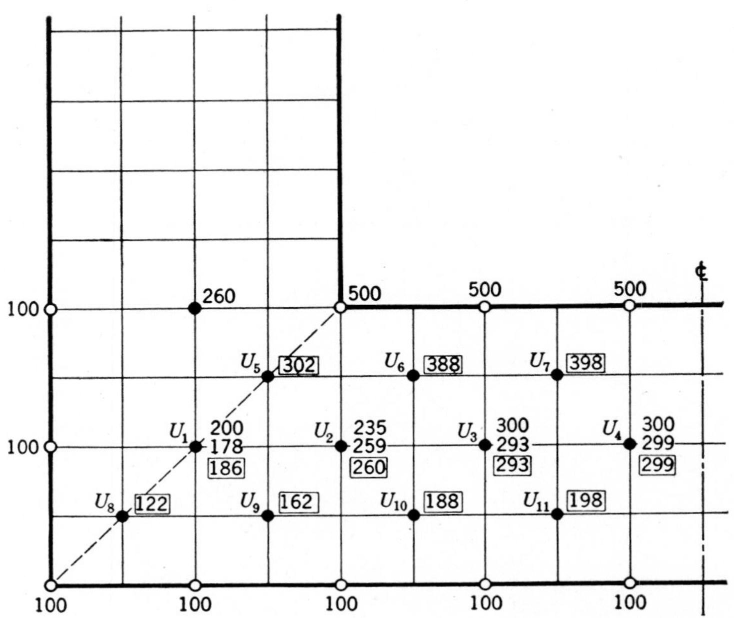

FIG. 8.38 Temperature Distribution in the Furnace of Fig. 8.36 Determined by Block Iteration Using Eq. (8.22) and Two-Line Rosettes for Initial Values.

The method of derivation of the basic formulas for regular figures, the forms of the final equations, the general method of harmonization, and especially the difference method are essentially the same as those developed here for Laplace's equation.

For a detailed discussion of this topic as it relates to torsion the reader is referred to the paper by Weller, Shortley, and Fried.[1] Rectangular areas are treated by Moskovitz.[2]

[1] "The Solution of Torsion Problems by a Numerical Integration of Poisson's Equation," by R. Weller, G. H. Shortley, and B. Fried, *Journal of Applied Physics*, Vol. II, No. 4, pp. 283–290, April, 1940.

[2] "The Numerical Solution of Laplace's and Poisson's Equations," D. Moskovitz, *Quarterly of Applied Mathematics*, Vol. II, July, 1944.

APPENDIX A

§8.25 The Four-Point Influence Equation by Taylor's Series.[1]

Let $U(x, y)$ be a function[2] of two variables, whose partial derivatives at the point (x, y) will be denoted by U_x, U_y, U_{xx}, U_{xy}, U_{yy}, U_{xxx}, U_{xxy}, U_{xyy}, U_{yyy}, where U_{xxy} for example denotes $\partial^3 U/\partial x^2\, \partial y$. We can then approximate $U(x + a, y + h)$ by a portion of its Taylor series expansion. Neglecting terms of higher degree than the third in a and b, we have

$$\begin{aligned} U(x + a, y + b) = U(x, y) &+ aU_x + bU_y + \tfrac{1}{2}[a^2 U_{xx} + 2abU_{xy} \\ &+ b^2 U_{yy}] + \tfrac{1}{6}[a^3 U_{xxx} + 3a^2 b U_{xxy} \\ &+ 3ab^2 U_{xyy} + b^3 U_{yyy}]. \end{aligned} \tag{8.60}$$

Applying eq. (8.60) to write approximate values for

$$U(x + r_1 h, y), \quad U(x - r_2 h, y), \quad U(x, y + s_1 h), \quad U(x, y - s_2 h)$$

we have, neglecting terms of higher degree in h than the third,

$$\left.\begin{aligned} U(x + r_1 h, y) &= U(x, y) + r_1 h U_x + \tfrac{1}{2} r_1{}^2 h^2 U_{xx} \\ &\quad + \tfrac{1}{6} r_1{}^3 h^3 U_{xxx}, & (a) \\ U(x - r_2 h, y) &= U(x, y) - r_2 h U_x + \tfrac{1}{2} r_2{}^2 h^2 U_{xx} \\ &\quad - \tfrac{1}{6} r_2{}^3 h^3 U_{xxx}, & (b) \\ U(x, y + s_1 h) &= U(x, y) + s_1 h U_y + \tfrac{1}{2} s_1{}^2 h^2 U_{yy} \\ &\quad + \tfrac{1}{6} s_1{}^3 h^3 U_{yyy}, & (c) \\ U(x, y - s_2 h) &= U(x, y) - s_2 h U_y + \tfrac{1}{2} s_2{}^2 h^2 U_{yy} \\ &\quad - \tfrac{1}{6} s_2{}^3 h^3 U_{yyy}. & (d) \end{aligned}\right\} \tag{8.61}$$

To derive the Liebmann formula from eqs. (8.61), put $r_1 = r_2 = s_1 = s_2 = 1$, add the four equations, and, remembering that

$$U_{xx} + U_{yy} = 0, \tag{8.1}$$

we have

$$\begin{aligned} U(x + h, y) + U(x - h, y) + U(x, y + h) + U(x, y - h) \\ = 4U(x, y), \end{aligned} \tag{8.62}$$

[1] For this derivation the author is indebted to Dr. David Moskovitz, Associate Professor of Mathematics at the Carnegie Institute of Technology.

[2] We assume that $U(x, y)$ is a function whose partial derivatives of all needed orders exist, and those of higher order than the first are independent of the order of differentiation.

from which

$$U(x, y) = \tfrac{1}{4}[U(x + h, y) + U(x - h, y) + U(x, y + h) + U(x, y - h)], \quad (8.63)$$

which is obviously the Liebmann formula.

When the four quantities r_1, r_2, s_1, s_2 are not equal to each other we rewrite eqs. (8.61) without the last term of each equation. This amounts to neglecting terms in h of higher degree than the second. Multiply the resulting four equations respectively by r_2, r_1, s_2, and s_1, then add the first two and the second two, obtaining

$$\left.\begin{aligned} r_2U(x + r_1h, y) + r_1U(x - r_2h, y) &= (r_1 + r_2)U(x, y) \\ &\quad + \tfrac{1}{2}h^2r_1r_2(r_1 + r_2)U_{xx}, \qquad (a) \\ s_2U(x, y + s_1h) + s_1U(x, y - s_2h) &= (s_2 + s_1)U(x, y) \\ &\quad + \tfrac{1}{2}h^2s_1s_2(s_1 + s_2)U_{yy}. \qquad (b) \end{aligned}\right\} (8.64)$$

Divide eq. (8.64*a*) by $r_1r_2(r_1 + r_2)$, then divide eq. (8.64*b*) by $s_1s_2(s_1 + s_2)$, then add the resulting equations, and, again remembering that

$$U_{xx} + U_{yy} = 0, \quad (8.1)$$

we have

$$\frac{r_2U(x + r_1h, y) + r_1U(x - r_2h, y)}{r_1r_2(r_1 + r_2)} + \frac{s_2U(x, y + s_1h) + s_1U(x, y - s_2h)}{s_1s_2(s_1 + s_2)} = \left(\frac{1}{r_1r_2} + \frac{1}{s_1s_2}\right)U(x, y). \quad (8.65)$$

In terms of the notation of Fig. 8.1, observing that $x = y = 0$, $r_1 = a$, $r_2 = c_1$, $s_1 = b$, and $s_2 = d$, the last expression reduces to eq. (8.4), which is the four-point influence formula.

APPENDIX B

Rectangular Areas by Means of Tables

§8.26 Solution of Rectangular Areas by Means of Tables. It can be shown that, in any rectangle ($m \times n'$), $m = 3, 4$, n' any number, the key values are linear functions of all Laplacian perimeters u_1 to u_k inclusive. Thus

$$\boldsymbol{u}_i = \boldsymbol{C}_1\boldsymbol{P}_1 + \boldsymbol{C}_2\boldsymbol{P}_2 + \cdots + \boldsymbol{C}_i\boldsymbol{P}_i \cdots + \boldsymbol{C}_k\boldsymbol{P}_k, \quad (8.66)$$

in which $C_1, C_2 \cdots C_k$ are constant coefficients for each u_i. Table A gives coefficients C_1 to C_k inclusive *for the last key value* in rectangles $(4 \times n')$ respectively.[1] Thus in a rectangle (4×5.5), Table A,

$$u_k = u_2 = 0.02703P_1 + 0.16216P_2.$$

This table is sufficient to determine all key values in rectangles $(4 \times n')$, for values of n' between 2 and infinity. The procedure is as follows:

First calculate the last key value u_k using the appropriate coefficients in the table. We can then treat the rectangle as if it were shorter, and its length n an even integer. Next we find u_{k-1} and then view the rectangle as if it were further shortened by 2 units. We thus can find u_{k-2}, u_{k-3}, etc., and continue the process until all key values are found.

It should be observed that in calculating u_{k-1} the last perimeter P_{k-1} must be modified by the addition of u_k. In general, in calculating u_i we add u_{i+1} to P_i. Thus

$$u_i = C_1P_1 + C_2P_2 + \cdots C_i(P_i + u_{i+1}). \tag{8.67}$$

Inspection of Table A shows that the coefficients for u_k rapidly approach convergence. In rectangles $(4 \times n')$, Table A convergence is reached at $n = 13$. For values of n greater than 13, C_k, C_{k-1}, C_{k-2}, C_{k-3} are the same as C_6, C_5, C_4, and C_3 respectively at $n = 13$ or $n = 12$, depending on whether n is odd or even. The coefficients for values of δ other than those given in Table A can be found by interpolation.

§8.27 Auxiliary Tables. In long rectangles it is desirable to be able to find directly interior values of u_i, without having to find first $u_k, u_{k-1} \cdots u_{i+1}$. This can be done by means of Table B, which gives the coefficients for any $u_i < u_k$ independent of all other key values. *Table B is for regular rectangles, with integral lengths.* If the length is not an integer it is necessary first to find u_k.

Another advantage of Table B lies in the fact that all key values are given in terms of the one set of P's calculated for the rectangle $(4 \times n)$, and no modification of these is needed.

Inspection of Table B shows that when n equals 14 the coefficients have become stabilized and that these coefficients may be used for all subsequent values of n. Specifically, for any integral value of n greater than 14.

[1] These coefficients can be obtained by combining the formulas for the elementary cases derived in Part I. For an analytical treatment and construction of these tables see author's paper "The Numerical Solution of Laplace's Equation in Composite Rectangular Areas," *Journal of Applied Physics*, September, 1946.

(*a*) The coefficients of u_1, u_2, and u_3 are the same as of u_1, u_2, and u_3 for $n = 14$.

(*b*) For n even, the coefficients C_k, C_{k-1}, C_{k-2}, etc., of u_{k-1} and u_{k-2} are the same as of u_5 and u_4 respectively at $n = 14$. For n odd, the corresponding coefficients are the same as of u_5 and u_4 respectively at $n = 13$.

(*c*) The coefficients of u_i, $(3 < i < k - 2)$, are constant, and essentially the same as for u_3 in $n = 14$. Thus, to four decimal places, n odd or even,

$$u_i = 0.1768P_i + 0.0303(P_{i-1} + P_{i+1}) + 0.0052(P_{i-2} + P_{i+2}) + 0.0009(P_{i-3} + P_{i+3}); \tag{8.68}$$

since the last perimeter in eq. (8.68) is P_{i+3} it follows that u_i is affected by a relatively small length of immediately adjacent boundaries. If we limit the accuracy of the coefficients to four decimal places it is seen that in rectangles $(4 \times n)$ the length of the influencing boundary does not extend beyond six lattice units measured from point (i) in either direction. In rectangles $(3 \times n)$ the corresponding length is only four lattice units. These facts are useful in approximate solutions.

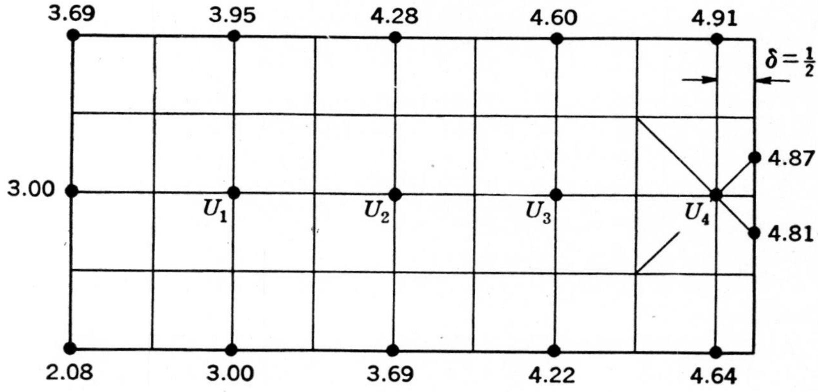

FIG. 8.39 Boundary Values for Example 8.8.

Example 8.8. Given a rectangle (4×8.5) with boundary values as shown in Fig. 8.39. Required to find all key values.

Solution. (*a*) We begin by calculating P_1, P_2, P_3, and p_4, the first three of which are found from eq. (8.31*b*) and the last from eq. (8.34*c*). Thus

$$P_1 = 0.5(4.28 + 3.69 + 2.08 + 3.69) + 3.95 + 3.00 + 3.00 = 16.82,$$

$$P_2 = 0.5(4.60 + 3.95 + 3.00 + 4.22) + 4.28 + 3.69 = 15.86,$$

$$P_3 = 0.5(4.91 + 4.28 + 3.69 + 4.64) + 4.60 + 4.22 = 17.58,$$

$$p_4 = 0.5(4.60 + 4.22 + 4.91 + 4.64) + 4(4.87 + 4.81) = 47.91.$$

We next find $u_k = u_4$. From Table A we have

$$u_4 = 0.00045P_1 + 0.00272P_2 + 0.01584P_3 + 0.09235p_4 = 4.754.$$

We now view the rectangle as a (4×8) and find u_3. Thus, by eq. (8.67),

$$u_3 = 0.00490P_1 + 0.02941P_2 + 0.17157(P_3 + u_4) = 4.381.$$

Considering the remaining figure as a (4×6) we have

$$u_2 = 0.02857P_1 + 0.17143(P_2 + u_3) = 3.950.$$

Lastly

$$u_1 = 0.16667(P_1 + u_2) = 3.462.$$

(*b*) *Alternative Procedure for u_1 and u_2.* After finding u_4 and u_3 we take coefficients from Table B and write

$$u_2 = 0.02941P_1 + 0.17647P_2 + 0.02941(P_3 + u_3) = 3.939,$$

$$u_1 = 0.17155P_1 + 0.02941P_2 + 0.00490(P_3 + u_3) = 3.460.$$

The exact values of u_4, u_3, u_2, and u_1 are 4.7536, 4.3820, 3.9512, 3.4657, which differ but slightly from those given by our method. From the key values all remaining values can be calculated by the Liebmann formula.

TABLE A $4(n + \delta)$

u	$n \downarrow$	$\delta \rightarrow$	0.1	0.2	0.3	0.4	0.5	0.6	0.7	0.8	0.9	1.0
u_1	2	C_1	0.02326	0.04348	0.06122	0.07692	0.09091	0.10345	0.11475	0.12500	0.13433	0.14286
u_1	3	C_1	.14667	.15000	.15294	.15556	.15789	.16000	.16190	.16364	.16522	.16667
u_2	4	C_1	.00389	.00730	.01031	.01299	.01538	.01754	.01950	.02128	.02290	.02439
		C_2	.02335	.04380	.06186	.07792	.09231	.10526	.11699	.12766	.13740	.14634
u_2	5	C_1	.02506	.02564	.02616	.02662	.02703	.02740	.02773	.02804	.02832	.02857
		C_2	.15034	.15385	.15694	.15970	.16216	.16438	.16639	.16822	.16990	.17143
u_3	6	C_1	.00067	.00125	.00177	.00223	.00264	.00301	.00334	.00365	.00393	.00418
		C_2	.00400	.00751	.01061	.01336	.01583	.01805	.02007	.02190	.02357	.02510
		C_3	.02335	.04380	.06187	.07795	.09235	.10532	.11706	.12774	.13749	.14644
u_3	7	C_1	.00430	.00440	.00449	.00457	.00464	.00470	.00476	.00481	.00486	.00490
		C_2	.02579	.02639	.02692	.02740	.02782	.02820	.02855	.02886	.02915	.02941
		C_3	.15045	.15396	.15706	.15982	.16229	.16451	.16653	.16836	.17003	.17157
u_4	8	C_1	.00011	.00021	.00030	.00038	.00045	.00052	.00057	.00063	.00067	.00072
		C_2	.00069	.00129	.00182	.00229	.00272	.00310	.00344	.00376	.00404	.00431
		C_3	.00401	.00752	.01062	.01337	.01584	.01807	.02008	.02192	.02359	.02513
		C_4	.02335	.04381	.06187	.07795	.09235	.10532	.11706	.12774	.13750	.14645
u_4	9	C_1	.00074	.00075	.00077	.00078	.00080	.00081	.00082	.00083	.00083	.00084
		C_2	.00443	.00453	.00462	.00470	.00477	.00484	.00490	.00495	.00500	.00505
		C_3	.02581	.02642	.02695	.02742	.02784	.02823	.02857	.02889	.02917	.02944
		C_4	.15045	.15396	.15706	.15982	.16229	.16452	.16653	.16836	.17004	.17157

u_5	10	C_1	.00002	.00004	.00005	.00007	.00008	.00009	.00010	.00011	.00012	.00012
		C_2	.00012	.00022	.00031	.00039	.00047	.00053	.00059	.00064	.00069	.00074
		C_3	.00069	.00129	.00182	.00229	.00272	.00310	.00345	.00376	.00405	.00431
		C_4	.00401	.00752	.01062	.01337	.01584	.01807	.02008	.02192	.02359	.02513
		C_5	.02335	.04381	.06187	.07795	.09235	.10532	.11706	.12774	.13750	.14645
u_5	11	C_1	.00013	.00013	.00013	.00013	.00014	.00014	.00014	.00014	.00014	.00014
		C_2	.00076	.00078	.00079	.00081	.00082	.00083	.00084	.00085	.00086	.00087
		C_3	.00443	.00453	.00462	.00470	.00478	.00484	.00490	.00496	.00501	.00505
		C_4	.02581	.02642	.02695	.02742	.02784	.02823	.02857	.02889	.02917	.02944
		C_5	.15045	.15396	.15706	.15982	.16229	.16452	.16653	.16836	.17004	.17157
u_6	12	C_1	.00000	.00001	.00001	.00001	.00001	.00002	.00002	.00002	.00002	.00002
		C_2	.00002	.00004	.00005	.00007	.00008	.00009	.00010	.00011	.00012	.00013
		C_3	.00012	.00022	.00031	.00039	.00047	.00053	.00059	.00065	.00069	.00074
		C_4	.00069	.00129	.00182	.00229	.00272	.00310	.00345	.00376	.00405	.00431
		C_5	.00401	.00752	.01062	.01337	.01584	.01807	.02008	.02192	.02359	.02513
		C_6	.02335	.04381	.06187	.07795	.09235	.10532	.11706	.12774	.13750	.14645
u_6	13	C_1	.00002	.00002	.00002	.00002	.00002	.00002	.00002	.00002	.00002	.00002
		C_2	.00013	.00013	.00013	.00014	.00014	.00014	.00014	.00015	.00015	.00015
		C_3	.00076	.00078	.00079	.00081	.00082	.00083	.00084	.00085	.00086	.00087
		C_4	.00443	.00453	.00462	.00470	.00478	.00484	.00490	.00496	.00501	.00505
		C_5	.02581	.02642	.02695	.02742	.02784	.02823	.02857	.02889	.02917	.02944
		C_6	.15045	.15396	.15706	.15982	.16229	.16452	.16653	.16836	.17004	.17157

TABLE B (4 × n)

n	u	C_1	C_2	C_3	C_4	C_5	C_6
5	u_1	0.17073	0.02439				
6	u_1	.17143	.02857				
7	u_1	.17155	.02929	0.00418			
	u_2	.02029	.17573	.02510			
8	u_1	.17157	.02941	.00490			
	u_2	.02941	.17647	.02941			
9	u_1	.17157	.02943	.00503	0.00072		
	u_2	.02943	.17660	.03015	.00431		
	u_3	.00503	.03015	.17588	.02513		
10	u_1	.17157	.02944	.00505	.00084		
	u_2	.02944	.17662	.03028	.00505		
	u_3	.00505	.03028	.17662	.02944		
11	u_1	.17157	.02944	.00505	.00086	0.00012	
	u_2	.02944	.17662	.03030	.00517	.00074	
	u_3	.00505	.03030	.17675	.03018	.00431	
	u_4	.00086	.00517	.03018	.17588	.02513	
12	u_1	.17157	.02944	.00505	.00087	.00014	
	u_2	.02944	.17662	.03030	.00519	.00087	
	u_3	.00505	.03030	.17677	.03030	.00505	
	u_4	.00087	.00519	.03030	.17662	.02944	
13	u_1	.17157	.02944	.00505	.00087	.00015	0.00002
	u_2	.02944	.17662	.03030	.00519	.00089	.00013
	u_3	.00505	.03030	.17677	.03032	.00518	.00074
	u_4	.00087	.00520	.03032	.17675	.03018	.00431
	u_5	.00015	.00089	.00518	.03018	.17589	.02513
14	u_1	.17157	.02944	.00505	.00087	.00015	.00002
	u_2	.02944	.17662	.03030	.00520	.00089	.00015
	u_3	.00505	.03030	.17677	.03033	.00520	.00087
	u_4	.00087	.00520	.03033	.17677	.03030	.00505
	u_5	.00015	.00089	.00520	.03030	.17662	.02944

CHAPTER 9

CONFORMAL TRANSFORMATIONS

THE USE OF POLAR AND BIPOLAR COORDINATES IN HARMONIZATION

§9.1 Equations of Transformation, Corresponding Points and Curves. In many problems in which we have to deal with curvilinear boundaries such as circular rings, or bars with grooves or circular holes, it

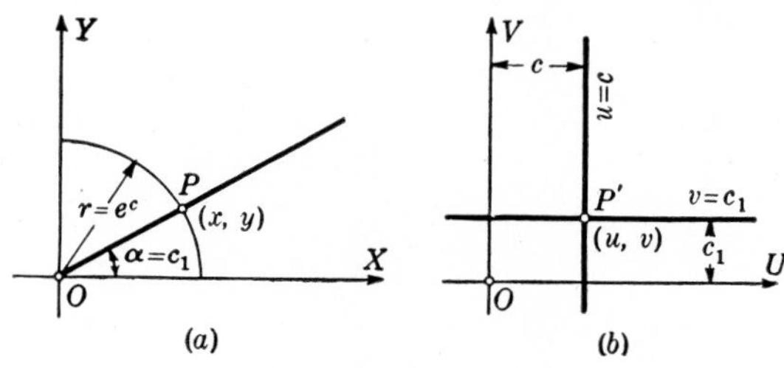

FIG. 9.1

is convenient to introduce in place of the ordinary cartesian coordinates (x, y) other cartesian coordinates (u, v) so chosen that u or v is constant over the curved boundaries in question. For example, let us assume that in Fig. 9.1

$$u = \log (x^2 + y^2)^{1/2} = \log r$$

and

$$v = \tan^{-1} \frac{y}{x} = \alpha.$$

In such a case all points lying on a circle of radius $r = e^c$ (c = a constant) with center at the origin in the (x, y) plane would in the (u, v) plane fall on a vertical line $u = c$. Likewise, all points on the radial line OP in the (x, y) plane which makes an angle $\alpha = c_1$ with the X axis would in the (u, v) plane fall on a horizontal line $v = c_1$, Fig. 9.1. The equations giving u and v in terms of x and y are known as the *equations of transformation.* In general, these equations will be expressed as

$$u = u(x, y), \quad v = v(x, y), \tag{9.1}$$

where $u(x, y)$, $v(x, y)$ are specific given functions of x and y.

If P is a point in the (x, y) plane of coordinates (x, y), then the point P' in the (u, v) plane whose coordinates (u, v) are given by the equations of transformation is said to be *a corresponding point.*

The equations of transformation transform a locus of points in the (x, y) plane into some definite locus in the (u, v) plane. Curves made up of corresponding points will be spoken of as *corresponding curves.*

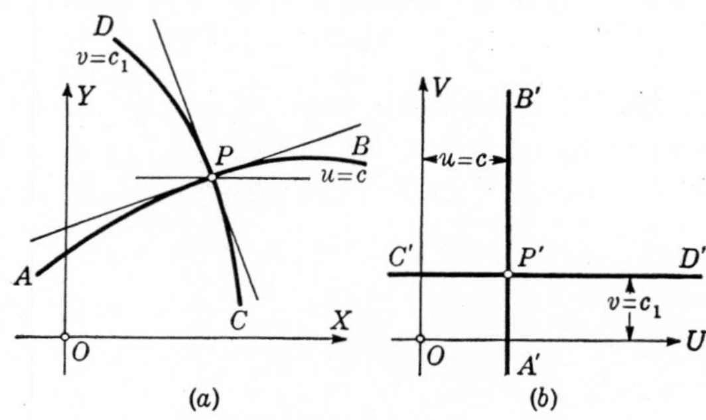

FIG. 9.2

§9.2 **Orthogonal Transformations.** In Fig. 9.2 let P' and P be a pair of corresponding points, and let the curves APB and CPD be the curves through P which correspond to the straight lines $A'P'B'$ and $C'P'D'$, for which $u = c$ and $v = c_1$ respectively. Since

$$u = u(x, y)$$

it follows that

$$du = \frac{\partial u}{\partial x}\,dx + \frac{\partial u}{\partial y}\,dy.$$

For the curve APB u is a constant, and therefore

$$du = 0.$$

Hence $(dy/dx)_{ab}$, the slope at every point on the curve APB, is given by

$$\left(\frac{dy}{dx}\right)_{ab} = -\frac{\partial u/\partial x}{\partial u/\partial y}\cdot \tag{9.2}$$

We assume that $\partial u/\partial y$ does not vanish. Similarly,

$$v = v(x, y)$$

and

$$dv = \frac{\partial v}{\partial x}\,dx + \frac{\partial v}{\partial y}\,dy.$$

Clearly, for curve CPD, v is a constant, and therefore $(dy/dx)_{cd}$, the slope at every point on curve CPD, is given by

$$\left(\frac{dy}{dx}\right)_{cd} = -\frac{\partial v/\partial x}{\partial v/\partial y}. \tag{9.3}$$

Thus far we have assumed that the transformations are effected by arbitrary u and v functions. Suppose, however, that we restrict these functions to the real and imaginary parts of an analytic function of a complex variable. Thus if

$$z = x + iy$$

then

$$f(z) = u(x, y) + iv(x, y), \tag{9.4}$$

in which u is the real and v the imaginary part.

It is shown in advanced calculus that there exists a fundamental relationship between the $u(x, y)$ and $v(x, y)$ of eq. (9.4) or more briefly between the u and v parts of a function of a complex variable, namely, if $f(z)$ is an analytic function, then

$$\frac{\partial u}{\partial x} = \frac{\partial v}{\partial y} \qquad (a)$$

and

$$\frac{\partial u}{\partial y} = -\frac{\partial v}{\partial x}. \qquad (b) \qquad (9.5)$$

These equations are known as *the Cauchy-Riemann equations.* Two functions which satisfy the Cauchy-Riemann equations are called *conjugate functions.* It follows that ***each of a pair of conjugate functions is a harmonic function, i.e., if u and v are a pair of conjugate functions, then***

$$\frac{\partial^2 u}{\partial x^2} + \frac{\partial^2 u}{\partial y^2} = 0 \tag{9.6}$$

and

$$\frac{\partial^2 v}{\partial x^2} + \frac{\partial^2 v}{\partial y^2} = 0. \tag{9.7}$$

To obtain eq. (9.6) we differentiate eq. (9.5*a*) with respect to x, and eq. (9.5*b*) with respect to y, and add. Similarly, to obtain eq. (9.7) we differentiate eq. (9.5*a*) with respect to y, and eq. (9.5*b*) with respect to x, and subtract the results.

Substituting from the Cauchy-Riemann equations in the expression for $(dy/dx)_{cd}$, eq. (9.3), we obtain

$$\left(\frac{dy}{dx}\right)_{cd} = \frac{\partial u/\partial y}{\partial u/\partial x}\cdot \tag{9.8}$$

The two slopes $(dy/dx)_{ab}$, eq. (9.2), and $(dy/dx)_{cd}$, eq. (9.8), are thus negative reciprocals. Therefore, ***each pair of curves in the (x, y) plane, which corresponds to a pair of straight lines in the (u, v) plane for which $u = c$ and $v = c_1$ respectively, always intersects at right angles. Such curves are said to form an orthogonal system.***

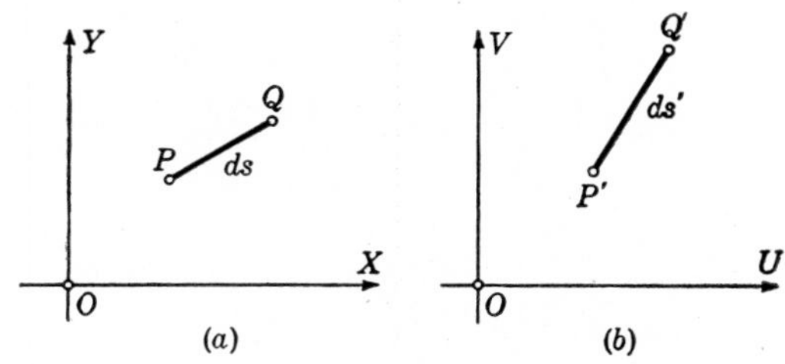

FIG. 9.3

§9.3 Stretch Ratio. Consider now two points P and Q distant ds from each other in the (x, y) plane and the corresponding pair P' and Q' distant ds' from each other in the (u, v) plane, Fig. 9.3. We wish to derive an expression for the ratio

$$J = \frac{ds'}{ds}\cdot \tag{9.9}$$

The quantity J will be referred to as *the stretch ratio.* To obtain this ratio we write

$$ds = \sqrt{dx^2 + dy^2},$$

$$ds' = \sqrt{du^2 + dv^2}.$$

Since u and v are functions of (x, y) we have

$$du = \frac{\partial u}{\partial x}\,dx + \frac{\partial u}{\partial y}\,dy,$$

$$dv = \frac{\partial v}{\partial x}\,dx + \frac{\partial v}{\partial y}\,dy,$$

so that

$$(du)^2 = \left(\frac{\partial u}{\partial x}\right)^2 dx^2 + \left(\frac{\partial u}{\partial y}\right)^2 dy^2 + 2\frac{\partial u}{\partial x}\frac{\partial u}{\partial y}\,dx\,dy,$$

$$(dv)^2 = \left(\frac{\partial v}{\partial x}\right)^2 dx^2 + \left(\frac{\partial v}{\partial y}\right)^2 dy^2 + 2\frac{\partial v}{\partial x}\frac{\partial v}{\partial y}\,dx\,dy.$$

Adding and remembering the Cauchy-Riemann relations we obtain

$$(du^2 + dv^2) = \left[\left(\frac{\partial u}{\partial x}\right)^2 + \left(\frac{\partial x}{\partial v}\right)^2\right](dx^2 + dy^2),$$

or

$$(ds')^2 = \left[\left(\frac{\partial u}{\partial x}\right)^2 + \left(\frac{\partial v}{\partial x}\right)^2\right](ds)^2.$$

Hence, ***the stretch J, which is inherently a positive quantity, is given by***

$$J = \sqrt{\left(\frac{\partial u}{\partial x}\right)^2 + \left(\frac{\partial v}{\partial x}\right)^2}. \tag{9.10}$$

Inspection of eq. (9.10) shows that J is independent of the directions of PQ and $P'Q'$. It is thus a constant for a given point although it varies from point to point.

§9.4 Conformal Transformations. Referring to Fig. 9.4(a), we have, from the well-known cosine law,

$$\cos\alpha = \frac{a^2 + b^2 - c^2}{2ab}.$$

In terms of the x and y projections, which we denote by a_x, a_y, b_x, b_y, as shown in Fig. 9.4(a), the lengths a, b, c are given by

$$a^2 = a_x^2 + a_y^2,$$

$$b^2 = b_x^2 + b_y^2,$$

$$c^2 = (a_x - b_x)^2 + (a_y - b_y)^2.$$

Substituting and simplifying, we obtain

$$\cos\alpha = \frac{a_x b_x + a_y b_y}{ab}. \tag{9.11}$$

Consider now two corresponding angles θ and θ', defined as the angles between corresponding segments, as shown in Fig. 9.4(b) and 9.4(c).

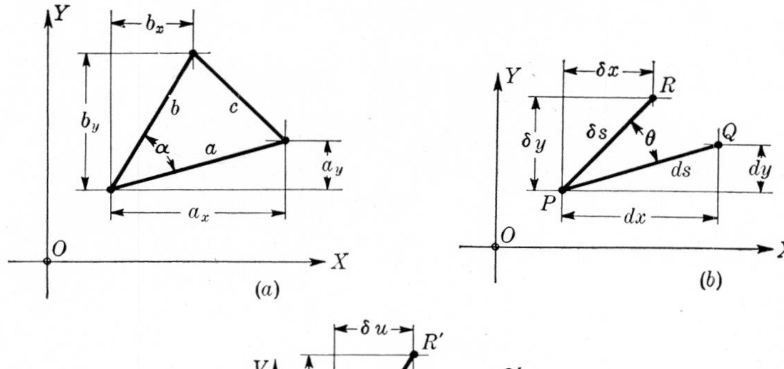

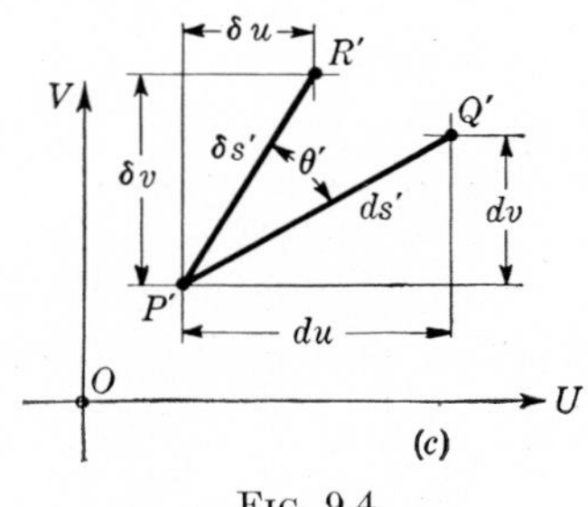

FIG. 9.4

By eq. (9.11)

$$\cos\theta = \frac{dx\,\delta x + dy\,\delta y}{ds\,\delta s}, \qquad (a)$$

and

$$\cos\theta' = \frac{du\,\delta u + dv\,\delta v}{ds'\,\delta s'}. \qquad (b) \qquad (9.12)$$

Now

$$du = \frac{\partial u}{\partial x}\,dx + \frac{\partial u}{\partial y}\,dy,$$

and

$$\delta u = \frac{\partial u}{\partial x}\,\delta x + \frac{\partial u}{\partial y}\,\delta y.$$

Multiplying, we get

$$du\,\delta u = \left(\frac{\partial u}{\partial x}\right)^2 dx\,\delta x + \left(\frac{\partial u}{\partial y}\right)^2 dy\,\delta y + \frac{\partial u}{\partial x}\frac{\partial u}{\partial y}(dx\,\delta y + dy\,\delta x). \qquad (a)$$

Similarly

$$dv\,\delta v = \left(\frac{\partial v}{\partial x}\right)^2 dx\,\delta x + \left(\frac{\partial v}{\partial y}\right)^2 dy\,\delta y + \frac{\partial v}{\partial x}\frac{\partial v}{\partial y}(dx\,\delta y + dy\,\delta x). \qquad (b) \qquad (9.13)$$

Adding, and remembering the Cauchy-Riemann equations, we obtain

$$du\,\delta u + dv\,\delta v = \left[\left(\frac{\partial u}{\partial x}\right)^2 + \left(\frac{\partial v}{\partial x}\right)^2\right](dx\,\delta x + dy\,\delta y),$$

or by eq. (9.10)

$$du\,\delta u + dv\,\delta v = J^2(dx\,\delta x + dy\,\delta y). \tag{9.14}$$

Since the stretch ratio J is a constant at a point we may write

$$ds' = J\,ds,$$

$$\delta s' = J\,\delta s,$$

so that

$$ds'\,\delta s' = J^2\,ds\,\delta s,$$

and

$$J^2 = \frac{ds'}{ds}\frac{\delta s'}{\delta s}. \tag{9.15}$$

Substituting this expression for J^2 in eq. (9.14), and dividing by $ds'\,\delta s'$, we obtain

$$\frac{du\,\delta u + dv\,\delta v}{ds'\,\delta s'} = \frac{dx\,\delta x + dy\,\delta y}{ds\,\delta s}. \tag{9.16}$$

Hence by eq. (9.12)

$$\cos\theta' = \cos\theta$$

and

$$\theta' = \theta. \tag{9.17}$$

It follows that ***a transformation by means of conjugate functions leaves corresponding angles unchanged in magnitude and sense at all points where J is finite but not equal to zero. Such transformations are said to be conformal.***

From the fact that the stretch ratio at a point is constant and the further fact that the magnitudes of corresponding angles are preserved it follows that in a conformal transformation small figures in the (x, y) plane transform into similar figures in the (u, v) plane. The orthogonal character of the transformation by means of conjugate functions discussed in §9.2 is now seen to follow also from the general conformal character of the transformation.

§9.5 The Essential Character of a Harmonic Function is Not Changed by a Conformal Transformation. It is clear that the transformation of any function $\phi(x, y)$ into a function $\phi(u, v)$ by means of arbitrary equations

$$u = f_1(x, y), \quad v = f_2(x, y),$$

does not change the value of the function at corresponding points. Thus if (x_i, y_i) and (u_i, v_i) are the coordinates of a pair of corresponding points then

$$\phi(x_i, y_i) = \phi(u_i, v_i).$$

We will now show that ***when a harmonic function is transformed by means of conjugate functions the harmonic character of the function is preserved;*** i.e., given $\phi(x, y)$, so that

$$\frac{\partial^2\phi(x, y)}{\partial x^2} + \frac{\partial^2\phi(x, y)}{\partial y^2} = 0, \qquad (a)$$

then

$$\frac{\partial^2\phi(u, v)}{\partial u^2} + \frac{\partial^2\phi(u, v)}{\partial v^2} = 0. \qquad (b) \tag{9.18}$$

Differentiating $\phi(u, v)$ with respect to x we have

$$\frac{\partial\phi}{\partial x} = \frac{\partial\phi}{\partial u}\frac{\partial u}{\partial x} + \frac{\partial\phi}{\partial v}\frac{\partial v}{\partial x}$$

and

$$\frac{\partial^2\phi}{\partial x^2} = \frac{\partial\phi}{\partial u}\frac{\partial^2 u}{\partial x^2} + \frac{\partial u}{\partial x}\left(\frac{\partial^2\phi}{\partial u^2}\frac{\partial u}{\partial x} + \frac{\partial^2\phi}{\partial u\,\partial v}\frac{\partial v}{\partial x}\right) + \frac{\partial\phi}{\partial v}\frac{\partial^2 v}{\partial x^2} + \frac{\partial v}{\partial x}\left(\frac{\partial^2\phi}{\partial v\,\partial u}\frac{\partial u}{\partial x} + \frac{\partial^2\phi}{\partial v^2}\frac{\partial v}{\partial x}\right),$$

or

$$\frac{\partial^2\phi}{\partial x^2} = \frac{\partial\phi}{\partial u}\frac{\partial^2 u}{\partial x^2} + \frac{\partial\phi}{\partial v}\frac{\partial^2 v}{\partial x^2} + \frac{\partial^2\phi}{\partial u^2}\left(\frac{\partial u}{\partial x}\right)^2 + \frac{\partial^2\phi}{\partial v^2}\left(\frac{\partial v}{\partial x}\right)^2 + 2\frac{\partial^2\phi}{\partial u\,\partial v}\frac{\partial u}{\partial x}\frac{\partial v}{\partial x}. \tag{9.19}$$

Similarly

$$\frac{\partial^2\phi}{\partial y^2} = \frac{\partial\phi}{\partial u}\frac{\partial^2 u}{\partial y^2} + \frac{\partial\phi}{\partial v}\frac{\partial^2 v}{\partial y^2} + \frac{\partial^2\phi}{\partial u^2}\left(\frac{\partial u}{\partial y}\right)^2 + \frac{\partial^2\phi}{\partial v^2}\left(\frac{\partial v}{\partial y}\right)^2 + 2\frac{\partial^2\phi}{\partial u\,\partial v}\frac{\partial u}{\partial y}\frac{\partial v}{\partial y}. \tag{9.20}$$

Remembering that ϕ, u, and v are all harmonic functions, and that by eqs. (9.5)

$$\left(\frac{\partial u}{\partial x}\right)^2 + \left(\frac{\partial u}{\partial y}\right)^2 = \left(\frac{\partial v}{\partial x}\right)^2 + \left(\frac{\partial v}{\partial y}\right)^2,$$

and also that

$$\frac{\partial u}{\partial x}\frac{\partial v}{\partial x} + \frac{\partial u}{\partial y}\frac{\partial v}{\partial y} = 0,$$

we obtain upon addition of eqs. (9.19) and (9.20) and simplification

$$\left(\frac{\partial^2\phi}{\partial u^2} + \frac{\partial^2\phi}{\partial v^2}\right)\left[\left(\frac{\partial u}{\partial x}\right)^2 + \left(\frac{\partial u}{\partial y}\right)^2\right] = 0. \tag{9.21}$$

Having assumed in §9.2 that $(\partial u/\partial y)$ does not vanish, it follows that the Laplacian in eq. (9.21) vanishes, i.e.,

$$\frac{\partial^2\phi}{\partial u^2} + \frac{\partial^2\phi}{\partial v^2} = 0, \tag{9.22}$$

which shows that the $\phi(u, v)$ is a harmonic function.

This fact is of great importance in many problems in elasticity and physics and will prove of special value in applying the process of harmonization to problems involving sources of stress concentration such as circular holes, grooves, etc. By means of suitable conformal transformations an orthogonal system of curves which includes the curved boundary forming the sources of stress concentration is transformed into a square network. ***Since a transformation does not alter the value of the function at corresponding points, the boundary values of $\Sigma = p + q$ at corresponding points are taken the same in both the (x, y) and (u, v) planes.***

But by eq. (9.22) $\phi(u, v) = \Sigma$ is a harmonic function so that the values of Σ at all net points in the (u, v) plane can be found by harmonization, and the values so obtained represent also the values of Σ at the corresponding points in the (x, y) plane.

Several types of conformal transformations are of special interest in practical problems in harmonization. To these belong polar coordinates and bipolar coordinates. Two other types of conformal transformations, inversion and elliptical coordinates, are frequently met with in the theory of elasticity.

§9.6 Polar Coordinates. Consider the analytic function

$$(x + iy) = e^{f(z)}. \tag{9.23}$$

Solving for $f(z)$ we have

$$\begin{aligned} f(z) &= \log\,(x + iy) \\ &= \log\,(r \cos\theta + ir \sin\theta) \\ &= \log\,[r\,(\cos\theta + i \sin\theta)] \\ &= \log\,(re^{i\theta}) \\ &= \log r + i\theta \\ &= \log\,(x^2 + y^2)^{1/2} + i \tan^{-1}\frac{y}{x} \\ &= u(x, y) + iv(x, y). \end{aligned} \tag{9.24}$$

Hence

$$\left.\begin{aligned} u(x, y) &= \log r = \log\,(x^2 + y^2)^{1/2}, &\quad (a)\\ v(x, y) &= \theta = \tan^{-1}\frac{y}{x}\cdot &\quad (b)\end{aligned}\right\}(9.25)$$

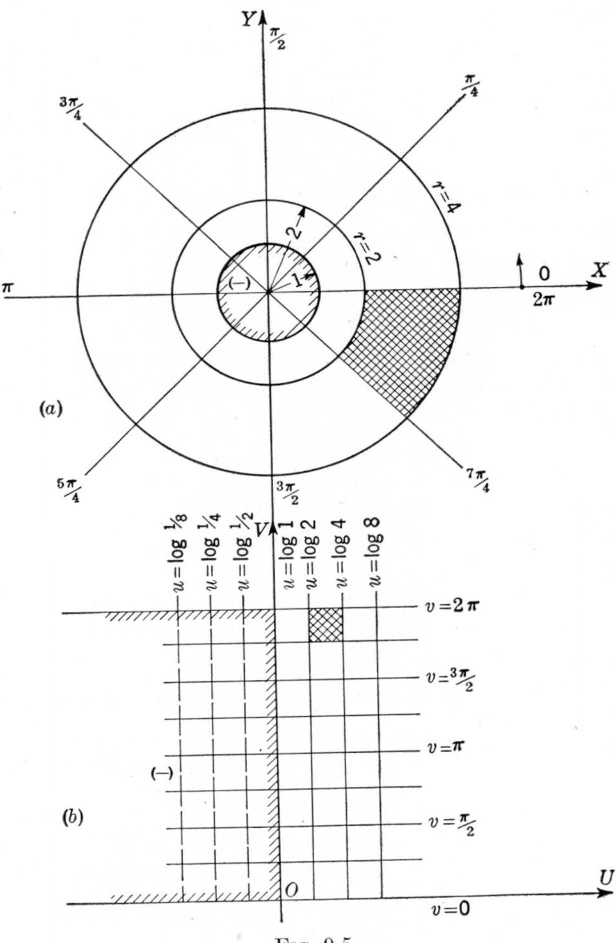

FIG. 9.5

The resulting equations of transformation thus are

$$\left.\begin{aligned} u &= \log r, &\quad (a)\\ v &= \theta. &\quad (b)\end{aligned}\right\}(9.26)$$

As already pointed out in §9.1 the first of these equations transforms concentric circles with centers at the origin into straight lines parallel to the V axis, and the second equation transforms radial lines into lines parallel to the U axis, as shown in Fig. 9.5.

We note that the circle of unit radius is transformed into the V axis and that the X axis is transformed into the U axis. All circles lying inside the unit circle give negative values. These transformations are shown by the full and dashed vertical lines in the (u, v) plane, Fig. 9.5(b). We further note that the entire (x, y) plane is transformed into a strip of width equal to 2π in the V direction and of infinite length in the U direction.

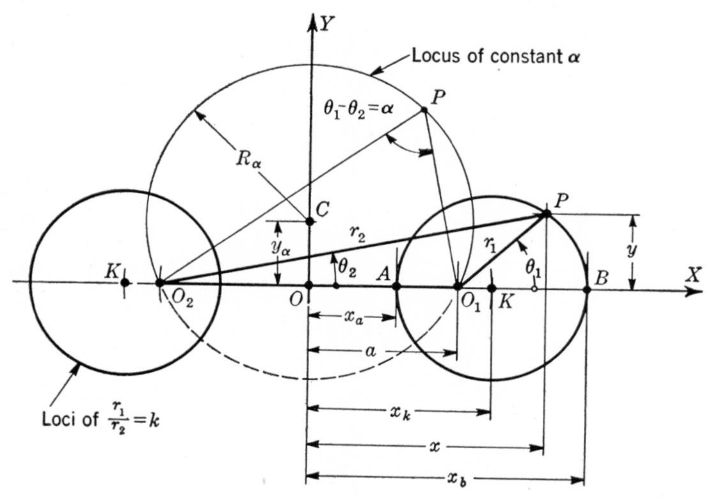

FIG. 9.6

§9.7 Bipolar Coordinates. Consider next the analytic function

$$f(z) = \log\left(\frac{z - a}{z + a}\right) \tag{9.27}$$

$$= \log (z - a) - \log (z + a).$$

Now let

$$z - a = r_1 e^{i\theta_1}, \quad z + a = r_2 e^{i\theta_2}, \tag{9.28}$$

where r_1 and r_2 are measured from two new origins O_1 and O_2, known as poles, distant $\pm a$ from the original origin O, Fig. 9.6.

In terms of r_1, θ_1, r_2, and θ_2

$$f(z) = \log r_1 e^{i\theta_1} - \log r_2 e^{i\theta_2}$$

$$= (\log r_1 + i\theta_1) - (\log r_2 + i\theta_2),$$

whence

$$f(z) = \log \frac{r_1}{r_2} + i(\theta_1 - \theta_2). \tag{9.29}$$

The equations for a conformal transformation, therefore, are

$$\left.\begin{aligned} u &= u(x, y) = \log \frac{r_1}{r_2}, & (a) \\ v &= v(x, y) = \theta_1 - \theta_2. & (b) \end{aligned}\right\} \tag{9.30}$$

These functions satisfy the Cauchy-Riemann equations. We now investigate the locus $u = c$, a constant. It is clear that u is a constant when

$$\frac{r_1}{r_2} = k, \quad \text{a constant.}$$

Squaring we get

$$r_1^2 = k^2 r_2^2.$$

From Fig. 9.6

$$r_1^2 = (x - a)^2 + y^2,$$
$$r_2^2 = (x + a)^2 + y^2.$$

Hence

$$(x - a)^2 + y^2 = k^2[(x + a)^2 + y^2],$$

and

$$x^2 + y^2 + a^2 - \left(\frac{1 + k^2}{1 - k^2}\right) 2ax = 0, \tag{9.31}$$

which is the equation of a circle with center on the X axis, that is, the line determined by the poles O_1O_2. The curves corresponding to a constant value of u are thus two families of circles with centers on the X axis as shown in Figs. 9.6 and 9.8.

Now let

$$f = \frac{1 + k^2}{1 - k^2}.$$

Then

$$x^2 + y^2 + a^2 - 2afx = 0. \tag{9.32}$$

Putting $y = 0$ we obtain for the x intercepts x_a, x_b, Fig. 9.6,

$$x_a = a(f - \sqrt{f^2 - 1}),$$
$$x_b = a(f + \sqrt{f^2 - 1}).$$

The distance x_k from the origin O to the center K of the circle then becomes

$$x_k = \tfrac{1}{2}[a(f + \sqrt{f^2 - 1}) + a(f - \sqrt{f^2 - 1})]$$
$$= af = a\left(\frac{1 + k^2}{1 - k^2}\right) \tag{9.33}$$

The corresponding radius R_k of the circle is given by

$$R_k = \tfrac{1}{2}(x_b - x_a)$$
$$= a\sqrt{f^2 - 1}$$
$$= a\left(\frac{2k}{1 - k^2}\right)\cdot \tag{9.34}$$

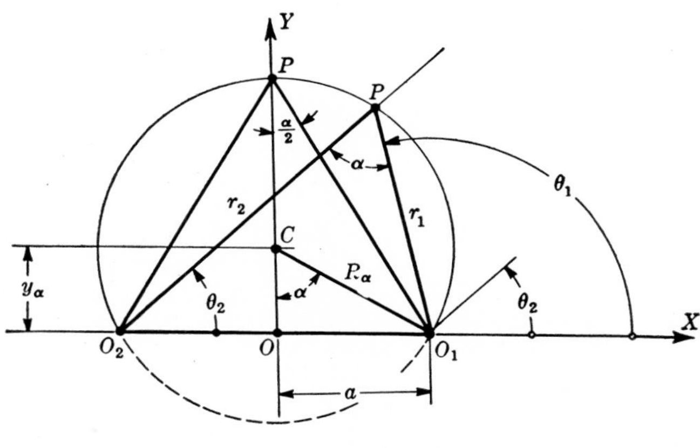

FIG. 9.7

It is also easy to see that the locus of points corresponding to constant differences $\theta_1 - \theta_2 = \alpha$ are portions of circles which pass through the poles O_1 and O_2 and whose centers lie on the Y axis, which is the perpendicular bisector of the pole distance O_1O_2.

Obviously for all points P which lie on one side of the X axis on such a circle the angles O_1PO_2 are all equal, Fig. 9.7.

Referring to Fig. 9.7 it can be seen that y_α, the distance from the origin O to the center C of the circle corresponding to $\theta_1 - \theta_2 = \alpha$, is given by

$$y_\alpha = a \cot \alpha, \tag{9.35}$$

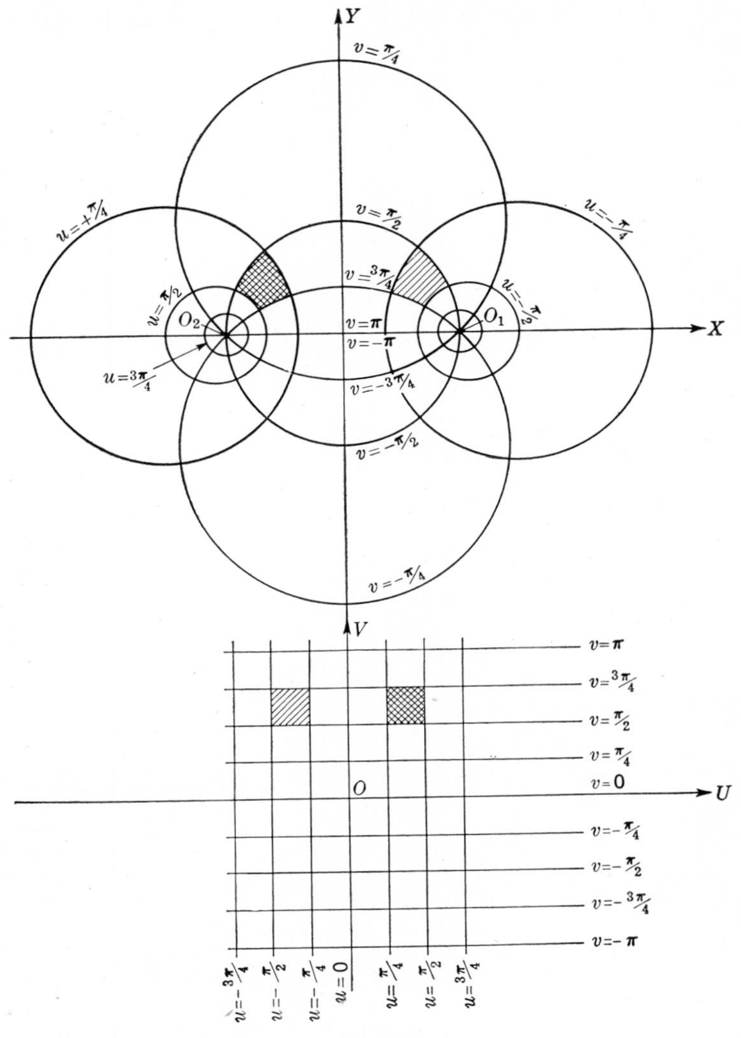

FIG. 9.8

and that R_α, the radius of the same circle, is given by

$$R_\alpha = a \sec \alpha. \tag{9.36}$$

Inspection of Fig. 9.7 further shows that the center C and the radius R_α can be determined graphically by drawing a line through O_1 which makes an angle α with the Y axis, as shown. Obviously O_1C represents the radius, and OC the distance y_α.

As in the case of polar coordinates the entire (x, y) plane is transformed into a narrow strip 2π units in width and of infinite length, Fig. 9.8. The X axis represents the limiting circles for which

$$\theta_1 - \theta_2 = \pm\pi.$$

In the transformed infinite strip, the circle for which α approaches plus π gives the upper boundary $v = \pi$, and the circle for which α approaches minus π gives the lower boundary $v = -\pi$. The Y axis represents the circle whose center is at infinity on the X axis. For this circle

$$\frac{r_1}{r_2} = 1$$

and

$$u = \log 1 = 0.$$

Hence, the Y axis is transformed into the V axis.

The U axis, $v = 0$, corresponds to the circle of infinite radius and center on the Y axis. The circles whose centers approach as a limit the poles O_1 and O_2 give limiting ratios r_1/r_2 equal to zero and infinity respectively. The corresponding vertical lines are at infinity.

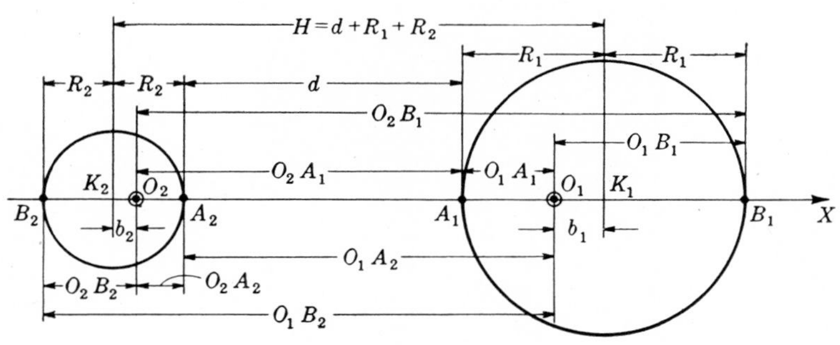

FIG. 9.9

§9.8 Two Circles Determine the Positions of the Poles. Consider two circles of radii R_1 and R_2, with centers K_1 and K_2 respectively, distant H apart, as shown in Fig. 9.9. We wish to find the positions of the poles O_1 and O_2 so that the two given circles will form a part of a bipolar system.

From Fig. 9.9 we have

$$O_1A_2 = H - b_1 - R_2,$$

$$O_2A_2 = R_2 - b_2,$$

$$O_1B_2 = H - b_1 + R_2,$$

$$O_2B_2 = R_2 + b_2.$$

Referring to the circle with center at K_2, let

$$\frac{r_1}{r_2} = k_2 = \frac{O_1A_2}{O_2A_2} = \frac{O_1B_2}{O_2B_2}\cdot$$

In terms of H, b_1, b_2, and R_2 we obtain

$$\frac{H - b_1 - R_2}{R_2 - b_2} = \frac{H - b_1 + R_2}{R_2 + b_2},$$

whence

$$b_1 = H - \frac{R_2^2}{b_2}\cdot \tag{9.37a}$$

For the circle whose center is at K_1 we have, by analogy,

$$b_2 = H - \frac{R_1^2}{b_1}\cdot \tag{9.37b}$$

Solving eqs. (9.37a) and (9.37b) for b_1 and b_2, we obtain

$$\left.\begin{aligned} b_1 &= \frac{H^2 + R_1^2 - R_2^2}{2H} - \frac{1}{2}\sqrt{\left(\frac{H^2 + R_1^2 - R_2^2}{H}\right)^2 - 4R_1^2}, \quad (a)\\ b_2 &= \frac{H^2 + R_2^2 - R_1^2}{2H} - \frac{1}{2}\sqrt{\left(\frac{H^2 + R_2^2 - R_1^2}{H}\right)^2 - 4R_2^2}. \quad (b)\end{aligned}\right\} \tag{9.38}$$

When

$$R_1 = R_2 = R,$$

$$b_1 = b_2 = b = \frac{H - \sqrt{H^2 - 4R^2}}{2}\cdot \tag{9.39}$$

It follows also that in this special case

$$O_1O_2 = 2a = H - 2b$$

and

$$a = \frac{H - 2b}{2}\cdot \tag{9.40}$$

ILLUSTRATIVE PROBLEMS

Example 9.1. Concentrated Load Acting Normally to a Semi-Infinite Plate. Consider a concentrated load acting normally to the straight edge of a semi-infinite plate. By §2.2, Fig. 2.5, such a load can be replaced by a distributed system of boundary stresses along a small semicircular arc, which are given by

$$\sigma_r = -\frac{2P}{\pi t}\frac{\cos\theta}{r}\cdot \tag{2.8}$$

We lay down a network of polar coordinates, Fig. 9.10(*a*), and make a conformal transformation by means of the equations

$$\left.\begin{aligned} u &= \log r, &&(a)\\ v &= \theta, &&(b)\end{aligned}\right\}(9.26)$$

which were derived in §9.6. We choose small angular increments, say $\Delta\theta = 15°$. Then

$$\Delta v = \Delta\theta = 15° = \frac{\pi}{2}\cdot\frac{1}{6} = 0.2618.$$

In order to obtain perfect squares in the (u, v) plane we put

$$\Delta u = \Delta v = 0.2618.$$

We can now calculate the values of r which are necessary in order that the polar network shall correspond to the square network in the (u, v) plane, Fig. 9.10(*b*).

From eq. (9.26*a*)

$$r = e^u = e^\theta.$$

Hence

$$r_0 = e^0 = 1,$$

$$r_1 = e^{0.2618} = 1.30,$$

$$r_2 = e^{(0.2618\times 2)} = 1.69, \text{ etc.}$$

In this manner we determine the dimensions for the polar network shown in Fig. 9.10(*a*). The corresponding boundary stresses shown in the same figure were calculated by eq. (2.8). The values at all interior points were then determined by block iteration using eq. (8.22) and twelve key points $E3$, $E5 \cdots A3$, $A5 \cdots A9$.

We start the solution with a coarse network in which $C5$ and $C9$ are the only key points, and find approximate values from two simultaneous eqs. (8.22) and (8.19). We next resolve $C5$ and $C9$ by means of the Liebmann formula to obtain initial values for all other key values. We then write down the necessary twelve equations (8.22), taking into consideration the facts of symmetry about the U axis, and solve by iteration. The remaining values are all found by the Liebmann formula.

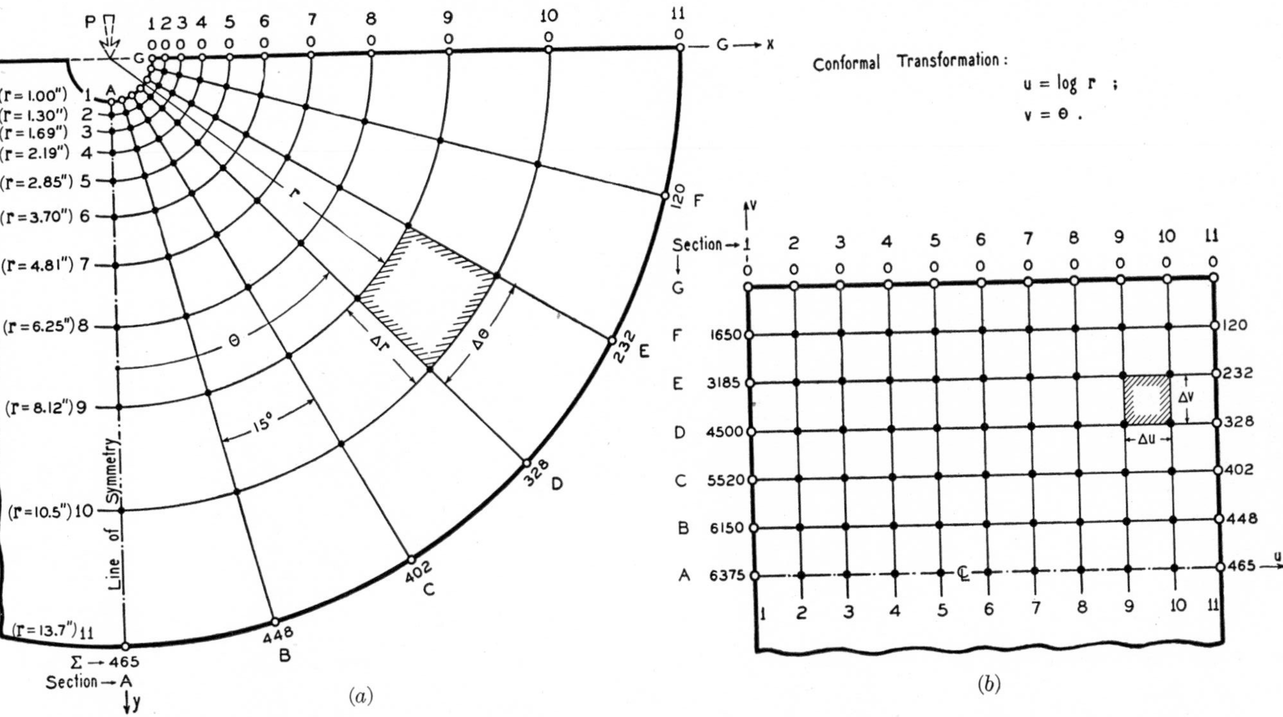

FIG. 9.10 Conformal Transformation for a Normal Concentrated Load Acting on the Straight Edge of a Semi-Infinite Plate.

$P = 10{,}000$ lb.; $t = 1$ in.; boundary values in pounds per square inch calculated by eq. (2.8).

Contours. Fig. 9.11 shows the contours or isopachic curves as determined from the values obtained by harmonization. The curves of Σ for the radial sections A to F inclusive are shown on the left side of Fig. 9.11. The contours

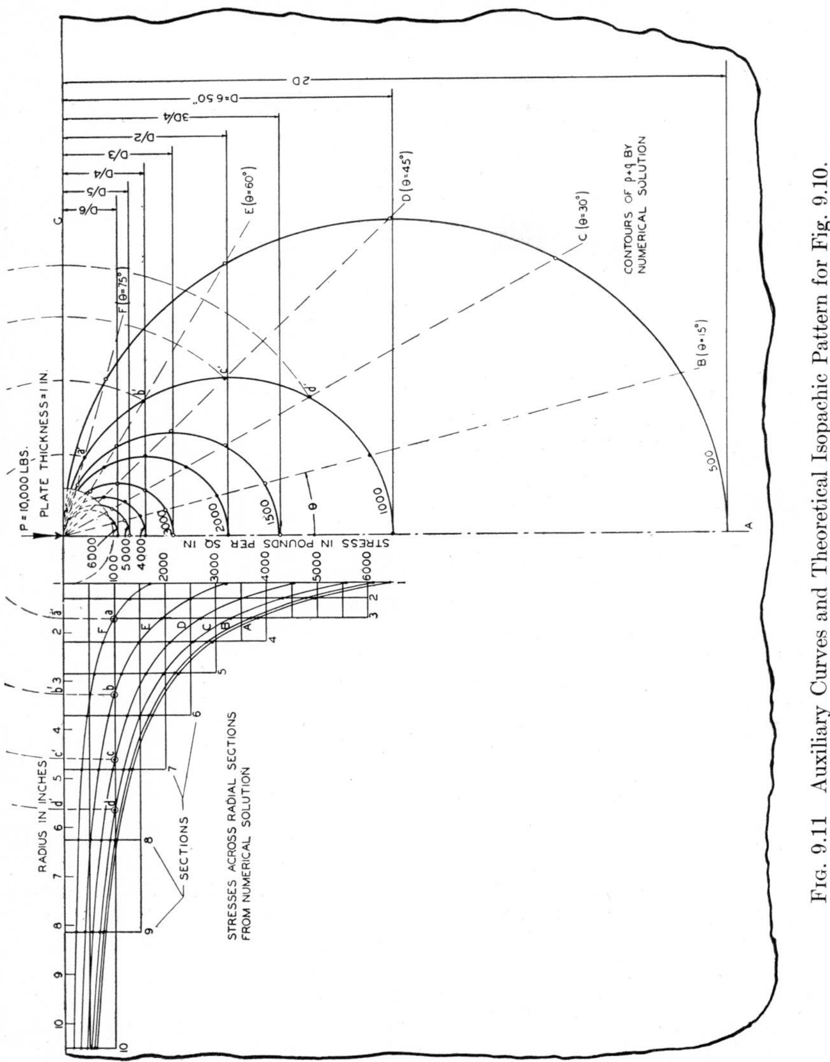

FIG. 9.11 Auxiliary Curves and Theoretical Isopachic Pattern for Fig. 9.10.

for any one value of Σ are obtained from the points of intersection of the stress curves for the radial sections with the horizontal line drawn through the point on the stress scale corresponding to the given stress. Thus, for $\Sigma = 1000$ the points are a, b, c, d, Fig. 9.11. These points of intersection are projected on the line giving the scale for the radial distances, the horizontal line OG, Fig

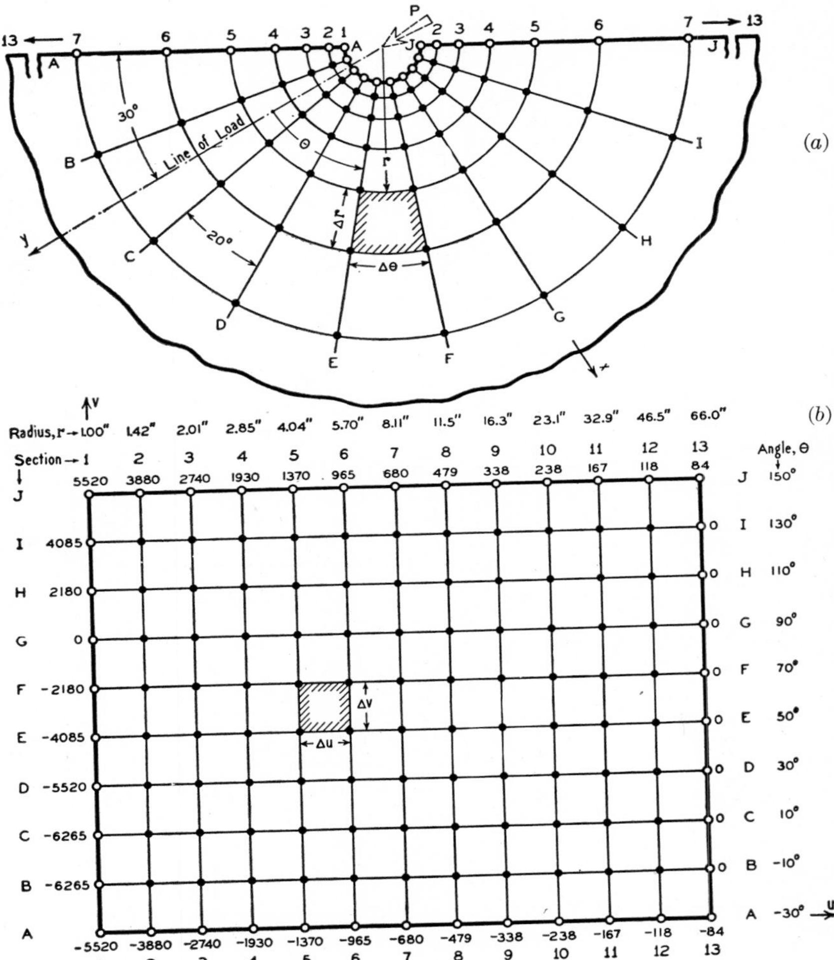

FIG. 9.12 Conformal Transformation for an Inclined Load Acting on a Semi-Infinite Plate.

P = 10,000 lb.; t = 1 in.; load inclined 30° to plate edge; boundary values of Σ in pounds per square inch calculated by eq. (2.8).

9.11. For $\Sigma = 1000$ the projections are a', b', c', and d'. The distances from the origin O to the points of projection are then transferred with a compass to the respective radial lines, as shown in Fig. 9.11.

In §2.2 it was shown that the distribution produced by a concentrated load is purely radial. Hence, the loci of constant values of Σ, that is, contours or isopachic curves, are circles tangent to the straight edge of the semi-infinite plate and having their centers on the line of the load. The contours obtained from harmonization and shown in Fig. 9.11 are evidently such circles.

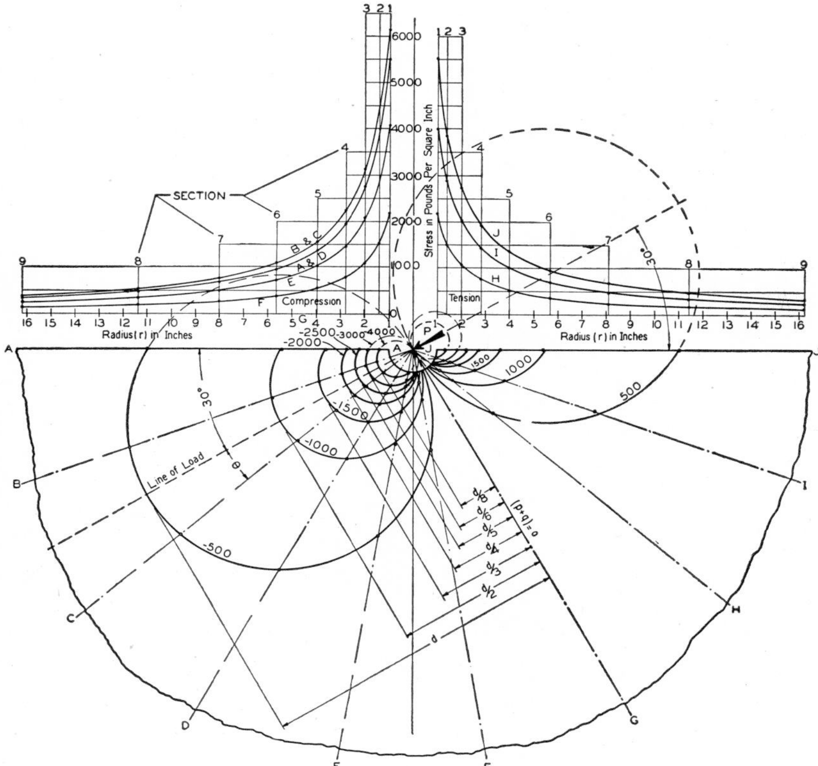

FIG. 9.13 Theoretical Isopachic Pattern for Inclined Concentrated Load of Fig. 9.12. Upper curves show $(p + q)$ across radial sections A–A, B–B . . . J–J. Lower figure shows isopachic curves for increments of 500 psi.

Example 9.2. Inclined Load on a Semi-Infinite Plate. We next consider an inclined concentrated load which makes an angle of 30° with the straight edge of a semi-infinite plate, Fig. 9.12.

A polar network and the corresponding square network were determined in the same manner as in the preceding example. The radius of the semicircular groove near the load was taken as unity and the maximum radius as 66 in. The angular intervals were taken 20° apart. A portion of the polar network is shown in Fig. 9.12(*a*). The complete corresponding square network for a range of r from 1 to 66 resulting from the conformal transformation is shown in Fig. 9.12(*b*).

The theoretical numerical values of the boundary stresses $\sigma_r = \Sigma$ are shown in the rectangular network of Fig. 9.12. On the semicircular boundary where $r = 66$ in. the stresses were assumed to vanish.

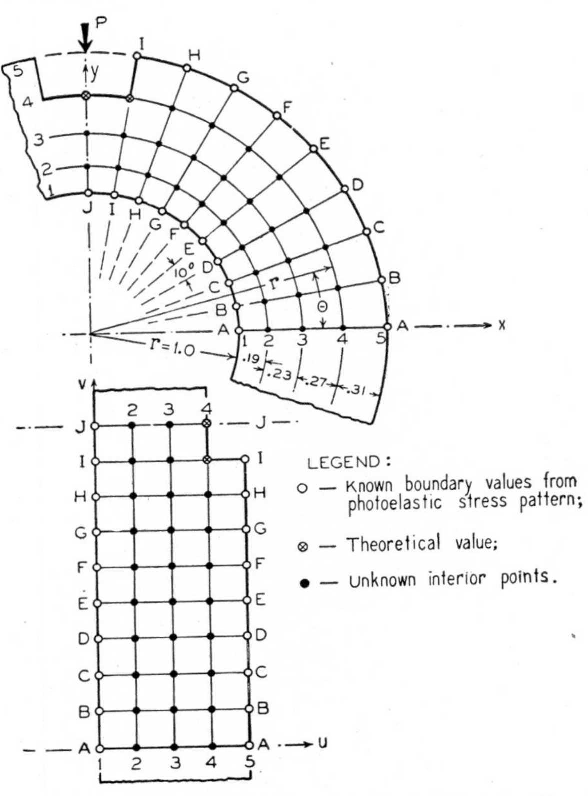

FIG. 9.14 Conformal Transformation of a Circular Ring.

The isopachic curves for the example under consideration are shown in Fig. 9.13 and agree completely with the corresponding curves from theoretical considerations which were discussed in §2.7.

Example 9.3. Circular Ring under Concentrated Diametral Loads. Polar coordinates are especially useful in bodies having circular boundaries and sources of stress concentrations. In such cases the polar coordinate system automatically gives a finer network in the regions surrounding the source of stress concentration, which gradually becomes coarser as the radial distances increase. An ideal example is found in the circular ring of Fig. 6.15. The

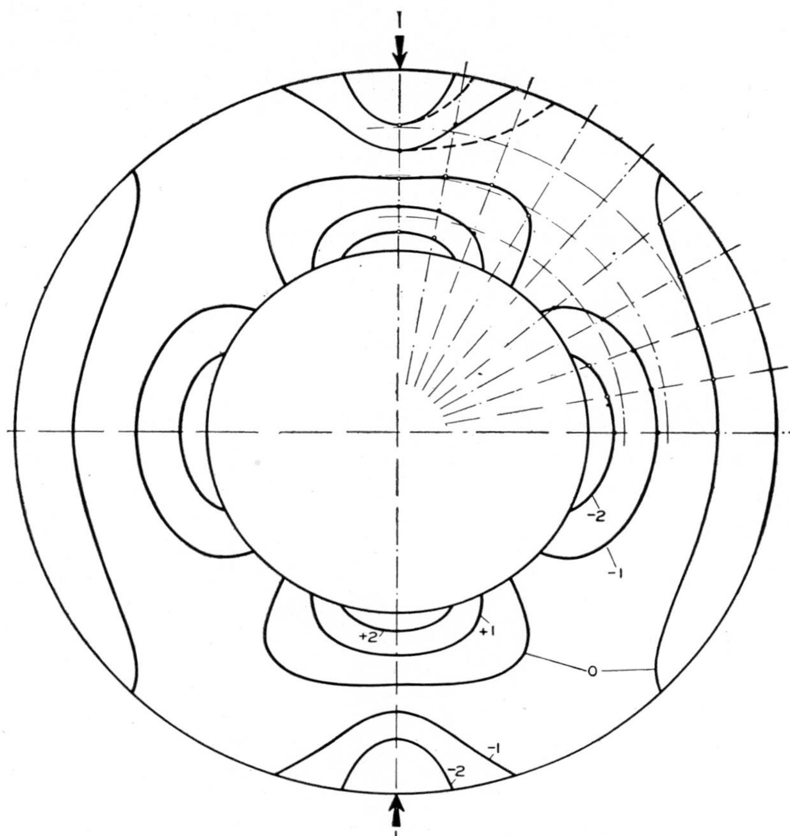

FIG. 9.15 Theoretical Isopachic Stress Pattern for a Circular Ring under Diametral Compression Obtained by Using the Conformal Transformation Shown in Fig. 9.14 and the Boundary Values Given by the Stress Pattern of Fig. 6.15.

All interior values obtained by means of block iteration. For corresponding experimental pattern from a steel ring see Fig. 7.16.

dimensions of the polar coordinates which are necessary in order to transform the ring into an approximately square network and the square network itself are shown in Fig. 9.14. In the regions near the concentrated loads small rectangular pieces are removed and stresses from a radial distribution are assumed, eq. (2.8).

In calculating the dimensions of the polar network the order is the reverse of the order used in the examples of the concentrated loads. Here r_1 and r_2, the inner and outer radii of the ring, are given as equal to 1 and 2 units respectively.

In order to have a square network it is obviously necessary to divide the interval A–A, Fig. 9.14, into an integral number of equal intervals, say four. The value of Δu representing one side of the transformed squares is then given by

$$\Delta u = \frac{\log 2 - \log 1}{4} = 0.1735.$$

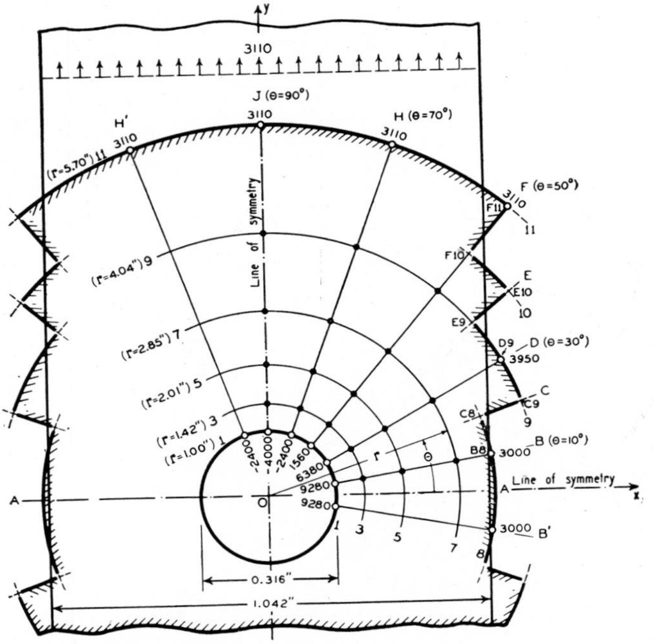

FIG. 9.16 Dimensions for the Conformal Transformation of a Bar with a Circular Hole in Uniform Tension.

Boundary values from Fig. 8.12; $t = 0.258$ in.; $P = 278.5$ lb.

But for a square network

$$\Delta v = \Delta u.$$

Hence

$$\Delta\theta = \Delta v = 0.1735 \text{ radian} = 10° \quad \text{approximately.}$$

The resulting contours for the ring under consideration are shown in Fig. 9.15. In this network there are five key points, $A3$, $C3$, $E3$, $G3$, and $I3$. The harmonization is effected as in Example 8.2.

Example 9.4. A Bar in Tension with a Central Circular Hole. Polar coordinates may be used to advantage even when not all the boundaries are circular. Consider, for example, the tension bar of Fig. 9.16.

The polar network shown will expedite materially the determination of the value of Σ. It is clear that the circular boundaries $r = 1$ and $r = 5.7$ in the (x, y) plane go into straight vertical lines in the (u, v) plane. On the circular boundary corresponding to $r = 5.7$ the stresses may be assumed as constant and equal to the uniform applied tension, which in the given example is 3110 psi.

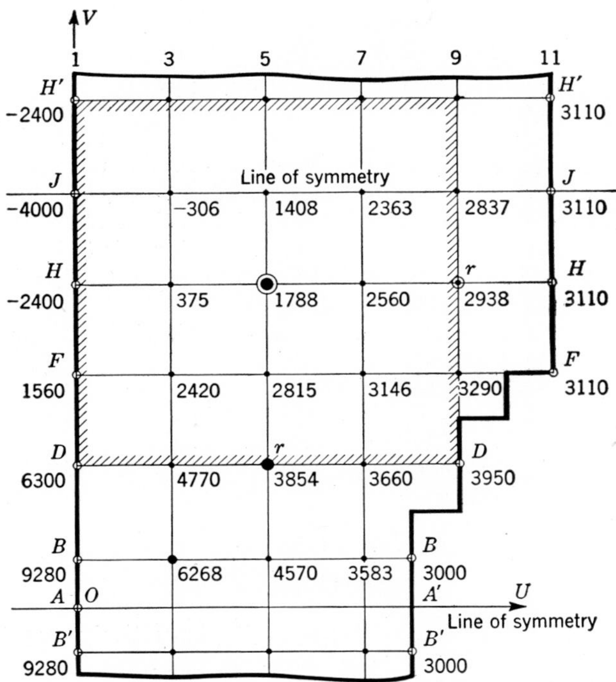

FIG. 9.17 Sketch Showing Conformal Transformation of Fig. 9.16 and Final Values Obtained by Harmonization.

Initial values for $H9$, $D5$, and $B'5$ from rosettes. Because of symmetry $H9 = H'9$ and $H5 = H'5$, so that $H5$, which is the center of the (4×4) square, can be calculated by eq. (8.22). We next calculate $F3$, $F7$, $B3$, and $B7$ (using diagonal neighbors and the fact that $B'3 = B3$) and improve $D5$. Similarly we calculate $J7$ and $F7$ and improve $H9$. We then improve the key point $H5$.

Further, the lines of symmetry, the X and Y axes, Fig. 9.16, are transformed into horizontal lines in the (u, v) plane. To take care of the outer straight vertical edges we replace them by artificial, broken boundaries as shown in Fig. 9.16. The five net points $F10$, $E10$, $E9$, $C9$, and $C8$ on the right broken boundary do not enter into the calculations of the values of Σ on the coarse network shown. The values of Σ at the remaining three points $F11$, $D9$, and

$B8$ are assumed to be equal to the nearest boundary values and were taken from the stress pattern shown in Fig. 8.12.

The square network and boundary values corresponding to the polar system of Fig. 9.16 are shown in Fig. 9.17. These values were harmonized and from them the values of Σ for a finer network determined. The resulting contours are shown in Fig. 9.18. Comparison with contours from a solution using a rectangular network shows that the accuracy of the results near the hole is somewhat better from the polar system. To obtain contours of the same degree of accuracy using a rectangular network would necessitate considerably more labor.

Example 9.5. Deep Grooves in Tension. Bipolar Coordinates. Consider next a long bar with two deep, symmetrical semicircular grooves in a field of pure tension, as shown in Fig. 9.19. We will determine the values of Σ by harmonization and bipolar coordinates.

It is obviously desirable that the semicircles at the roots of the grooves should form a part of the bipolar circles. Assuming this to be a necessary condition in the solution of the problem, we can by eq. (9.39) calculate the positions of the poles O_1 and O_2, Fig. 9.20.

From eq. (9.39) the distance b from the center of the circle fitting a groove to the nearest poles is

$$b = \frac{H - \sqrt{H^2 - 4R^2}}{2}.$$

In the particular problem,

$$H = 0.6275 \text{ in.},$$
$$R = 0.0975 \text{ in.}$$

Substituting these values in eqs. (9.39) and (9.40) respectively, we get

$$b = 0.0157 \text{ in.} \quad \text{and} \quad a = 0.298 \text{ in.}$$

We can now determine the necessary values of the bipolar network, that is, of x_k, R_k, y_α, and R_α, so that when these values are transformed by eqs. (9.30) we will obtain a network of perfect squares

As pointed out in §9.7 the Y axis is transformed into the V axis. For the circle fitting the left groove

$$\begin{aligned} u &= \log \frac{r_1}{r_2} = \log \frac{O_1A_2}{O_2A_2} \\ &= \log \frac{H - R - b}{R - b} \\ &= \log \frac{0.6275 - 0.0975 - 0.0157}{0.0975 - 0.0157} = \log 6.286, \end{aligned}$$

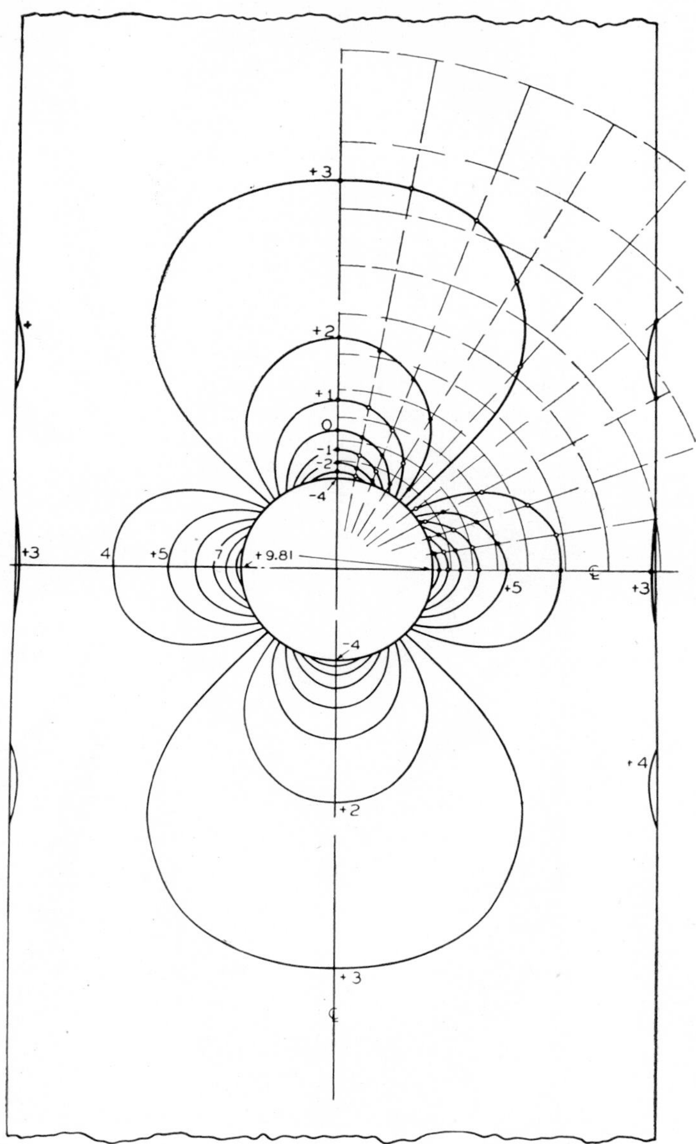

Fig. 9.18 Isopachic Stress Pattern for Fig. 9.16 Based on the Values in Fig. 9.17. One fringe = 333 psi.

FIG. 9.19 Photoelastic Stress Pattern of a Bar with Deep Grooves in Pure Tension.

Radius of grooves = 0.0975 in.; depth = four times the radius; width of bar = 1.213 in.; width of minimum section = 0.433 in.; t = 0.172 in.; P = 214.8 lb.; $2F$ = 500 psi. tension; uniform stress in bar = 2.06 fringes; maximum stress at grooves = 12.00 fringes.

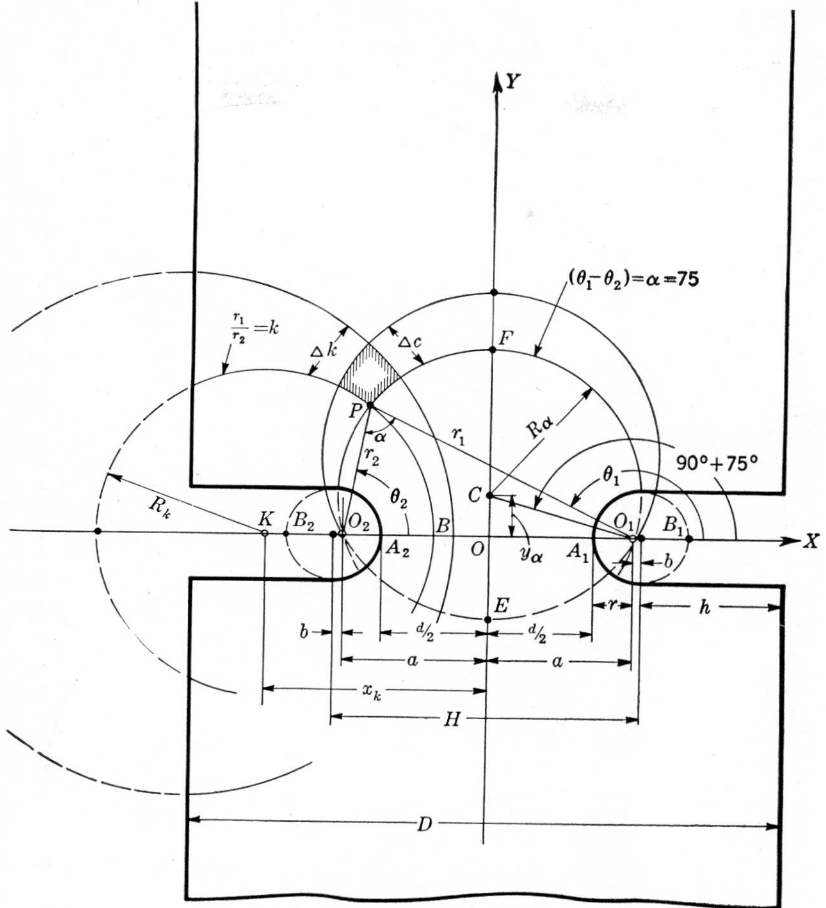

FIG. 9.20 Notation for Conformal Transformation of Bar with Deep Grooves.

or

$$u = 1.838.$$

The interval OA_2 in the (u, v) plane, Fig. 9.20, we divide into an arbitrary number of equal parts, say seven. This gives

$$\Delta u = \frac{1.838}{7} = 0.2626.$$

For a square network

$$\Delta v = \Delta u = (\theta_1 - \theta_2) = \alpha = 0.2626 \text{ radian}.$$

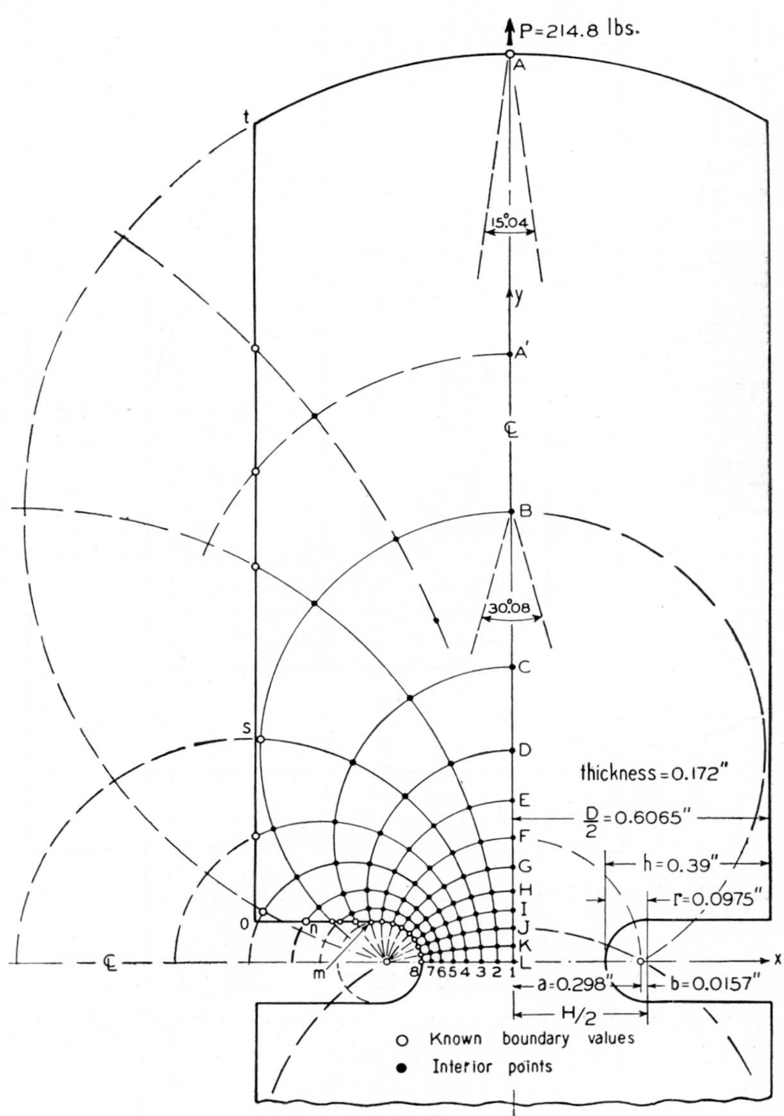

FIG. 9.21 Conformal Transformation for Fig. 9.20.

Hence

$$\alpha = 15.044°.$$

The values x_k and R_k corresponding to the orthogonal network shown in Figs. 9.20 and 9.21 can be calculated from the expressions

$$x_k = a\left(\frac{1+k^2}{1-k^2}\right), \tag{9.33}$$

$$R_k = a\left(\frac{2k}{1-k^2}\right). \tag{9.34}$$

Table 9.1 shows the final values of x_k and R_k for sections 1 to 8 inclusive, as well as for an additional section, 1′, located between sections 1 and 2, which it was found useful to introduce. The complete bipolar network is shown in Fig. 9.21 and the transformation in Fig. 9.22.

TABLE 9.1

SECTION	u	$e^u = \frac{r_1}{r_2} = k$	CENTER x_k		RADIUS R_k	
			x_k/a	inches	R_k/a	inches
1	0.000	1.00				
2	0.2626	1.30	−3.90	−1.165	3.76	1.123
3	0.5252	1.69	−2.07	−0.620	1.82	0.544
4	0.7878	2.20	−1.52	−0.454	1.145	0.342
5	1.0504	2.86	−1.28	−0.382	0.796	0.238
6	1.3130	3.72	−1.155	−0.345	0.579	0.173
7	1.5756	4.83	−1.088	−0.325	0.432	0.129
8	1.8382	6.286	−1.051	−0.314	0.327	0.0976
1′	0.1313	1.14	−7.667	−2.29	7.60	2.27

The centers and radii of the circles with centers on the Y axis, Fig. 9.21, corresponding to the horizontal lines A to L inclusive in the (u, v) plane, Fig. 9.22, were determined graphically by the procedure described in §9.7. The vertical section of symmetry is given by the V axis, and the semicircle fitting the groove is transformed into the extreme left straight-line boundary which is parallel to the V axis, section 8–8, Fig. 9.22. The horizontal section of symmetry on which the poles are located is transformed into the straight line L–L parallel to the U axis. The portion of the groove which is given by the straight line m–n–o goes into the curve m'–n'–o', and the left vertical edge o–s–t goes into the curve o'–s'–t'. The extreme circle for which $\alpha = 15.044°$ is transformed into the straight-line portion of section A–A near the V axis.

The boundary values shown in Fig. 9.22 were taken from the photoelastic stress pattern, Fig. 9.19. The final values of Σ are given in Fig. 9.22.

In order to construct a set of coutours from these results it is convenient to plot the values of Σ corresponding to each circle around that circle as in polar coordinates. The isopachic curves based on the results from the bipolar

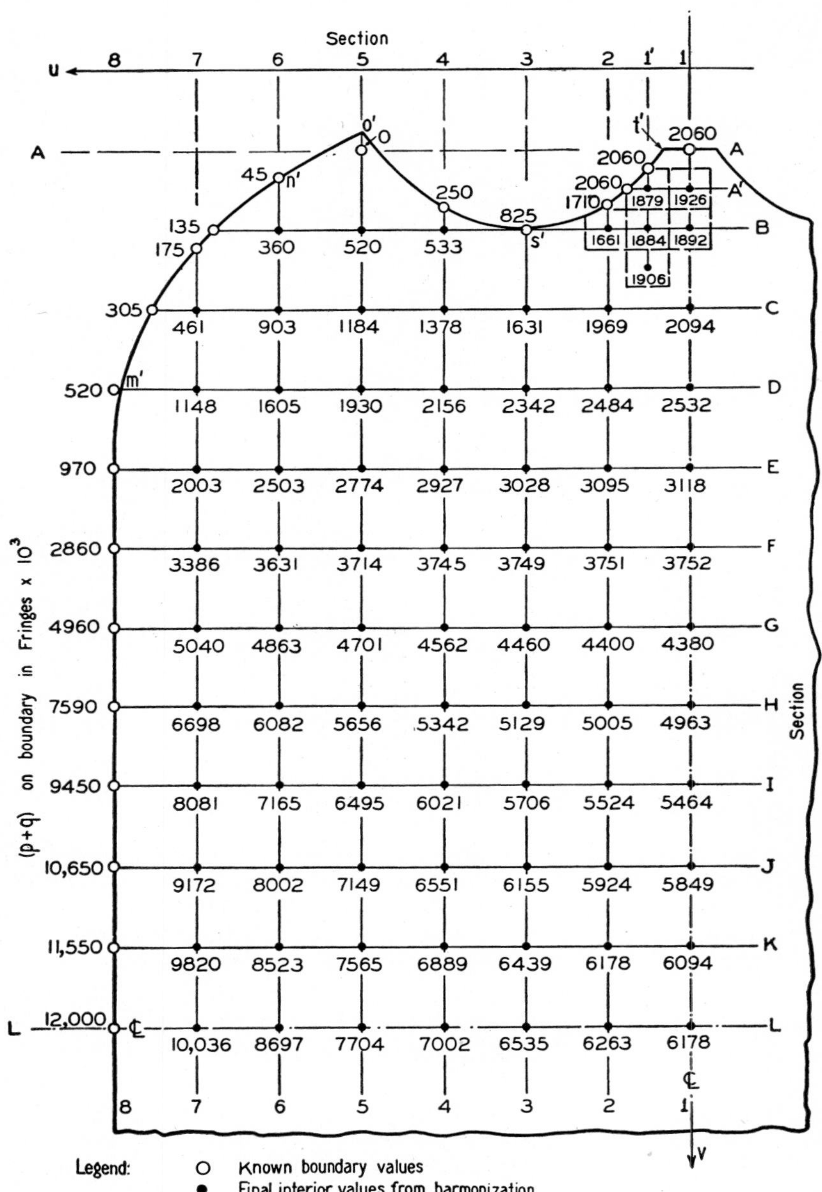

FIG. 9.22 Drawing Showing Transformed Area of Fig. 9.21 and Final Values of Σ from the Numerical Solution Using Bipolar Network.

system are shown in Fig. 9.23. They agree with the contours obtained by harmonization using the mixed rectangular network shown in Fig. 9.24.

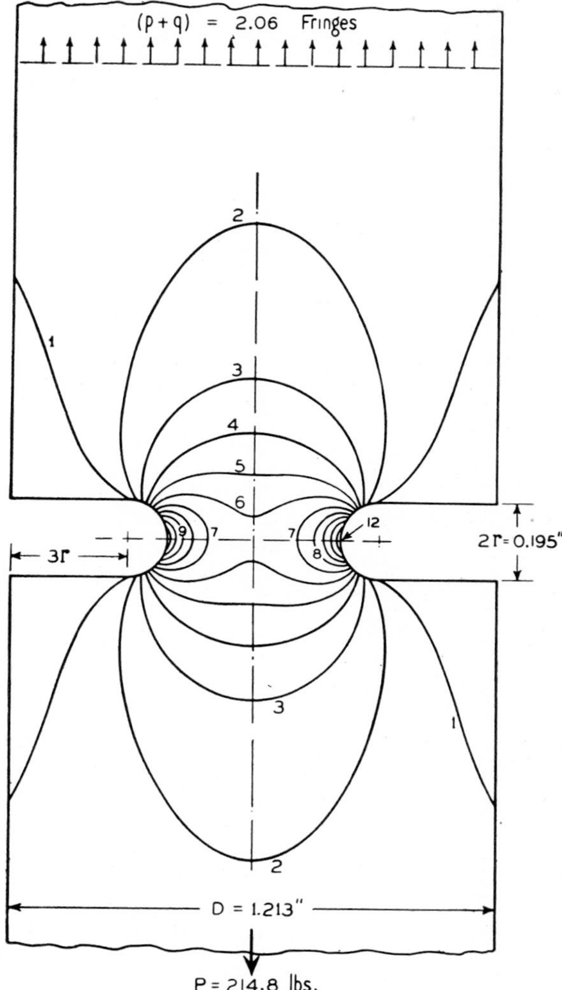

FIG. 9.23 Isopachic Pattern for Bar with Deep Grooves in Fig. 9.19. One fringe = 500 psi.

Fig. 9.25 shows comparative curves of the values of Σ across the sections of symmetry from the mixed rectangular network shown in Fig. 9.24 and the bipolar network of Fig. 9.21. It is seen that they are in close agreement.

In order to verify the results the principal stresses p and q across the symmetrical sections through the grooves were determined and a static check

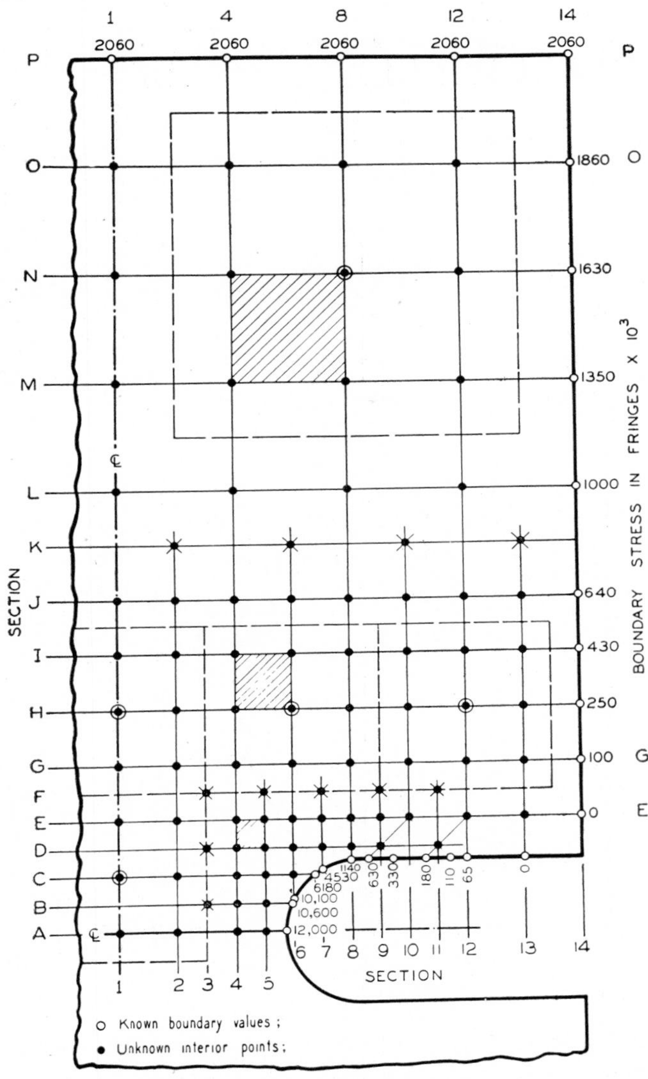

FIG. 9.24 Drawing Showing Mixed Rectangular Network for Bar with Deep Grooves of Fig. 9.19.

made. The results are shown in Fig. 9.26. Corresponding to an applied load of 214.8 lb. we have for the sum of the p stresses across the maximum section a value of 212 lb. The conditions of equilibrium are thus satisfied within 1.3 per cent.

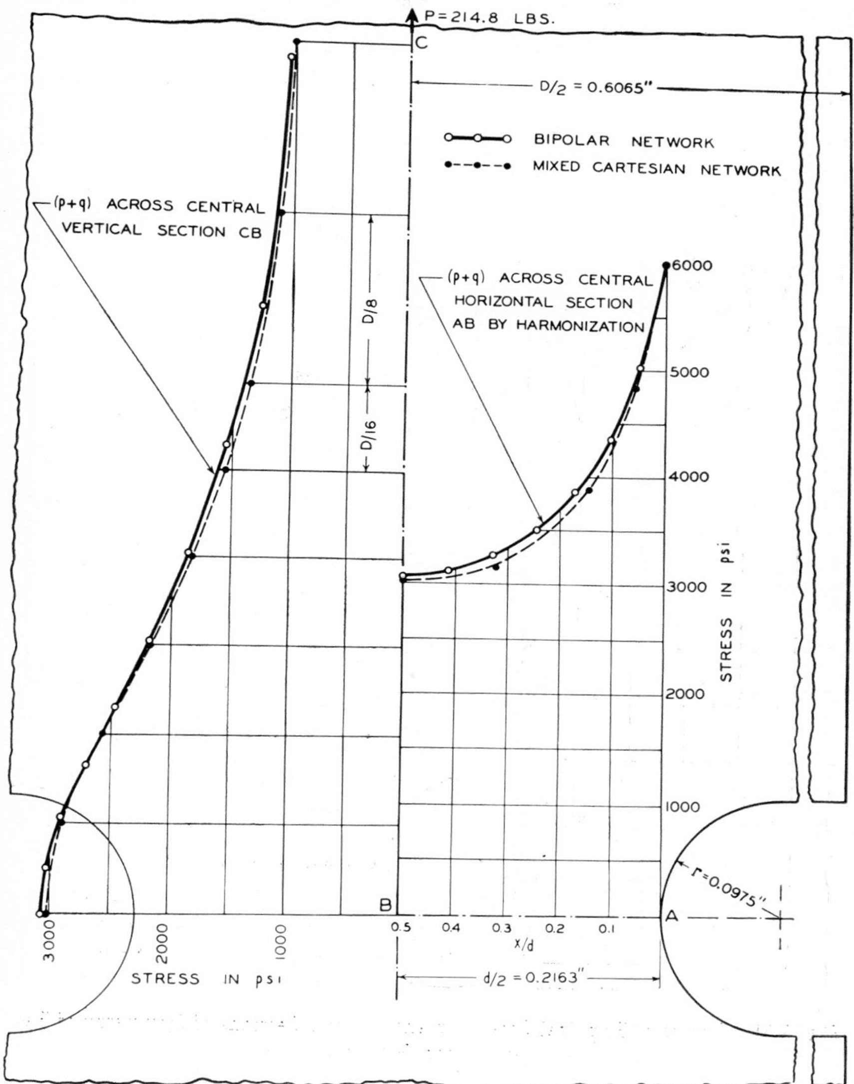

FIG. 9.25 Curves of $(p + q)$ across Sections of Symmetry of Bar with Deep Grooves Obtained from Bipolar and Mixed Rectangular Networks.

Bipolar coordinates involve a little more work in calculating the network and in plotting of contours than a mixed rectangular network. Nevertheless, where there are two complete circular grooves or holes it will be found that the use of bipolar coordinates will result in a measurable saving of time as well as an increase in the accuracy. The saving of labor is due to a reduction in the

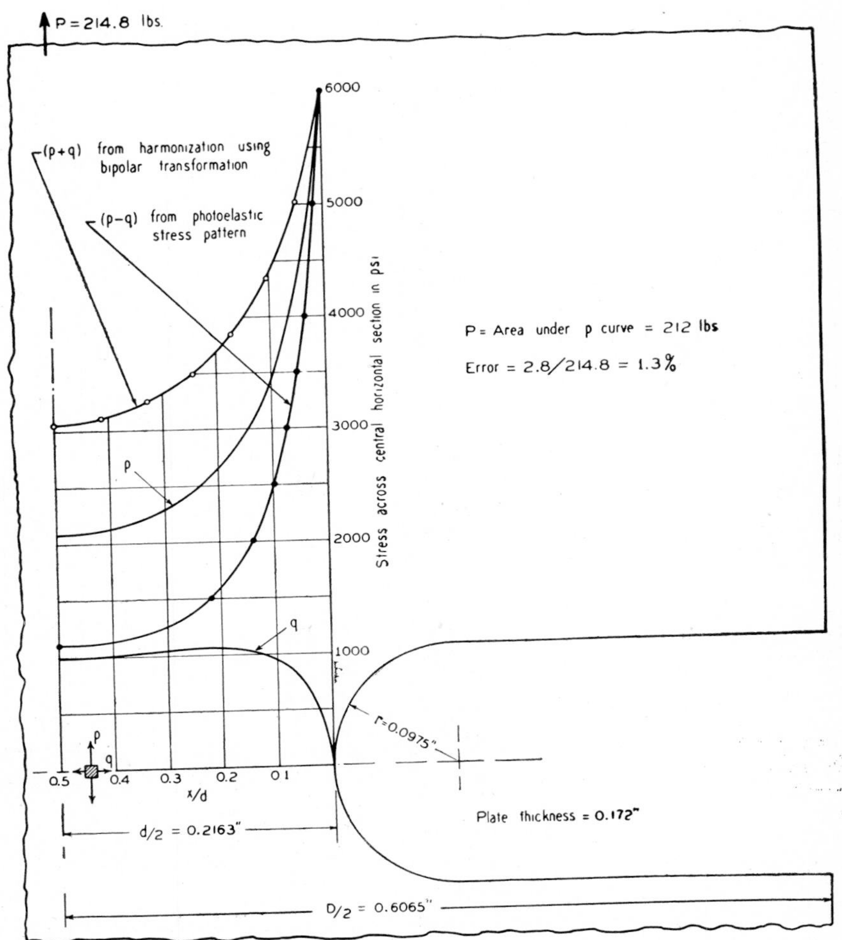

FIG. 9.26 Curves of Principal Stresses p and q across Sections of Symmetry of Bar with Deep Grooves.

total number of net points, a better distribution of these points, and fewer correction factors. The greater accuracy is due to the greater role which the boundary stresses around the sources of stress concentration are made to play and the fineness of the network near these sources.

CHAPTER 10

THE STRESS-OPTIC LAW IN THREE DIMENSIONS

10.1 Introduction. In Vol. I we discussed the stress-optic law in two dimensions. We proved this law by means of direct photoelastic evidence. It was shown that, for incidence normal to the plane of the principal stresses p and q, the retardation n in fringes is given by

$$n = Ct(p - q), \qquad [(5.3), \text{Vol. I}]$$

in which C is the stress-optic coefficient, and t is the thickness of the model parallel to the ray, i.e., the length of the light path.

In the present chapter we discuss the stress-optic law in three dimensions and similarly demonstrate it by direct photoelastic evidence.

§10.2 Secondary Principal Stresses. The optical effects resulting from the transmission of polarized light through three-dimensionally stressed bodies, or from oblique incidence in two-dimensional problems, is connected with the concept of *secondary principal stresses,* a concept which is generally not treated in elasticity or strength of materials. Consider, for example, the element in Fig. 10.1. For an arbitrary set of coordinate axes the stress system consists of six independent components: σ_x, σ_y, σ_z, τ_{xy}, τ_{yz}, and τ_{xz}. ***We define secondary principal stresses for a given direction (i) as the principal stresses resulting from the stress components which lie in a plane normal to the given direction (i), and denote these by $(p', q')_i$.*** Thus the secondary principal stresses for the Z axis are the principal stresses resulting from the stress components σ_x, σ_y, and τ_{xy}. Specifically

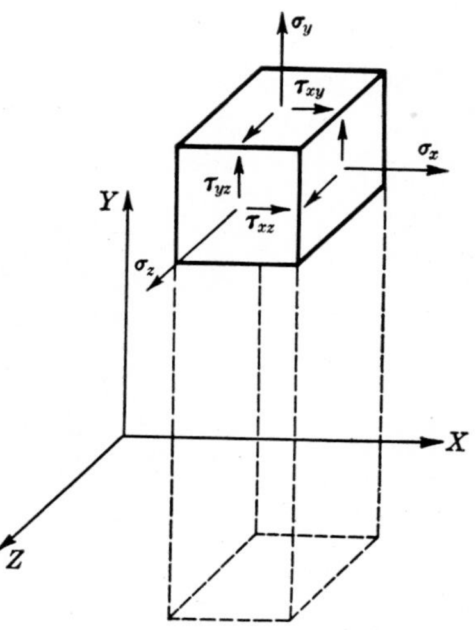

FIG. 10.1 Sketch Showing Stress Components on a Three-Dimensional Element.

$$(p', q')_z = \frac{\sigma_x + \sigma_y}{2} \pm \frac{1}{2}\sqrt{4\tau_{xy}^2 + (\sigma_x - \sigma_y)^2},$$

with corresponding directions given by

$$\tan\,(2\theta)_z = \frac{2\tau_{xy}}{\sigma_x - \sigma_y}.$$

Similarly, the secondary principal stresses for the Y axis are the principal stresses which result from the stress components σ_x, σ_z, and τ_{xz}.

We observe that secondary principal stresses differ radically from the primary or ordinary principal stresses. ***At each point of a stressed body there exists only one set of primary principal stresses. However, there exists at the same point an infinite number of secondary principal stresses,*** depending on the choice of the direction through the given point, although for each particular line or direction the pair of secondary principal stresses becomes unique.

§10.3 The Stress-Optic Law in Three Dimensions. The stress-optic law in three dimensions may be stated in the form of several propositions, as follows:

A. Resolution of Light Vector and Light Vibrations: (*a*) ***When a polarized beam enters a stressed medium it is resolved into components which are parallel to the secondary principal stresses corresponding to the given ray at the point of entrance, Fig. 10.2(a).***

(*b*) ***The vibrations associated with the beam of light traveling through the stressed body are at each point parallel to the directions of the secondary principal stresses, for the given ray.*** If the latter directions are constant between the point of entrance O and the point of exit O_1, Fig. 10.2(*a*), then the directions of the vibrations are also constant. If, however, the directions of the secondary principal stresses for the given ray rotate as the light advances, then the directions of vibration of the components of the light vector also rotate through the same angle.

(*c*) ***When rotation is present a plane-polarized beam entering parallel to one of the secondary principal stress directions generally emerges elliptically polarized.*** However, when the ratio of the angle of rotation to the retardation is small, that is for appreciable stress, the ellipticity is small and the emergent beam may, for practical purposes, be considered plane polarized. The entering light vector rotates with the secondary principal plane along which it entered, and produces a component vibration in a transverse direction of negligible amplitude.[1] This is evidenced by the fact that if the beam is plane polarized and enters parallel to, say, p', Fig. 10.2(*b*), full extinction can be obtained only by placing the

[1] See "Stress Analysis by Three-Dimensional Photoelastic Methods" by Daniel C. Drucker and Raymond D. Mindlin, *Journal of Applied Physics*, Vol. 11, No. 11, pp. 724–732, November, 1940.

principal plane of the analyzer perpendicular to the direction of p' at the point of exit; i.e., the analyzer and polarizer are no longer crossed at extinction but are inclined to each other at an angle of $(90° - \alpha)$, where α is the angle of rotation.

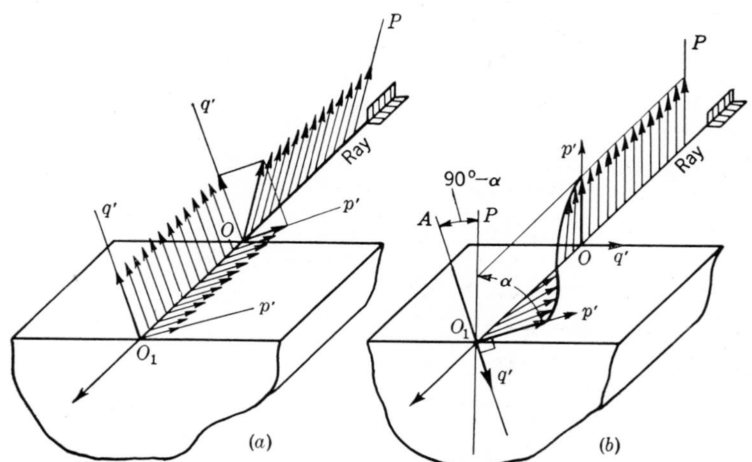

Fig. 10.2 Sketches Showing the Manner in Which a Beam of Plane-Polarized Light Travels through Secondary Principal Planes.

(*a*) Directions of vibration remain constant. (*b*) A plane-polarized beam entering parallel to p' rotates through an angle α and can be extinguished by setting the analyzer A perpendicular not to the polarizer P, but to p' at the point of exit O_1.

B. Retardations: (*a*) ***When the secondary principal stresses remain constant between the point of entrance O and the point of exit O_1, Fig. 10.2, the retardation in wave lengths or fringes is given by***

$$n = Ct'(p' - q'), \tag{10.1a}$$

in which C is the usual stress-optic coefficient, t' is the actual light path, and (p', q') are the secondary principal stresses for the direction of the given ray.

(*b*) ***If only the directions of the secondary principal stresses remain constant and the magnitudes vary, then***

$$n = C \int_0^{t'} (p' - q')\, dt'. \tag{10.1b}$$

(*c*) ***When the directions of the secondary principal stresses rotate, the rotation tends to increase the resulting retardation.*** The increase, however, is small and may for most practical purposes be neglected. In any event, the exact relation between this rotation and its effect on the retardations is at present not fully established.[1]

The law given by eq. (10.1) is generally derived from equations relating the indices of refraction to the secondary principal stresses. Thus, if n_p, n_q are refractive indices of the polarized waves with vibrations parallel to p' and q' respectively, n_o the index of refraction of the unstressed material, and r' the normal stress parallel to the direction of the ray (i), then, on the basis of the historical experimental evidence,

$$\left.\begin{aligned} n_p - n_o &= C_1 p' + C_2(q' + r'), & (a)\\ n_q - n_o &= C_1 q' + C_2(p' + r'), & (b) \end{aligned}\right\}(10.2)$$

in which C_1, C_2 are stress-optic coefficients. From eqs. (10.2) we have

$$\begin{aligned} n_p - n_q &= (C_1 - C_2)(p' - q') \\ &= C'(p' - q'), \end{aligned}$$

where C' is the relative stress-optic coefficient. Multiplying by t'/λ we get

$$(n_p - n_q)\frac{t'}{\lambda} = C'\frac{t'}{\lambda}(p' - q') = n,$$

whence the retardation n is

$$\boldsymbol{n = Ct'(p' - q')},$$

which is obviously eq. (10.1a).

Instead of reproducing the historical evidence[2] for eqs. (10.2) we proceed to establish eqs. (10.1) by direct photoelastic demonstration. Experimental and theoretical stress distributions are shown for a series of basic cases of oblique incidence of a parallel beam, which are believed to establish the validity of the fundamental propositions stated in this section.

§10.4 Normal Stresses Parallel to the Ray. We begin by showing that normal stresses parallel to the ray do not produce any photoelastic effects. To this end we freeze[3] a system of pure bending stresses into a rectangular beam, and cut from it a transverse strip of width h, Fig. 10.3(a). Two stress patterns from this strip corresponding to different directions of the ray are shown in Figs. 10.3(c) and 10.3(e). The first

[1] See reference on p. 334.

[2] For a discussion of the historical development of this subject the reader is referred to Chapter III, in *Treatise on Photoelasticity* by Coker and Filon, Cambridge University Press, London, 1931, or Macmillan, New York.

[3] See §§10.7–10.11, Vol. I, *Photoelasticity*, for the theory and properties of the frozen stress patterns.

of these patterns, Fig. 10.3(*c*), is of the conventional type and corresponds to a ray which is perpendicular to the plane of the bending stresses, Fig. 10.3(*b*). The fringes are here straight, parallel, and equidistant, and the distribution is linear. Fig. 10.3(*e*) represents the effect

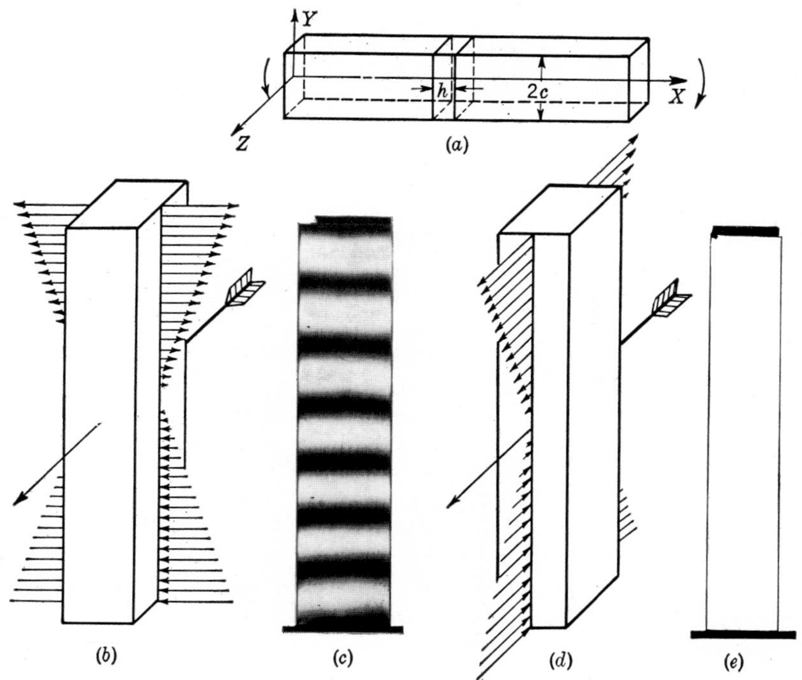

FIG. 10.3 (*a*) Sketch of Beam with Frozen Stresses in Pure Bending Showing Transverse Section of Width h. (*c*) Stress Pattern Obtained from Above Section When Light is Normal to the Stresses Shown in (*b*). Here Photoelastic Effects are Produced. (*e*) Stress Pattern of Zero Fringe Order Obtained When Light is Parallel to the Stresses Shown in (*d*). This Produces No Photoelastic Effect.

$2c = 1.022$ in.; $h = 0.229$ in.; $t = 0.176$ in.

obtained from the same strip when the ray is parallel to the bending stresses, i.e., parallel to the axis of the bar, Fig. 10.3(*d*). The experiment shows zero or no photoelastic effect, either for the tension or compression side, for the full range of stresses from zero to the maximum values. We thus conclude that ***normal stresses parallel to the ray produce no photoelastic effects,*** at least when acting alone.

Further corroboration of this effect is provided by the stress patterns of Figs. 10.6 and 10.12(*a*).

§10.5 Shear Stresses which are Coplanar with the Ray. We consider next systems of pure shear which lie in one plane with the axis of propagation, and are parallel and perpendicular to the ray, Fig. 10.4(*b*).

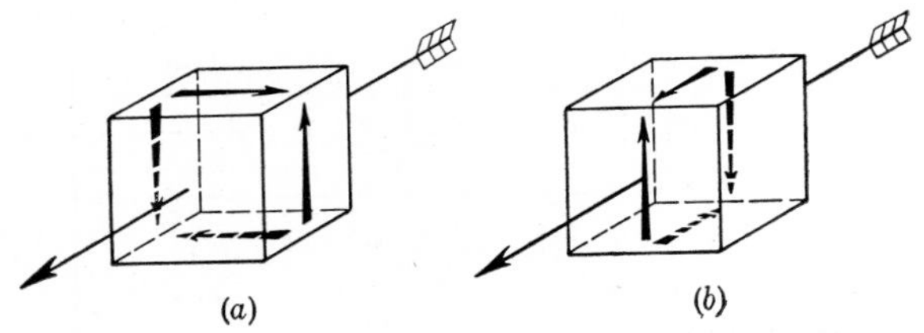

FIG. 10.4 Sketches Showing Two Basic Orientations of Systems of Pure Shear Stresses with Respect to the Direction of the Ray.

(*a*) Produces photoelastic effects. (*b*) Produces no photoelastic effects.

To this end we take a transverse or inclined section from a circular shaft, Fig. 10.5, into which pure shear stresses were frozen, and allow a beam of polarized light to travel through it in a direction parallel to the axis of the shaft. It is clear that at every point through which the light

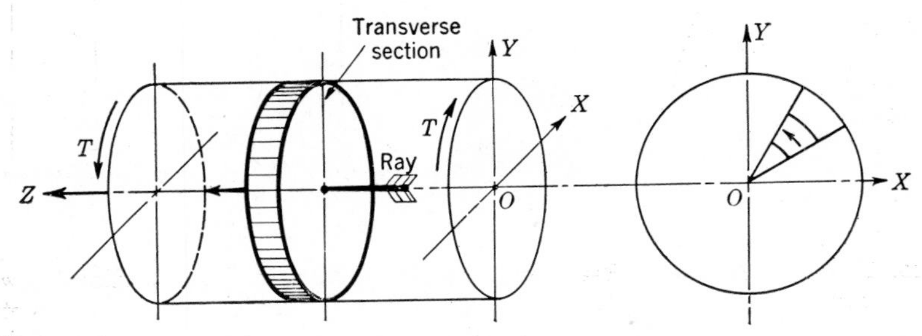

FIG. 10.5 Sketch Showing Transverse Section Cut from a Shaft in Pure Torsion; Also Ray Normal to Section.

travels the stresses consist of pure shears of the type shown in Fig. 10.4(*b*). The resulting stress patterns, Fig. 10.6, are of zero fringe order. Hence, ***systems of shear stresses which are coplanar with the direction of the ray, and the components of which are parallel and perpendicular to the ray, produce no photoelastic effects.***

The effects of systems of shear thus depend on whether all four components or only two of them are perpendicular to the ray. In the first instance, Fig. 10.4(*a*), photoelastic effects are produced. In the second instance, Fig. 10.4(*b*), there are no photoelastic effects.

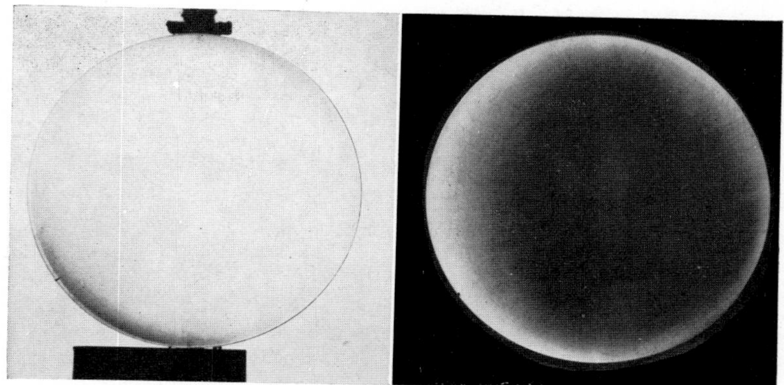

FIG. 10.6 Stress Patterns of a Thin Transverse Section Cut from a Circular Shaft in Pure Torsion, with the Light Normal to the Face of Disk, Fig. 10.5.

Except for small time stresses the patterns show zero fringe orders, i.e., no photo-elastic effects.

§10.6 Secondary Principal Stresses from Pure Tension. Consider now an element subjected to uniform tensile stresses σ_t, Fig. 10.7(a) and placed in the polariscope so that the ray which lies in the XZ plane makes an angle θ with the direction of the stress. For concreteness we assume that the tensile stresses lie in the XY, or vertical, plane.

The stress components acting on an element with faces parallel and perpendicular to the ray, Fig. 10.7(b), are

$$\left.\begin{aligned} \sigma_{x'} &= \sigma_t \sin^2\theta, && (a)\\ \sigma_{z'} &= \sigma_t \cos^2\theta, && (b)\\ \tau_{x'z'} &= \frac{\sigma_t}{2}\sin 2\theta, && (c) \end{aligned}\right\}(10.3)$$

in which Z' is the direction of the ray, and X' is normal to it.

Of the above stresses the only component which lies in a plane transverse to the ray is the component

$$\sigma_{x'} = \sigma_t \sin^2\theta.$$

The secondary principal stresses therefore are

$$\left.\begin{aligned} p' &= \sigma_t \sin^2\theta, && (a)\\ q' &= 0. && (b) \end{aligned}\right\}(10.4)$$

Hence, by eq. (10.1a), noting that $t' = t/\sin\theta$ in the unshaded region b,

Fig. 10.7 (*a*),

$$\left.\begin{aligned} n &= t(C\sigma_t)\sin\theta \qquad &(a) \\ &= N't\sin\theta, \qquad &(b) \end{aligned}\right\} \tag{10.5}$$

in which $N' = C\sigma_t$ represents the frozen tensile stress in fringes per inch of light path at normal incidence, i.e., the normal fringe intensity.

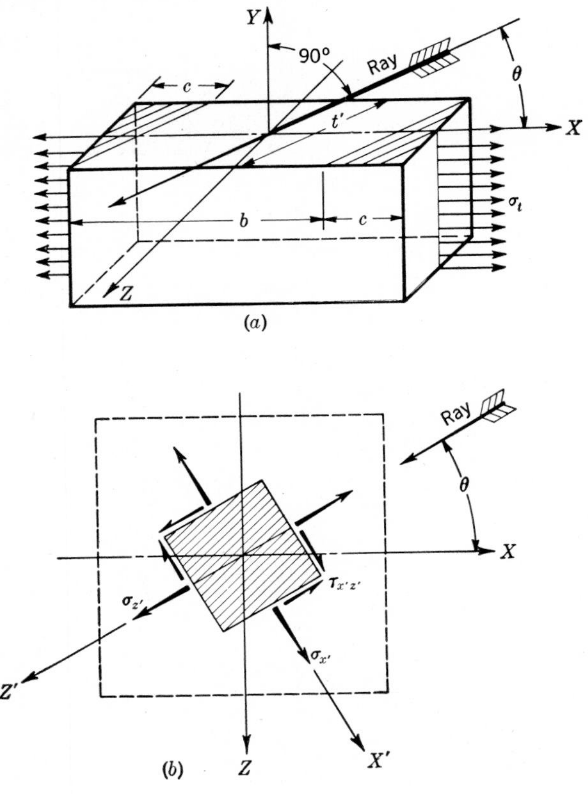

FIG. 10.7 (*a*) An Element in Pure Tension under Oblique Incidence. (*b*) Secondary Principal Stresses.

Referring to Fig. 10.7 (*a*) it is clear that this equation will hold in the unshaded region *b*, in which t' is constant. The stress pattern for that region should be of one fringe order. However, in the end intervals marked *c*, t' varies linearly from zero at the ends to t'.

The stress pattern for the end regions will consist of vertical parallel, equidistant lines, varying from a zero order at the ends to a value of n in region b. A stress pattern for $\theta = 68° 40'$, and $N' = 7.92$ fringes per inch, is shown in Fig. 10.8(a). The comparative curves of theoretical and experimental results, Fig. 10.8(b), show that the retardation is a function of the secondary principal stresses only. The maximum fringe order from the stress pattern is 5.2. The corresponding theoretical value given by eq. (10.5) is

$$n_{\text{max.}} = 0.712 \times 7.92 \times 0.932 = 5.25 \text{ fringes.}$$

It is thus seen that the normal stress $\sigma_{z'}$ parallel to the ray, and the shear stresses $\tau_{x'z'}$ lying in one plane with the ray, produce no photoelastic effect, not only when they act alone, as in Figs. 10.3 and 10.6, but even when they act in conjunction with secondary principal stresses.

Fig. 10.9 shows a stress pattern, and comparative theoretical and experimental curves of n, for a disk cut transversely from a circular shaft into which a uniform tension was fixed by freezing. The basic treatment is the same as for the block in Fig. 10.8.

§10.7 Secondary Principal Stresses from Pure Bending. (a) *Strip from a rectangular bar.* ***A general demonstration of the effect of secondary principal stresses from tension and compression is provided by a transverse strip cut from a bar with fixed system of pure bending stresses,*** Fig. 10.10(a). If this strip be placed in the polariscope so that the ray is parallel to the neutral surface and inclined to the stresses at an angle θ, the secondary principal stresses are again given by eqs. (10.3), in which, however, the bending stress σ_b replaces the tensile stress σ_t. Recalling that

$$\sigma_b = \frac{My}{I}, \tag{10.6}$$

where y is the distance from the neutral axis, M is the bending moment, and I is the moment of inertia, we obtain

$$n = Ct\frac{M}{I}y \sin \theta. \tag{10.7}$$

Hence for the region in which t' is constant the stress pattern consists of straight, parallel, equidistant fringes. The resulting stress pattern for $\theta = 60°$ and comparative curves are given in Figs. 10.10(b) and 10.10(c).

(b) *Disks from a Circular Shaft.* Fig. 10.11(a) shows a sketch of a disk cut transversely from a circular shaft into which was frozen a system of pure bending stresses. The ray is assumed to lie in the neutral surface and to be inclined to the bending stresses, which are parallel to the axis of the shaft, by an angle θ.

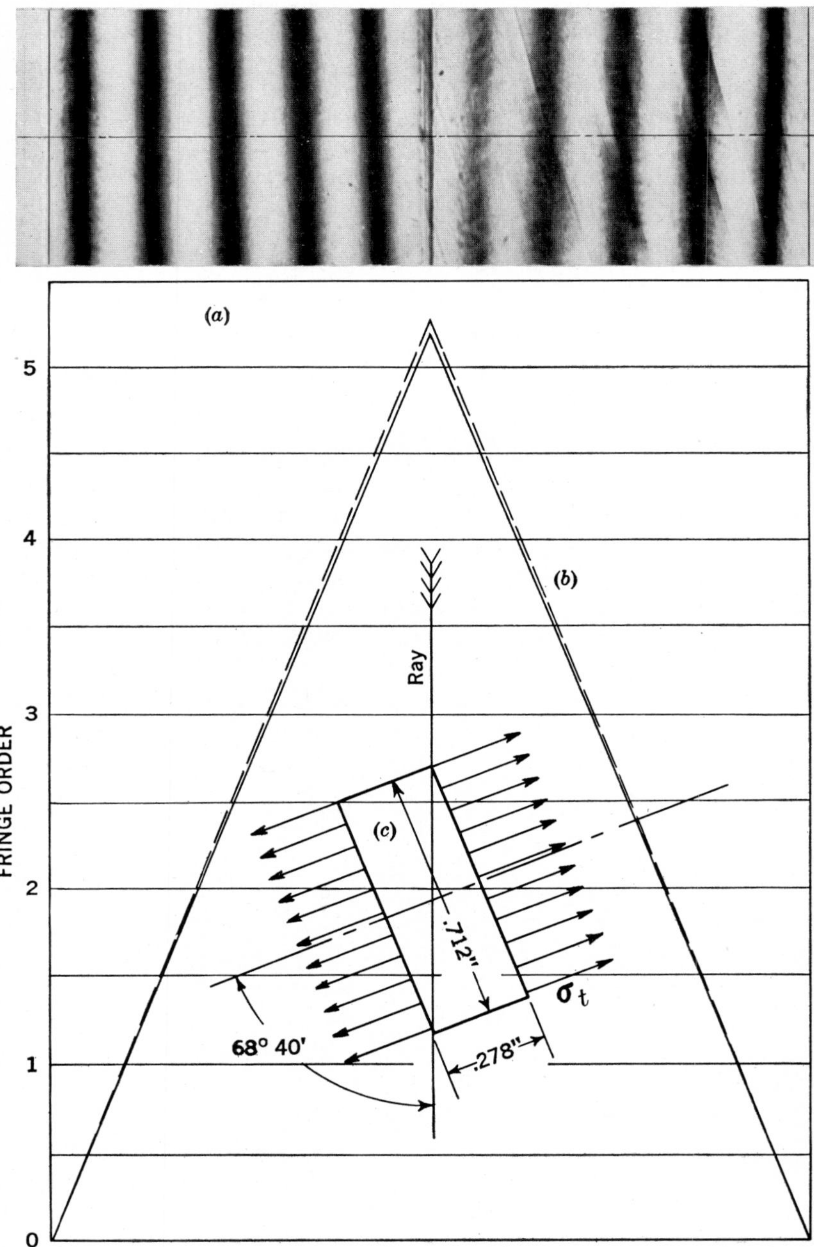

FIG. 10.8 (*a*) Stress Pattern of a Rectangular Block with Frozen Tensile Stresses under Oblique Incidence. (*b*) Theoretical and Experimental Fringe Orders. Dashed curve—theoretical; full curve—experimental. (*c*) Dimensions of Block and Angle of Incidence. $N' = 7.92$ fr./in.

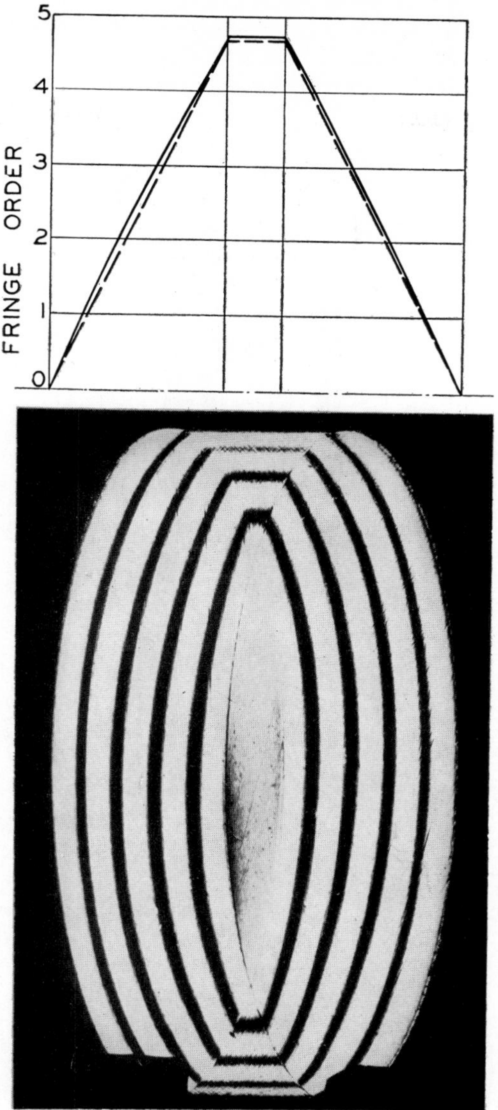

FIG. 10.9 Stress Pattern of a Circular Disk Cut from a Shaft in Tension under Oblique Incidence.

$D = 0.940$ in.; $t = 0.257$ in.; $N' = 7.185$ fr./in. at normal incidence; angle θ between ray and axis of shaft 70° approximately. Maximum fringe order = 4.7 from stress pattern, and 4.68 theoretically. It is also to be noted that n is constant where t' is constant.

When θ is small, Fig. 10.11 (b), the distance t' traversed by the ray is constant except for the shaded regions near the corners. Therefore the retardation along a chord parallel to the neutral axis and distant y from it is given by eq. (10.7).

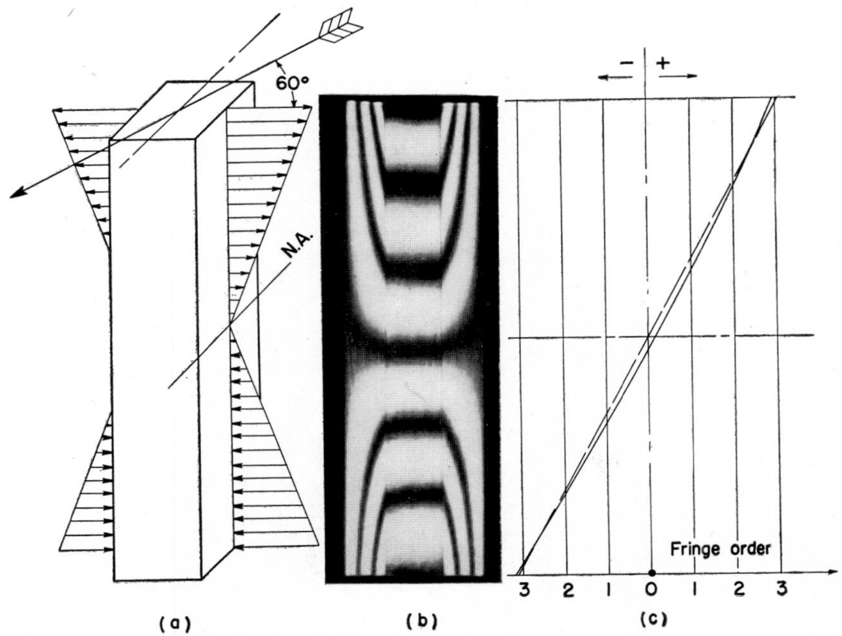

FIG. 10.10 Transverse Section from a Beam in Pure Bending under Oblique Incidence.

(a) Direction of ray; (b) stress pattern; (c) theoretical and experimental curves. Maximum stress $N' = 20$ fr./in. of light path at normal incidence. Maximum fringe order for 60° view is approximately 3, both experimentally and theoretically. Dimensions of bar same as in Fig. 10.3.

Hence the pattern for the region for which t' is constant consists of equidistant straight lines parallel to the neutral surface, Fig. 10.12 (b).

When the angle θ which the ray makes with the bending stress becomes large, specifically, when, Fig. 10.11 (c),

$$|\tan \theta| \geq \frac{2r}{t},$$

the beam is no longer incident on the flat surface of the disk but on the

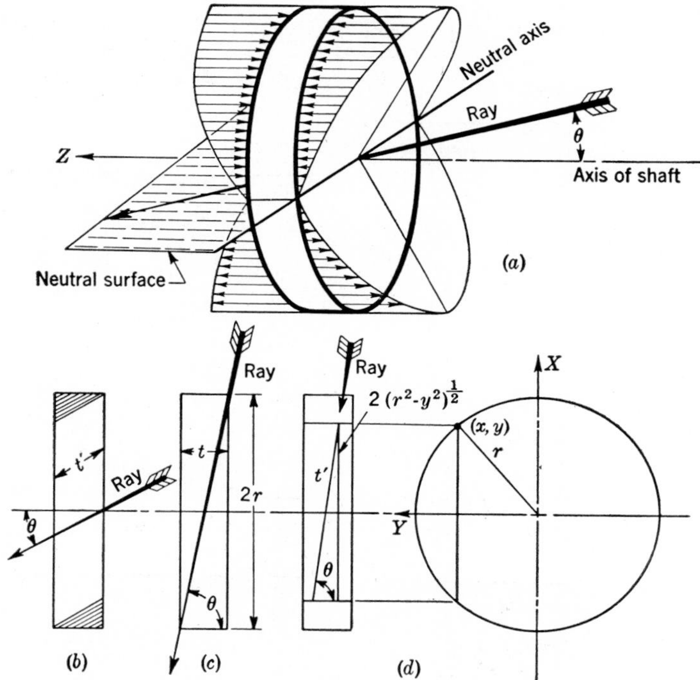

Fig. 10.11 Sketches for Transverse Section Cut from a Circular Shaft in Pure Bending under Different Degrees of Oblique Incidence.

curved surface, so that the distance traversed by the light diminishes as the distance y from the neutral surface increases. The retardation is therefore no longer given by eq. (10.7). In this case, Fig. 10.11 (*d*),

$$t' = \frac{2(r^2 - y^2)^{1/2}}{\sin\theta}, \tag{10.8}$$

$$\left.\begin{aligned} p' &= \frac{M}{I}\, y \sin^2\theta, && (a) \\ q' &= 0, && (b) \end{aligned}\right\} (10.9)$$

so that

$$n = C2(r^2 - y^2)^{1/2}\,\frac{M}{I}\, y \sin\theta,$$

$$= N'\,\frac{y}{c}\, 2(r^2 - y^2)^{1/2} \sin\theta, \tag{10.10}$$

in which

$$N' = \frac{1}{2f} \times \frac{Mc}{I} = C\frac{Mc}{I}. \tag{10.11}$$

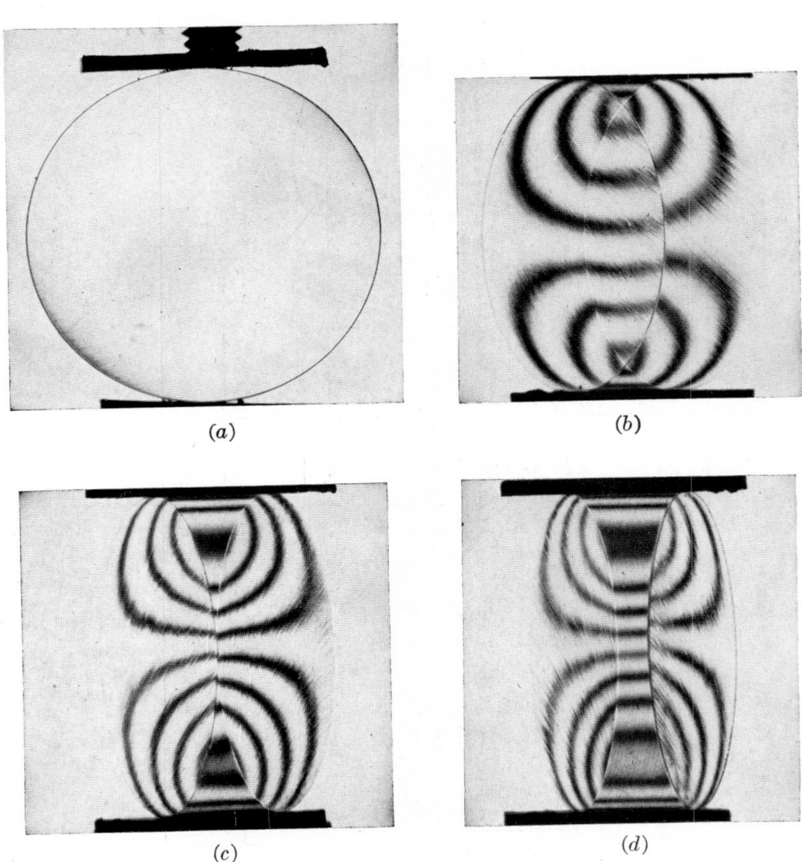

(a) (b) (c) (d)

FIG. 10.12 Stress Patterns of a Transverse Disk Cut from a Circular Shaft with Frozen Pure Bending Stresses for Normal and Oblique Incidence.

(a) $\theta = 0°$, (b) $\theta = 56°$, (c) $\theta = 69°$, (d) $\theta = 74° \, 34'$. D of shaft $= 1.0465$ in.; bending moment $= 3.35$ in.-lb.; d of disk $= 0.930$ in.; $t = 0.347$ in.; $N' = 8.28$ fr./in.

As in eq. (10.5), N' denotes the maximum stress in fringes per inch of light path at normal incidence.

Four stress patterns for different angles of θ are shown in Fig. 10.12. Theoretical and experimental curves of n for Fig. 10.12(d) are shown in Fig. 10.13.

§10.8 Variable Secondary Stresses. ***We next consider secondary principal stresses of constant directions but of variable magnitudes.*** Such systems can also be obtained from a bar in pure bending. Refer-

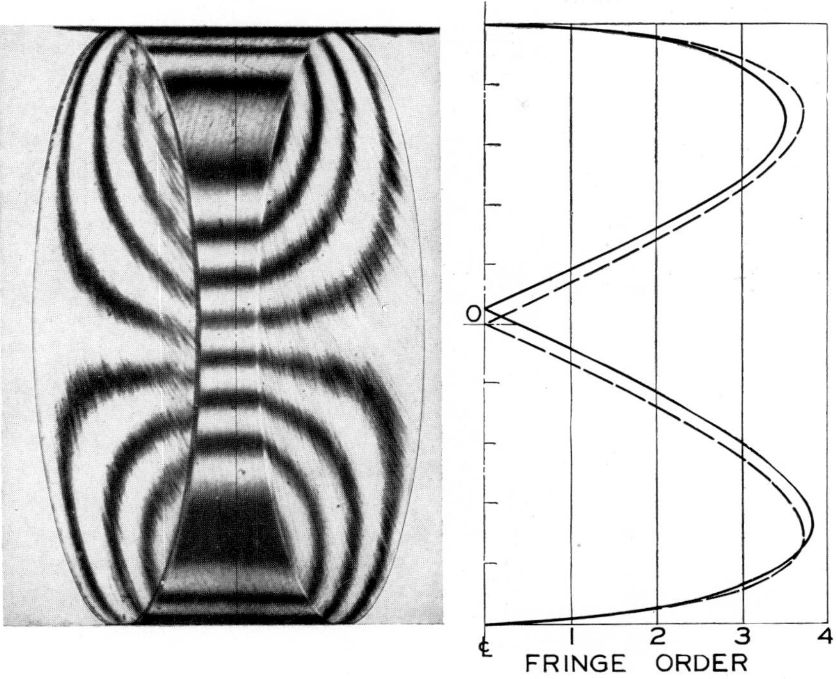

Fig. 10.13 Theoretical and Experimental Curves of Fringe Orders for Case (*d*) of Fig. 10.12.

ring to Fig. 10.14 we cut a small cube from the bar with frozen bending stresses and allow a beam of polarized light to pass through it in such a way that the beam is parallel to the plane of the bending stresses. The secondary principal stresses in this case are

$$p' = \frac{My}{I}\sin^2\theta,$$

$$q' = 0,$$

and

$$n = C\int_0^{t'}(p' - q')\,dt'$$

$$= \frac{CM}{I}\sin^2\theta\int_0^{t'} y\,dt'.$$

Observing that

$$dt' = -\frac{dy}{\sin\theta},$$

we have

$$\left.\begin{aligned} n &= \frac{CM}{I}\sin\theta\int_{y_o}^{c} y\,dy & (a)\\ &= \frac{CM}{I}\sin\theta\,\frac{(c^2 - y_o^{\,2})}{2} & (b)\\ &= N'\,\frac{\sin\theta}{2c}\,(c^2 - y_o^{\,2}), & (c) \end{aligned}\right\}\quad(10.12)$$

in which N' is as in eq. (10.11).

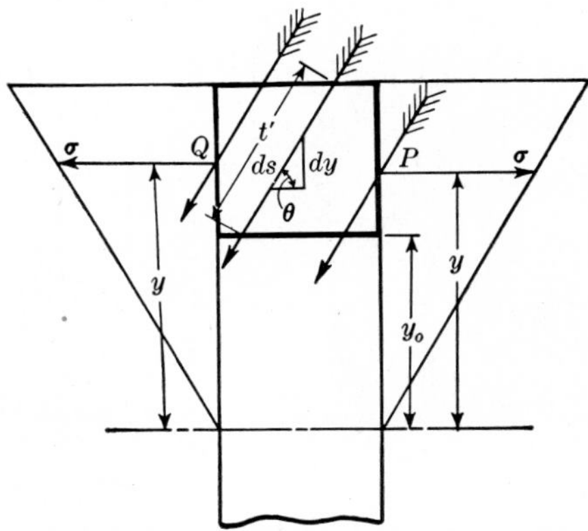

FIG. 10.14 Sketch of an Element from a Beam in Pure Bending under Oblique Incidence with the Ray in the Plane of the Stresses.

It is thus seen that n follows a parabolic distribution.

Eq. (10.12) holds for rays which enter on the outside horizontal surface where $y = c$, and emerge on the lower horizontal surface where $y = y_o$, Fig. 10.14. For rays entering at points on the right vertical face or leaving through the left vertical face the respective retardations are

$$n = N'\,\frac{\sin\theta}{2c}\,(y^2 - y_o^{\,2}), \qquad (a)$$

and

$$n = N'\,\frac{\sin\theta}{2c}\,(c^2 - y^2). \qquad (b) \qquad (10.13)$$

Comparative curves of experimental and theoretical values of n for

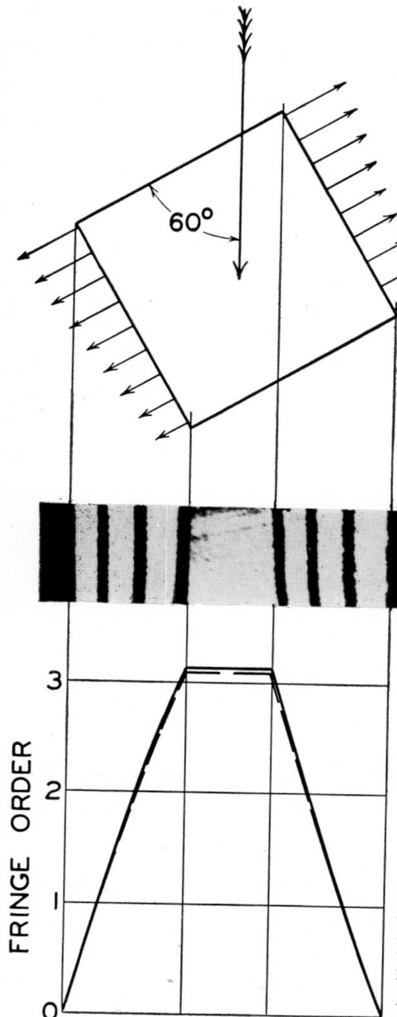

FIG. 10.15 Stress Pattern and Comparative Curves for a Small Cube with Frozen Bending Stresses under Oblique Incidence, Fig. 10.14.

The cube was cut from the tension part of the beam in Fig. 10.3 and contains the Extreme Fibers. Dimensions: face 0.229 in. × 0.229 in.; t = 0.176 in.; $2c$ = 1.022 in. $N_{max.}'$ = 20 fr./in. at normal incidence.

$\theta = 60°$ are shown in Fig. 10.15. Using the data in the legend of Fig. 10.15 and eq. (10.12c) we have

$$n_{max.} = \frac{20 \times 0.866}{1.022}(0.51^2 - 0.28^2) = 3.07 \text{ fringes.}$$

The corresponding experimental value is 3.15 approximately.

§10.9 Secondary Principal Stresses from a Circular Disk. *We consider next the secondary principal stresses arising in a circular disk when it is subjected to concentrated diametral loads and rotated in the polariscope about one of the axes of symmetry, Fig. 10.16.*

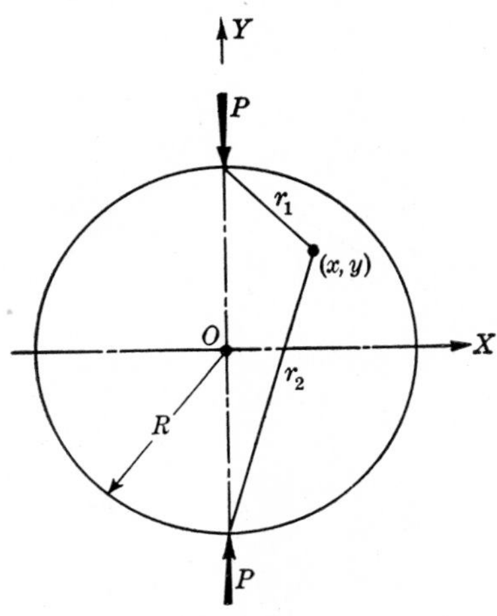

FIG. 10.16 Sketch Showing Notation Used for a Circular Disk Subjected to Concentrated Diametral Loads.

The expressions for the rectangular stress components for this case were derived in Chapter 4 and are given by

$$\left.\begin{aligned}\sigma_x &= -\frac{2P}{\pi t}\left[\frac{(R-y)x^2}{{r_1}^4} + \frac{(R+y)x^2}{{r_2}^4} - \frac{1}{d}\right], && (a)\\ \sigma_y &= -\frac{2P}{\pi t}\left[\frac{(R-y)^3}{{r_1}^4} + \frac{(R+y)^3}{{r_2}^4} - \frac{1}{d}\right], && (b)\\ \tau_{xy} &= \frac{2P}{\pi t}\left[\frac{(R-y)^2x}{{r_1}^4} - \frac{(R+y)^2x}{{r_2}^4}\right], && (c)\end{aligned}\right\}(4.11)$$

where

$$\left.\begin{aligned}{r_1}^2 &= x^2 + (R-y)^2, && (a)\\ {r_2}^2 &= x^2 + (R+y)^2. && (b)\end{aligned}\right\}(4.12)$$

The secondary stress components depend on the axis of rotation and are clearly variable. For simplicity we consider only rotations about the X or Y axis in which cases the mean stresses are closely approximated by the stresses at the midpoints of the optical paths.

For a rotation θ_x about the X axis, Fig. 10.17(*a*), the secondary stress components are

$$\left.\begin{aligned}\sigma_{x'} &= \sigma_x, &(a)\\ \sigma_{y'} &= \sigma_y \cos^2 \theta_x, &(b)\\ \tau_{x'y'} &= \tau_{xy} \cos \theta_x. &(c)\end{aligned}\right\}(10.14)$$

Similarly for a rotation θ_y about the Y axis, Fig. 10.17(*b*),

$$\left.\begin{aligned}\sigma_{x''} &= \sigma_x \cos^2 \theta_y, &(a)\\ \sigma_{y''} &= \sigma_y, &(b)\\ \tau_{x''y''} &= \tau_{xy} \cos \theta_y. &(c)\end{aligned}\right\}(10.15)$$

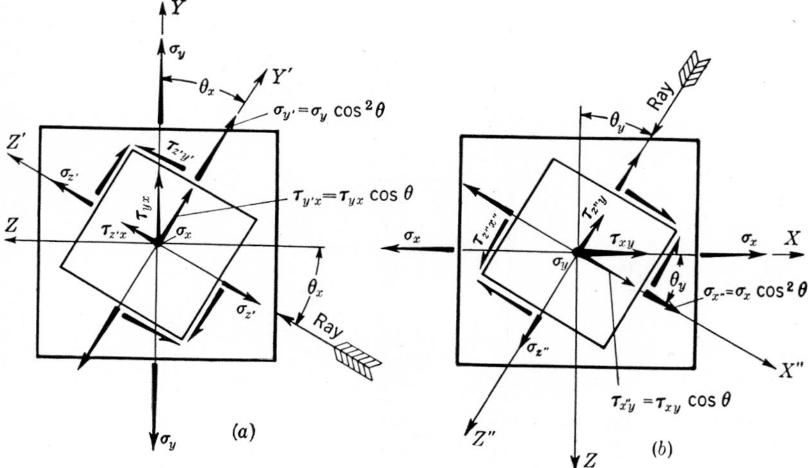

FIG. 10.17 Sketches Showing Secondary Principal Stresses Resulting from Rotation of the Disk in Fig. 10.16 about the X Axis and Y Axis respectively.

The differences between the secondary principal stresses $(p' - q')$ then are [see eq. (1.14), Vol. I],

$$\left.\begin{aligned}(p' - q')_{z'} &= \sqrt{4(\tau_{xy} \cos \theta_x)^2 + (\sigma_x - \sigma_y \cos^2 \theta_x)^2}, &(a)\\ (p' - q')_{z''} &= \sqrt{4(\tau_{xy} \cos \theta_y)^2 + (\sigma_x \cos^2 \theta_y - \sigma_y)^2}, &(b)\end{aligned}\right\}(10.16)$$

For points on the X axis, which is clearly an axis of symmetry, $\tau_{xy} = 0$ and

$$\left.\begin{aligned}(p' - q')_{z'} &= \sigma_x - \sigma_y \cos^2 \theta_x, &(a)\\ (p' - q')_{z''} &= \sigma_x \cos^2 \theta_y - \sigma_y. &(b)\end{aligned}\right\}(10.17)$$

The resulting retardations, which we denote by $n_{z'}$, and $n_{z''}$, then are

$$\left.\begin{aligned} n_{z'} &= \frac{(p' - q')_{z'}}{2F_{z'}}, & (a) \\ n_{z''} &= \frac{(p' - q')_{z''}}{2F_{z''}}, & (b) \end{aligned}\right\} \quad (10.18)$$

where $F_{z'}$ and $F_{z''}$ are the fringe values in psi. shear, corresponding to the optical paths parallel to Z' and Z'' respectively.

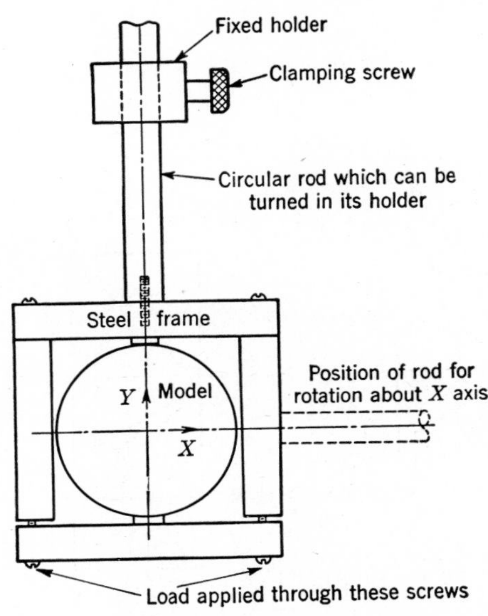

FIG. 10.18 Sketch of Jig Used to Load and to Rotate Model in Oil Tank.

§10.10 Stress Patterns from a Disk under Oblique Incidence. A Bakelite disk 1.846 in. in diameter and 0.153 in. thick was placed in a small rectangular frame which was equipped with a rod about whose axis a rotation could be produced, Fig. 10.18. The loads were applied through the lower two screws, and stress patterns were obtained for normal and oblique incidence with the disk and frame immersed in a glass tank filled with Halowax oil. The resulting stress patterns are shown in Figs. 10.19 and 10.20.

The load was calculated from the expression

$$P = \frac{n_c \pi f R}{2}, \qquad (4.73)$$

FIG. 10.19 Stress Patterns of a Circular Disk in Diametral Compression for Normal and Oblique Incidence with Rotation about the Vertical Axis of Symmetry.

(*a*) Normal view. (*b*) Angle θ between ray and normal to face of disk = 30°. (*c*) $\theta = 45°$. $D = 1.846$ in.; $t = 0.153$ in.; $F = 281$ psi. shear; $P = 364$ lb.

in which n_c is the fringe order at the center of the disk for normal incidence, f is the material fringe value in shear and equals 43 psi., and R is

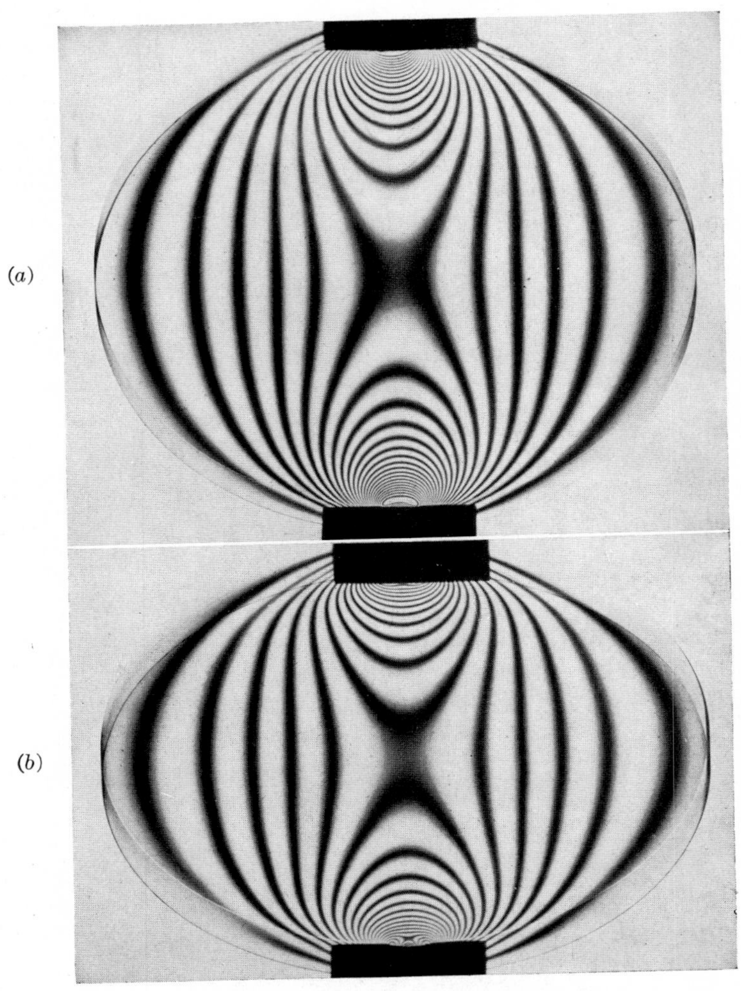

FIG. 10.20. Stress Patterns of Disk in Fig. 10.19 Resulting from a Rotation about the Horizontal Axis. (a) $\theta = 30°$; (b) $\theta = 45°$.

the radius of the disk in inches. The value of n_c at the center of the disk was determined from the curves of n for the horizontal and vertical axes using both dark and bright backgrounds. This value was found to be

5.84 fringes. Eq. (4.73) then gives

$$P = 5.84 \times \pi \times 43 \times \frac{0.923}{2} = 364 \text{ lb.}$$

After the stress patterns were obtained the disk was removed from the clamp, placed in the regular straining frame, and subjected to gradually

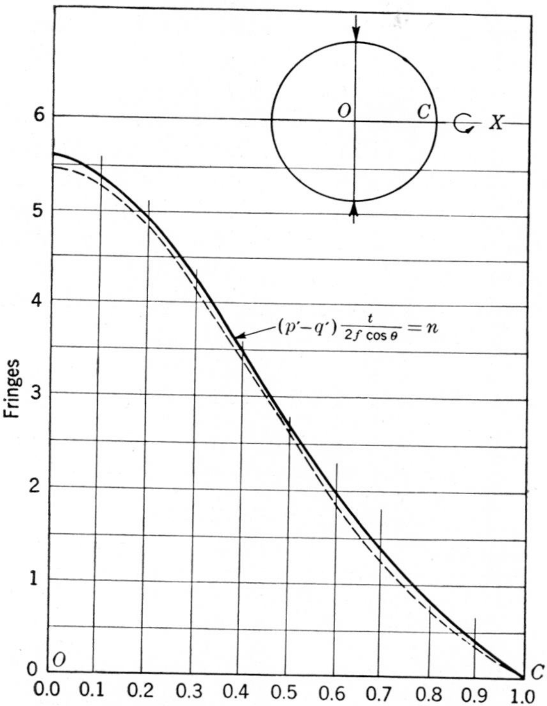

FIG. 10.21 Theoretical and Experimental Curves of n along the X Axis Resulting from a Rotation of 30°.

Experimental results shown by full curve are based on the stress pattern in Fig. 10.20(*b*).

increasing concentrated loads. A curve of n_c at the center of the disk versus the applied load was plotted from which the load for any fringe order could be determined. Although the model was then one week old the load necessary to produce 5.84 fringes at the center was approximately the same as that given by eq. (4.73).

Theoretical curves of n were then determined for the X axis and for a section parallel to it halfway between the center and the top. In these calculations which are based on the equations in §10.9 the sequence is as follows: first we find σ_x, σ_y, τ_{xy}; then $\sigma_{x'}$, $\sigma_{y'}$, $\tau_{x'y'}$; next we calculate $(p' - q')$; and last we find n.

Comparative values of n as obtained experimentally and theoretically are shown in Tables 10.1, 10.2, and 10.3 and in Figs. 10.21 and 10.22.[1]

It was found necessary to carry the calculations of n to better than slide-rule accuracy in order to match the precision of the experimental results. ***The degree of agreement between theory and experiment is indeed remarkable, as can be seen from inspection of the tables and curves.*** The slight deviations are in the main due to errors in the angles of rotation, to the load, and to the average secondary stresses. It is to be noted that the greatest discrepancy occurs in the values from a rotation about the X axis of 45° (see Tables). This seems altogether reasonable since the stresses at the midpoint of the optical path are in this case definitely not the mean stresses, especially for large values of σ_x. In addition there exists a relatively large rotation in the directions of the secondary principal stresses.

TABLE 10.1

COMPARISON OF THEORETICAL AND EXPERIMENTAL VALUES OF n IN FRINGES FOR A HORIZONTAL DIAMETRAL SECTION

Rotation about Vertical Axis

	Normal View		30° Rotation		45° Rotation	
Point x/R	Theoretical n	Experimental n	Theoretical n	Experimental n	Theoretical n	Experimental n
0	5.84	5.84	6.32	6.24	7.22	7.00
0.1	5.67	5.64	6.14	6.05	7.02	6.80
0.2	5.19	5.15	5.62	5.54	6.45	6.24
0.3	4.47	4.42	4.85	4.81	4.60	5.39
0.4	3.66	3.57	4.00	3.90	4.62	4.42
0.5	2.80	2.73	3.08	3.04	3.59	3.38
0.6	2.02	1.96	2.23	2.20	2.62	2.44
0.7	1.34	1.28	1.50	1.46	1.77	1.60
0.8	0.78	0.72	0.88	0.81	1.06	0.86
0.9	0.34	0.29	0.34	0.33	0.47	0.31
1.0	0	0	0	0	0	0

[1] Similar results have been obtained by D. C. Drucker for a square plate under diagonal loads. See his paper "Photoelastic Separation of Principal Stresses by Oblique Incidence," *Journal of Applied Mechanics, Trans., A.S.M.E.*, Vol. 10, No. 3, September, 1943.

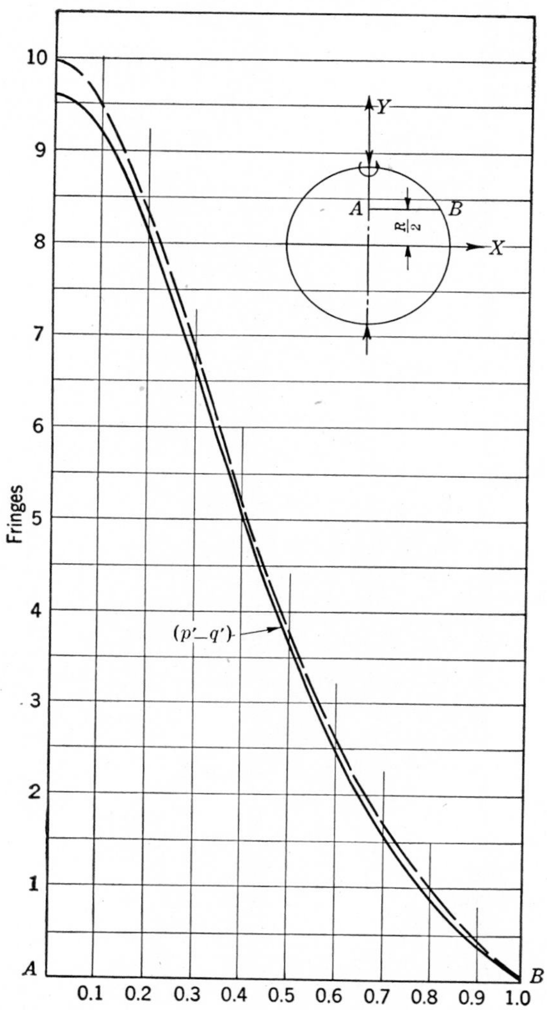

FIG. 10.22 Theoretical and Experimental Curves of n for Section A–B Resulting from a Rotation of 45° about the Y Axis.

Experimental results shown by full curve are based on the stress pattern of Fig. 10.19(c).

TABLE 10.2

COMPARISON OF THEORETICAL AND EXPERIMENTAL VALUES OF n IN FRINGES FOR A HORIZONTAL DIAMETRAL SECTION

Rotation about Horizontal Axis

	Normal View		30° Rotation		45° Rotation	
Point x/R	Theoretical n	Experimental n	Theoretical n	Experimental n	Theoretical n	Experimental n
0	5.84	5.84	5.48	5.62	5.16	5.37
0.1	5.67	5.64	5.31	5.42	5.00	5.21
0.2	5.19	5.15	4.85	4.96	4.54	4.76
0.3	4.47	4.42	4.16	4.30	3.88	4.10
0.4	3.66	3.57	3.39	3.51	3.13	3.34
0.5	2.80	2.73	2.58	2.68	2.35	2.56
0.6	2.02	1.96	1.84	1.96	1.65	1.86
0.7	1.34	1.28	1.21	1.33	1.07	1.28
0.8	0.78	0.72	0.70	0.81	0.60	0.80
0.9	0.34	0.29	0.30	0.38	0.25	0.39
1.0	0	0	0	0	0	0

TABLE 10.3

COMPARISON OF THEORETICAL AND EXPERIMENTAL VALUES OF n FOR A SECTION MIDWAY BETWEEN LOAD AND HORIZONTAL DIAMETER OF DISK

Rotation about Vertical Axis

	Normal View		30° Rotation		45° Rotation	
Point x/R	Theoretical n	Experimental n	Theoretical n	Experimental n	Theoretical n	Experimental n
0	7.80	7.68	8.58	8.42	9.98	9.61
0.1	7.46	7.38	8.20	8.08	9.50	9.21
0.2	6.59	6.55	7.19	7.11	8.30	8.09
0.3	5.43	5.39	5.90	5.83	6.72	6.58
0.4	4.20	4.22	4.54	4.48	5.13	5.08
0.5	3.08	3.09	3.31	3.24	3.72	3.62
0.6	2.14	2.11	2.28	2.25	2.57	2.45
0.7	1.38	1.37	1.47	1.43	1.66	1.54
0.8	0.79	0.78	0.85	0.81	0.96	0.84
0.9	0.34	0.36	0.36	0.33	0.41	0.33
1.0	0	0	0	0	0	0

§10.11 Rotational Effects. ***We now proceed to demonstrate the two rotational effects stated in §10.3: first, that the vibrations travel in the rotating principal planes, and second, that the rotation increases the retardation.*** These effects can be demonstrated by superimposing a linear bending stress σ_b over an initial system of uniform tension or compression σ_t, which is inclined to the bending stress at an arbitrary angle θ (θ not equal to zero).[1] Experimentally this can be attained by freezing a system of pure tension σ_t into a plate of Bakelite, Fig. 10.23, cutting out of it a bar at some arbitrary angle θ to the direction of the frozen tension, and then subjecting this bar to bending moments about an axis which lies in the plane of the tensile stresses and is normal to the long edge of the bar, i.e., about the Y' axis, Fig. 10.23.

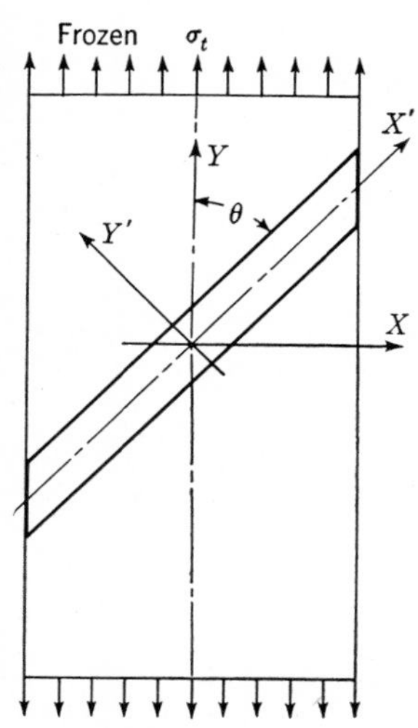

FIG. 10.23 Sketch Showing Inclined Bar Cut from a Plate with Frozen Pure Tensile Stresses.

The rectangular stress components and the general direction of the principal stresses at points of entrance and exit of the ray are shown in Fig. 10.24. Denoting the maximum bending stress by σ_{bm}, and the ratio σ_{bm}/σ_t by m, the difference between the principal stresses at any point (i) distant z from the center of the beam is

$$p - q = \frac{\sigma_t}{t}\sqrt{t^2 + 2mzt\cos 2\theta + m^2z^2}, \tag{10.19}$$

and the directions of the principal stresses are given by

$$\tan 2\phi = \frac{mz\sin 2\theta}{t + mz\cos 2\theta}. \tag{10.20}$$

At point A, σ_b is negative, and at B it is positive. Also, at A, $z = t$, so that

$$\left.\begin{aligned} \tan\,(2\phi)_a &= \frac{-m\sin 2\theta}{1 - m\cos 2\theta} \qquad (a) \\ \text{and} \qquad \tan\,(2\phi)_b &= \frac{m\sin 2\theta}{1 + m\cos 2\theta}. \qquad (b) \end{aligned}\right\} \tag{10.21}$$

Hence the angle of rotation α, Fig. 10.24(d), is given by

$$\alpha = (\phi_p)_b - (\phi_p)_a, \tag{10.22}$$

where $(\phi_p)_a$ and $(\phi_p)_b$ denote the directions of the maximum stresses p_a

[1] See "Photoelastic Analysis of Transverse Bending of Plates," by D. C. Drucker, *Journal of Applied Mechanics, Trans. A.S.M.E.*, Vol. 9, No. 4, December, 1942.

and p_b at A and B respectively. From eqs. (10.21)

$$\sin 2\theta = \frac{m^2 - 1}{2m} \tan 2\alpha. \tag{10.23}$$

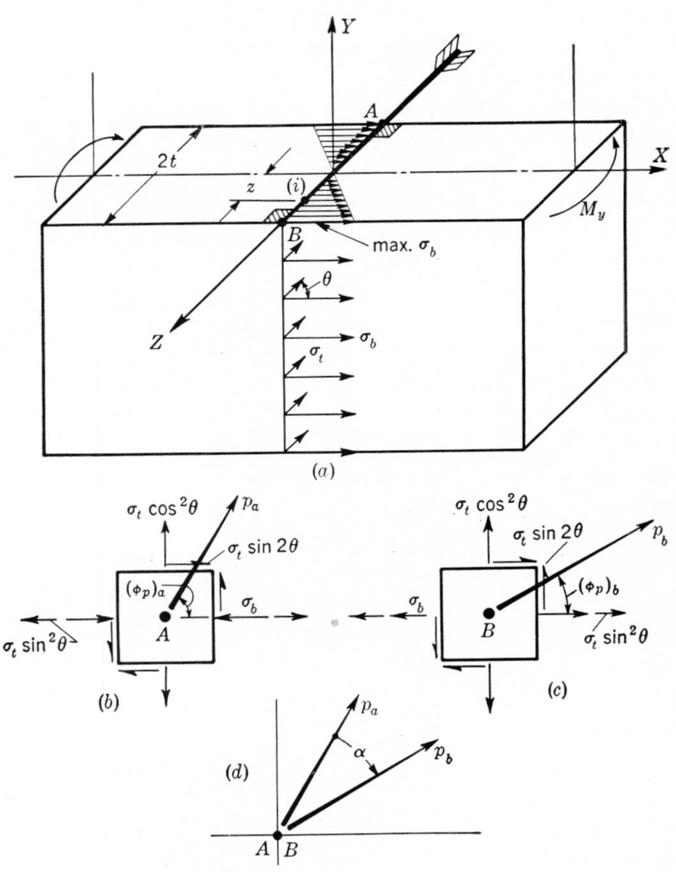

FIG. 10.24 (*a*) Sketch Showing the Superposition of Pure Bending over the Frozen Pure Tension in the Bar of Fig. 10.23. (*b*) and (*c*) Stress Components at Points *A* and *B* Respectively. (*d*) Angle of Rotation α.

Also, neglecting the rotational effect, the retardation n is given by

$$n = \int_{-t}^{t} \frac{(p - q)}{2f} dz, \tag{10.24}$$

where f is the shear fringe value of the material.

Substituting $(p - q)$ from eq. (10.19), integrating, and replacing $\sigma_t/2f$ by n_t, we obtain

$$\frac{n}{n_t} = \frac{1}{4m}\left\{(m + \cos 2\theta)\sqrt{1 + 2m \cos 2\theta + m^2}\right.$$

$$+ (m - \cos 2\theta)\sqrt{1 - 2m \cos 2\theta + m^2}$$

$$\left. + \sin^2 2\theta\left[\sinh^{-1}\left(\frac{m + \cos 2\theta}{|\sin 2\phi|}\right) + \sinh^{-1}\left(\frac{m - \cos 2\theta}{|\sin 2\theta|}\right)\right]\right\}. \quad (10.25)$$

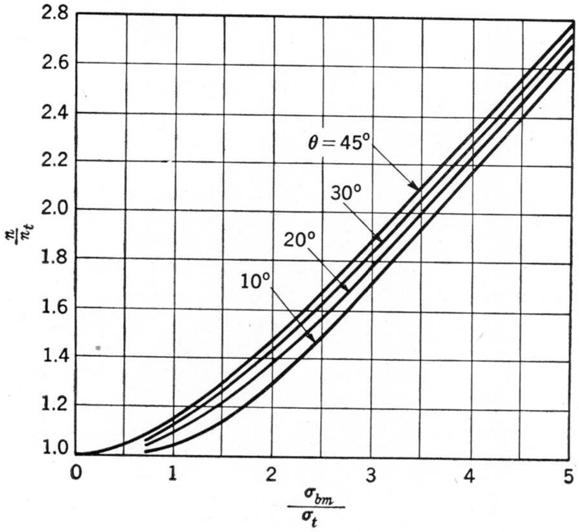

FIG. 10.25 Curves for the Evaluation of (n/n_t) for Different Angles of θ and Ratios $m = \sigma_{bm}/\sigma_t$. (From Drucker.)

The ratios n/n_t for different values of m and θ have been calculated by Drucker[1] and are given by the curves of Fig. 10.25. Values of θ from zero to 45° are sufficient for the whole range from 0 to 90°, since angles $\pm\theta$ or $\pm(90 - \theta)$ lead to the same results, so that n/n_t for 60° is the same as for 30°.

§10.12 Experimental Verification. ***The theory developed in the preceding section is confirmed experimentally.*** Comparative results for n and α from a pure bending test are given by the curves of Fig. 10.26. In this test the beam was 1.173 in. by 0.371 in., θ was 45°, and the frozen σ_t was 2.75 fringes. The beam was strained to give an integral number of

[1] See reference on p. 359.

fringes, and the bending stresses were determined. Corresponding to fringes of order 3, 4, 5, 6, 7, the values of $m = \sigma_{bm}/\sigma_t$ came out to be 0.7, 1.71, 2.52, 3.43, and 4.17. The theoretical values of n could then be read off the 45° curve of Fig. 10.25. Inspection of the curves in Fig. 10.26(a) shows that the theoretical values are consistently somewhat lower than the experimental values and that the difference increases as m

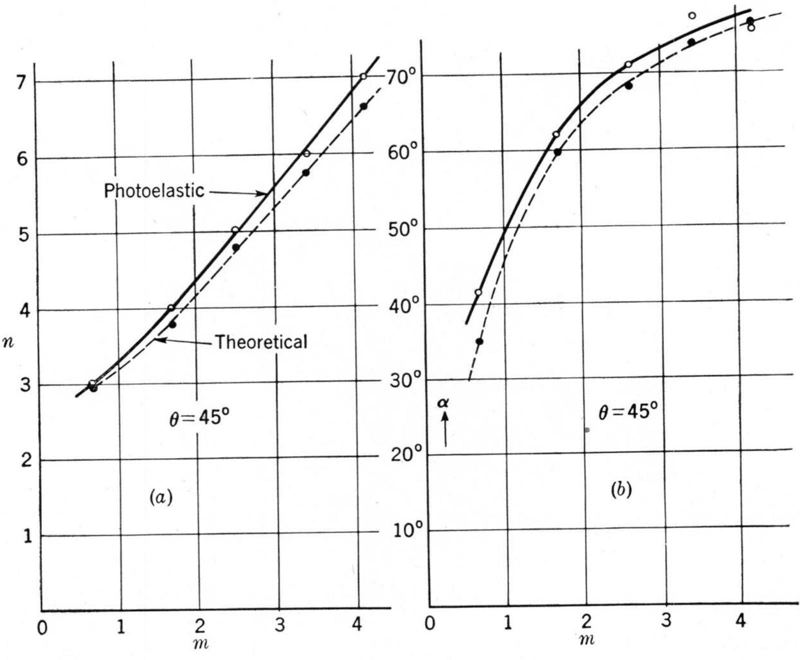

FIG. 10.26 Theoretical and Experimental Values of n and α as Functions of m Illustrating Rotational Effects.

increases. The rotational effect upon the retardation is thereby confirmed.

Fig. 10.26(b) shows comparative curves for the angle of rotation α. For an arbitrary non-integral retardation this angle can be determined only by trial. Using plane-polarized light, the polarizer is set at random and the analyzer is rotated from an arbitrary position through 180°. If no extinction is obtained the polarizer is moved through a small angle, say 5°, and extinction sought again by rotating the analyzer. The process is repeated until extinction is obtained, for there will always be one setting of the polarizer for which its principal axis will be parallel to the direction of a principal stress at the point of entrance. For that position of the polarizer extinction will be attained when the analyzer is at right angles to the direction of vibration at the point of emergence, point B, Fig. 10.24. The rotation of the light α is then given by the angle through which the analyzer must be turned from the crossed position corresponding to the last setting of the analyzer which gives extinction, Fig. 10.27.

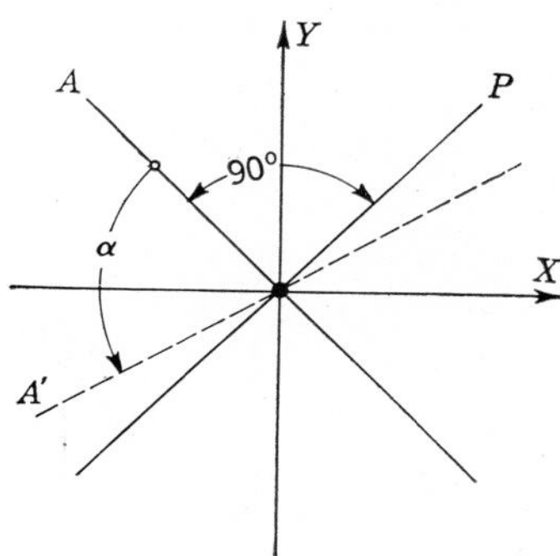

FIG. 10.27 Sketch Showing the Angular Rotation of the Analyzer Necessary to Produce Extinction of the Emerging Ray in Which the Direction of Vibration Has Been Changed.

In the particular case when the retardation is an integral number of fringes, extinction can be effected in a considerably simpler manner, for in this instance extinction can be produced for all positions of the polarizer. This follows from eq. (3.27), Vol. I, which shows that for a retardation equal to an integral number of wave lengths the resulting beam is plane polarized, and the vibrations are parallel to the principal plane of the polarizer. Hence, it is only necessary to start with a crossed analyzer and polarizer, and to rotate the analyzer, until extinction is obtained. The angle of rotation α is the angle through which the analyzer is turned from its crossed position.

Inspection of Fig. 10.26(b) shows good agreement between the theoretical and experimental results. Several applications of oblique incidence are described in Chapter 12.

CHAPTER 11

THREE-DIMENSIONAL TECHNIQUE

§11.1 Introduction. In this chapter we discuss general questions of technique which arise in the application of the method *of freezing and slicing and transmitted parallel light.* These techniques often differ from those used in two-dimensional photoelasticity. Although they are relatively simple to apply it took considerable time and much labor to discover and to test them. The final procedures described in this chapter are based on the accumulated experience during some eight years of work in three-dimensional problems. They are presented here in the belief that they may save much time and cost to other workers in the field and will materially add to the quality of the work. Essential equipment is also described.

§11.2 Materials and Preparation. The primary material used in this country at the present time in three-dimensional photoelastic investigations is the same which proved so successful in two-dimensional work, namely Bakelite BT-61-893. This material possesses the essential diphase characteristics which permits of the freezing or fixing of an elastic pattern into a three-dimensional model, which is not disturbed by slicing.[1] The only objections to Bakelite are the limitations in size of the virgin plates, the tendency to develop time stresses, and the high cost. Chief among these are the relatively small dimensions of the plates which the Bakelite Corporation has so far been able to put on the market. These dimensions are roughly 12 in. by 6 in. by 1 in., and all monolithic models have to be cut from such plates. The problem of time stresses, although annoying, can be overcome. This is discussed in the next sections. The possibility of cemented models still needs exploration.

The virgin plates contain considerable initial stresses. Experience has shown that these can be appreciably reduced by repeated annealing. We have used as many as 5 to 10 cycles of annealing with good results. The annealing procedure has been fully described in §10.13, Vol. I. The only revision we wish to make here is in regard to temperature. In thick plates the temperature should be 260° F. to 270° F. instead of 230° F. to 260° F.

[1] For a detailed discussion of these characteristics the reader is referred to §§10.7–10.13, Vol. I.

§11.3 Methods of Loading for Circular Shafts. (*a*) *Tension.* Uniform tension is a state of stress often assumed in theoretical discussions of problems in elasticity. It is an ideal condition for which mathematical analysis is much simplified. However, it is doubtful whether such a stress can ever be fully realized in practice in thick bars or shafts. Even in the laboratory it is extremely difficult to produce a good approximation to a state of uniform tension in bars 3 in. wide, 1 in. thick, and 10 in. or 12 in. long.

Attempts to produce sensibly uniform tension with a variety of rigid mechanical clevices of the universal type proved unsuccessful. Best results are obtained when the rigid clevices are replaced by loops of strong but flexible twine or strings. The twine or strings should be formed into closed bands, put over rollers having a diameter equal to that of the shaft, and slipped over the transverse pins passing through the shaft, Fig. 11.1. Precautions must be taken to make sure that the strings do not slip along the pins, as that will produce eccentric loading and bending. Small pulleys fixed so that they are free to turn but cannot move along the pins are desirable.

To reduce the effects of accidental bending it is further desirable to place the transverse holes for the load-carrying pins at right angles to the hole, or other discontinuity in the shaft where the stresses are required, Fig. 11.1.

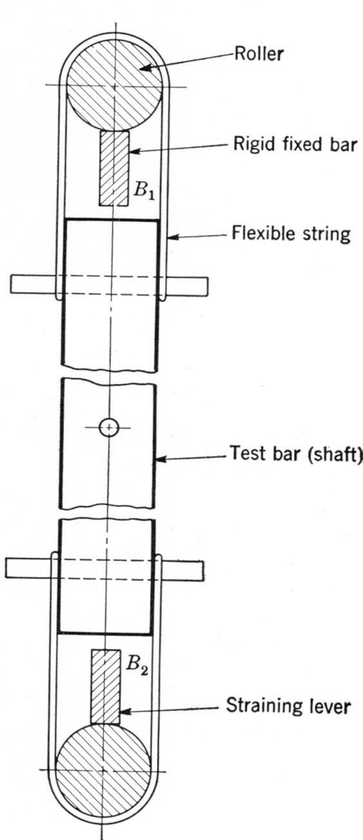

FIG. 11.1 Sketch Showing Method of Loading a Circular Shaft in Tension.

The two bars B_1 and B_2 are a part of the straining frame built into the furnace.

With the above precautions it is possible to obtain sensibly uniform tension in a shaft 1 in. in diameter with a symmetrically located circular hole when the distance between the loading pins is approximately 6 in.

(*b*) *Compression.* Except in very short blocks it is extremely difficult to produce uniform compression. The slightest eccentricity produces buckling.

(*c*) *Bending.* As in tension, flexible strings are better than clevices. In order to eliminate axial stresses the strings should be fairly long. ***In order to obtain a reliable measure of the bending moment it is absolutely***

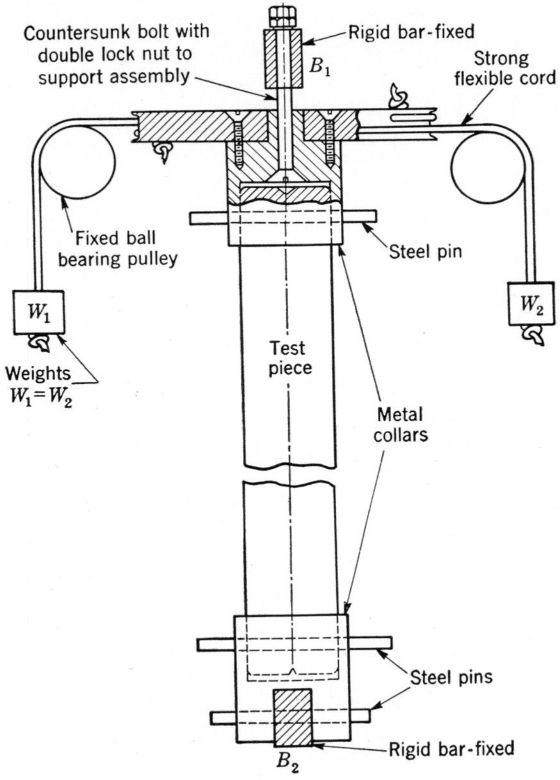

FIG. 11.2 Sketch of the Loading Mechanism Used to Apply Torsion.

Rigid bars B_1 and B_2 and pulleys are all part of the straining frame inside the furnace.

essential that the axes of pins which carry the loads should lie in the neutral surface of the shaft. Important as this precaution was at room temperature (two dimensions), it is vastly more so at high temperatures.

(*d*) *Torsion.* Torsion has been successfully produced by means of the set-up shown in Fig. 11.2.

§11.4 Tension in Thick Plates.[1] In thick slotted plates, of cross section (3 in. by 1 in.) approximately, the distribution of the tensile stresses in the regions surrounding the slot, for the type of head shown in Fig. 11.3, is a function of the ratio $L'/t = m$, where L' is the distance

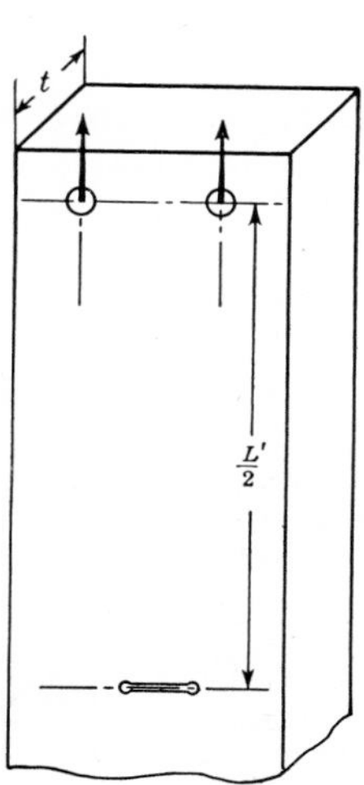

FIG. 11.3 Sketch of a Thick Plate Showing Head Design and Notation.

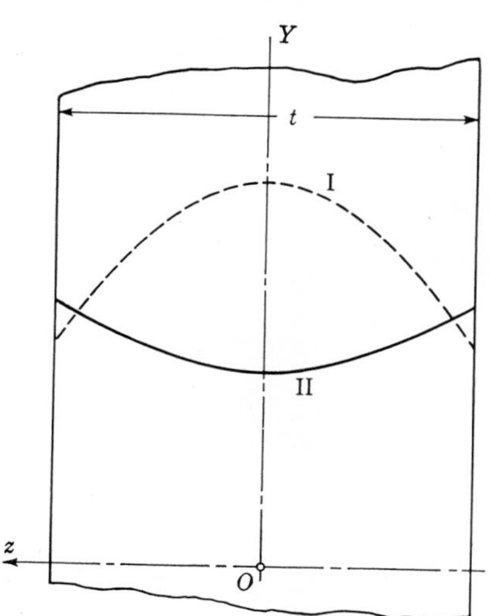

FIG. 11.4 Sketch Showing Reversal in the Shape of the σ_y-Curve at the Root of the Slot in Plate of Fig. 11.3. Curves I and II refer respectively to short and intermediate plates.

between the pins parallel to the loads and t is the thickness of the plate. Experiments show that, for m less than 8 approximately, σ_y follows curve I, Fig. 11.4, which is characterized by the fact that the maximum is at the center, where $z = 0$. In longer plates, $8 < m < 15$ approximately, the curve of σ_y reverses its shape and the minimum is at the center, curve II, Fig. 11.4.

A steady state of uniform tension is developed for values of m greater than 15, and an accidental or transient approximation to uniform tension may occur at m = 7.8 or 8 approximately.

The experimental facts on which the above statements rest are shown in Fig. 11.5, where the variation in the shape of the curve is represented by the ratio R of the stress at the center of the plate divided by the stress

[1] The data in §§11.4 and 11.5 are reproduced from an investigation made by the author for the U. S. Navy, David Taylor Model Basin. See reference 1, p. 17.

at the ends, i.e.,

$$R = \frac{(\sigma_y)_{z=0}}{(\sigma_y)_{z=t/2}}. \tag{11.1}$$

Inspection of this graph shows that the values of R drop as m increases up to approximately a value of m equal to 10, then slowly increase to approach the line A–A, where $R = 1$, which denotes uniform tension. The part of the curve which lies above line A–A represents a distribution

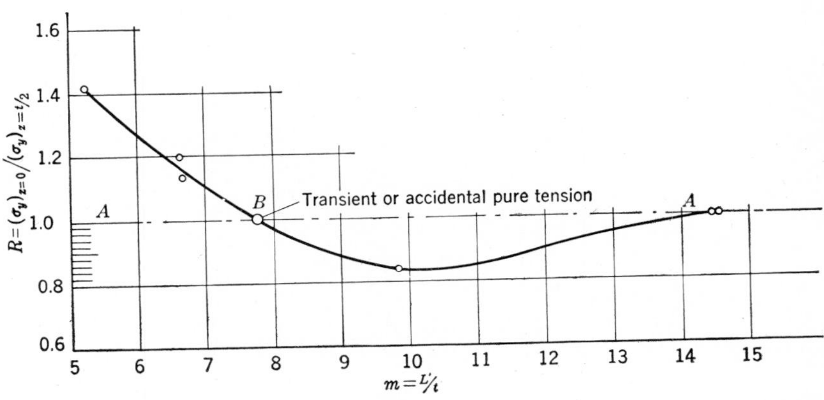

FIG. 11.5 Curve Showing the Manner of Variation of the Maximum Values of σ_y across the Root of the Slot for the Type of Loading Shown in Fig. 11.3.

Line A–A represents a uniform stress distribution which is attained when $m = 15$ approximately. At point B transient pure tension is developed.

of σ_y with a peak at the center, curve I, Fig. 11.4. The part of the curve which lies below A–A similarly denotes a distribution of σ_y with a minimum at the center, curve II, Fig. 11.4.

Point B in Fig. 11.5, where the curve crosses the horizontal line A–A, is of special interest. It indicates that for $m = 7.8$ approximately a transient or accidental state of uniform tension may be developed.

From the above discussion of the available experimental facts it follows that stable pure tension cannot be developed in a plate 1 in. thick, in which the loads are applied as shown in Fig. 11.3. To develop such a stress the plate would have to be 15 or 16 in. long, and the available photoelastic Bakelite has a maximum length of approximately 12 in. Fig. 11.6 shows a typical stress pattern of a thick slotted plate in tension.

Two ways are open to attain this result in a plate 1 in. thick. We might try a plate 7.8 in. between the loads and trust that transient pure tension will develop, or we might change the manner of loading. Fig. 11.7 shows a sketch of a modified type of head design, which might produce a closer approximation to uniform tension than the head design of Fig. 11.3. This requires further study. However, experiments show

FIG. 11.6 Stress Pattern of a Thick Slotted Plate in Tension. Dimensions of cross section 3 in. by 1 in.; length of slot 0.5 in.

that at $m = 7.8$ a transient state of approximately uniform tension actually exists.

§11.5 Tensile Strength of Bakelite at High Temperatures. ***The ultimate tensile strength of Bakelite BT-61-893 at 260° F. in a three-hour test is only partially known. From the data which are available this ultimate tensile strength varies from 100 to 180 psi., approximately.***

Heads of the type shown in Fig. 11.1 have withstood an average stress of 50 psi. approximately. Heads of the type shown in Fig. 11.3 have safely carried an *average stress* of 35 psi. approximately. This stress is probably fairly close to the breaking point. Plate heads with a single pin in the center instead of two as shown in Fig. 11.3 are definitely weaker.

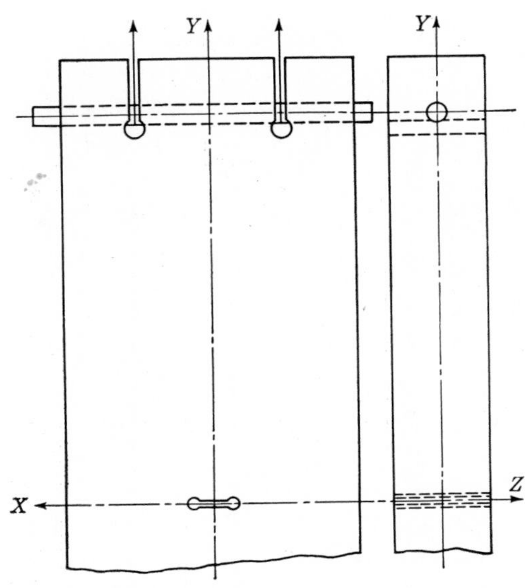

FIG. 11.7 Sketch of a Modified Head Design for Obtaining an Approximate Uniform Stress Distribution above and below the Slot.

§11.6 Furnace and Heating. ***When heating large, thick models, say plates 3 in. by 1 in. in cross section, or even 1-in. shafts, it is absolutely essential that the temperature around the model should be sensibly uniform.***

The furnace must be specially designed to give this result. Heating coils should be symmetrically distributed underneath the floor. Heating units should also be attached to or imbedded in the walls. It is desirable to arrange these heating units into several independent elements each of which can be controlled by an independent rheostat. In addition, the furnace should be equipped with a fan to provide effective circulation of the air.

Thermometers must be attached to opposite faces of the models, and the temperature should be read at frequent intervals during both the heating and cooling period. The ***difference in temperature between***

FIG. 11.8 Photograph of Furnace with Loading Frame Built Integrally into It with Only the Loading Beam Protruding.

Photograph also shows indicator to measure deformation of specimens. Indicator is operated by a flexible string wrapped around pulleys and attached to loading beam.

opposite faces should be controlled at least to within ±5° F. Uneven temperature distributions in the furnace invariably produce disturbances in the stress distribution even when the loads are axial.

The equalization of the temperature in a large model requires considerable time. ***Large models should be kept at 260° F.–265° F. for not less than two hours and preferably longer.*** In our practice the model is allowed to cool overnight for a period of about twelve to sixteen hours.

In order to observe the model and the attached thermometers during the heating process, the furnace should be equipped with glass windows on opposite walls, and the thermometer should be so adjusted that readings can be taken without opening the door. The mercury bulb should be kept in contact with the specimen; ordinary Scotch tape is sufficient for the purpose.

§11.7 The Loading Frame. ***In three-dimensional work it is best to build the loading frame integrally into the furnace.*** The interior dimensions of the furnace should therefore be large enough to accommodate the largest model from a standard Bakelite plate. Such furnaces are not available on the market and must be built for each laboratory. The interior dimensions of such a furnace should be approximately 24 in. by 28 in. for the floor and about 28 in. high. Fig. 11.8 shows the furnace and loading machine used by the author.

The columns of the loading frame are rectangular steel bars 1½ in. by ⅝ in. The upper horizontal bar is 12 in. long and 1½ in. by ⅝ in. in cross section. The straining lever is about 30 in. long, measured from the fulcrum, and is equipped with a small ball bearing at the pivot, and a counterbalance.

The columns are equipped with ½-in. holes spaced 1 in. apart to permit adjustments for models of different lengths. The horizontal bars have ¼-in. holes, 1 in. apart.

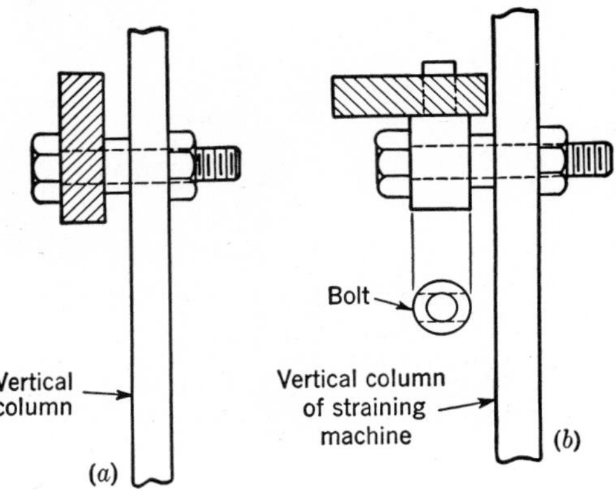

FIG. 11.9 Sketches of Fixture Used with Loading Frame in Furnace to Permit Cantilever-Type Loading Shown in Fig. 11.10.

§11.8 Fixtures. Several simple fixtures will be found useful. The bolt shown in Fig. 11.9(*b*) permits the use of the upper cross bar to produce cantilever bending about the flat side of the model, Fig. 11.10.

The pulley arrangement shown in Fig. 11.8 serves as a reliable indicator to measure the deformation at high temperatures. This is very useful when studying the fundamental strain-temperature curves for constant stress and the stress-strain curves for constant temperatures in different plastics.

§11.9 Models. The outstanding feature of three-dimensional models consists of the inevitable, relatively large deformations which are produced at 260° F. These deformations have two significant consequences. First, the final shape may be considerably different from the initial form.

Second, the results must always be interpreted as referring to the final shape of the model after cooling. When this latter condition is encountered the initial shape must be deliberately modified by trial and error so that the final shape represents a close approximation to the problem at hand.

Such a problem arises for instance in the study of valves of the type shown in Fig. 11.11. The deformation here may be very great. In

FIG. 11.10 Inside View of Furnace Showing Several Cantilever Beams.

some cases the heads completely buckled like an umbrella against the wind, Fig. 11.11(*b*). In addition the models are extremely small. The mechanician's technique becomes of considerable importance in these investigations.

§11.10 Method of Slicing. Two methods of slicing, the *plate method* and the *difference method*, may be used. In the plate method thin plates are actually sawed out of the model and each plate is examined in the polariscope. In the difference method the shaft is not sawed into plates but is gradually reduced in thickness, and the difference between the fringe orders at a point between successive patterns is taken to represent the fringe order or stress in a plate of a thickness equal to that of the materials removed, Fig. 11.12.

The difference method is in a sense equivalent to making sections with

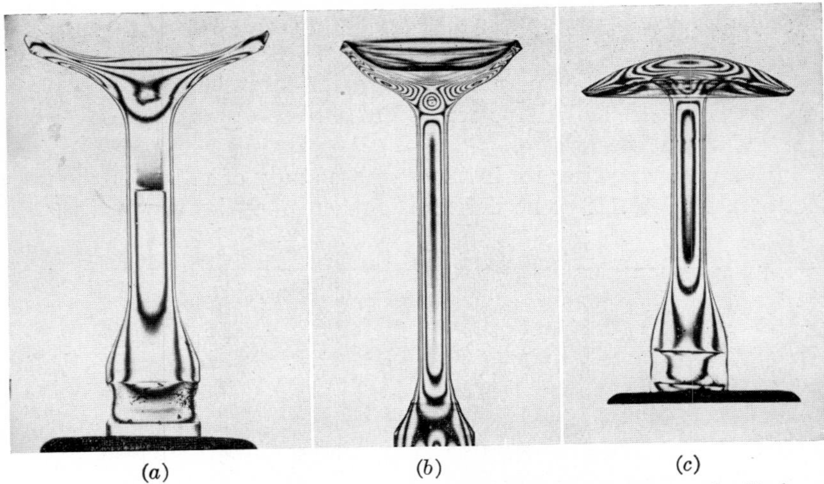

(a) (b) (c)

FIG. 11.11 Stress Patterns of Three Models from an Investigation on the Design of Diesel-Engine Valves. The Diameters of the Heads Were about 1 in.; the Shaft Diameter about 0.19 in.

(a) Stress pattern of a diametral section of an originally flat valve under a load of 1.458 lb., at 260° F. the head assumed the shape shown.

(b) Stress pattern of a valve which completely buckled under a load of 2.042 lb. The original shape was similar to that in (c).

(c) Stress pattern of a valve of slightly heavier design than (b) which retained its mushroom shape under a load of 2.042 lb.

a knife of zero thickness. Were it not for the inevitable boundary vagueness resulting from the three-dimensional deformations which increases with the thickness, the difference method would have much in its favor. No material, and therefore no pertinent part of the model, would be lost in slicing. The stress patterns could be made to have a rather large number of fringes at relatively small stresses, and so the changes in the curvature at the sources of stress concentrations could be materially reduced. However, all these advantages seem to be offset by the accumulation of space effects or shadows and the subsequent necessity for large extrapolations. The disadvantage of the plate method lies in the small number of fringes that can be frozen into the plates without large deformations. The stresses in thin plates are sharp, however, and the accuracy may be greater even though the number of fringes is small. A doubling polariscope carefully used may be of some assistance.

If the error in the maximum fringe order is about ¼ of a fringe then a plate with 5 fringes would give the maximum stress within 5 per cent. It is advisable to start with plates about ¼ in. thick, and then to reduce the thickness by sanding off equal amounts from opposite faces. This affords a means of getting several values and, therefore, a check on the maximum stress at the center of the plate.

The plate method is also somewhat shorter. The whole shaft can be

(a)

(b)

FIG. 11.12 Frozen Stress Patterns of Sections from a Circular Shaft with a Transverse Hole in Tension, Obtained by Milling off Equal Amounts from Opposite Sides Illustrating the *Difference Method*. $D = 0.963$ in.; $r/d = 0.187$.

(a) $t = 0.635$ in.; $n_{\text{max.}} = 17.8$ fringes.
(b) $t = 0.401$ in.; $n_{\text{max.}} = 11.9$ fringes.

sliced without being removed from the vise in the machine. Generally we prefer the plate method, although there are occasions when the difference method is indicated.

Considerable time can be saved by reducing the length of the plates. To this end we first cut off roughly one end of the shaft to within, say, ½ in. or ¾ in. from the edge of the hole, Fig. 11.13, then grip the other end in the milling machine and cut plates to a suitable depth, say 1 in. to 1½ in. The plates are then cut off along section *B–B*. Section *A–A* can be made on a jigsaw. The other operations are best performed on a milling machine. A small Atlas machine of type M-F (bench model) is quite sufficient.

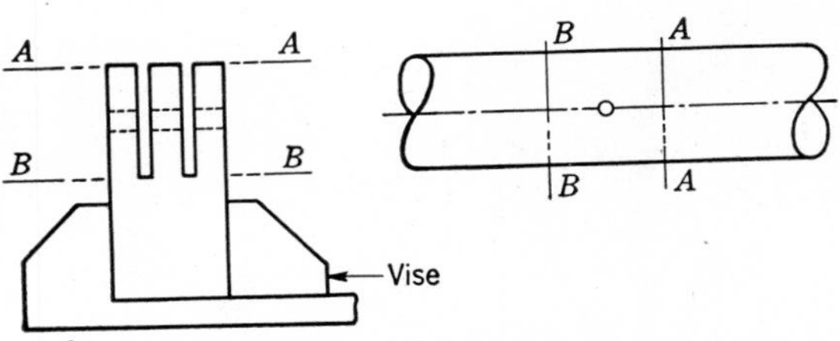

FIG. 11.13 Sketch Showing Method of Slicing a Shaft.

In all these operations there are just a few basic requirements. ***The tools must be sharp. They must be restricted in their use to the plastic models only. The cuts should be of moderate size, and the cutting must be done at moderate speeds with an effective coolant. In this connection cold soda water has been found better than oil. The main rule in machining is never to rush the work by cutting too fast or too deep.***

The cutters or saws should obviously be as thin as possible. Circular saws 1/16 in. thick and 4 in. in diameter have been found to be sufficiently rigid. Cutters 1/32 in. thick have also been used.

Upon removal from the furnace the model should be examined photoelastically for symmetry. If the inspection reveals an unsatisfactory general distribution of stress the model can be annealed and the loading repeated.

§11.11 Time Stresses. It is known that Bakelite models free from external loads will in a period of several hours develop internal stresses. It has been shown that the formation of these stresses is connected with the absorption of moisture from the air.[1] These stresses, which are known as ***time stresses, are compressive on the outer surface and tensile in the interior.*** It has been found that the depth of penetration of these compressive stresses is a function of several variables such as time and

[1] See papers by Walter Leaf, " Time Edge Effect," Fifteenth Eastern Photoelasticity Conference, held at Massachusetts Institute of Technology, June, 1942; also " Additional Data on Time Edge Effect," presented at the Sixteenth Eastern Photoelasticity Conference held at Illinois Institute of Technology, November, 1942.

atmospheric conditions. Depths as great as ⅛ in. have been observed, Fig. 11.14. The magnitude of these stresses increases with time and in a few days may reach an intensity of 4 to 6 fringes per inch of thickness. In a period of several months these intensities may be doubled.[1]

In two-dimensional problems time stresses were eliminated by speedy uninterrupted work, the effect of which was to arrest their development. This expedient cannot be used in three-dimensional problems in which freezing and slicing are employed. At least 24 hours, and possibly more, will always elapse before the slices are ready for inspection.

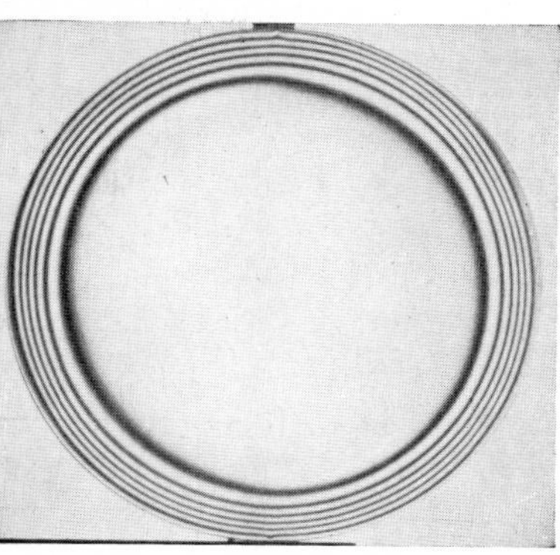

FIG. 11.14 Stress Pattern of a Disk Cut from a Shaft with Frozen Tensile Stresses Showing Deep Time Stresses Which Have Developed in Approximately Three Months. $D = 1.038$ in.; $t = 0.424$ in.; $n_{max.}$ at edge = 6 fringes approximately.

The time stresses on a transverse section of a circular shaft probably follow a distribution similar to that indicated in Fig. 11.15. They consist of a narrow outer circular ring in compression and a much larger central core in tension. These internal, or time, stresses form a system in equilibrium over any section which divides the body in two. The basic relation between the compressive stresses σ_c and the tensile stresses σ_t is given by the expression

$$\int_a^R \sigma_c 2\pi r\, dr = \int_o^a \sigma_t 2\pi r\, dr$$

or

$$\int_a^R \sigma_c r\, dr = \int_o^a \sigma_t r\, dr. \tag{11.2}$$

Consider now a diametral section, such as the part between lines B–B and C–C, Fig. 11.15. We observe that in order to have equilibrium among the stresses on that section it is necessary that

$$\int_a^R \sigma_c\, dr = \int_o^a \sigma_t\, dr. \tag{11.3}$$

In view of eq. (11.2) the last condition is possible only if r is constant,

[1] See Figs. 11.1 and 11.13 in Vol. I.

which it clearly is not. Hence, on a diametral section, there is no equilibrium between the time stresses.

Another way of arriving at the same conclusion is to consider the forces acting on the section $CCBB$, Fig. 11.15. Clearly the time stresses acting

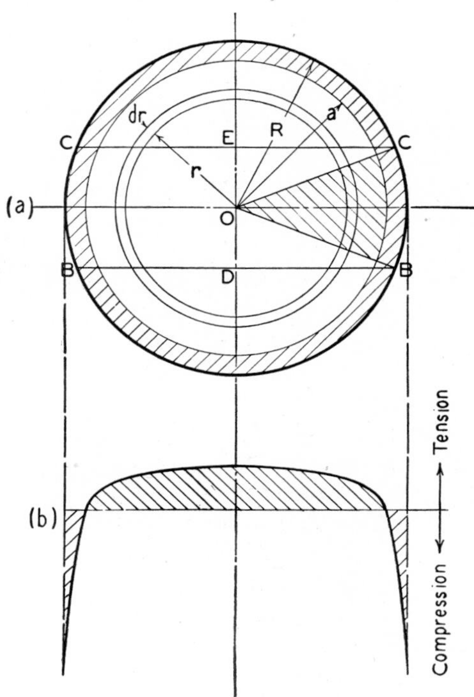

FIG. 11.15 Sketch Showing Probable Distribution of Time Stresses and the Inherent Absence of Equilibrium on Section BB–CC.

on the curved triangle OBC are in equilibrium. It follows that the tensile forces on the triangles OBD and OCE have no compressions to neutralize them. Hence, on a diametral section the time stresses are unbalanced and the tensions are roughly twice as great as the compressions.

Owing to the absence of equilibrium, redistribution and release of the time stresses in a thin plate may logically be expected. Experiments show that the expectation is actually fulfilled. If a section is cut from a shaft or thick plate and sufficient time is allowed for recovery, the time stresses, including the compressions on the boundary, gradually diminish. The recovery is rather slow, often requiring several days. Sur-

prisingly enough, no new time stresses seem to develop during the time of recovery. This phenomenon of release of internal stresses has been found to be the most effective method to eliminate time stresses in three-dimensional work employing Bakelite models. Clearly this process is the very opposite to that employed in two-dimensions where speed is relied upon to arrest the development of time stresses.

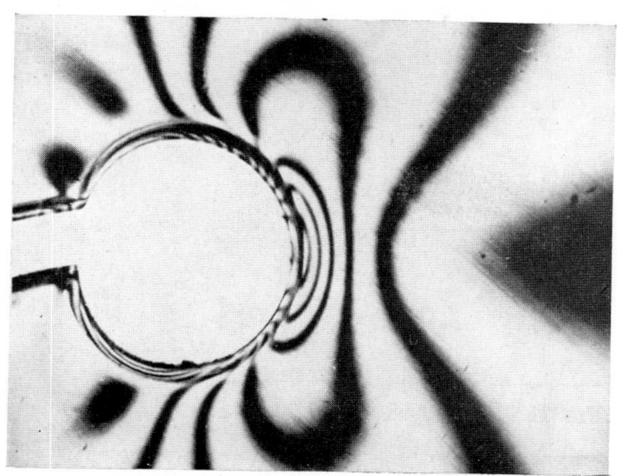

FIG. 11.16 Stress Pattern of the Outside Section Cut from a Thick (1 in.) Slotted Plate in Tension, Fig. 11.3, Showing Pronounced Time Stresses.

Photograph was taken immediately after slicing. Specimen was not sanded. $t = 0.207$ in.

Convincing evidence on the process of release and recovery is believed to be shown in the stress patterns of Figs. 11.16 to 11.19. Fig. 11.16 was taken immediately after slicing. The region around the hole is badly distorted by time stresses. Note for instance the complete absence of the singular points. The highest visible fringe order here is 7 approximately. Fig. 11.17 shows the rearrangement 18 hours later. Although marked disturbances are still present the condition is much improved. A stress pattern 66 hours after slicing is shown in Fig. 11.18. The singular points begin to be discernible. Fig. 11.19 shows the results 70 hours after slicing. Here the thickness was reduced somewhat from 0.207 in. by sanding both sides equally. The time stresses are almost completely gone, the singular points are clearly visible, and the maximum fringe order can be counted without extrapolation to be 6.6 approximately. Similar results have been obtained from a large number of other experiments. *In order to retard the formation of new or additional time stresses during the period of recovery the sections are kept in oil.*

The rearrangement and release can be accelerated by physically removing the outer skin containing the compressive stresses. The actual motion of the stresses (fringes) resulting from the rearrangement of the

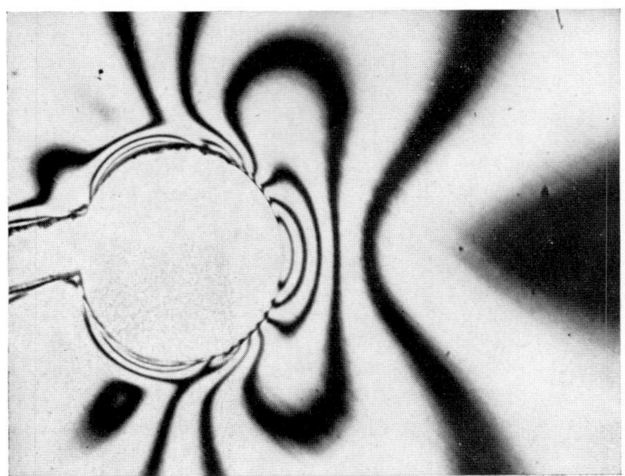

FIG. 11.17 Same as Fig. 11.16, 18 Hours after Slicing.

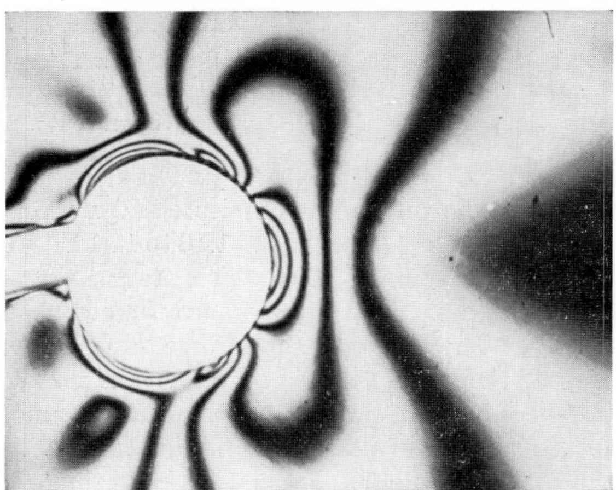

FIG. 11.18 Same as Fig. 11.16, 66 Hours after Slicing.

time stresses can often be seen with the naked eye. Fig. 11.20 shows several stress patterns of disks cut from circular shafts in which the skin was removed by turning. The removal of the time stresses by machining off the skin is not recommended where the skin contains a source of stress concentration.

Instructive stress patterns of the redistribution of the stresses in a ring upon being split are shown in Fig. 11.21.

To summarize: ***time stresses in three-dimensional photoelasticity employing Bakelite models can generally be reduced, or completely removed, by waiting for a rearrangement in the internal stresses. The interval of time necessary to bring about this release may be several days. Time stresses can also be reduced by removing the skin to a suitable depth.*** See Fig. 11.25. In such cases the rearrangement proceeds rapidly, often in a matter of minutes. If the time of recovery is long the sections should be stored in oil.

FIG. 11.19 Stress Pattern of Section Shown in Fig. 11.16, Somewhat Thinner, Taken 70 Hours after Slicing.

Comparison with Fig. 11.16 shows that time stresses almost completely disappeared. Note the clarity of the singular points. However, further work is required.

§11.12 Determination of Fringe Orders. ***In two-dimensional photoelasticity we use one of two basic methods for the determination of fringe orders. One method may be called static, the other dynamic.*** There are stress patterns which contain singular or isotropic points, i.e., fringes of order zero. A beam in pure bending is a typical illustration. In such cases the fringe order at any point can be determined from a single or *static* photograph, provided, of course, we also know the manner in which the pattern forms. Generally, however, the fringe of zero order is not retained in a stress pattern and the formation may be rather complicated. In such cases the most practical method to determine the fringe order at a point is by repeated loading and unloading and con-

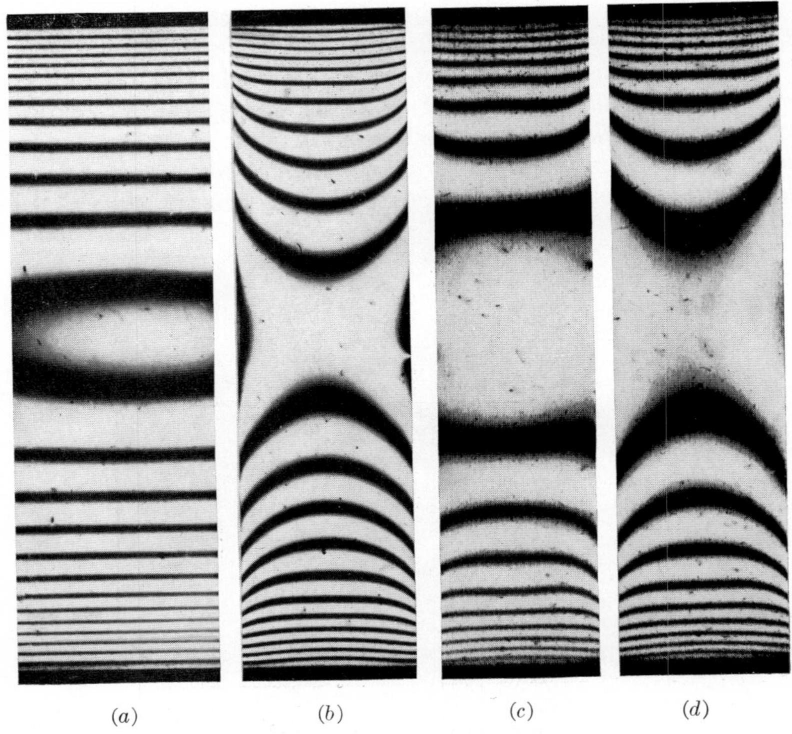

(a) (b) (c) (d)

FIG. 11.20 Stress Patterns Showing Rapid Rearrangement of Time Stresses.

(a) Stress pattern of region in shaft from which disk was cut; $D = 1.036$ in. (b) Stress pattern of disk immediately after cutting; $t = 0.273$ in. (c) Stress pattern of the same disk about half a minute after reducing diameter to 1.007 in. (d) Same disk about 10 minutes later.

tinuous observation of fringe formation. We may call this the *dynamic* method. ***This method can obviously not be employed in a frozen stress pattern. The static method will work in some cases but not in others. However, it is always possible to determine the fringe order at any point with great accuracy by compensation.***

§11.13 The Compensator Method. This method is basically the same as that used by Professor Coker for the evaluation of $(p - q)$. Using white light as a source we superimpose a uniform tension or compression over the point under inspection until a dark zone forms. From the isochromatic or stress in the compensator strip at compensation the fringe order at that stress can be readily found. Using white light the load is measured at compensation. The white light is then replaced by a monochromatic source, and the fringe order in the compensating strip at that load is determined. The fringe order in the compensating strip at compensation equals the fringe order of the compensated point. The usual compensators are made for a small range of stress and are not suitable for this purpose. However, the compensation can easily be effected by inserting a small tension specimen of arbitrary thickness into the main straining or loading machine, placing the annealed or frozen shaft (or other body) next to it at proper orientation, and measuring the

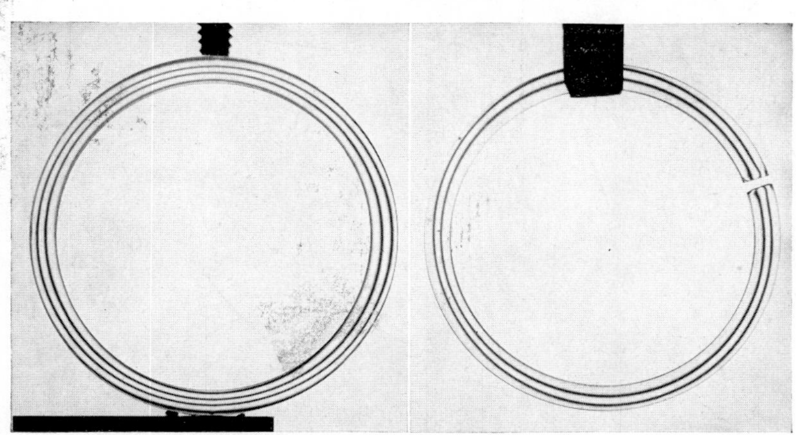

FIG. 11.21 (*a*) Stress Pattern of Outside Ring Machined from the Circular Disk of Fig. 11.14. $D = 1.039$ in.; $d = 0.887$ in.; $t = 0.228$ in. (*b*) Stress Pattern of Ring in (*a*) after Being Split. $D = 1.0356$ in.; $d = 0.885$ in. Splitting had the effect of reducing the maximum fringe order.

stress in the tension specimen at the instant compensation is obtained. The fringe order in the tension strip at compensation equals the fringe order of the compensated point. Another possibility is to combine a bar of fixed fringe order, say 2 or 3, with a Babinet compensator.

In the case of shafts in tension the fringes at the edges are rather crowded. Because of this it will be found more convenient to compensate the region along the axis of the shaft, where the fringes or isochromatics are broadest, Fig. 11.22.

§11.14 The Geometric Method. In circular shafts in uniform tension another method, which does not rest on compensation, may be followed. Let A, B, C, Fig. 11.23, represent the position of three successive fringes of order n_i, n_{i-1}, n_{i-2}. We project these points on the diameter X of the circle representing the cross section of the shaft, and draw chords $A'-A'$, $B'-B'$, $C'-C'$, Fig. 11.23. The difference $2h$ between

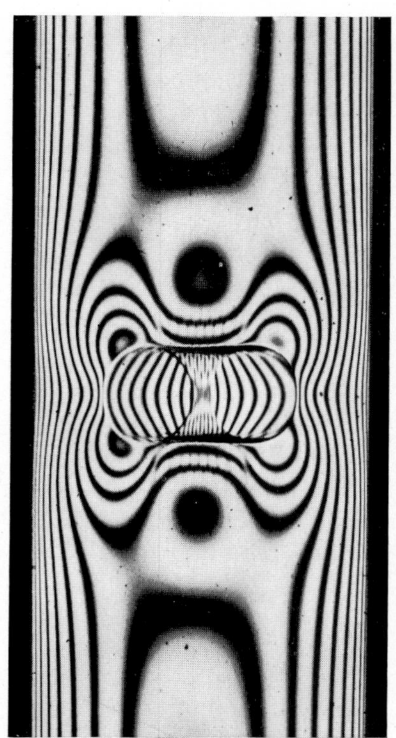

FIG. 11.22 (*a*) Frozen Stress Pattern of a Circular Shaft with a Transverse Hole in Tension.

Direction of ray inclined with respect to axis of hole 20° approximately. D = 0.963 in.; r = 0.131 in.; r/d = 0.187; P = 20.95 lb.; f (nominal) = 1.60 psi. shear; $N_{\text{unf.}}$ = 9.0 fringes.

FIG. 11.22 (*b*) Frozen Stress Pattern of the Same Shaft with the Direction of the Ray Perpendicular to the Axis of the Hole.

the successive lengths of these chords is the thickness needed to produce one fringe. Clearly then, if a line be drawn parallel to the X axis, Fig. 11.23, distant h from it, this line would locate a point on the circumference of the circle where fringe 1 must be placed. It will be noted that this fringe is extremely close to the edge. The order at any other point is obtained by dividing the chord through that point, such as A'–A', by $2h$.

Furthermore, denoting the maximum fringe order at the center D, Fig. 11.23, by N, and that at any other point C by n, and assuming a

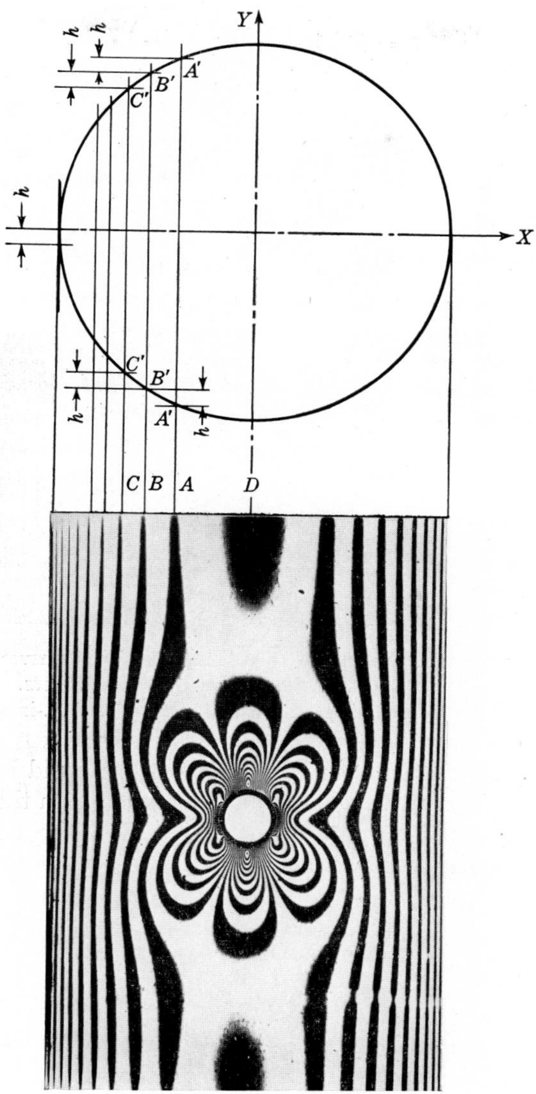

FIG. 11.23 Sketch Illustrating Geometric Method of Determining Fringe Order.

uniform tension, it is easy to show that the distance δ from point C to the nearest edge of the shaft of radius R is given by

$$\delta = R\left(1 - \frac{\sqrt{N^2 - n^2}}{N^2}\right). \tag{11.4}$$

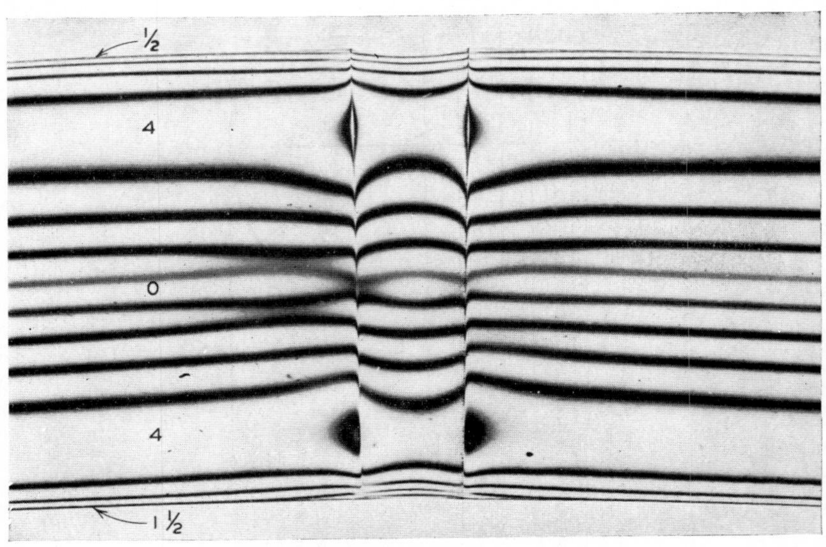

FIG. 11.24 Frozen Stress Pattern of a Circular Shaft with Transverse Hole in Pure Bending Showing Effect of Time Stresses on Extreme Fibers. $D = 0.980$ in.; $r = 0.110$ in.; $r/d = 0.145$ (initial dimensions); $M = 2.57$ lb.-in.

From this equation a theoretical stress pattern could be constructed readily for any assumed value of N and compared with the photoelastic pattern. In this way the true value of N could be found. Assuming N to be 10, a simple calculation shows that

$$\delta_1 = 0 \text{ approximately},$$

$$\delta_2 = 0.02R,$$

$$\delta_3 = 0.046R,$$

in which the subscripts denote the fringe orders. It is seen that the distances from the edge of the shaft to the first three fringes are extremely small and could readily be lost in photography or printing. Thus, if one were to rely on this equation he might be led to conclude that in Fig. 11.23 the first visible fringe near the edge is, say, 3, instead of 2, making $N = 12.7$ instead of the given 11.7. However, ***this method of fringe***

order determination is unreliable, owing to the presence of compressive time stresses in the outer layers of the shaft, the effect of which is to increase the values of δ near the edges, i.e., to spread the fringes apart. This effect is clearly demonstrated by the stress pattern of a shaft in pure bending, Fig. 11.24.

Here the fringe of zero order forms the neutral surface and appears clearly in the central portion of the beam. This provides a reliable origin from which all other fringe orders can be determined. Inspection of Fig. 11.24 shows that on the tension side we can clearly identify the fringe of order $\frac{1}{2}$ and even zero, whereas on the compressive side the lowest fringe which is definitely visible is approximately of order $\frac{3}{2}$. The effect of the initial compression on the edges is thus to spread the fringes apart and to make them more easily identifiable. Striking evidence of time stresses in bending and their complete elimination by removing the skin is shown in Fig. 11.25.

In bending, the true maximum fringe order can be obtained by taking the average of the fringe orders on opposite sides. The effect of the time stresses is then canceled out.

The geometric method would give accurate results if, and only if, a portion of the shaft could be found where the state of stress is absolutely uniform. Such an ideal condition is practically impossible to obtain, even if the applied loads are truly axial and the shaft is free from bending or twisting. The time stresses combine with the uniform tension to produce a non-uniform state of stress, with the result that the fringe order ceases to be proportional to the distance traversed by the light. In our case these distances are represented by the chords such as $A'–A'$, Fig. 11.23. Because of these unavoidable disturbances in the uniformity of the stress distribution, ***the geometric method and eq. (11.4) may lead to considerable errors in the fringe order. The most reliable method for the determination of fringe orders is, therefore, that of compensation.***

§11.15 Fringe Value. ***The presence of the time stresses also complicates the determination of fringe values.*** Were it not for these stresses the model fringe value F could be readily found once the fringe order N at the center of the shaft is accurately determined. Thus, denoting the load and cross-sectional area by P and A respectively,

$$N = \frac{P}{A2F},$$

so that

$$2F = \frac{P}{AN}.$$

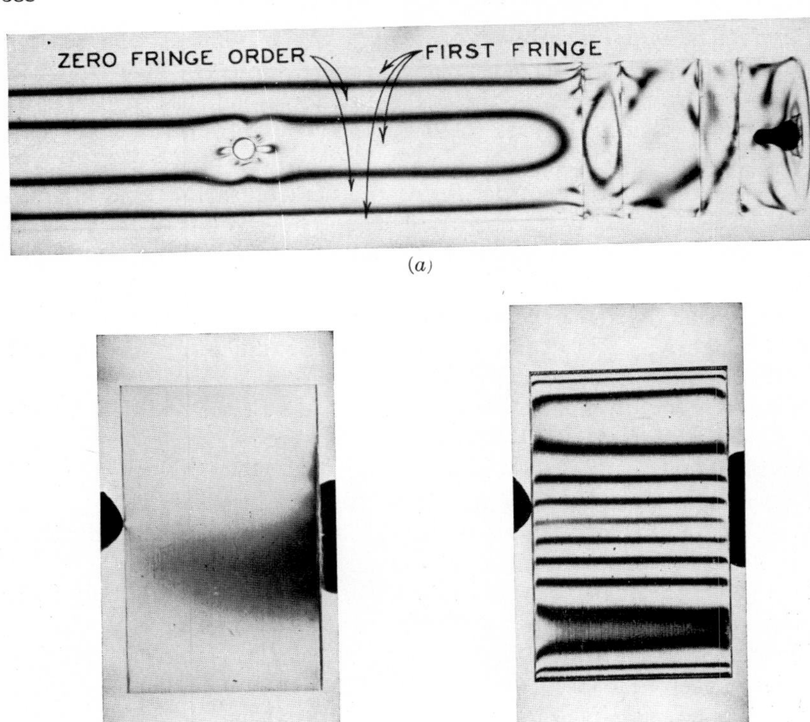

(a)

(b)

(c)

FIG. 11.25 (a) Frozen Stress Pattern of a Circular Shaft with Transverse Hole in Pure Bending. Plane of bending and direction of ray parallel to axis of hole, showing optical effects due to time stresses. $D = 1.058$ in.; $r = 0.065$ in.; $r/d = 0.070$; $M = 3.33$ lb.-in. (b) View of a Section Cut from the Shaft in (a) after a Layer $\frac{1}{16}$ in. Thick Has Been Removed by Turning. Note the complete elimination of the time stresses. (c) Same as (b) with the Light Perpendicular to the Plane of Bending Showing the Bending Stresses.

Recalling that the fringe value of the material $f = FD$, where D is the diameter of the shaft, we get

$$f = \frac{PD}{2AN}. \tag{11.5}$$

However, the effect of the time stresses is to produce an additional tension over a relatively large central core. As already stated the resultant of the tensile stresses over a diametral section is greater than that of the compressive stresses. The net result of this state of stress is to increase the fringe order N over what it would be if there were no time stresses. The fringe value f obtained from eq. (11.5), which we will refer to as the *nominal* fringe value, is, therefore, smaller than its true value. Thus, in certain shafts we found nominal fringe values as low as 1.42 and in others 1.49, which are considerably smaller than the fringe value of 1.59 psi. previously found for two-dimensional flat bars.

However, by removing the compressive layer and allowing the tensions to become released the fringe value gradually returns to its normal value of 1.59.

It is the difference between the true and the nominal fringe values which makes it impossible to obtain the actual fringe order at a point in the stress pattern from the true fringe value.

§11.16 Stress Patterns from Curved or Irregular Models. Photoelastic materials generally have indices of refraction greater than unity. Hence, a parallel beam of light on passing through an irregular model will be refracted as indicated in Fig. 11.26.

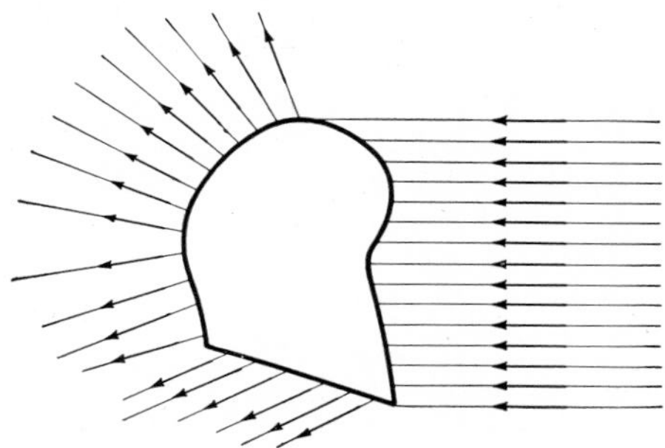

FIG. 11.26 Sketch Illustrating the Manner in Which a Parallel Beam of Light Becomes Refracted When Passing through an Irregular Object.

The most practical way to prevent this scatter and to obtain an unrefracted parallel beam and hence a reliable stress pattern is to immerse the specimen in a liquid having substantially the same index of refraction as the model. The first to suggest and to use this procedure was Z. Tuzi.[1] He worked with Phenolite models which have an index of refraction of 1.64, for which carbon bisulphide, having an index of 1.62, was a suitable liquid.

In current American practice, in which Bakelite specimens are used (index 1.573), Halowax oil (*RD* 11-1), obtainable from the Bakelite

[1] See *Scientific Papers of the Institute of Physical and Chemical Research*, Nos. 112–114, pp. 97–102, Tokyo, Japan, October, 1927.

Corporation, has been found most effective. All the stress patterns of three-dimensional models in this book have been obtained by immersion of the specimens in this oil.

This procedure necessitates, of course, a glass tank with good flat surfaces. Such tanks can be home-made, using a suitable cement. Ready-made tanks of different sizes are also available.

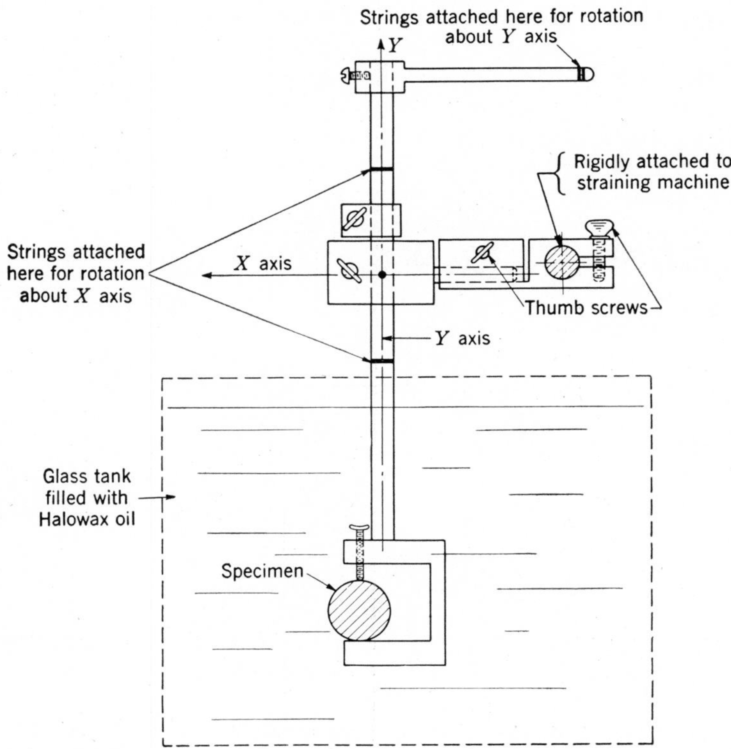

FIG. 11.27 Sketch of a Universal Jig Used to Hold and to Rotate a Small Section in Halowax Oil for Adjustment of Model with Respect to the Light.

One useful consequence of the immersion process is the elimination of the need for polishing the sections or plates cut from the specimens. Good clear patterns can be obtained from unpolished machined surfaces. A tank 3 in. by 8 in. and 8 in. high has been found of sufficient size for most work. Fig. 11.27 shows a sketch of a three-way universal jig or holder which facilitates the manipulation of the sections in the glass tank.

Simple remote control, in fact, plain long strings, can be used to adjust the specimen in the tank until clear boundaries and boundary stresses are attained. *As in two dimensions, it is suggested that the photographs taken be developed immediately.* The photographic procedures are the same as in two dimensions. See Vol. I. To obtain good, clear boundary stresses bright backgrounds are recommended.

CHAPTER 12

APPLICATIONS OF OBLIQUE INCIDENCE AND OF ROTATIONAL EFFECTS

§12.1 Introduction. If an arbitrary section such as A–A, Fig. 12.1, parallel to the XZ plane, be made through a three-dimensionally stressed body each element in that plate must be assumed to be subjected to a general stress system consisting of six rectangular stress components σ_x,

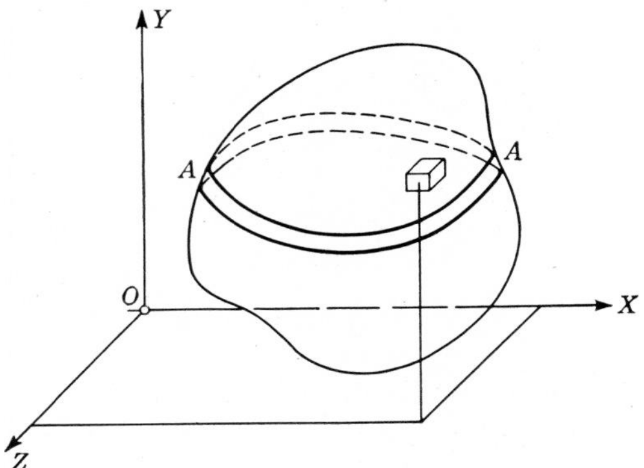

FIG. 12.1

σ_y, σ_z, τ_{xy}, τ_{yz}, and τ_{xz}. A normal stress pattern, i.e., one obtained from a ray normal to its face, would give data from which the difference between the secondary principal stresses in the plane of the section only could be obtained. These would be a function of σ_x, σ_z, and τ_{xz}.

Consider now an oblique beam. Specifically for a ray in the XY plane making a positive or counterclockwise angle θ with the Y axis the difference between the secondary principal stresses is given by

$$(p' - q')_\theta^2 = (\sigma_x \cos^2\theta + \sigma_y \sin^2\theta + \tau_{xy} \sin 2\theta - \sigma_z)^2 + 4(\tau_{xz} \cos\theta + \tau_{yz} \sin\theta)^2.$$

Inspection of the coefficients shows that there exists one independent relation between them, i.e., $\sin^2\theta + \cos^2\theta = 1$. This has the effect of reducing the number of independent equations to five.

Replacing the first coefficient by $(1 - \sin^2 \theta)$ and simplifying, we obtain

$$(p' - q')_\theta^2 = [(\sigma_x - \sigma_z) + (\sigma_y - \sigma_x)\sin^2\theta + \tau_{xy}\sin 2\theta]^2 + 4(\tau_{xz}\cos\theta + \tau_{yz}\sin\theta)^2.$$

The five quantities $(\sigma_x - \sigma_z)$, $(\sigma_y - \sigma_x)$, τ_{xy}, τ_{xz}, and τ_{yz} can be determined from five stress patterns of different inclinations θ. These in turn determine the third stress difference $(\sigma_y - \sigma_z)$. This is the theoretical limit in the method of oblique incidence. The principal stresses, or the normal stress components, cannot be found by this method, although the principal shears are obtainable.

General considerations lead to the same conclusion regarding the normal stresses. It is well known that isotropic stresses produce no optical effects. Consequently two stress systems in which the shears are the same and the normal stresses differ by a constant are photoelastically indistinguishable.

Unfortunately, the realization of even the limited possibilities is connected with practical difficulties, and the resulting accuracy may not be great.

However, the method has been found effective in certain special cases and these are treated in the present chapter. Specifically we describe, the determination of stresses in Saint Venant torsion, the separation of the principal stresses in two dimensions, and the determination of the maximum bending stresses in plates with holes, grooves, or fillets the axes of which are perpendicular to the neutral surface.

PART I SAINT VENANT TORSION[1]

§12.2 Basic Equation for Pure Torsion. ***It is shown in the theory of elasticity that, in cylindrical shafts subjected to pure torsion, Saint Venant's theory, the general stress system is reduced to two shear components only, lying in planes parallel to those of the applied twisting couples.***[2] Choosing the axis of the shaft as the Z axis, Fig. 12.2, the stress components induced by pure torsion are τ_{xz} and τ_{yz}. All other stress components vanish; i.e.,

$$\sigma_x = \sigma_y = \sigma_z = \tau_{xy} = 0.$$

Assume now that a ray of polarized light lying in a plane parallel to the XZ plane passes through an element subjected to pure torsion, the ray

[1] This method was first published by the author in the *Journal of Applied Mechanics, Trans. A.S.M.E.*, Vol. XI, No. 4, December, 1944. For another method, see Chapter 14.

[2] See *Theory of Elasticity* by S. Timoshenko, p. 229, McGraw-Hill Book Co.

being inclined at an arbitrary angle θ to the axis of the shaft, the Z axis, Fig. 12.3. The direction of the light we designate by Z', and the line perpendicular to it, lying in the XZ plane, by X', Fig. 12.3. We now wish to determine the photoelastic effect of the stresses resulting from pure torsion on the light passing through an element subjected to it. From the general stress-optic law we know that this optical effect is pro-

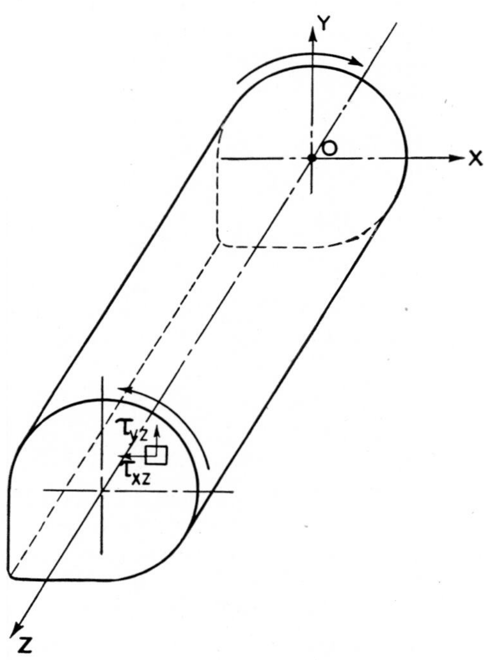

FIG. 12.2 Sketch of a Cylindrical Shaft in Pure or Saint Venant Torsion.

duced by the difference between the secondary principal stresses $(p' - q')$ lying in a plane transverse to the assumed axis of propagation, i.e., in a plane parallel to the $X'Y$ plane, Fig. 12.3. The problem thus is reduced to determining the secondary principal stresses and their difference for the specified direction of the light.

To this end we consider each of the two stress systems, τ_{xz} and τ_{yz}, separately. The first of these components τ_{xz} is shown in Fig. 12.4(a). Consider next an element with faces parallel and perpendicular to the ray, the shaded element, Figs. 12.4(b) and 12.4(c). The stresses $\sigma_{x'}$, $\sigma_{z'}$, and $\tau_{x'z'}$ induced on such an inclined element by the component τ_{xz}

are given by the expressions

$$\left.\begin{aligned} \sigma_{x'} &= \tau_{xz} \sin 2\theta, & (a) \\ \sigma_{z'} &= -\tau_{xz} \sin 2\theta, & (b) \\ \tau_{x'z'} &= \tau_{xz} \cos 2\theta. & (c) \end{aligned}\right\} \quad (12.1)$$

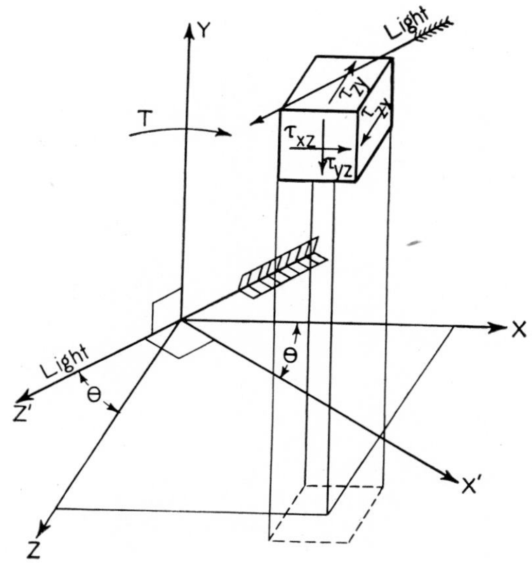

FIG. 12.3 Sketch Showing an Element from a Shaft in Pure Torsion under Oblique Incidence.

Ray is inclined at an angle θ to axis of shaft, Z.

The secondary principal stresses for this case are therefore completely determined by the horizontal stress component $\sigma_{x'}$. Hence

$$\left.\begin{aligned} p' &= \sigma_{x'} = \tau_{xz} \sin 2\theta, & (a) \\ q' &= 0. & (b) \end{aligned}\right\} \quad (12.2)$$

We next turn our attention to the second stress component τ_{yz}, which is shown in Fig. 12.5(a). On an inclined element whose faces are parallel and perpendicular to the ray, Figs. 12.5(b) and (c), this stress gives rise to two shear systems

$$\left.\begin{aligned} \tau_{x'y} &= \tau_{zy} \sin \theta, & (a) \\ \tau_{z'y} &= \tau_{zy} \cos \theta. & (b) \end{aligned}\right\} \quad (12.3)$$

Of these only the component $\tau_{x'y}$ will influence the secondary principal stresses for the given ray.

By superimposing the two stress systems given by eqs. (12.2a) and (12.3a) we obtain the secondary principal stresses resulting from pure torsion.

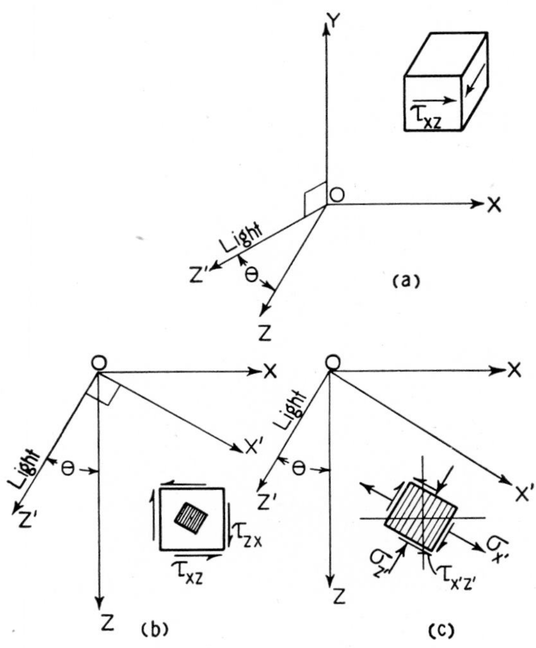

FIG. 12.4 Sketches Showing Secondary Principal Stresses Arising from Stress Component τ_{xz}.

For a ray parallel to the Z' axis only the component σ_x', shown in (c), produces photoelastic effects.

From elementary considerations it then follows that the secondary principal stresses p' and q' are given by

$$p', q' = \frac{\sigma_{x'}}{2} \pm \tfrac{1}{2}\sqrt{\sigma_{x'}^2 + 4\tau_{x'y}^2}$$

$$= \tfrac{1}{2}\tau_{xz}\sin 2\theta \pm \tfrac{1}{2}\sqrt{\tau_{xz}^2\sin^2 2\theta + 4\tau_{zy}^2\sin^2\theta}. \quad (12.4)$$

Hence

$$p' - q' = \sqrt{\tau_{xz}^2\sin^2 2\theta + 4\tau_{zy}^2\sin^2\theta},$$

or

$$p' - q' = 2 \sin \theta \sqrt{\tau_{xz}^2 \cos^2 \theta + \tau_{zy}^2}. \tag{12.5}$$

The photoelastic effect, i.e., the retardation n in fringes, is given by

$$n = Ct'(p' - q'). \tag{10.1a}$$

From (12.5) and (10.1a) we obtain

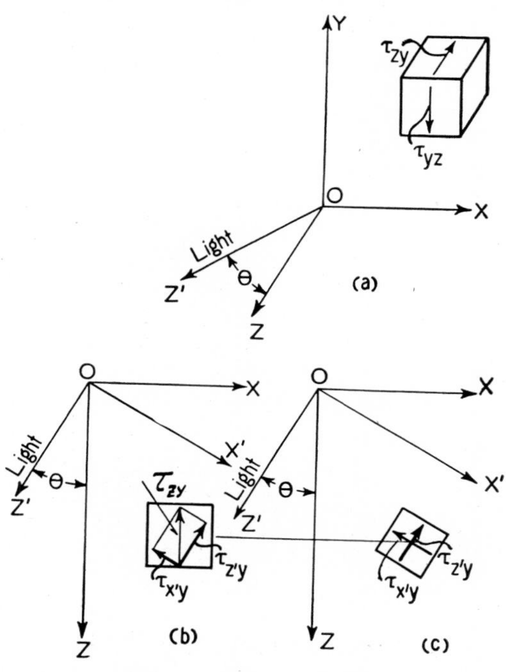

FIG. 12.5 Sketches Showing Secondary Principal Stresses Arising from Stress Component τ_{yz}.

For a ray parallel to the Z' axis only $\tau_{z'y}$ produces photoelastic effects.

$$n'f = \sin \theta \sqrt{\tau_{xz}^2 \cos^2 \theta + \tau_{yz}^2}, \tag{12.6}$$

in which

$$f = \frac{1}{2C}$$

and

$$n' = \frac{n}{t'};$$

i.e., n' is the fringe intensity, or the number of fringes per inch of optical path, and the units of τ_{xz} and τ_{yz} are those of the fringe value f, that is, pounds per square inch. If the constant f be omitted from eq. (12.6) the effect of this omission is merely to change the units of the stress components to fringes per inch. Dropping this constant we obtain

$$n' = \sin\theta\sqrt{\tau_{xz}^2\cos^2\theta + \tau_{yz}^2}. \tag{12.7}$$

This is the fundamental stress-optic equation for pure torsion of cylindrical shafts.

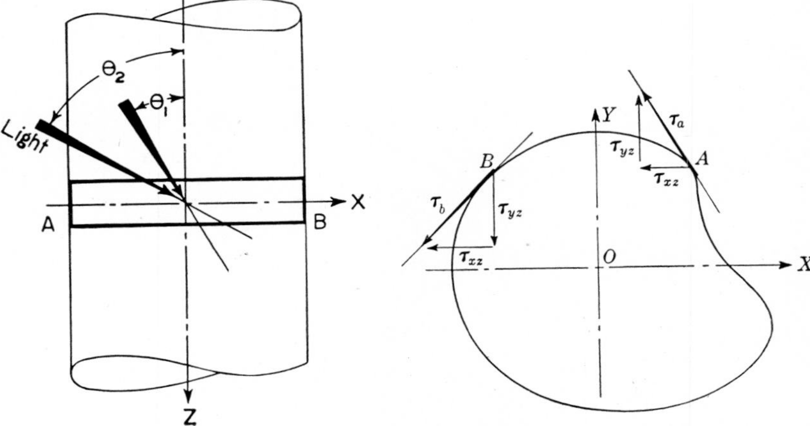

FIG. 12.6 Sketch of a Transverse Section Cut from a Circular Shaft in Torsion under Oblique Incidence.

FIG. 12.7 Sketch Showing Boundary Conditions in Pure Torsion.

Inspection of ***the last equation shows that the stress components τ_{xz} and τ_{yz} can be determined from two stress patterns of an arbitrary slice or plate cut from the shaft for which the light has different inclinations θ_1 and θ_2 (θ not equal to zero).*** To make the idea concrete, let us assume that we cut a transverse slice AB, Fig. 12.6, out of the shaft into which pure torsion stresses have been fixed. Two stress patterns in which the light has different and arbitrary directions θ_1 and θ_2, Fig. 12.6, will give the necessary and sufficient experimental data to evaluate the stress components τ_{xz} and τ_{yz} at any point in the cross section. By inserting the angles θ_1 and θ_2 and the fringe intensities n_1' and n_2' at a given point into eq. (12.7) we obtain the two equations

$$\left.\begin{aligned} n_1' &= \sin\theta_1\sqrt{\tau_{xz}^2\cos^2\theta_1 + \tau_{yz}^2}, \qquad (a)\\ n_2' &= \sin\theta_2\sqrt{\tau_{xz}^2\cos^2\theta_2 + \tau_{yz}^2}, \qquad (b)\end{aligned}\right\}(12.8)$$

which upon solution give the required stress components τ_{xz} and τ_{yz}, and from these the total shear stress can be found.

§12.3 Boundary Stresses. ***The maximum shear stresses generally occur on the boundary, and they are of special practical significance. The method under consideration is even simpler for the determination of boundary stresses. These can be evaluated from only one stress pattern for an arbitrary value of θ, not equal to zero.*** This simplification is made possible by the well-known property of tangency of boundary stresses; i.e., at the boundary the stresses are tangent to the boundary, Fig. 12.7. At each point of the boundary the relation between the components τ_{xz} and τ_{yz} is therefore completely determined by the geometry, i.e., the shape of the cross section. It follows that one stress pattern is sufficient to determine the boundary stresses. Denoting the fringe intensity at the boundary by N' we have from the fundamental eq. (12.7)

$$N' = \sin \theta \sqrt{{\tau_{xz}}^2 \cos^2 \theta + {\tau_{yz}}^2}. \tag{12.9}$$

Also from the contour of the cross section we have

$$\tau_{yz} = r\tau_{xz}, \tag{12.10}$$

in which r is a known ratio. Substituting in eq. (12.9) we obtain

$$\boldsymbol{N' = \sin \theta \, \tau_{xz} \sqrt{\cos^2 \theta + r^2},} \tag{12.11}$$

which gives τ_{xz} directly.

An alternative procedure for the determination of boundary stresses is possible. From eq. (12.7) it follows that, for $\theta = 90°$,

$$\boldsymbol{n' = \tau_{yz}.} \tag{12.12}$$

This means that ***a stress pattern obtained from a ray perpendicular to the axis of the shaft gives directly the component τ_{yz} at every point of the cross section, including the boundary.*** Since at the boundary the direction of the total shear is known it follows that this boundary stress can be determined from the one component τ_{yz}. In this method, however, the slice cannot be a transverse section but has to be inclined to the axis of the shaft at some convenient angle α, Fig. 12.8. It should also be noted that at the boundary the thickness t' is no longer constant, but varies linearly, and this variation must be considered when calculating n'. However, there will always be boundary regions at which the ray is parallel to the surface, and these yield the most reliable results. It is therefore advisable to orient the model so that the rays are parallel to the most highly stressed parts.

Theoretically the two methods are equally effective. Practical considerations, however, make the first method, in which a transverse slice may be used, generally preferable. This is due to the relatively large distortions which must be given to a Bakelite shaft in order to obtain sufficiently large stresses for optical observation. If the section is inclined as in Fig. 12.8, the shape of the boundary at the ends of the plate

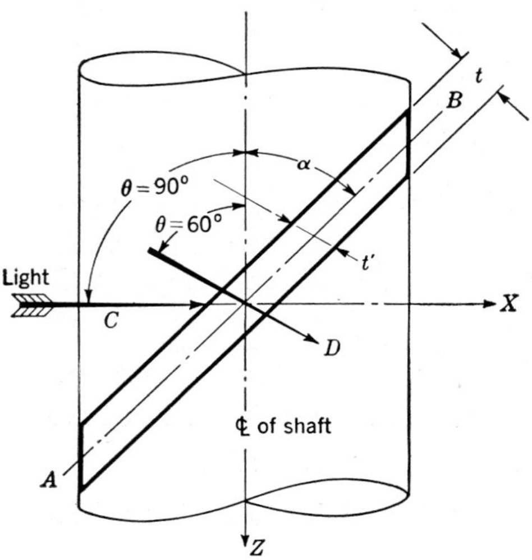

FIG. 12.8 Sketch of an Inclined Section from a Shaft in Torsion.

All shear stresses can be determined from two stress patterns of different angles θ not equal to zero. Boundary stresses can be determined from the stress pattern corresponding to $\theta = 90°$.

may be considerably distorted from the normal shape. The resulting difficulties are eliminated by a transverse section. However, for circular shafts the method based on eq. (12.12) is very effective.

§12.4 Stresses in a Circular Shaft. Since the state of stress in a circular shaft in pure torsion is known with precision the proposed method is first tested on such a shaft. To this end a circular shaft made of Bakelite BT-61-893 and approximately 1 in. in diameter was subjected to a pure torque and the shear system frozen into it in the usual manner. The time stresses were completely eliminated by removing the outer skin. The final diameter after turning was 0.908 in.

From this reduced shaft a slice 0.119 in. thick and inclined at 45° to the axis of the shaft, Fig. 12.8, was carefully cut out. In the cutting process the axis of the shaft was kept horizontal and the face of the cutter vertical, so that the axis of the shaft and the minor axis of the elliptical slice were perpendicular to each other.

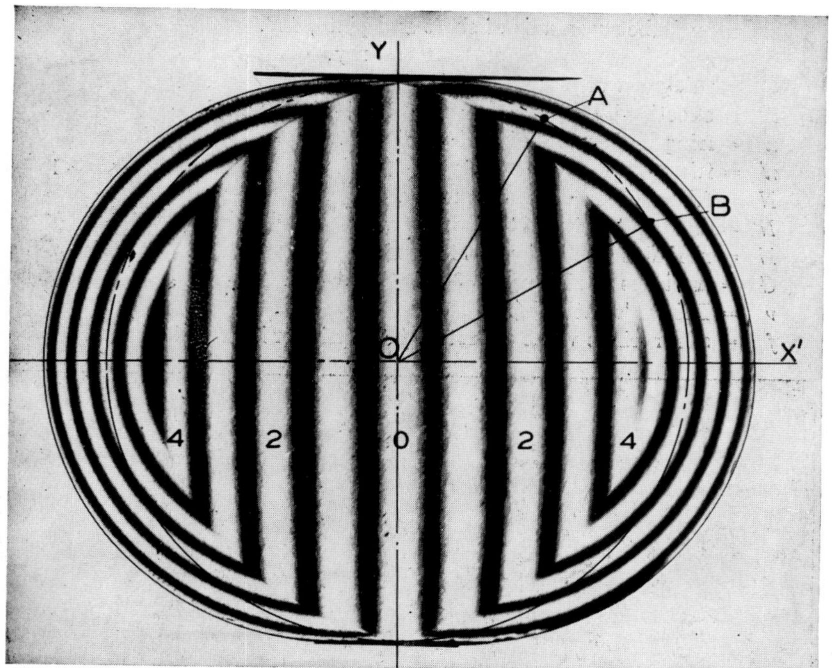

FIG. 12.9 Stress Pattern of a Section from a Circular Shaft in Pure Torsion Making an Angle of 45° with Axis of Shaft.

Light is normal to axis of shaft, i.e., $\theta = 90°$. $D = 0.908$ in.; $t = 0.119$ in.; $t' = 0.1685$ in.; N on X' axis at boundary $= 5.5$ fringes. Edges of plate have been marked for clarity.

Two stress patterns of this plate were taken, Figs. 12.9 and 12.10. In one, Fig. 12.9, $\theta = 90°$, i.e., the axis of the circularly polarized beam was perpendicular to the axis of the shaft; and in the other, Fig. 12.10, this angle was 60°. See also Fig. 12.8. The customary procedure of immersing the slice in a bath of Halowax oil was followed.

The general dimensions, notation, and relevant data are as follows:

Material: Bakelite *BT*-61-893.
$D = 2R$ = diameter of shaft = 1.005 in. both before and after twisting.
D' = diameter of shaft after removal of time stresses, 0.908 in.
L = length between couples, 6 in.
Overall length = 7 in.
Time and temperature of heating: 3 hours at 260° F.
θ = angle of twist, 107° or 1.867 radians in 6 in.
T = applied torque, 11.42 lb.-in.

α = angle between axis of shaft and plate, 45°.
θ = angle between axis of shaft and ray.
t = thickness of plate, 0.119 in.
t' = effective light path, $t' = t/\sin(\alpha + \theta)$, Fig. 12.8.
n = fringe order at an interior point.
n' = fringe intensity, i.e., fringes per inch of thickness at an interior point.
N = fringe order at the boundary.
N' = fringe intensity at the boundary.
E = modulus of elasticity, 1100 psi.
G = modulus of rigidity, 366 psi.
ν = Poisson's ratio, ½.
f = shear fringe value of material, 1.6 psi. per inch of thickness.

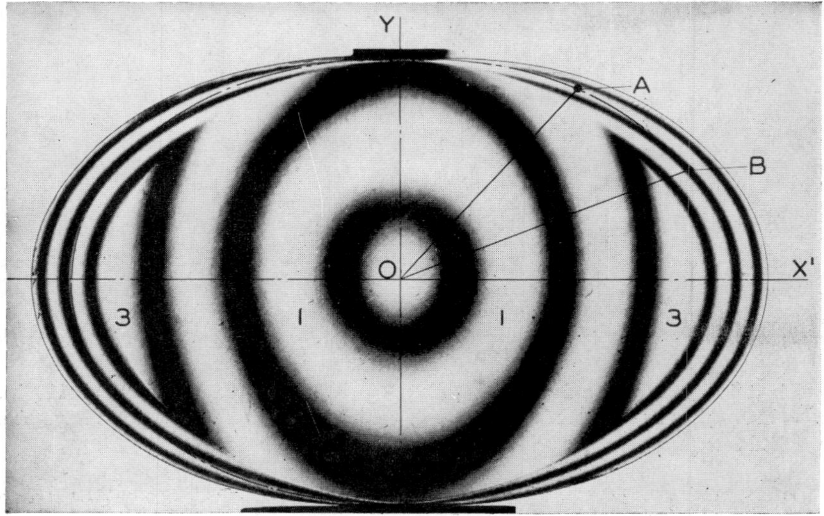

FIG. 12.10 Stress Pattern of the Same Section Shown in Fig. 12.9 with the Light at an Angle of 60° to the Axis of Shaft.
N on X' axis at boundary = 3.72 fringes. Edges have been marked for clarity.

§12.5 Boundary Stresses. The boundary stresses were determined by means of eq. (12.12) and the fringe orders N from the stress pattern shown in Fig. 12.9.

Fig. 12.11 shows the actual procedure in the numerical evaluation of all boundary stresses. Curve I represents the values of τ_{yz} along the circumference of the shaft, laid off radially, which are obtained from the stress pattern in Fig. 12.9. For example, on the Y axis $\tau_{yz} = 0$, and on the X axis $\tau_{yz} = 5.5$ fringes. At some general point P, $\tau_{yz} = PA$. From P as a center we draw an arc of radius PA, to obtain point B, so that

$$PB = PA = (\tau_{yz})_p.$$

In order to obtain the total boundary shear stress at P we draw a tangent at P and a horizontal line through B to obtain the point of intersection C. The length PC gives the required boundary stress.

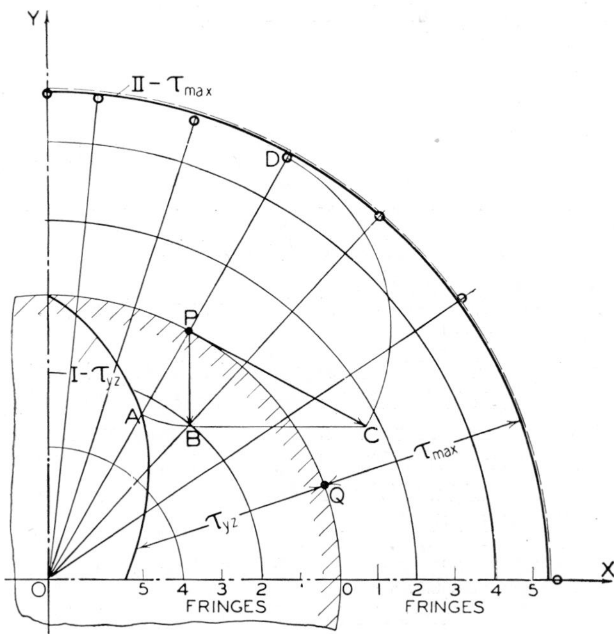

FIG. 12.11 Curves of τ_{yz} and $\tau_{\max.}$ Obtained from Stress Pattern Fig. 12.9; Method of Obtaining $\tau_{\max.}$ Is Also Shown.

Curve I is curve of fringe orders from Fig. 12.9. Curve II is mean value of $\tau_{\max.}$ derived from curve I; $N = 5.33$ fringes. Dashed curve is theoretical fringe order as calculated from applied torque of 11.42 lb.-in.; $N = 5.46$ fringes.

For purposes of comparison of the magnitudes of the boundary stresses we lay off radially $PD = PC$, so that PD is equal to the maximum or boundary stress at point P. In a circular shaft these boundary stresses are clearly of equal magnitude, and they should therefore fall on a circle, with center at O. Curve II, Fig. 12.11, represents the mean experimental value of the maximum shears, which is 5.33 fringes, and shows the degree of deviation of the experimental values from a circular locus. It is seen that ***the theoretical requirement that the boundary stresses in a circular shaft be of constant magnitude is completely satisfied.***

The dashed curve in Fig. 12.11 falling slightly outside curve II represents the theoretical boundary shears based on the applied torque of 11.42 lb.-in. Thus

$$\tau_{\text{max.}} = \frac{11.42 \times 0.502 \times 32}{\pi \times 1.005^4} = 57.4 \text{ psi.}$$

From eq. (10.1a), remembering that $C = 1/2f$,

$$N = \frac{\tau_{\text{max.}}\, t'}{f}$$

$$= \frac{57.4 \times 0.1685}{1.6} = 6.05 \text{ fringes approximately.}$$

Remembering that in Fig. 12.11 the diameter is only 0.908 in. as compared with 1.005 in. in the original shaft, we obtain

$$N = \frac{6.05 \times 0.908}{1.005} = 5.46 \text{ fringes approximately.}$$

This is the fringe order which corresponds to the experimental value of 5.33 given by curve II of Fig. 12.11, giving an error of about 2½ per cent.

The maximum shear stress was also determined from five additional stress patterns obtained from two thicker plates. One of these was a transverse section 0.245 in. thick; the other was a section inclined at 45° to the axis and 0.246 in. thick. The mean value of the maximum shear from these plates is also 57.4 psi. and agrees completely with the value given by the applied torque.

We thus see not only that the boundary stresses satisfy the requirement that they be of constant magnitude but also that these magnitudes agree with the required theoretical values. It should be emphasized that ***the boundary stresses were determined completely from the one stress pattern shown in Fig. 12.9.***

§12.6 Stresses across Radial Lines. We next determine the stresses across an arbitrary radial line OA inclined at an angle of 60° to the X axis, Fig. 12.9. To this end two stress patterns with different angles of incidence of the light are needed. We choose those shown in Figs. 12.9 and 12.10, in which $\theta = 90°$ and $\theta = 60°$ respectively, Fig. 12.9 being chosen because it gives τ_{yz} directly. The final stresses for section OA are given by the curve in Fig. 12.12. We note that at A the resultant stress is 5.35 fringes, which provides an additional corroboration for the boundary stresses. The fringe order curves which are necessary for the calculation of τ_{yz} and τ_{xz} across section OA are shown in Fig. 12.13.

Two further checks can now be made. First the distribution of the resultant stresses must be linear, and second, the stresses must be normal to the radius vector OA, Fig. 12.12, i.e., must be tangent to the stress contours which in this case are obviously circular. Inspection of the

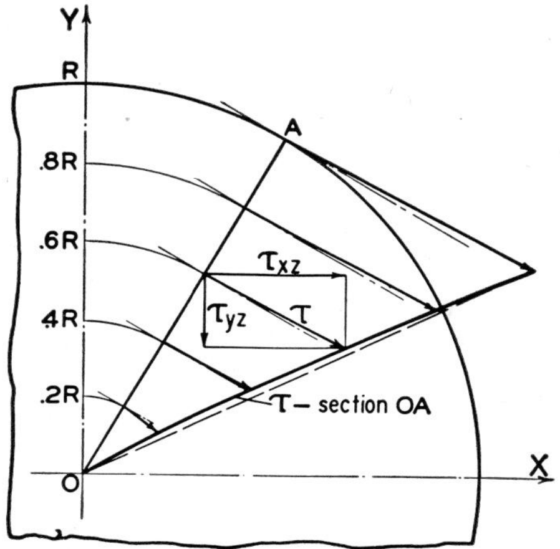

FIG. 12.12 Curve of τ across Radial Line OA Obtained Photoelastically from the Two Stress Patterns in Figs. 12.9 and 12.10.

Deviation from theoretical direction is indicated by tangents drawn at each point. Deviation from linearity is indicated by straight dashed line drawn through origin.

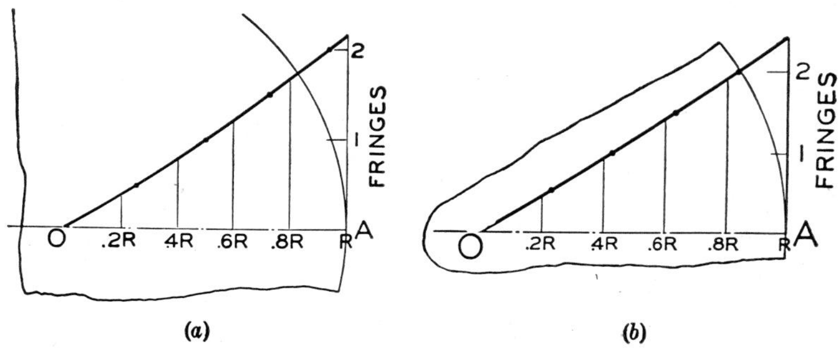

FIG. 12.13 Curves of Fringe Orders for Section OA Obtained from Figs. 12.10 and 12.9. (a) $\theta = 60°$; (b) $\theta = 90°$.

figure shows that the experimental results essentially satisfy both requirements. ***All theoretical requirements for the stress system in a circular shaft are thus met.***

§12.7 Approximate Theoretical Stress Patterns in Torsion. Consider an arbitrary point (i) of coordinates (x, y) in the plane of symmetry

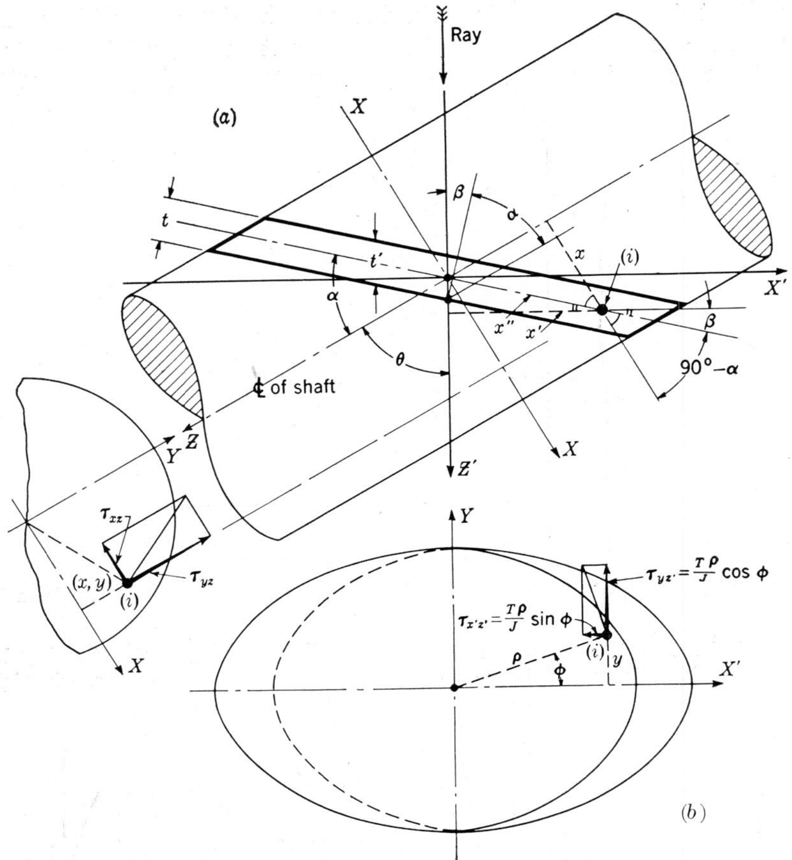

FIG. 12.14 Sketches for the Derivation of an Approximate Theoretical Stress Pattern in Torsion.

of the plate, Fig. 12.14(a). The shear stress at that point consists of two components τ_{xz} and τ_{yz} which are given by

$$\left.\begin{aligned} \tau_{xz} &= \frac{Ty}{J}, & (a)\\ \tau_{yz} &= \frac{Tx}{J} = \frac{Tx' \sin \alpha}{J \sin (\alpha + \theta)}, & (b) \end{aligned}\right\} \quad (12.13)$$

the X' axis being in the plane of the stress pattern itself, i.e., in a plane normal to the direction of the ray, Fig. 12.14(b).

Substituting the expressions for τ_{xz} and τ_{yz} from eqs. (12.13) in eq. (12.5) we have

$$p' - q' = 2 \sin \theta \frac{T}{J} \sqrt{\frac{x'^2 \sin^2 \alpha}{\sin^2 (\alpha + \theta)} + y^2 \cos^2 \theta}. \tag{12.14}$$

This may be written as

$$A^2 = \frac{x'^2 \sin^2 \alpha}{\sin^2 (\alpha + \theta)} + y^2 \cos^2 \theta, \tag{12.15}$$

where

$$A = \frac{(p' - q')J}{2T \sin \theta}, \tag{12.16}$$

which is clearly a constant for each fringe.

From eq. (12.15) we have

$$\frac{x'^2}{[A \sin (\alpha + \theta)/\sin \alpha]^2} + \frac{y^2}{(A/\cos \theta)^2} = 1. \tag{12.17}$$

The fringes corresponding to constant values of t' are therefore ellipses, with major and minor axes of a_y and $a_{x'}$, given by

$$\left.\begin{aligned} a_y &= \frac{A}{\cos \theta}, && (a) \\ a_{x'} &= \frac{A \sin (\alpha + \theta)}{\sin \alpha}, && (b) \end{aligned}\right\} \tag{12.18}$$

and

$$\frac{a_y}{a_{x'}} = \frac{\sin \alpha}{\sin (\alpha + \theta) \cos \theta}. \tag{12.19}$$

For a transverse section $\alpha = 90°$, $\sin \alpha = 1$ and eq. (12.17) reduces to

$$\frac{x'^2}{(A \cos \theta)^2} + \frac{y^2}{(A/\cos \theta)^2} = 1 \tag{12.20}$$

and

$$\frac{a_y}{a_{x'}} = \frac{1}{\cos^2 \theta}. \tag{12.21}$$

In deriving eqs. (12.14) and (12.17) we neglected the rotational effect of the secondary principal stresses and assumed that the mean stress along t' equals the stress at a point halfway between the points of entrance and exit of the ray. This treatment may be expected to give a good approximation in thin plates in regions close to the boundary of the disk, i.e., for fringes of maximum fringe order, where the rotation is small. However, for points lying on the axis of rotation, i.e., on the Y axis, and in particular for fringes of low fringe order, there exists a considerable rotation of the secondary principal stresses which increases as the center of the shaft is approached. Also, on the axis of rotation the mean shear stress is somewhat greater than that given by the value at the mid-point of the plate, so that on the Y axis the values of n corresponding to eq. (12.14) are considerably lower than the true values. The net result of neglecting the effect of rotation manifests itself in larger theoretical values for the major axis a_y. Hence the ratios $a_y/a_{x'}$ given by eq. (12.19), may be expected to be in general high and to fit more nearly the outer fringes than the inner ones, especially in thicker plates.

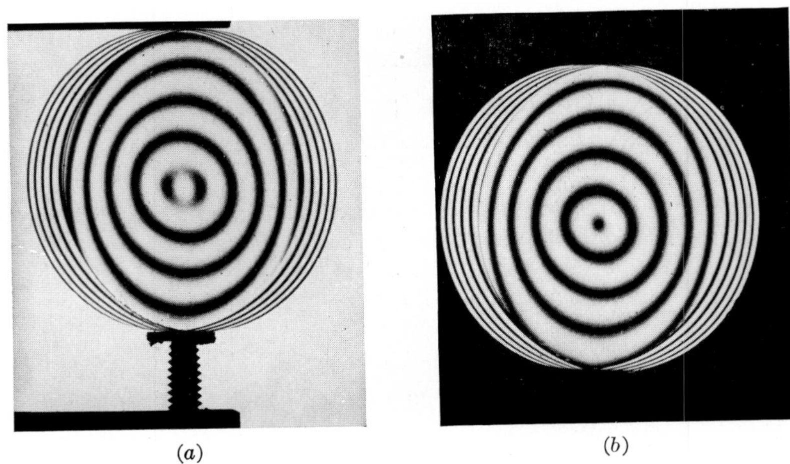

(a) (b)

FIG. 12.15 Stress Patterns of a Transverse Disk Cut from a Shaft in Pure Torsion.

Angle θ between ray and axis of shaft is 30° in both (a) and (b). $D = 1.005$ in.; $t = 0.245$ in.; $t' = 0.283$ in.; $T = 11.4$ lb.-in.

Inspection of ***the experimental stress patterns in Fig. 12.15 bears out the above predictions. Fringe 1 is nearly circular. The successive fringes are elliptical and become more oblong as the order of the fringes increases.*** Thus, in Fig. 12.15, $a_y/a_{x'} = 1.2$, 1.265, and 1.34 approximately for $n = 2$, 3, 4 respectively. The corresponding theoretical value as calculated by eq. (12.21) is 1.33.

From eq. (12.19) it also follows that, for $\theta = 90°$, a_y becomes infinite, which means that the fringes become straight. Inspection of the stress pattern of Fig. 12.9 shows that this is precisely what happens. Also, the ratios $a_y/a_{x'}$ from the thin plate, Fig. 12.10, are approximately 1.3 for $n = 1.5$ and 1.25 for $n = 1$. The corresponding theoretical value is 1.46. Further, for $\alpha = \theta = 45°$, $a_y/a_{x'} = 1$ and the fringes should be circular, eq. (12.19). The stress pattern of Fig. 12.16 shows that the outer fringes approach a circular shape.

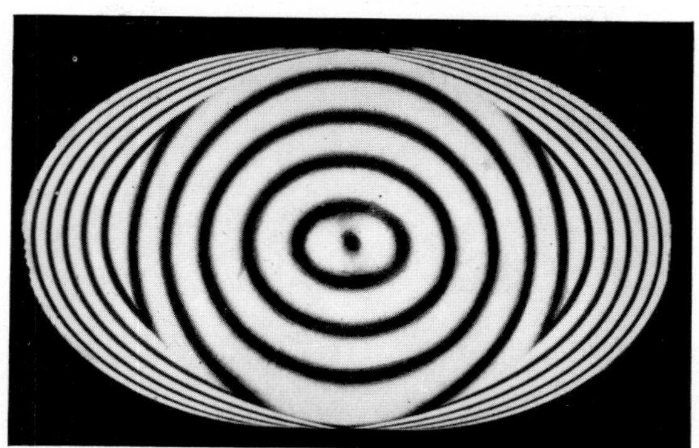

Fig. 12.16 Stress Pattern of a 45° Section Cut from a Shaft in Pure Torsion. Angle θ between ray and axis of shaft is 45°. $D = 1.005$ in.; $t = t' = 0.246$ in.; $T = 11.4$ lb.-in.

§12.8 Torsion of Circular Shafts of Variable Diameter. Stress Concentrations. *In circular shafts of variable diameters the stress system reduces to two shear components $\tau_{r\theta}$ and $\tau_{\theta z}$, Fig. 12.17(b). Of these, $\tau_{\theta z}$ becomes a maximum at the boundary where $\tau_{r\theta}$ vanishes. The method developed for Saint Venant's torsion can, with small modifications, also be applied to this case.*

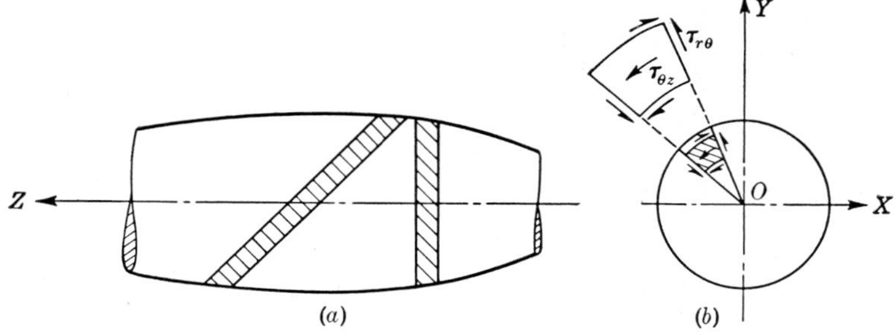

Fig. 12.17 Sketch Showing Shear Stresses in a Shaft of Variable Diameter in Torsion.

The first component $\tau_{r\theta}$ can be determined from transverse or inclined sections with the light parallel to the axis of the shaft. The second component $\tau_{\theta z}$ can be determined in one of several ways. We may cut chords from a transverse plate and use a beam which is normal to the chords, Fig. 12.18. We may also utilize the facts that the resultant fringe order from the whole disk, for a beam perpendicular to the axis, is zero, exactly as in bending, and that optical effects appear as successive chords are removed, Fig. 12.19. The stresses $\tau_{\theta z}$ can therefore be obtained by grinding off successive chords and determining the changes in the fringe

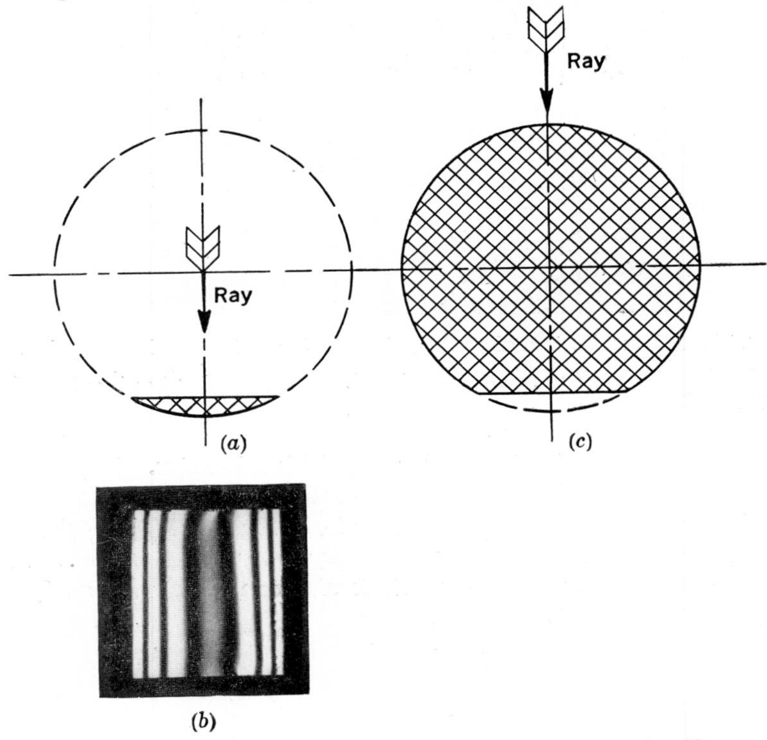

FIG. 12.18 Sketches and Stress Pattern Showing How to Determine Shears at the Boundary from a Segment.

Maximum t for segment $= 0.093$ in.; $D = 1.005$ in.; $T = 11.4$ lb.-in.

order in the remaining major part of the disk, the light still being normal to the chord.

If only the maximum values of $\tau_{\theta z}$ are required, i.e., the boundary values, they can be determined from oblique incidence of a transverse or inclined section, since at the boundary $\tau_{r\theta}$ vanishes. An inclined section similar to that of Fig. 12.9 with $\theta = 90°$ would then give directly the values of $\tau_{\theta z}$ at the boundary over a considerable length of the shaft. The boundary stresses $\tau_{\theta z}$ over the entire length of the shaft can also be obtained by oblique incidence from a longitudinal section containing the axis itself, Fig. 12.20.

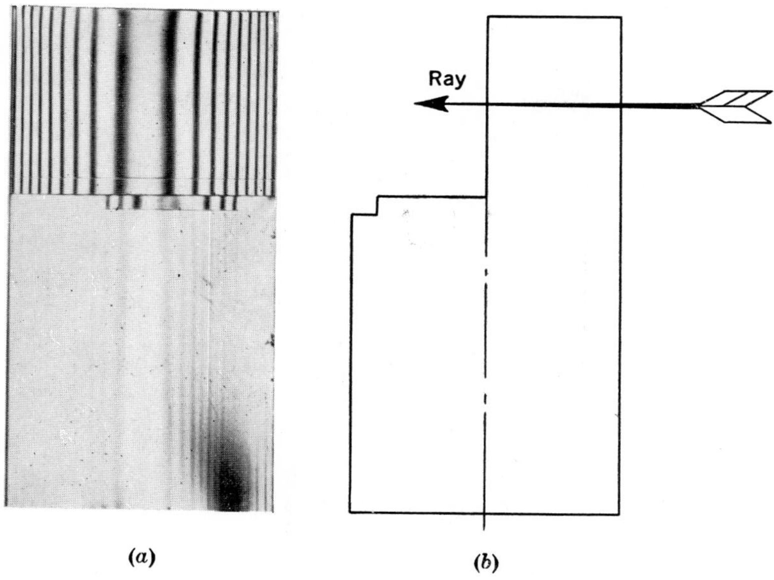

FIG. 12.19 Stress Pattern of a Section from a Twisted Circular Shaft Showing Cancellation of Optical Effects in Solid Portion and the Presence of Optical Effects Where Portions are Removed. $D = 1.005$ in.; $T = 11.4$ lb.-in.

Comparative curves of n for a longitudinal plate cut from the circular shaft in pure torsion which was discussed in §§12.4 to 12.6 are shown in Fig. 12.20. Here

$$\tau_{xz} = \frac{Ty}{J}, \tag{12.22}$$

and

$$n = \frac{\tau_{xz}}{F} = \frac{\tau_{\text{max.}}}{RF}\, y. \tag{12.23}$$

At point P, Fig. 12.20, $y = 0$, the shear AB is parallel to the ray, and therefore $n = 0$. The maximum value of n is at P_1 where $y = 0.4$ in. and is a maximum for the region in which t' is a constant. The value of n at that point is

$$(n)_{p_1} = \frac{57.4 \times 0.148 \times 1.414 \times 0.4}{0.502 \times 1.6} = 6 \text{ fringes approximately.}$$

The corresponding experimental value is 5.8, Fig. 12.20. By eq. (12.23), n follows a straight line between P and P_1, as is corroborated

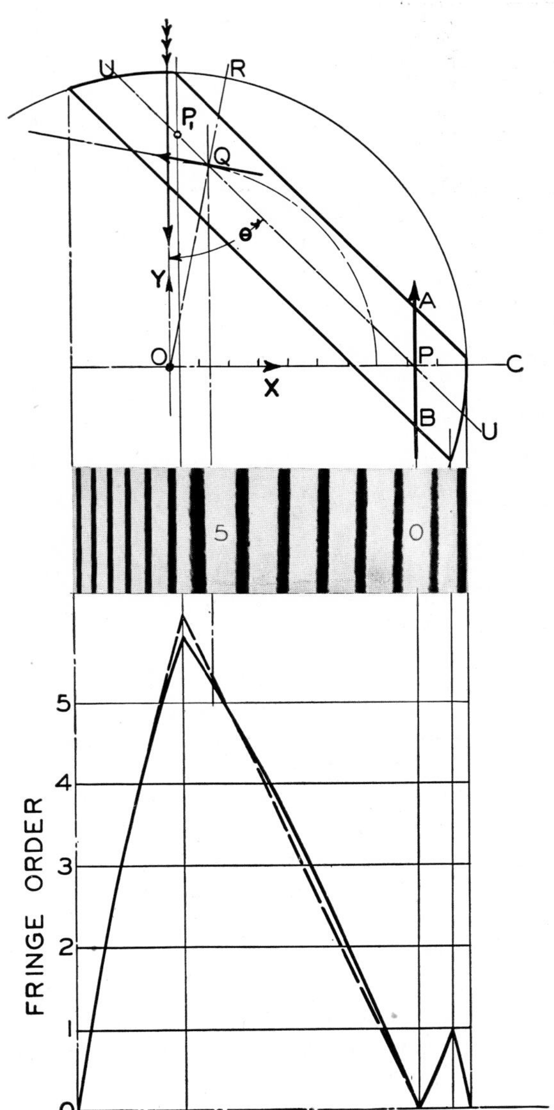

FIG. 12.20 Comparative Curves of n from a Longitudinal Plate Cut from a Twisted Circular Shaft.

D = 1.005 in.; maximum τ = 57.4 psi. = 35.9 fr./in.; maximum width of plate = 0.900 in.; t = 0.148 in.; θ = 45°.

FIG. 12.21 Stress Pattern of the Same Plate As in Fig. 12.20 Showing that at Normal Incidence the Fringe Order is Constant, Where the Thickness is Constant.

Maximum $n = 3.03$ fringes experimentally. Corresponding theoretical value of n is 3.18, eq. (12.23).

experimentally. Further, for a constant value of y, which means for normal incidence, n is constant. This is clearly shown by Fig. 12.21. It is thus seen that the results from longitudinal plates may be of high accuracy.

It should, therefore, be possible to determine photoelastically factors of stress concentration in torsion in circular shafts with grooves, fillets, or other discontinuities. Fig. 12.22 shows a stress pattern of a grooved shaft, in torsion, demonstrating again the complete cancellation of optical effect for the whole shaft. Figs. 12.23 are stress patterns of an inclined section through the groove. A tranverse section through the groove would also be desirable.

Three stress patterns of a circular shaft with an eccentric hole are given in Figs. 12.24. The first of these shows that in the vicinity of the hole there are radial and tangential shear stresses on planes normal to the face of the disk, $\tau_{r\theta}$ Fig. 12.17. Fig. 12.25 is an instructive stress pattern from a shaft with a keyway. Stress patterns indicating the possibilities in rectangular shafts are shown in Figs. 12.26 and 12.27.

§12.9 Separation of Principal Stresses in Two Dimensions. ***Another interesting application of oblique incidence is found in the sepa-***

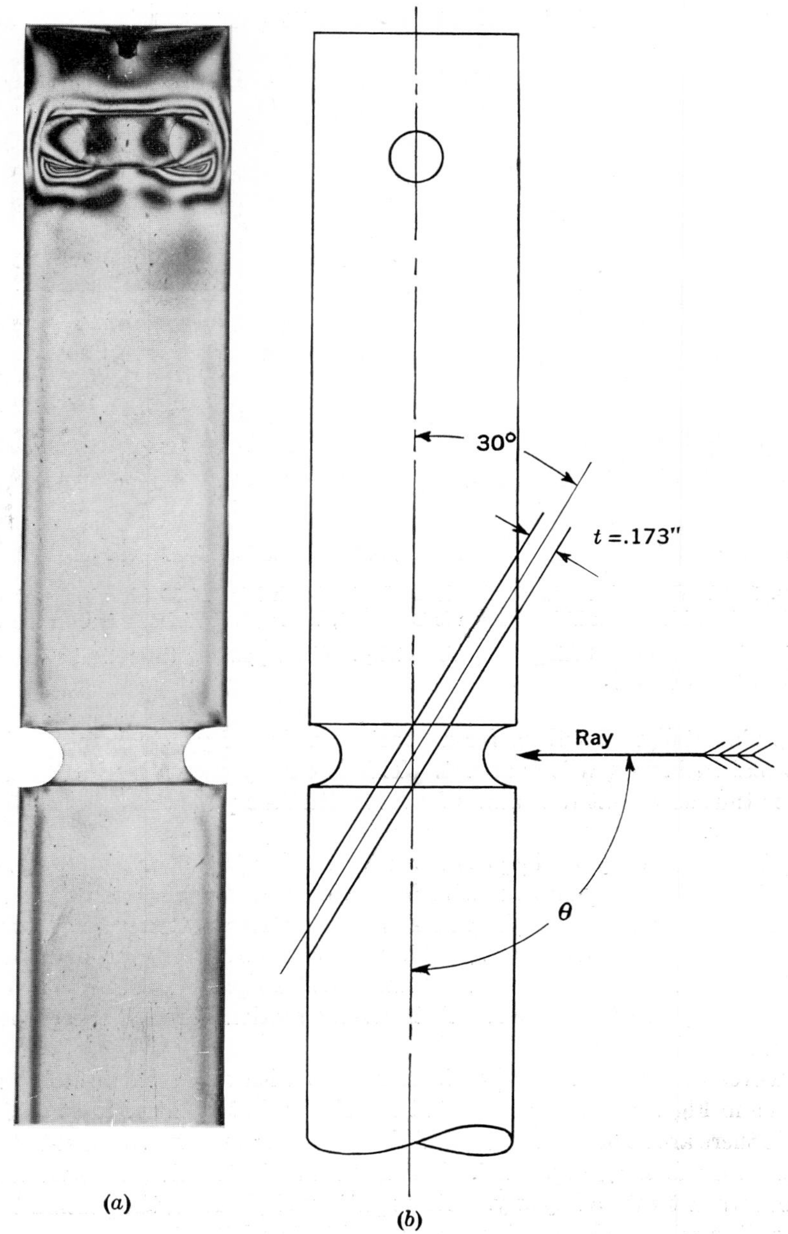

FIG. 12.22 Stress Pattern of a Grooved Circular Shaft in Pure Torsion.

Overall length = 6.5 in.; distance between holes = 5.5 in.; D = 0.90 in.; r = 0.130 in.; d = 0.53 in.; angle of twist 42.5° for 5.5 in. length; h/r = 1.42, where h is the depth of groove; r/d = 0.245.

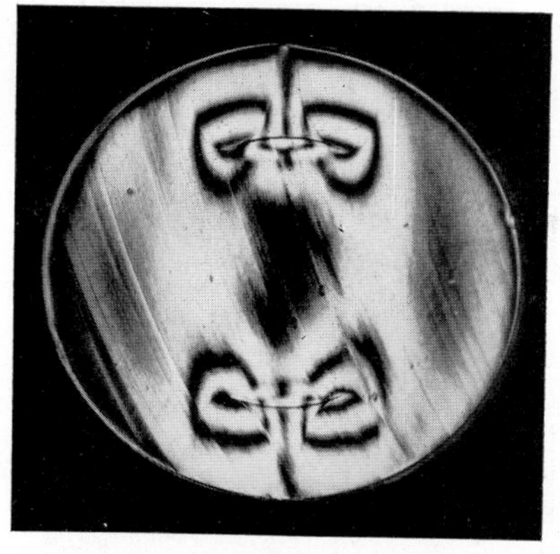

(*a*)

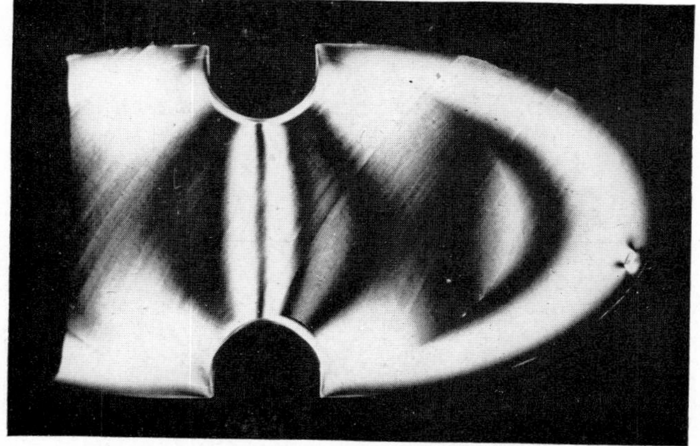

(*b*)

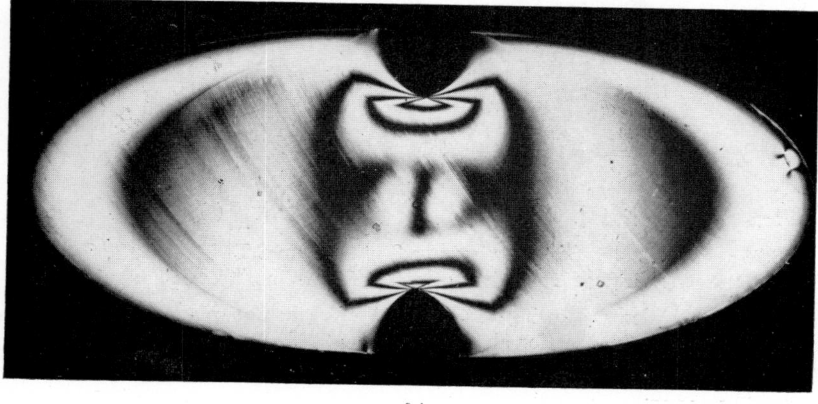

(*c*)

Fig. 12.23 Stress Patterns of Inclined Section as Shown in Fig. 12.22(*b*), t = 0.173 in. (*a*) $\theta = 0°$, light parallel to axis. (*b*) $\theta = 90°$. (*c*) $\theta = 60°$.

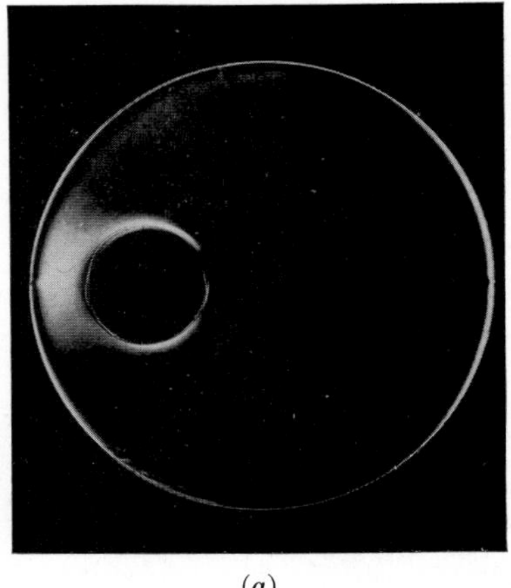

(a)

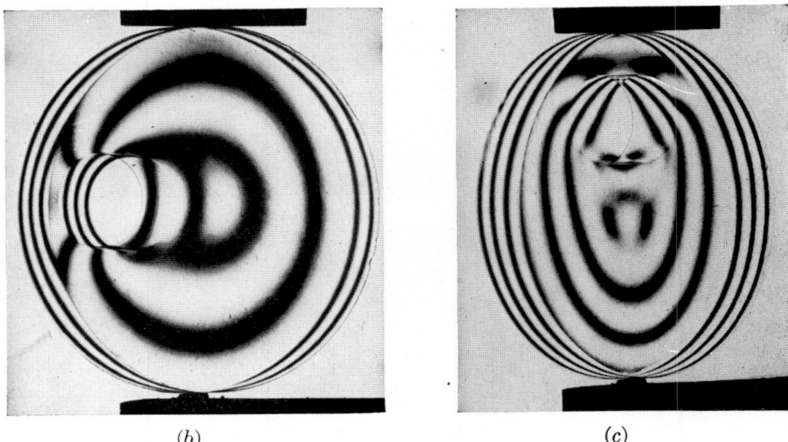

(b) (c)

FIG. 12.24 Stress Patterns of a Transverse Section from a Twisted Shaft, Containing an Eccentric Circular Hole Giving Data to Determine Stresses around Hole.

(a) Normal incidence showing the presence of shears on planes normal to the plane of the paper. (b) Rotation about Y axis, $\theta = 30°$. (c) Rotation about X axis, $\theta = 45°$. $D = 1.008$ in.; d of hole = 0.260 in.; eccentricity = 0.250. in; $T = 7.73$ lb.-in.; $t = 0.185$ in.

ration of the principal stresses in two-dimensional problems. Thus, eq. (10.16a) may be written

$$(n2F)^2 = 4(\tau_{xy} \cos \theta)^2 + (\sigma_x - \sigma_y \cos^2 \theta)^2 \qquad (10.16a)$$

in which F is the fringe value of the model in pounds per square inch shear for the particular angle θ. This equation may be viewed as a relation between the stress components and the retardation n resulting from a rotation θ about an arbitrary X axis.

It follows that, theoretically at least, the stress components for a two-dimensional problem can be determined from three stress patterns of

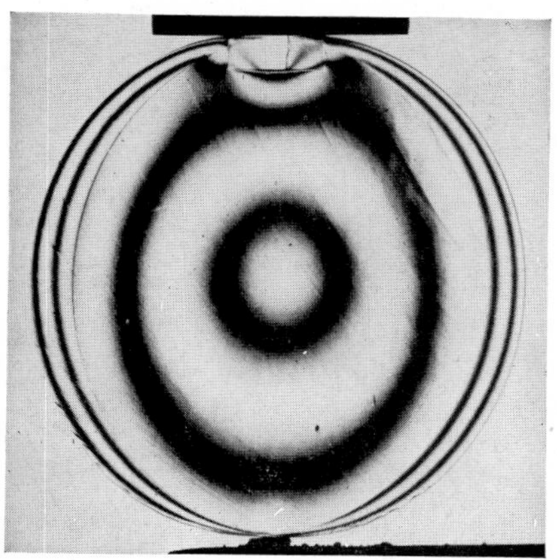

FIG. 12.25 Stress Pattern of a Transverse Section of a Twisted Circular Shaft Containing a Keyway.

Rotation about Vertical Axis, $\theta = 30°$. $D = 1.008$ in.; width of keyway $= 0.125$ in.; depth of keyway $= 0.070$ in.; $T = 7.73$ lb.-in.; $t = 0.183$ in.

oblique incidence Assuming a rotation about the X axis and denoting the angles by θ_1, θ_2, θ_3 and the corresponding fringe orders at a particular point by n_1, n_2, and n_3, we have, from eq. (10.16a),

$$\left.\begin{aligned}(n_1 2F_1)^2 &= 4(\tau_{xy} \cos \theta_1)^2 + (\sigma_x - \sigma_y \cos^2 \theta_1)^2, \quad (a)\\ (n_2 2F_2)^2 &= 4(\tau_{xy} \cos \theta_2)^2 + (\sigma_x - \sigma_y \cos^2 \theta_2)^2, \quad (b)\\ (n_3 2F_3)^2 &= 4(\tau_{xy} \cos \theta_3)^2 + (\sigma_x - \sigma_y \cos^2 \theta_3)^2. \quad (c)\end{aligned}\right\} (12.24)$$

We thus have three independent equations with three unknowns. Similar equations can be written for a rotation about the Y axis.

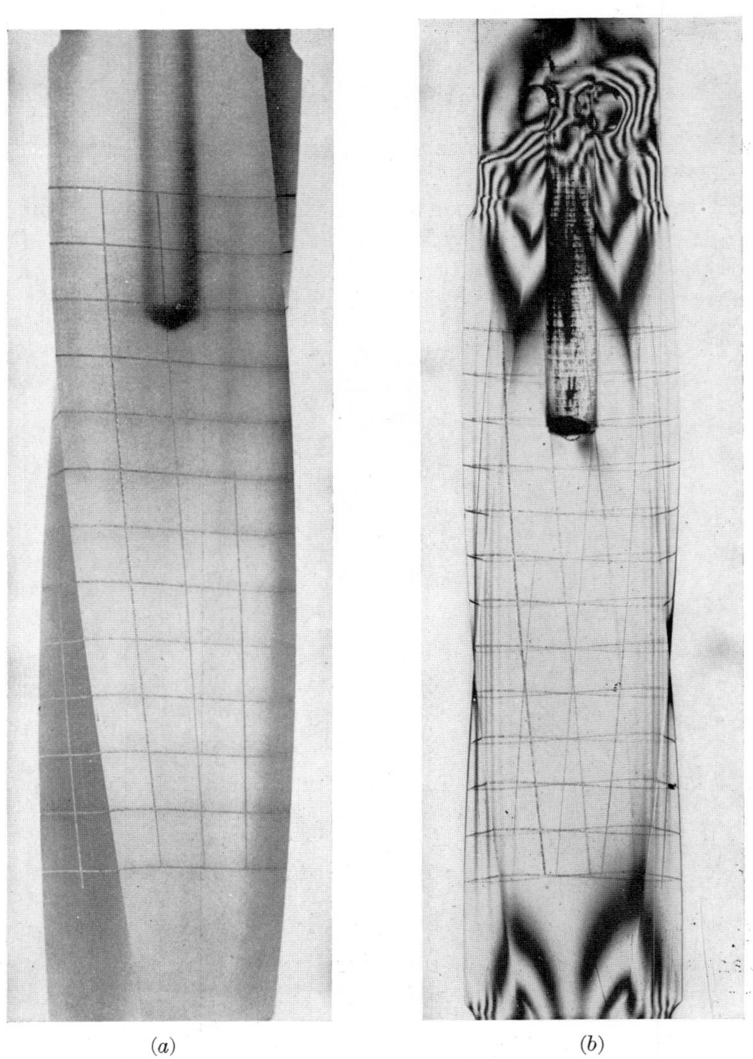

(a) (b)

FIG. 12.26 Photograph and Stress Pattern of a Twisted Rectangular Shaft Showing Warping.

Overall length = 6.5 in.; distance between pins = 5.5 in.; cross section = 1.012 in. by 0.506 in.; T = 5.32 lb.-in. approximately. Angle of twist 90° in 5.5 in.; d of hole = 0.253 in.; engraved lines ¼ in. apart.

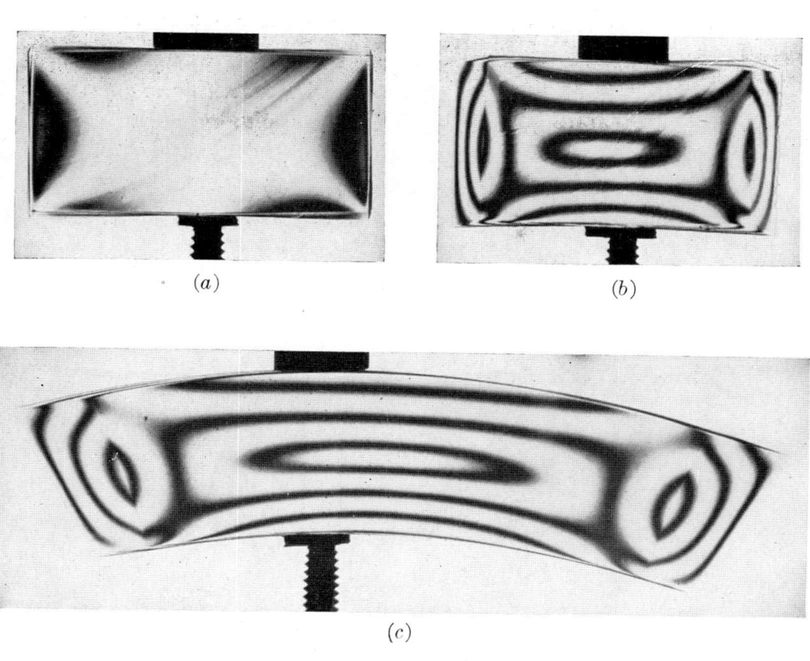

(a) (b)

(c)

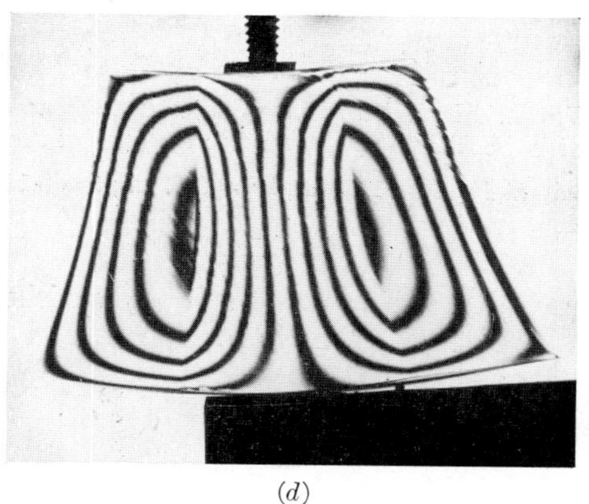

(d)

FIG. 12.27 Stress Patterns of Plates Cut from a Rectangular Shaft in Torsion.

Cross section of shaft = 1.020 in. × 0.508 in.; angle of twist = 86.5° in 5.5 in. (*a*) Transverse section normal to light; t = 0.183 in. (*b*) Transverse section; θ = 30°. (*c*) Section cut at an angle of 60° with long transverse edge; t = 0.127 in.; θ = 45°. (*d*) Section cut at an angle of 60° with short transverse edge; t = 0.181 in.; θ = 90°.

When the experimental values of n and θ are determined with precision the above equations will yield good results. However, ***the nature of the equations is such as to make them highly sensitive to small errors in n and θ and, therefore, rather impractical to apply.***

§12.10 Sections of Symmetry. Although the general eqs. (12.24) are somewhat impractical the separation of the principal stresses in special two-dimensional problems can nevertheless be determined by

FIG. 12.28 Stress Pattern of a Bakelite Ring Subjected to Concentrated Diametral Loads with the Light Rays Normal to the Face of the Ring.

$P = 54$ lb. approximately; $D = 1.02$ in.; $2r = 0.51$ in.; $t = 0.11$ in.; $F = 782$ psi. tension or compression.

oblique incidence with good accuracy. If τ_{xy} vanishes, eqs. (12.24) reduce to two unknowns. We then have

$$\left.\begin{aligned} (n_1 2F)^2 &= (\sigma_x - \sigma_y \cos^2 \theta_1)^2, \qquad (a) \\ (n_2 2F)^2 &= (\sigma_x - \sigma_y \cos^2 \theta_2)^2, \qquad (b) \end{aligned}\right\} (12.25)$$

and these equations yield satisfactory results.[1] Clearly, in order to eliminate the shear it is necessary to rotate the stressed model about a principal axis at each point. ***This calls for a point-by-point exploration***

[1] For a discussion of the errors, and the first published applications of this method, see "Photoelastic Separation of Principal Stresses by Oblique Incidence," by D. C. Drucker, *Journal of Applied Mechanics*, September, 1943.

and necessitates a knowledge of isoclinics. In such cases the method is only of academic interest. The procedure becomes more useful for

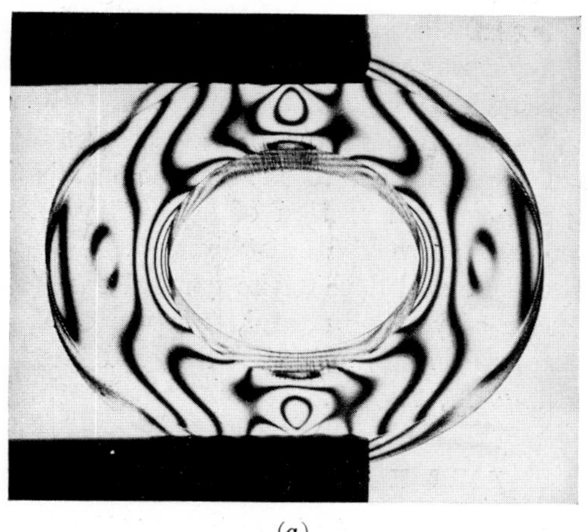

(a)

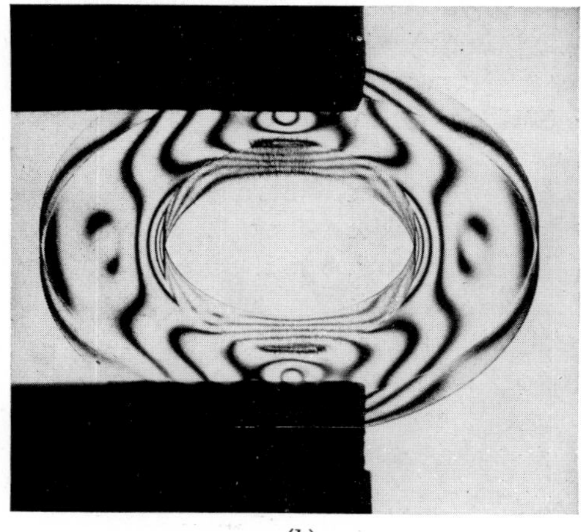

(b)

FIG. 12.29 Stress Patterns of the Ring in Fig. 12.28 Rotated about Its Horizontal Axis

(a) Angle θ between normal and ray is 30°; (b) $\theta = 45°$. Photographs taken with model in halowax oil.

sections of symmetry, where the shears inherently vanish. Two stress patterns obtained from a rotation about an axis of symmetry will give the necessary and sufficient data for the separation of the principal stresses on that axis.

An illustration of this method is shown in Figs. 12.28 and 12.29, in which a circular ring 1.02 in. in outside diameter, 0.51 in. in inside diameter and 0.11 in. thick was subjected to concentrated diametral loads.[1] Inspection of the curves in Fig. 12.30 shows that on the horizontal section of symmetry the method yielded reliable results. The errors at the free boundary can be readily corrected from the data in the normal view. However, along the vertical section of symmetry the results differed considerably from the known stress distribution.

It should perhaps be added that the general eqs. (12.24) have been tested on a number of problems, and, in spite of the large probable errors, the results are often useful in that they indicate the general shape of the stress distribution, Fig. 12.31.

PART II BENDING STRESSES

§12.11 Bending Stresses. ***An ingenious application of the rotational effect resulting from the combination of an initial tension superimposed over linear bending stresses, which was discussed in §10.11, was made by Drucker[2] in the determination of bending stresses and factors of stress concentration, in thin plates with holes, grooves, or fillets, which are perpendicular to the neutral surface, Fig. 12.32***

It is obvious that such bending stresses produce no optical effect when the ray is normal to the face of the plate, i.e., parallel to Z axis, Fig. 12.32. The effects of the tensions are then neutralized by the equal and opposite effects of the compressions. However, by freezing an initial tension into the plate at an angle θ to the bending stresses (θ not equal to zero), the resulting principal stresses are made to rotate, in the manner shown in Fig. 10.24, and a real photoelastic effect is produced, from which σ_{bm} can be calculated.

Two experimental procedures are possible: one is based on the determination of the resulting retardation n in fringes; the other, on the evaluation of the angle of rotation α. If n is determined experimentally we first calculate the ratio n/n_t, and then, using the curves of Fig. 10.25 and the known angle θ, we find the value of m corresponding to the ratio

[1] A solution for a square plate subjected to concentrated loads is given in the preceding reference.

[2] See " The Photoelastic Analysis of Transverse Bending of Plates in the Standard Transmission Polariscope," by D. C. Drucker, *Journal of Applied Mechanics, Trans. A.S.M.E.*, Vol. 9, No. 4, December, 1942.

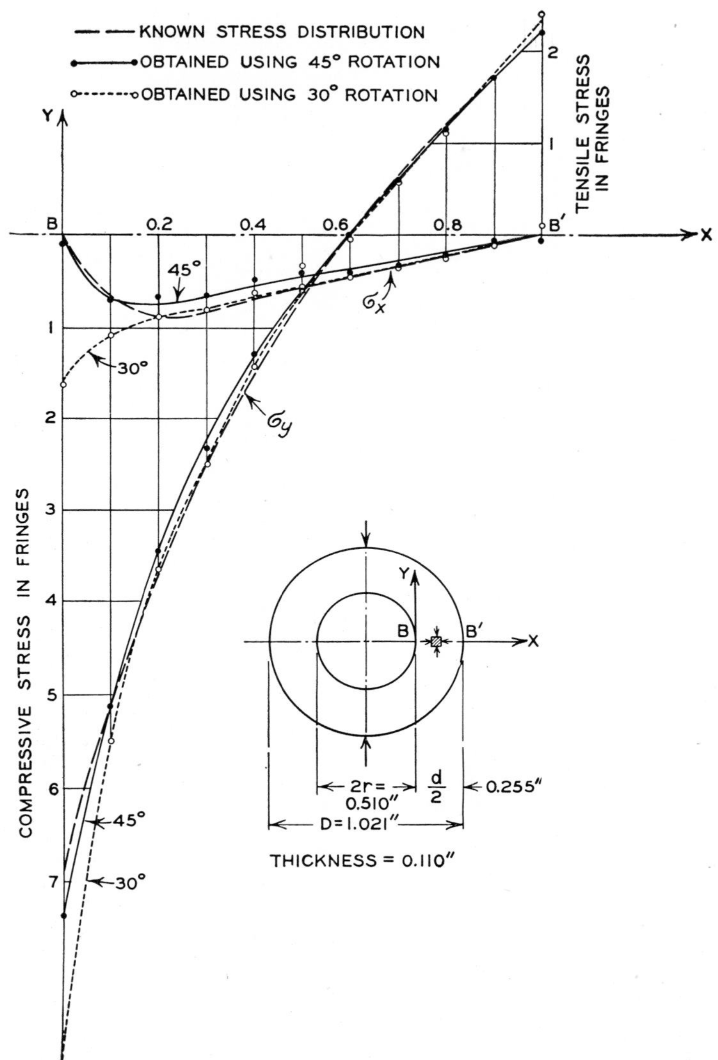

FIG. 12.30 Curves of Principal Stresses across the Horizontal Section of Symmetry in a Circular Ring Subjected to Diametral Loads Obtained by the Use of Oblique Incidence.

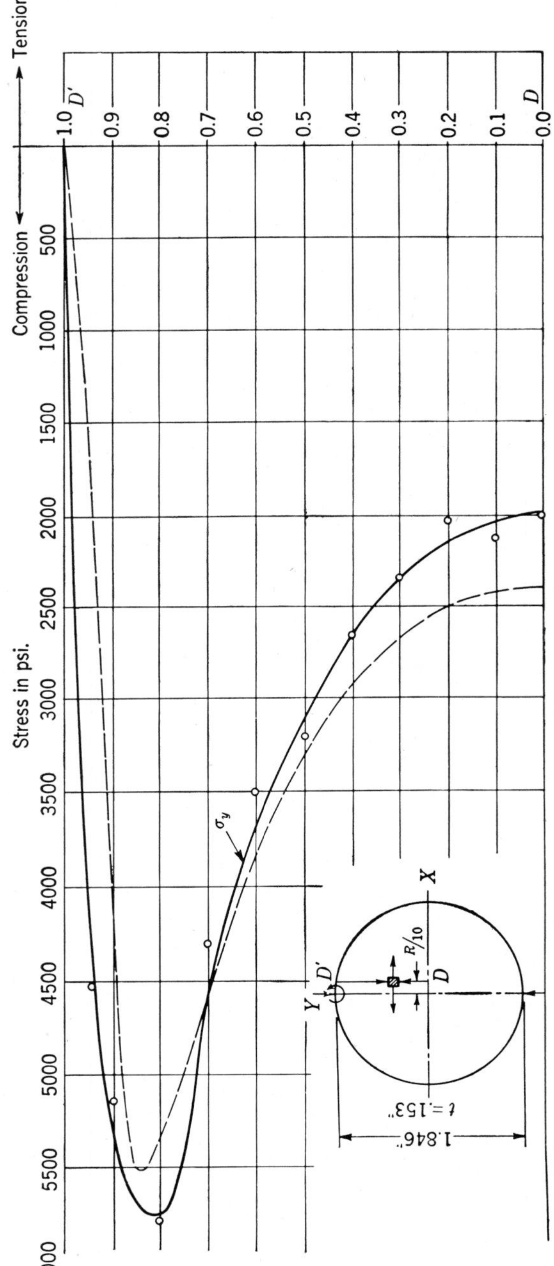

FIG. 12.31 Curves of σ_y along Section D–D', Based on Eqs. (12.24) with $\theta = 0°, 30°, 45°$; Rotation about Y Axis. For stress patterns see Fig. 10.19. Experimental results are shown by full curve. Theoretical distribution, dashed.

n/n_t. The value of σ_{bm} can then be readily calculated. If, on the other hand, the angle of rotation α is determined experimentally the ratio m can be calculated from eq. (10.23).

Of the two procedures the first is preferred, since retardations can be determined with greater accuracy than the angles of rotation.

Fig. 12.33 shows the results of some experiments by Drucker, in which he employed cantilever bars, on the theory that the transverse shears have no effect on the retardation. Using several bars with different values of θ, i.e., different directions of frozen tensions, he measured photoelastically the retardations n corresponding to applied bending stresses σ_{bm}, which were calculated by the usual flexure formula and are shown by the full straight line, Fig. 12.33. From the curves of Fig. 10.25, and the

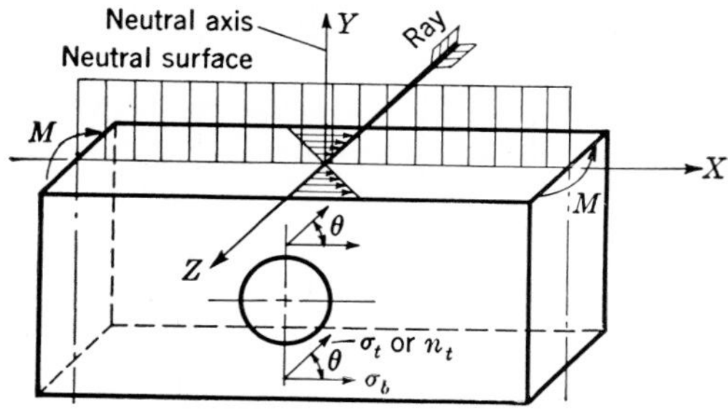

FIG. 12.32 Sketch Showing a Bar with a Hole Cut from a Plate with a Frozen Uniform Tension σ_t and Subjected to Bending σ_b about a Transverse Diameter of the Hole. See Fig. 10.23.

known values of n/n_t and θ, he then found the values m and the corresponding σ_{bm}.

Inspection of Fig. 12.33 shows excellent agreement between the experimental and theoretical results. It is to be noted that the greatest deviations are at $\theta = 40°$.

In the preceding discussion it was assumed that the bending moment induced only one longitudinal stress σ_{bm}. In plates with holes or other discontinuities the application of a bending moment induces in general two principal stresses of unknown directions at each point. The method based on rotational effects is also applicable to such problems. Here, however, the stress patterns yield the difference between the induced principal bending stresses, which will be denoted by $(p - q)\sigma_{bm}$. At free boundaries this reduces to a single stress of known direction and at sections of symmetry to two stresses of known directions.

Using this method Drucker determined the factors of stress concentration in bars with circular holes bent about a diameter of the hole. Stress patterns from such bars are shown in Fig. 12.34. The distributions of $(p - q)\sigma_{bm}$ on the outside surface of the bar for three different holes are shown in Fig. 12.35.

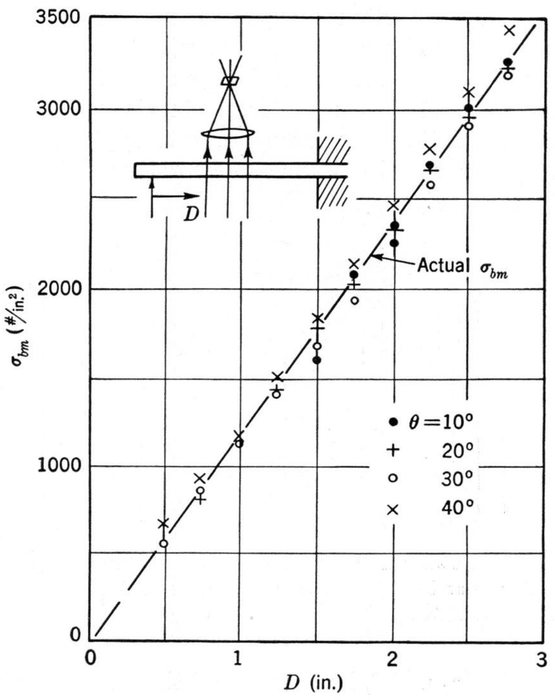

FIG. 12.33 Comparison of Theoretical and Experimental Values of Bending Stresses in Cantilever Beam Obtained by Superimposing Flexural Stresses over an Initial Frozen Tension Making an Angle θ with Bending Stresses. (From Drucker.)

As a result of these experiments Drucker concluded that in pure bending, for a hole of diameter equal to the thickness of the plate, the factor of stress concentration is 2.4, and that the factor is essentially the same for the semicircular groove of a diameter equal to the thickness.[1]

[1] This result is in good agreement with the theoretical results obtained by Reissner. See "The Effect of Transverse Shear Deformation on the Bending of Elastic Plates," by Eric Reissner, *Journal of Applied Mechanics, Trans. A.S.M.E.*, Vol. 12, No. 2, June, 1945. See also "The Influence of Circular and Elliptic Holes on the Transverse Flexure of Elastic Plates," by J. N. Goodier, *Philosophical Magazine*, Series 7, Vol. 22, pp. 69–80, 1936.

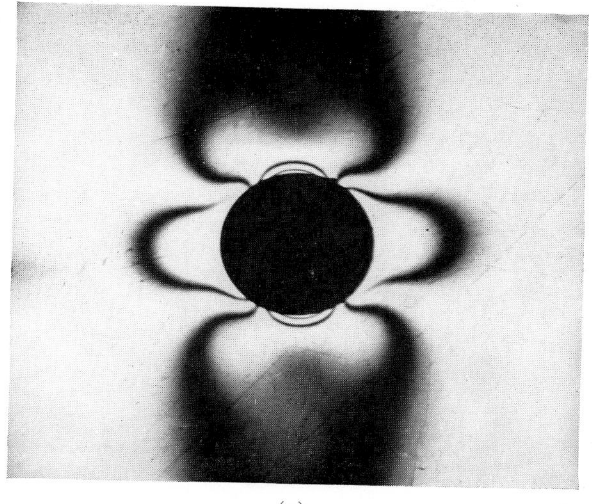

(a)

(b)

FIG. 12.34 Stress Patterns of Bars with Circular Holes Bent about the Transverse Diameter of the Hole.

Bending stresses made visible by combining them with an initial inclined frozen tension fixed into the bar, as in Figs. 10.24 and 12.32. (From Drucker.)

The above method is indicated in thin plates, where the assumption of linearity of the bending stresses is justified. However, ***it cannot be assumed without further investigation that the linear distribution of the bending stresses is also valid in thick plates. Here, the direct method of freezing the bending stresses into the plate and then slicing or grinding it should yield the desired results.***

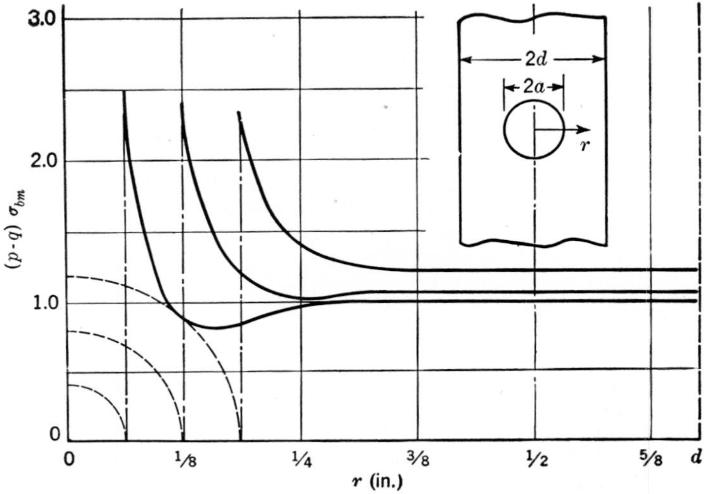

FIG. 12.35 Curves of Stress Distribution across Section of Symmetry through Hole in a Bar Bent about the Transverse Diameter of the Hole. (From Drucker.)

CHAPTER 13

CIRCULAR SHAFTS IN TENSION AND BENDING

PART I INTRODUCTION

§13.1 Scope of Chapter. The most useful practical results so far obtained from three-dimensional photoelasticity is in the relatively simple field of tension and bending. Here, quantitative data have been determined for several important cases of stress concentrations. In this chapter we describe photoelastic investigations of circular shafts with transverse circular holes in tension and bending, also shafts with grooves and fillets.

The chapter consists of four parts. In Part I we discuss methods to determine stress concentration factors. In Parts II and III we describe stress concentrations resulting from transverse holes in circular shafts in tension and bending respectively. These problems are of some practical importance. Open holes in shafts often form a part of the lubricating system of a machine; the oil holes in crankshafts are one example. Considerable research work in that direction has already been done by means of strain gages and fatigue tests.[1] The photoelastic results from bending are correlated with those from fatigue tests and strain measurement.

In Part IV we describe additional tension tests with circular shafts containing fillets or grooves.

All models were of Bakelite BT-61-893. The method of loading and fringe-order determination have already been discussed in chapter 11.

§13.2 Notation. The following notation will be used:

n = number of fringes at an arbitrary point (fringe order).

n' = fringe intensity, i.e., the number of fringes per inch of material measured parallel to the direction of the ray, $n' = n/t$, where t is the thickness of the plate. The stress σ is proportional to the fringe intensity; i.e., $\sigma = 2fn'$, where $2f$ is the tensile fringe value of the material.

[1] See "Two and Three Dimensional Cases of Stress Concentration and Comparison with Fatigue Tests," by R. E. Peterson and A. M. Wahl, *Journal of Applied Mechanics, Trans. A.S.M.E.*, Vol. 3, No. 1, March, 1936.

$N_{\text{unf.}}$ = maximum fringe order in that part of the shaft where the stresses are approximately uniform, best determined by compensation.

$N_{\text{unf.}}'$ = fringe intensity corresponding to $N_{\text{unf.}}$ If the diameter of the shaft where the stress is uniform is denoted by D, then

$$N_{\text{unf.}}' = \frac{N_{\text{unf.}}}{D}. \tag{13.1}$$

$n_{\text{ave.}}'$ = average fringe intensity in the minimum transverse area through the discontinuity.

$n_{\text{max.}}, n_{\text{max.}}'$ = maximum fringe order and maximum fringe intensity respectively, in any one section of arbitrary thickness t.

$N_{\text{max.}}'$ = maximum fringe intensity at the discontinuity.

$\sigma_{\text{max.}}, \sigma_{\text{ave.}}$ = maximum and average stress in pounds per square inch in the transverse sections through the discontinuity.

A = transverse area in the region of uniform stress.

A_1 = minimum area through the discontinuity.

P = total load on shaft in pounds.

§13.3 Factors of Stress Concentration. Methods. (*a*) *Definition.* ***The factor of stress concentration in three-dimensional work will be denoted by k_3 and defined by the simple expression***

$$k_3 = \frac{\sigma_{\text{max.}}}{\sigma_{\text{ave.}}} = \frac{N_{\text{max.}}'}{n_{\text{ave.}}'}. \tag{13.2}$$

Both fringe intensities $N_{\text{max.}}'$ and $n_{\text{ave.}}'$ can be determined with good engineering accuracy from a shaft with frozen stresses. (See §§11.12 to 11.14.)

(*b*) $N_{\text{max.}}'$. The maximum fringe intensity at the discontinuity can be obtained from one or more longitudinal sections parallel to the axis of the shaft, depending on the type of discontinuity. In cylindrical shafts, such as shafts with fillets or grooves, one central section is sufficient to determine $N_{\text{max.}}'$. Here $N_{\text{max.}}' = n_{\text{max.}}'$.

In shafts with transverse holes it is necessary to take several longitudinal sections transverse to the axis of the hole. The maximum intensity in each section is determined from the simple expression $n_{\text{max.}}' = n/t$. In thin plates the intensities $n_{\text{max.}}'$ may be assumed to represent the true stress at the center of the plate. A curve of n' can then be plotted from which $N_{\text{max.}}'$ can be determined.

(*c*) $n_{\text{ave.}}'$. The average fringe intensity across the minimum area of the discontinuity can be determined in one of two ways: by the fringe value method, or by what may be called a *photographic method.* In the first method

$$n_{\text{ave.}}' = \frac{\sigma_{\text{ave.}}}{2f} = \frac{P}{A_1 2f}, \tag{13.3}$$

in which $2f$ is taken equal to 3.2 as determined from thin bars at 260° F. This method yields best results when the time stresses are small.

In the photographic method $n_{\text{ave.}}'$ is found from $N_{\text{unf.}}'$ which is in turn obtained from $N_{\text{unf.}}$, eq. (13.1). Thus

$$n_{\text{ave.}}' = \frac{N_{\text{unf.}}' A}{A_1},$$

$$= \frac{N_{\text{unf.}}}{D} \frac{A}{A_1}. \tag{13.4}$$

In this procedure the value of $n_{\text{ave.}}'$ is independent of the fringe value. The accuracy depends on that of $N_{\text{unf.}}$.

Another photographic procedure is possible. Here

$$n_{\text{ave.}}' = n_{\text{unf.}}' \frac{A}{A_1}, \tag{13.5}$$

where $n_{\text{unf.}}'$ is determined by means of a Babinet compensator from $n_{\text{unf.}}$ in the plate itself, and not from $N_{\text{unf.}}$ for the whole shaft. In the absence of time stresses

$$N_{\text{unf.}}' = n_{\text{unf.}}'.$$

In very thin plates eq. (13.5) will yield good results. The several methods are illustrated in the cases which follow. Generally, the results do not differ greatly. In all cases the conservative, i.e., the lower, values of k_3 are plotted in the curves.

PART II SHAFTS WITH TRANSVERSE HOLE IN TENSION

§13.4 Case 1 $(r/d = 0.164)$. (a) *General Data.* We first consider the shaft shown in Fig. 13.1. Inspection of these stress patterns shows that the stresses in the shank are symmetrically distributed about the axis of the shaft. Fig. 13.2 further shows that the shaft is substantially free from transverse stresses. The general dimensions are:

Initial $D = 1.069$ in.	$A_1 = 0.599$ sq. in.
Final $D_f = 1.054$ in.	$A/A_1 = 1.46$
$2r = 0.265$ in.	$P = 22.15$ lb.
$d = D - 2r = 0.804$ in.	$\sigma = 25.3$ psi.
Initial $r/d = 0.164$	$\sigma_1 = 36.9$ psi.

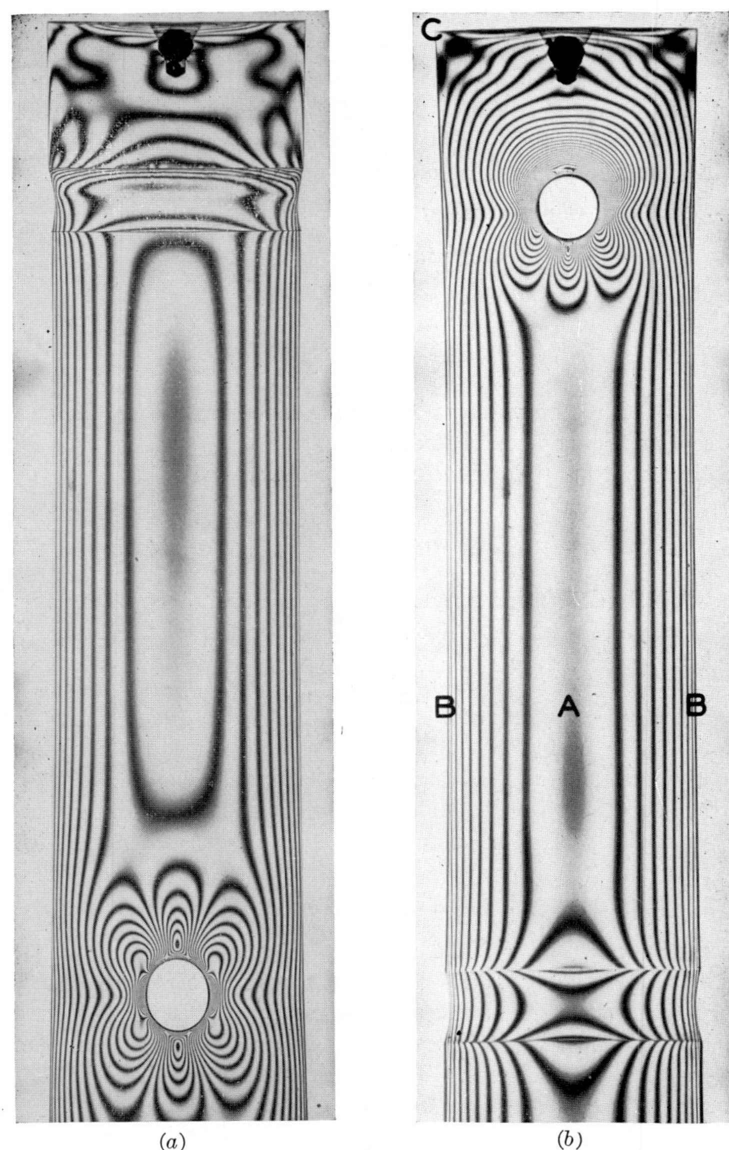

(a) (b)

FIG. 13.1 Frozen Stress Patterns of a Circular Shaft with a Transverse Hole Showing that the Stresses in the Shank are Symmetrically Distributed about the Axis; $r/d = 0.164$. See §13.4.

Final $r/d = r'/d' = 0.207$, approximately

$A = 0.874$ sq. in.

$N_{\text{unf.}} = 9.4$ fringes

$N_{\text{unf.}}' = N_{\text{unf.}}/D_f = 8.91$ fringes per inch

(a)

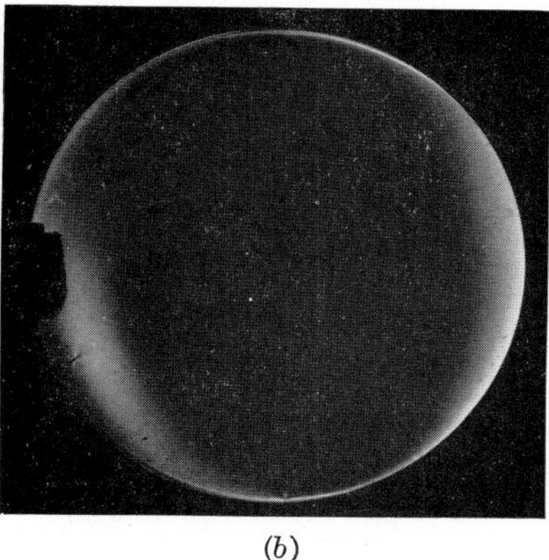

(b)

FIG. 13.2 (a) Enlargement of Pattern in Fig. 13.1(a); $r/d = 0.164$. (b) Stress Pattern of Section from Region of Uniform Stress Showing that Shaft is Substantially Free of Transverse Stresses; $t = 0.257$ in.

(b) $N_{\text{max.}}'$. In order to find the maximum stress around the hole, the shaft was sawed into five plates of equal thickness, $t = 0.177$ in., as shown in Fig. 13.3. From the stress patterns of the plates, Fig. 13.4, it can be seen that the stresses around the hole increase in magnitude as we approach the boundary of the shaft.

In order to determine the maximum stresses (fringe intensity) around the hole we divide the maximum number of fringes in each plate by the thickness of the plate and plot the curve shown in Fig. 13.3. This curve represents the tensile stresses around the hole along the shaded horizontal line in Fig. 13.3. From this curve $N_{\text{max.}}'$ is seen to be on the surface of the shaft and equals 33 fringes per inch. At the center of the shaft $n_{\text{max.}}'$ is only 26 fringes per inch. The difference is approximately 27 per cent.

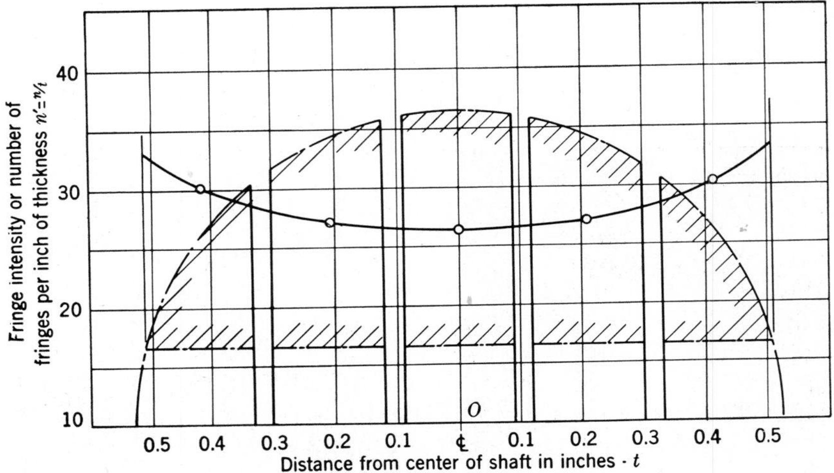

FIG. 13.3 Curve Showing the Variation of the Tensile Stress Intensity n' along the Edge of the Hole in Shaft of Fig. 13.1.

Figure also shows the manner in which plates were cut. $r/d = 0.164$; $t = 0.177$ in. for each plate; $N_{\text{max.}}' = 33$ fr./in.; n' at the center $= 26.5$.

(*c*) $n_{\text{ave.}}'$ *and* k_3. We next find the average stress across the minimum section through the hole. Using eq. (13.4) we obtain

$$n_{\text{ave.}}' = \frac{N_{\text{unf.}}'A}{A_1}$$

$$= 8.91 \times 1.46 = 13.$$

Hence,

$$k_3 = \frac{33}{13} = 2.54.$$

This is a conservative value, for, if $n_{\text{ave.}}'$ were based on the fringe value, eq. (13.3), k_3 would equal 2.87. As already observed, the curvature of the hole is somewhat altered by the deformations at high temperatures. The factor k_3 must be interpreted as referring to the final value of $r/d = 0.207$.[1]

[1] This material on stress concentration in tension is based on "Studies in Three-Dimensional Photoelasticity" by the author, published in the *Journal of Applied Physics*, Vol. 15, No. 1, January, 1944.

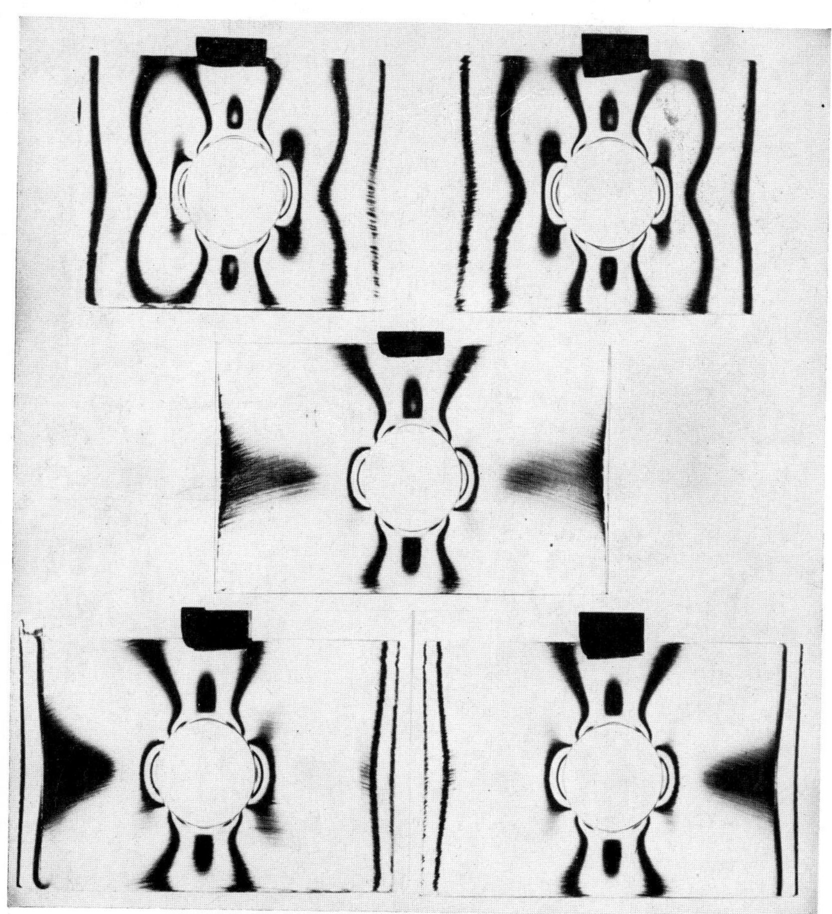

FIG. 13.4 Frozen Stress Patterns of Plates in Fig. 13.3, Showing the Variation in the Stresses along the Hole.

Upper row shows end plates; center pattern, center plate; and lower row, intermediate plates. The fringe order reaches a maximum of nearly five in the two end plates, whereas it is only four in the center plate. Note clarity of the four singular points around the hole showing the absence of marked time stresses.

FIG. 13.5 Frozen Stress Pattern of a Circular Shaft with a Transverse Hole; $r/d = 0.323$. See §13.5.

§13.5 Case 2 (r/d = 0.323). (*a*) *General Data.* Another shaft with a larger hole was next studied. A stress pattern of a portion of the shaft containing the hole is shown in Fig. 13.5. The general data are:

$D = 1.116$ in.	$A_1 = 0.491$ sq. in.
$D_f = 1.108$ in.	$A/A_1 = 1.96$
$2r = 0.438$ in.	$P = 18.48$ lb.
$d = 0.678$ in.	$\sigma = 19.2$ psi.
Initial $r/d = 0.323$	$\sigma_1 = 37.6$ psi.
Final $r/d = 0.385$	$N_{unf.} = 7.1$
$A = 0.964$ sq. in.	$N_{unf.}' = 6.41$ fringes per inch

As in the preceding case, the shaft was sawed into a number of sections, stress patterns were obtained, and the curve of n' was determined, Fig. 13.6. From this curve $N_{max.}'$ is again seen to be on the surface and is found to be 31.25 approximately.

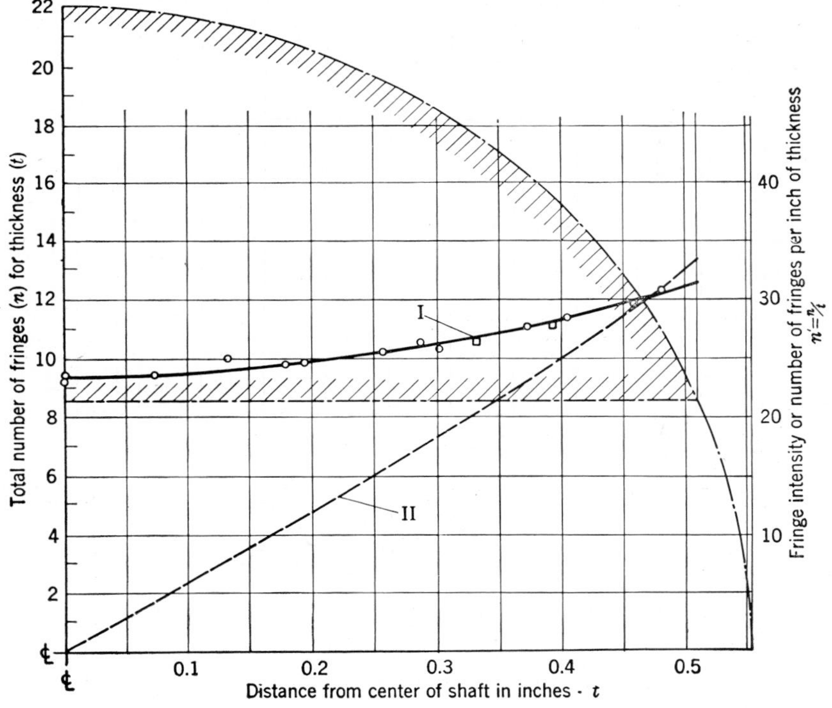

FIG. 13.6. Curves Giving the Variation of n' along Edge of Hole in the Shaft of Fig. 13.5; $r/d = 0.323$.

Curve I gives n'; curve II gives n. $N_{max.}' = 31.25$ fr./in.

By eq. (13.4) we find

$$n_{ave.}' = 6.41 \times 1.96 = 12.56 \text{ fringes per inch.}$$

Hence,

$$k_3 = \frac{31.25}{12.56} = 2.49.$$

We note that eq. (13.3) gives 11.72 for $n_{ave.}'$, and the corresponding k_3 equals 2.66.

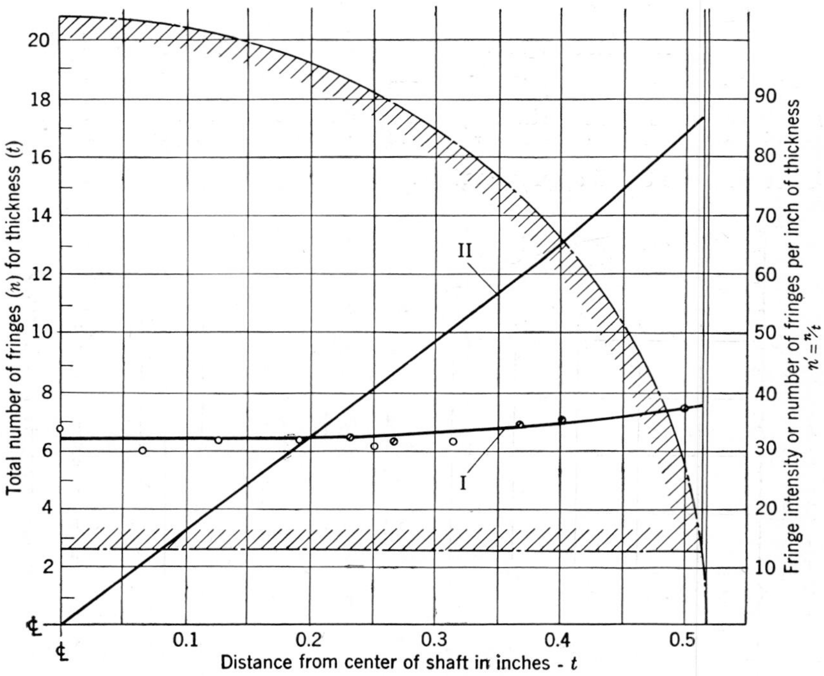

FIG. 13.7 Curves Showing the Variation in n' along Edge of Hole in a Circular Shaft for Which $r/d = 0.067$.

Curve I gives n'; curve II gives n. $N_{max.}' = 37.5$ fr./in.

§13.6 Case 3 (r/d = 0.067). (*a*) *General Data.* We last consider a shaft with a relatively small hole for which:

$D = 1.055$ in.	$A_1 = 0.713$ sq. in.
$D_f = 1.036$ in.	$A/A_1 = 1.185$
$2r = 0.124$ in.	$P = 28.47$ lb.
$d = 0.931$ in.	$\sigma = 33.9$ psi.

$r/d = 0.067$ $\sigma_1 = 40.0$ psi.
$r'/d' = 0.1$ $N_{unf.} = 11.7$ fringes
$A = 0.842$ sq. in. $N_{unf.}' = 11.3$ fringes per inch

The resulting distribution of $n_{max.}'$ is shown by curve I, Fig. 13.7, from which $N_{max.}' = 37.5$ fringes per inch, approximately. The average stress at the hole is 13.40, and the corresponding factor of stress concentration k_3 is 2.80.

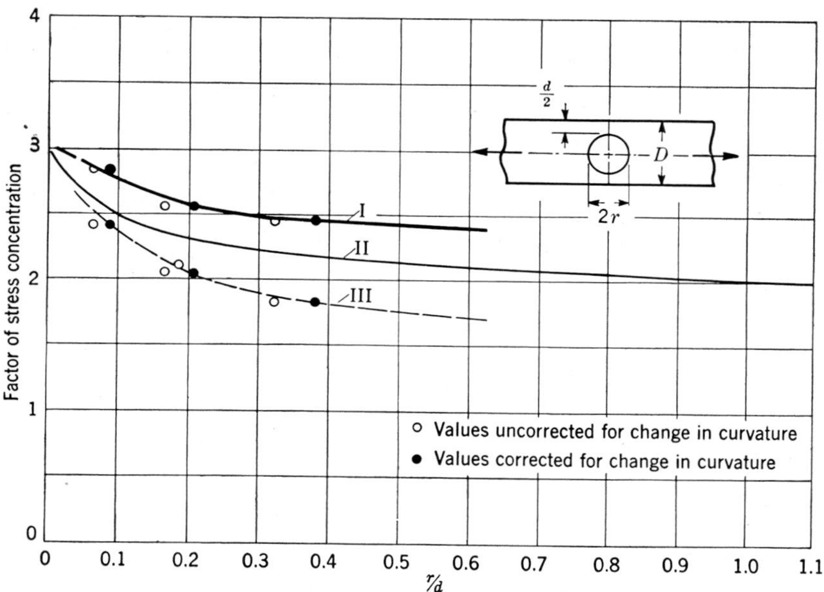

FIG. 13.8 Summary of Experimental Results for Shafts with Transverse Holes in Tension.

Curve I gives values of the three-dimensional factor of stress concentration, k_3; Curve II gives the two-dimensional factor k_2 for the same r/d; curve III gives k_3 based upon the tensile stress at the hole in the center of the shaft. This last value is shown only for comparison and should not be used in design.

§13.7 Relation between k_3 and k_2. The experimental results of all three cases discussed above are summarized in Fig. 13.8. Curve I gives the lower values of k_3 plotted against the final values of r/d. Curve II is the well-established curve of k_2 for the corresponding two-dimensional plates having the same ratios of r/d as the shafts.[1] It is seen that the k_3

[1] See author's paper "Photoelastic Studies in Stress Concentrations," *Mechanical Engineering, Journal of the A.S.M.E.*, August, 1936.

is somewhat larger than k_2, and that the difference is 14 per cent approximately. It is to be noted, however, that only conservative values of k_3 were used in curve I. The actual differences between k_3 and k_2 may therefore be greater than those indicated.

The values of k_3 given by curve I, Fig. 13.8, will be found to be closely approximated by the formula

$$k_3 = \left(1.1 + 7.1\frac{r}{d}\right)\frac{D}{d} \times \frac{A_1}{A} \times k_2. \tag{13.6}$$

The results given by curve I, Fig. 13.8, may be considered quite reliable in the range of r/d between 0.08 and 0.5 approximately. There is some doubt about the limiting or maximum value of k_3 as r/d approaches zero. Inspection of the curves giving n' in the three different cases, Fig. 13.9, shows that as the hole gets smaller the curves of n' flatten out and $N_{max.}'$ approaches the value of $n_{min.}'$ at the center of the shaft. Thus the ratio of $\dfrac{N_{max.}'}{n_{min.}'}$ is 1.353 and 1.186 for $r/d = 0.323$ and 0.067 respectively. It is therefore reasonable to conclude that for a very small hole the limiting value of k_3 is the same as for k_2, which has been established as 3.

Curve III, Fig. 13.8, gives the factors of stress concentration k_3 at the center of the shaft. These values are considerably smaller than k_3 on the surface and should not be used in design.

§13.8 Interpretation of Results. Independent Laminar Action. Inspection of curve I, Fig. 13.7, shows that in the interior, or central part, of the shaft the fringe intensity is constant. This is clearly true up to a point where $t = 0.25$ in. measured from the center of the shaft. Even beyond that point the rise is rather gradual. The interior part of the shaft thus behaves as if it consisted of vertical laminae or plates, transverse to the hole, each acting independently of the others. This is equivalent to saying that each transverse plate acts like a thin plate with a central circular hole in two-dimensional tension and that the factor of stress concentration for each plate, k_2, is determined by the ratio r/d', in which d' is the chord or effective width of the plate, Fig. 13.10.

Such a laminar action being assumed, the fringe intensities n' along the tensile edge of the hole can be expressed by the equation

$$n' = \frac{k_2 N_{unf.}' D'}{d'}, \tag{13.7}$$

in which D' and d' are as shown in Fig. 13.10, and $N_{unf.}'$ is the fringe intensity or stress in the region of pure tension. The values of n' given by eq. (13.7) we will refer to as theoretical intensities.

Fig. 13.11 shows a comparison of the experimental and the theoretical values of n', from which it can be seen that most of the shaft behaves as

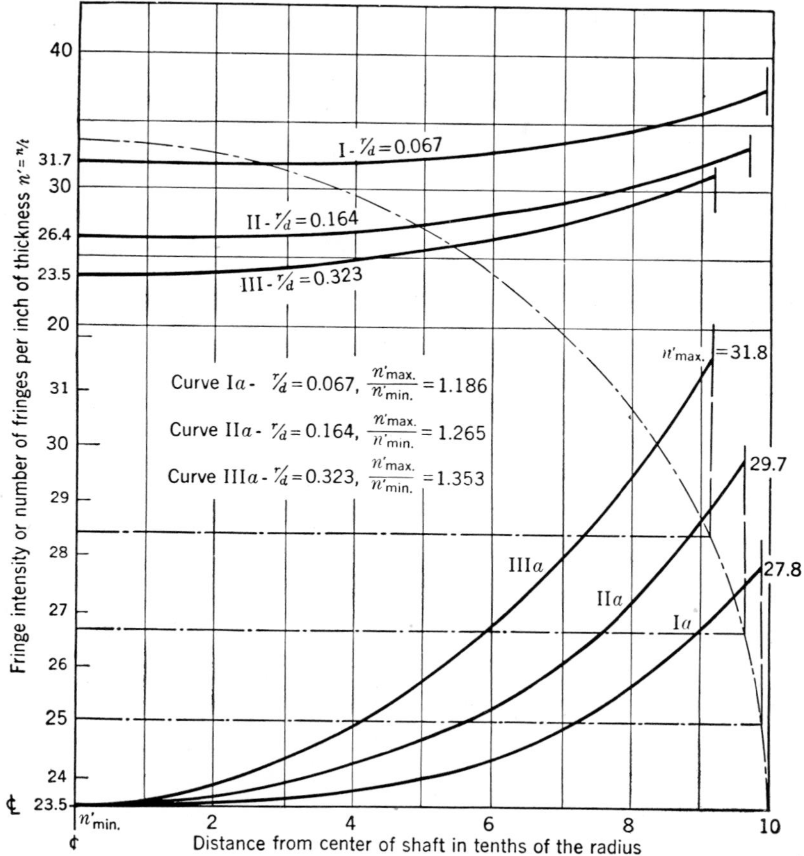

FIG. 13.9 Curves Showing Effect of r/d on Fringe Intensities.

Curves I, II, and III are taken from Figs. 13.7, 13.3, and 13.6 respectively. In order to bring the curves to one origin the loads on the three shafts were adjusted to produce the same stress at the center of the shaft. The stress chosen was $n_{min.}' =$ 23.5 fr./in., corresponding to $r/d = 0.323$, Fig. 13.6. The adjusted results are shown by curves I*a*, II*a*, and III*a*. The ratios of the maximum stresses to those at the center are 1.186, 1.265, and 1.353 for curves I*a*, II*a* and III*a*, respectively.

if it consisted of separate laminae. However, this is more nearly true for small holes than for large ones; i.e., when the holes are large in relation to the diameter of the shaft a smaller part of the shaft acts that way.

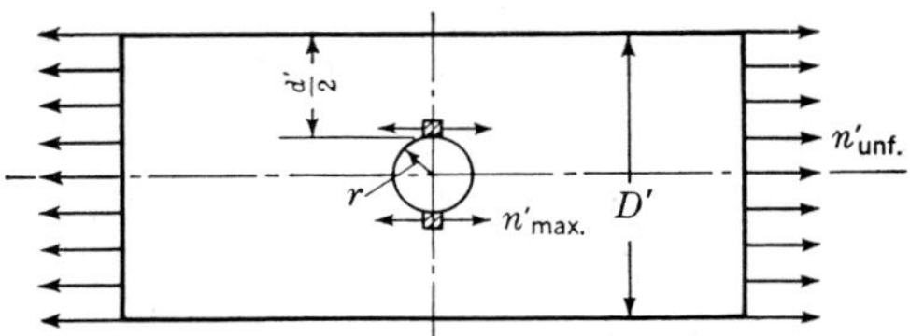

FIG. 13.10 Drawing Showing Notation Used for Plates Cut from Shafts with a Transverse Hole.

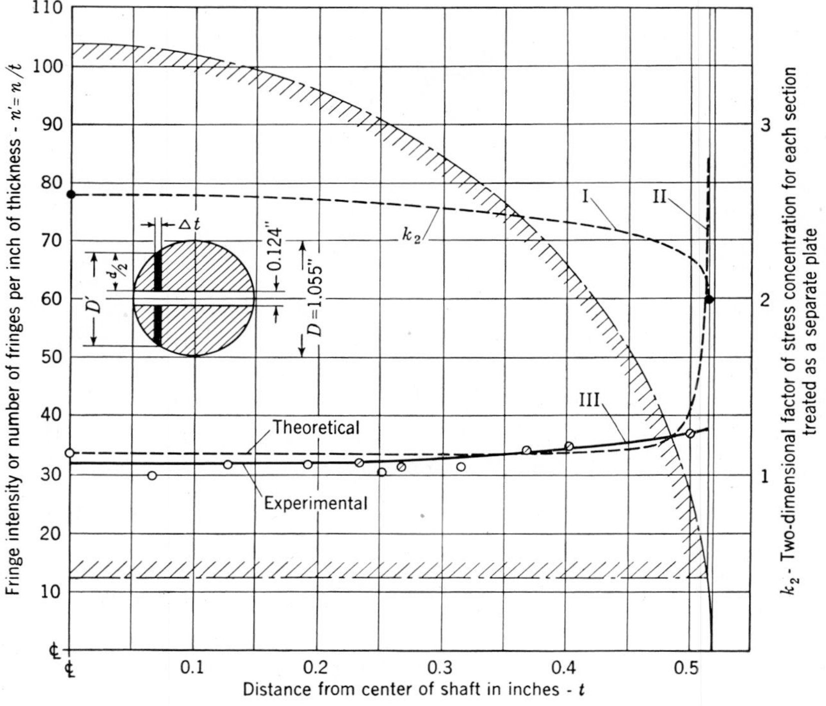

FIG. 13.11 Comparison of Values of n' from Theory of Laminar Action and Experiment.

Curve II is based on laminar values, eq. (13.7). Curve III gives corresponding photoelastic values. Curve I shows two-dimensional factors k_2 for bars in tension.

The deviations from the theoretical curve near the outside surface of the shaft are due to shear stresses.

PART III STRESSES IN BENT CIRCULAR SHAFTS WITH TRANSVERSE HOLES. CORRELATION WITH RESULTS FROM FATIGUE AND STRAIN MEASUREMENTS

§13.9 Stress Distribution in Solid Part of Shaft. Fig. 13.12 shows a typical stress pattern of a bent shaft. From this pattern the distribution of n' across the solid portion can be readily determined.

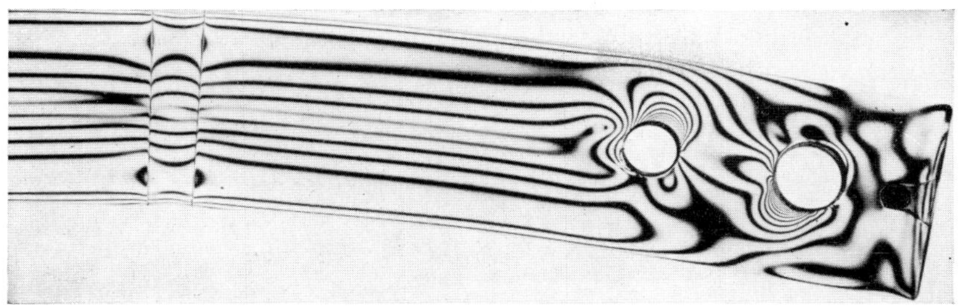

FIG. 13.12 Frozen Stress Pattern of a Circular Shaft with Transverse Hole in Pure Bending; $r/d = 0.145$. See §13.10.

The full curve of Fig. 13.13 shows the actual fringe intensities n' across the solid section which are defined as the number of fringes per unit of thickness measured along a line parallel to the direction of the light, i.e., parallel to the neutral axis in a transverse section of the shaft, such as line A–A. Owing to the fact that the time stresses are compressive on the surface of the shaft, the boundary stresses are considerably reduced on the tension side and increased on the compression side. The mean values of the fringe intensities on opposite sides of the neutral surface fall very close to the straight dashed line in Fig. 13.13, which is taken as a close approximation to the bending stresses in the solid part.

§13.10 Case 1 (r/d = 0.145). *General Dimensions:*

D = diameter of shaft before loading = 0.980 in.

$2r$ = diameter of hole = 0.220 in.

$d = D - 2r = 0.760$ in.

$r/d = 0.145$ (initial dimensions).

I_1 = moment of inertia of a solid transverse section = 0.0453 in.^{4} (initial dimensions).

I_2 = moment of inertia of transverse section through hole = 0.0286 in.^{4} approx. (initial dimensions).

P = load = 3.50 lb.

a = moment arm = 0.735 in. (final dimensions).

M = bending moment = 2.57 lb.-in.

N_1' = maximum fringe intensity at a solid transverse section in pure bending = 8.2.

N_2' = maximum fringe intensity at a transverse section through hole determined photoelastically = 25.5.

$(N_2')_{\text{nominal}}$ = nominal maximum fringe intensity at hole = 12.8.

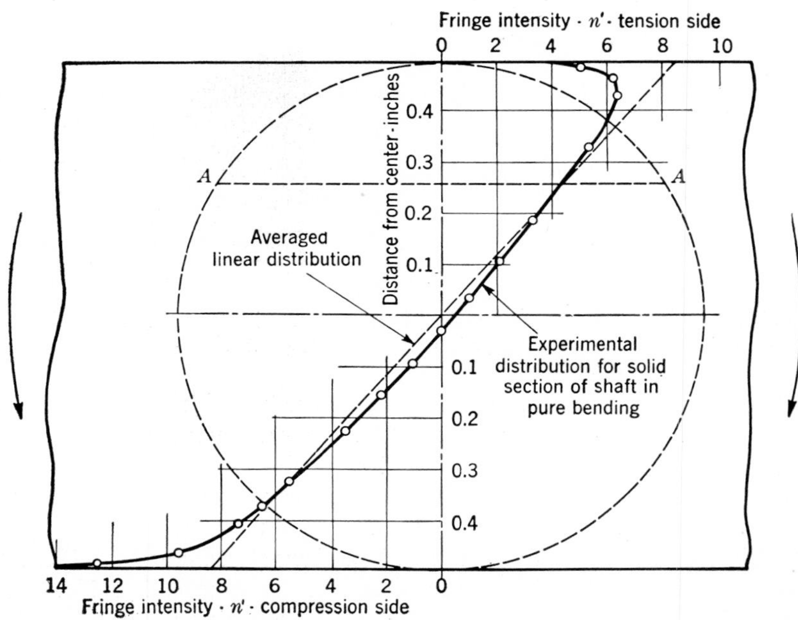

FIG. 13.13 Curve Showing Effect of Time Stresses on Fringe Intensities in Circular Shaft of Fig. 13.12, at a Section Some Distance from Hole.

Fig. 13.14 shows the dimensions of the four successive plates cut from the tension half of the shaft and the resulting curves of $(p - q)$. A typical stress pattern obtained from one plate is shown in Fig. 13.15. Fig. 13.16 shows the nominal and photoelastic stress distributions for a transverse section through the hole. Curve I gives the nominal stresses for a transverse section through a solid portion of the shaft in pure bending. This is the mean curve found in Fig. 13.13. Curve II of Fig. 13.16 is the nominal stress distribution through the hole. It is obtained from

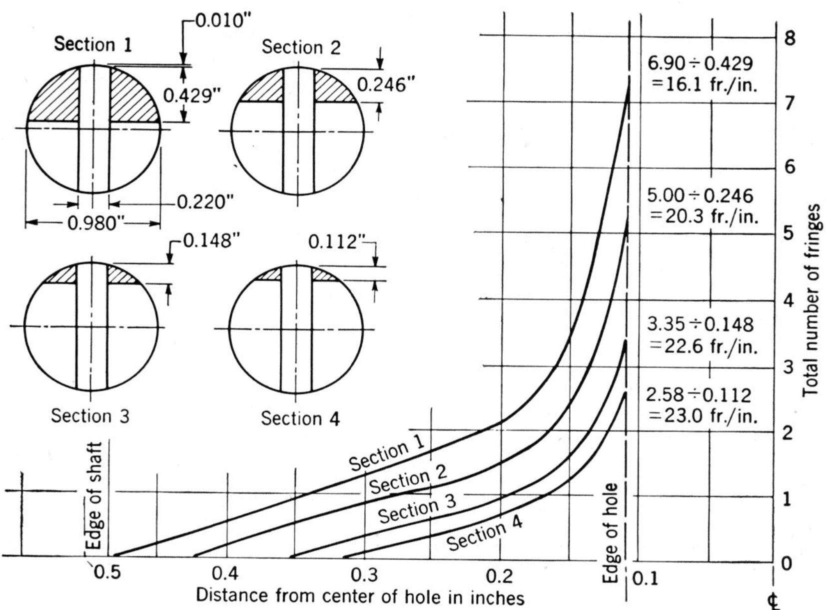

FIG. 13.14 Curves of $(p - q)$ from Four Successive Longitudinal Plates Taken from Tension Side of Circular Shaft in Fig. 13.12.

FIG. 13.15 Frozen Stress Pattern of the Tension Half of Circular Shaft with Transverse Hole in Pure Bending in Fig. 13.12. $r/d = 0.145$; $t = 0.430$ in.; $n_{\text{max.}} =$ 6.90 fringes.

curve I by means of the simple relation

$$(n_2')_{\text{nominal}} = n_1' \frac{I_1}{I_2}, \tag{13.8}$$

in which n_1' and n_2' are respectively the nominal stresses (in fringe intensities) in the same fiber in a solid section in pure bending, and at a section

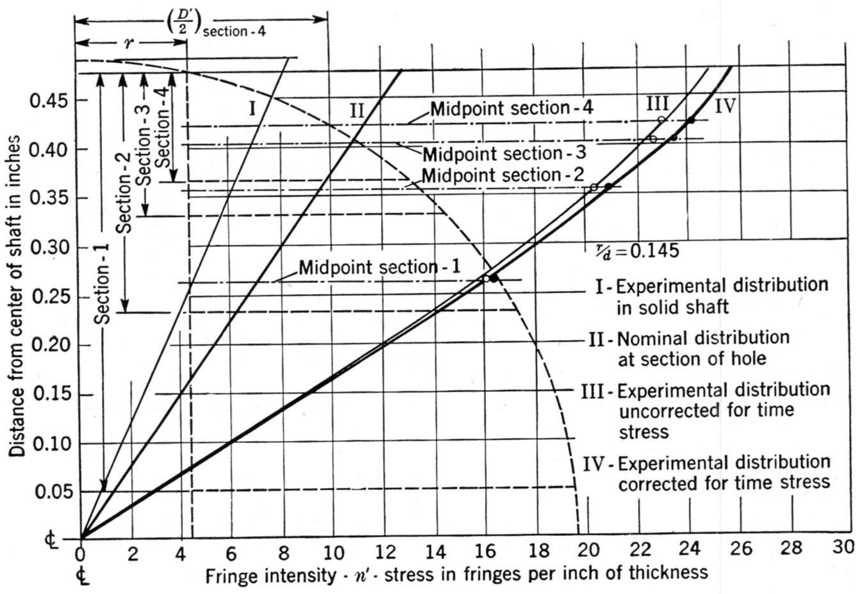

FIG. 13.16 Curves Showing Experimental Stress Distribution at Section through Hole for Tension Side as Determined from the Four Indicated Plates; $r/d = 0.145$.

through the hole. From eq. (13.8) it follows that:

$$(N_2')_{\text{nominal}} = N_1' \frac{I_1}{I_2}. \tag{13.9}$$

Curve III shows the photoelastically determined bending stresses at the hole. In plotting this curve the average fringe intensity obtained for a plate was placed at the midpoint of the plate. The curve obtained in this manner is straight for a considerable distance from the center of the shaft and does not differ radically from a straight line thereafter. The assumption that the mean stress intensity corresponds to the midpoint of the plate is therefore justified for all practical purposes. Curve IV gives the same data as curve III corrected for time stresses. The manner in which the correction is generally obtained in pure bending is shown in Fig. 13.13.

§13.11 Case 2 (r/d = 0.07). *General Data:*

$D = 1.058$ in.	$P = 4.44$ lb.
$2r = 0.13$ in.	$a = 0.75$ in.
$d = 0.928$ in.	$M = Pa = 3.33$ lb.-in.
$r/d = 0.07$.	$N_1' = 8.95$ fr./in.
$I_1 = 0.0615$ in.^{4}	$N_2' = 26$ fr./in. at extreme fibers.
$I_2 = 0.049$ in.^{4}	$(N_2')_{\text{nominal}} = 11.2$ fr./in.

A typical stress pattern from this shaft is shown in Fig. 13.17. The resulting stress distribution is shown by curve IV, Fig. 13.18.

§13.12 Photoelastic Factors of Stress Concentration. By definition the factor of stress concentration k_3 is given by

$$k_3 = \frac{\sigma_{\text{max.}}}{\sigma_{\text{nominal}}} \tag{13.10}$$

$$= \frac{N_2' \times 2f}{Mr/I_2}, \tag{13.11}$$

in which $2f$ is the fringe value in tension or compression per inch of thickness. Remembering that

$$2f = \frac{Mr}{I_1N_1'}, \tag{13.12}$$

we obtain after substitution

$$k_3 = \frac{N_2'I_2}{N_1'I_1}. \tag{13.13}$$

Combining with eq. (13.9), we have

$$k_3 = \frac{N_2'}{(N_2')_{\text{nominal}}}. \tag{13.14}$$

Eq. (13.13) shows that the factor of stress concentration k_3 can be calculated without the fringe value or bending moment, thereby eliminating one or two possible sources of error. The only experimental data needed to evaluate this factor are the maximum nominal fringe intensity N_1' in the solid portion of the shaft which is in pure bending, and the maximum photoelastic fringe intensity N_2' at the hole. The ratio I_1/I_2 is taken from the initial dimensions of the shaft, and this may introduce a small error.

FIG. 13.17 Frozen Stress Pattern of Tension Half of a Circular Shaft with Transverse Hole in Pure Bending. $r/d = 0.070$; $D' = 1.058$ in.; $n_{max.} = 7.30$ fringes. See §13.11.

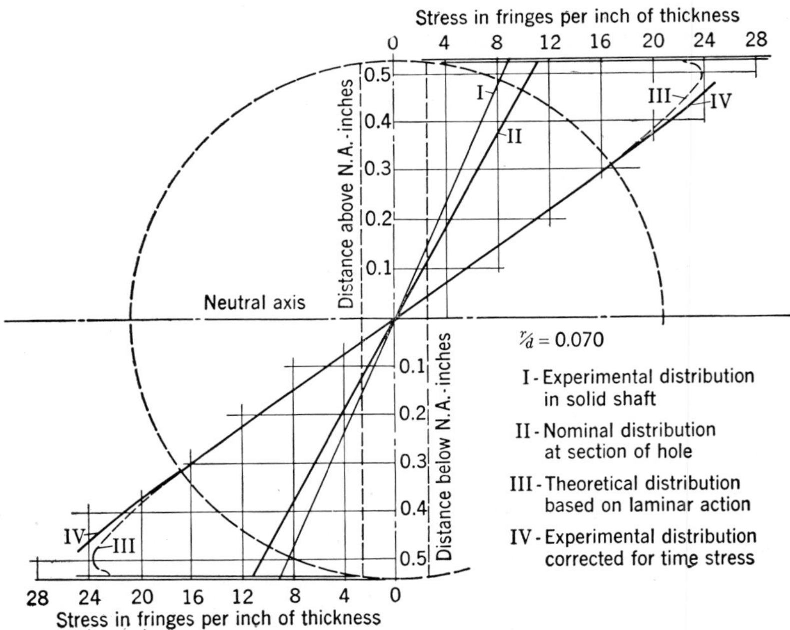

FIG. 13.18 Stress Distribution at Section through Hole; $r/d = 0.070$.

For purpose of calculation eq. (13.14) is the most convenient since both N_2' and $(N_2')_{\text{nominal}}$ are given directly by the curves of Figs. 13.16 and 13.18. Using these curves we find that

$$(k_3)_{r/d=0.145} = \frac{25.5}{12.8} = 2 \text{ approximately,}$$

and

$$(k_3)_{r/d=.07} = \frac{26}{11.2} = 2.32 \text{ approximately.}$$

A third case in which $r/d = 0.058$ was investigated; it gave a value for $k_3 = 2.16$.

In calculating these factors the experimental curves were extrapolated to the extreme fibers on the assumption that the maximum stresses occur there. It will be shown later that a strong probability exists that this assumption is not always true, and specifically that the maximum bending stress may actually be developed at a point some small distance away from the extreme fibers. The effect of this will be to reduce the factor k_3 for small values of r/d.

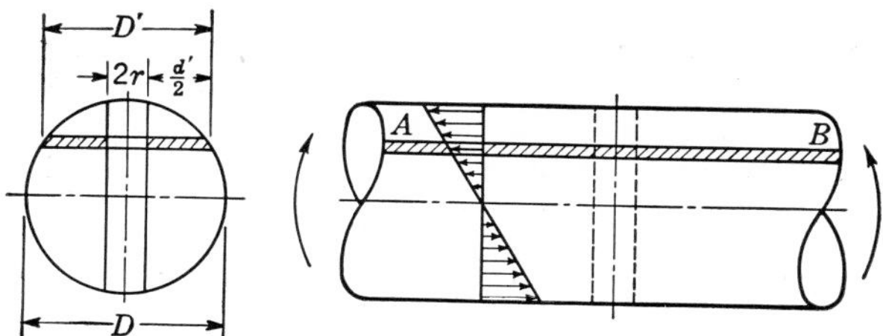

FIG. 13.19 Sketch Showing Notation and Meaning of Laminar Action for Circular Shafts in Bending.

§13.13 The Theory of Laminar Action. The experimental results shown in Figs. 13.16 and 13.18 can be explained by assuming: (*1*) *that, in transverse sections far from the hole, the longitudinal stresses follow the linear distribution given by the elementary flexure formula*

$$\sigma = \frac{My}{I}, \tag{13.15}$$

and (*2*) *that each thin plate, or lamina, parallel to the neutral surface behaves like a two-dimensional bar in pure tension or compression, Fig. 13.19.*

One consequence of this assumption is that the factor of stress concentration around the hole in each plate is exactly the same as the two-dimensional factor k_2 for the same ratio r/d, Fig. 13.20.

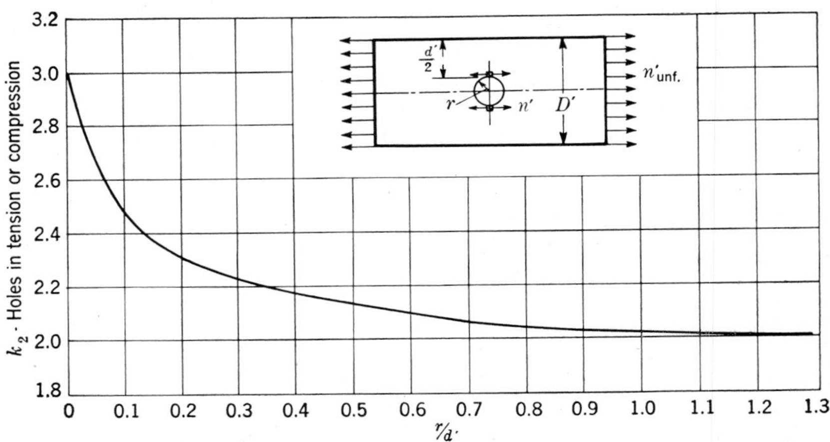

FIG. 13.20 Curve of k_2, for Bars with Holes in Tension As Applied to a Single Lamina in a Circular Shaft with Transverse Hole in Bending.

For this curve see *Strength of Materials* by N. C. Riggs and M. M. Frocht, p. 384, Ronald Press, New York.

As an illustration consider a shaft 2 in. in diameter with a ¼-in. hole, Fig. 13.21. At a point 0.5 in. above the neutral axis, the length of the

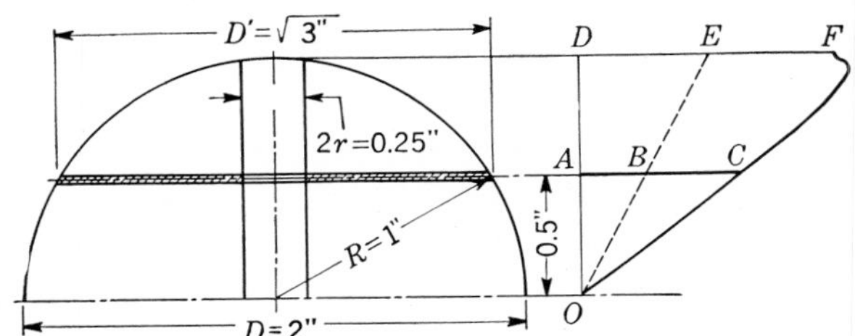

FIG. 13.21 Sketch Showing Application of Theory of Laminar Action to the Determination of the Stress Distribution in a Bent Shaft with a Transverse Hole. See §13.13.

chord $D' = \sqrt{3}$ in., and $d' = D' - 2r = 1.482$ in. The corresponding r/d' is given by

$$\frac{r}{d'} = \frac{0.125 \text{ in.}}{1.482 \text{ in.}} = 0.0843.$$

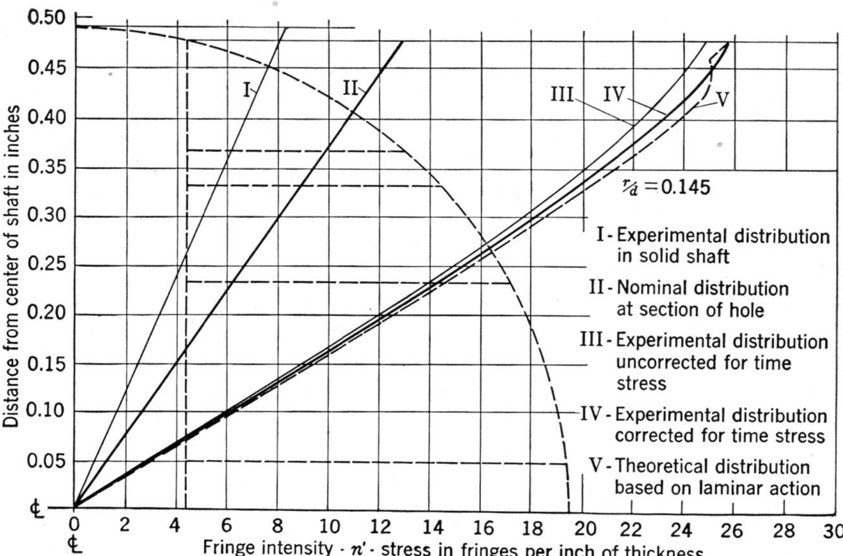

FIG. 13.22 Experimental and Theoretical Stress Distributions at Section through Hole; $r/d = 0.145$.

From the curve in Fig. 13.20 we find that the stress-concentration factor k_2 for this plate is 2.53 approximately. The maximum bending stress σ in this strip is then

$$\sigma = 2.53 \times \frac{My}{I} \cdot$$

The values of σ would then follow some such curve as OCF, Fig. 13.21, in which

$$\frac{AC}{AB} = (k_2)_{r/d'=0.0843} = 2.53$$

and

$$\frac{DF}{DE} = (k_2)_{r/d'=\infty} = 2.$$

The stress distributions which follow from the above assumptions, and the corresponding photoelastic values for $r/d = 0.145$ and $r/d = 0.070$, are shown in Figs. 13.22 and 13.18. The dashed curves represent the distribution from the assumption of laminar action. The other curves are the same as in Figs. 13.16 and 13.18.

The distribution of the bending stresses on the assumption of laminar action for nine different ratios of r/d are shown in Fig. 13.23(a), and an enlarged view of the same curves in the proximity of the extreme fibers is shown in Fig. 13.23(b). Inspection of these curves shows that for values of r/d less than 0.14 the maximum bending stresses may occur below the extreme fibers.

§13.14 Factors of Stress Concentration on the Assumption of Laminar Action. Assuming laminar action the three-dimensional factors of stress concentration k_3 would be given by

$$k_3 = \frac{k_2(My_m/I_2)}{Mr/I_2},$$

or

$$k_3 = k_2 \frac{y_m}{r}, \tag{13.16}$$

in which y_m denotes the distance from the neutral axis to the point of maximum bending stress, in what we may briefly call the theoretical curves, and, for small holes, r equals the radius of the shaft approximately. Inspection of Fig. 13.23(b) shows that $(r - y_m)$ is very small. Thus, for $r/d = 0.005$, $y_m = 0.965r$, and for $r/d = 0.09$, $y_m = 0.93r$ approximately.

Since y_m/r is never greater than unity, it follows that k_3 is never greater than the maximum value of k_2. From two-dimensional studies we know that the maximum value of k_2 is 3. Hence, assuming laminar action, k_3 cannot possibly exceed that value. For r/d greater than 0.14 the maximum bending stress occurs in the extreme fibers and $k_3 = 2$, and for r/d less than 0.14, k_3 is greater than 2.

§13.15 Comparison with Results from Fatigue Tests and Strain Measurements. Factors of stress concentration k_3 based on the assumption of independent laminar action, i.e., on the curves of Fig. 13.23, are given by curve I of Fig. 13.24.

Superimposed over this curve are the three points from the photoelastic tests and seven additional points from fatigue tests and strain measurements determined by Peterson and Wahl and reported in 1936.[1] Inspection of this curve shows that all the points from fatigue tests except the two from small shafts (0.5 diameter) fall well on the curve.

Moreover, there is some direct experimental evidence tending to show that in shafts with small holes the maximum stress is not developed in the extreme fibers, but at points some distance below. Examination of frac-

[1] See footnote 1 on p. 429.

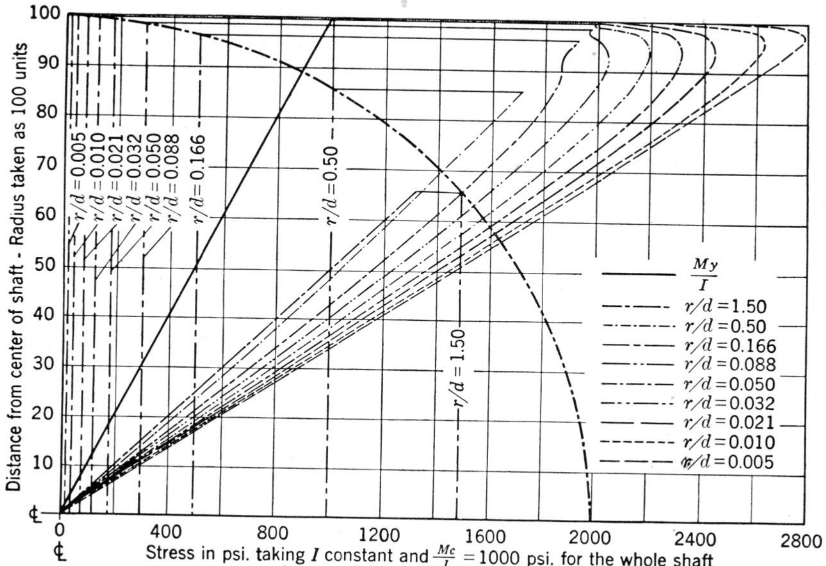

FIG. 13.23 (*a*) Curves Giving Theoretical Stress Distributions on Assumption of Laminar Action at Section through Hole.

Nine different values of r/d for circular shafts with transverse holes in bending are shown.

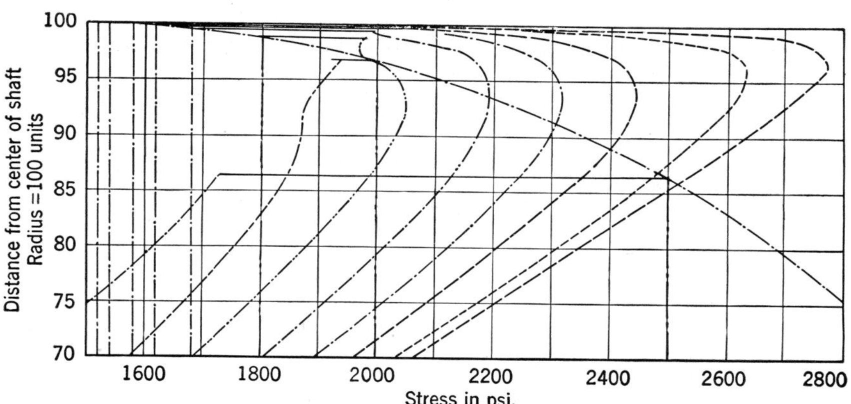

FIG. 13.23 (*b*) Enlargement of Top Portion of Curves in (*a*).

tures from fatigue tests seems to substantiate this conclusion. A photograph of one such fracture is shown in Fig. 13.25.

Inspection of this photograph shows a crack on both sides of the hole well below the extreme fibers. Further, the position of this crack agrees substantially with that given by the theoretical curve for the same ratio r/d.

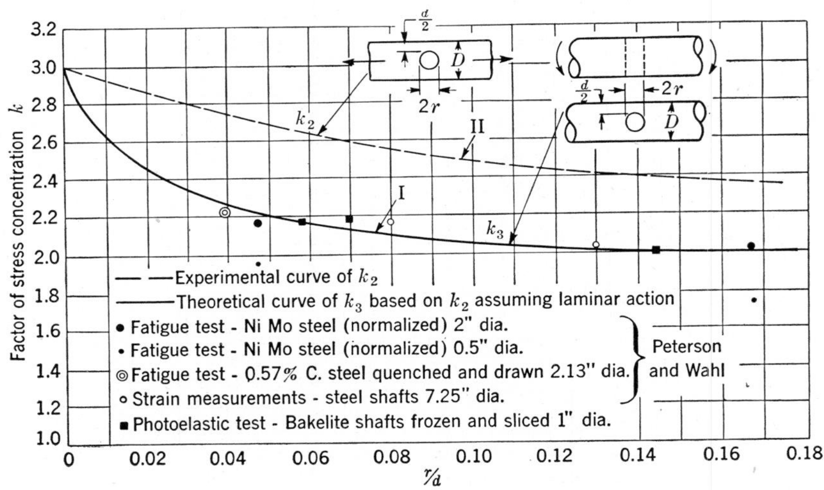

FIG. 13.24 Comparison of Theoretical and Experimental Values of k_3 for Circular Shafts with Transverse Holes in Bending.

Returning now to the photoelastic results for case 2, in which $r/d = 0.07$, and assuming that the maximum bending stresses do not occur at the extreme fibers but at the points indicated by the theoretical curves, the factor k_3 from the photoelastic data would become

$$k_3 = \frac{24.4}{11.2} = 2.18$$

instead of the previously calculated 2.32. This value is in closer agreement with the results from fatigue tests and strain measurements, as well as with the curve based on laminar action.

§13.16 Error from the Assumption of Laminar Action. Other Errors. ***The laws of equilibrium would be completely satisfied if the whole shaft lent itself to laminar representation.*** Since each lamina is in equilibrium, the total resisting moment would equal to the applied bending moment. However, the laminar representation breaks down in the extreme fibers above line A–A, and below line B–B, Fig. 13.26. In those regions the width of the plate is less than the diameter of the hole. The plates in those regions are, therefore, not continuous but consist of two disconnected parts separated by the hole. Owing to this geomet-

FIG. 13.25 Photograph of a Fatigue Fracture of a Steel Shaft Showing Crack Near Top of Hole. $D = 3$ in.; $r = 0.187$ in.; $r/d = 0.0334$. (Courtesy Mr. R. E. Peterson, Westinghouse Electric Corporation.)

ric limitation shear stresses must exist on the horizontal surfaces between the extreme plates. The effect is to increase, somewhat, the bending stresses on the extreme plates beyond those resulting from laminar action by an amount equal to the shear.

Inspection of Fig. 13.26 shows, however, that, for small holes, such as oil holes, the areas above line A–A and below B–B are small and approach zero as the diameter of the hole diminishes. It follows that ***for small holes the disturbance in equilibrium resulting from the breakdown of laminar representation, and its effect on the stresses, is a negligible quantity of no practical significance.*** This conclusion is supported by the fact that all experimental results from fatigue tests, strain measurements, and photoelasticity fall well on the curve of laminar action. For large holes, however, a correction would be necessary. It is doubtful whether such cases often occur in practice.

In the problem under consideration, ***the time stresses tend to cancel out, and the errors due to this cause are small.*** The same conclusion holds for the error arising from the changes in the values of r/d.

Since the fringe value and the bending moment do not enter into eq. (13.14), the expression used to calculate the value of k_3, it follows that the effect of friction on the load, and the accuracy of measuring the bending moment, do not affect the results, although precautions were taken to free the pivot in the straining machine of frictional forces and to measure the bending moment accurately. A small error may have been introduced by extrapolation.

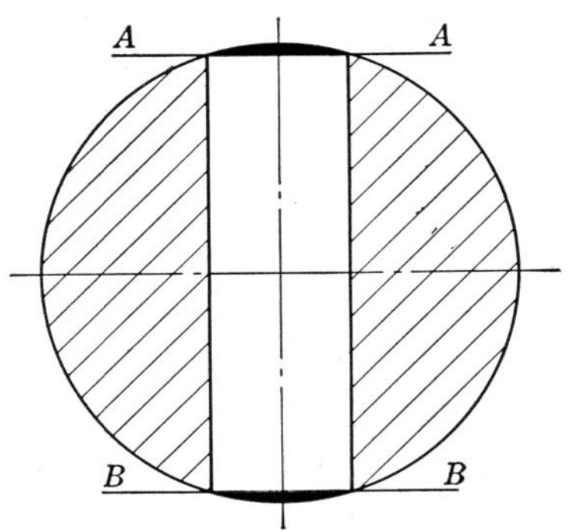

FIG. 13.26 Sketch in Connection with Laminar Action.

Solid areas above line A–A and below B–B cannot be represented by a continuous lamina. In practical cases, such as oil holes, these areas are small and their effect is negligible.

§13.17 Conclusions. The photoelastic results suggested the hypothesis of independent laminar action, which is strongly supported by the available data from fatigue tests and strain measurements. This hypothesis leads to a simple method of calculation of maximum bending stresses and theoretical factors of stress concentrations. ***The first important conclusion is that the theoretical stress-concentration curve obtained on the assumptions of laminar action is in good agreement with the results from fatigue tests, strain measurements, and the photoelastic tests. We thus have a simple and effective correlation between stress and failure. Large (2-in.) normalized Ni-Mo steel shafts with transverse holes in pure bending in fatigue seem to break at a stress equal to the endurance limit divided by the factor of stress concentration. The behavior of such shafts is then similar to that of a brittle material except that the endurance limit replaces the ultimate tensile strength.***

We further conclude that, except for the limiting values, the three-dimensional factors k_3 in bending are considerably smaller than the two-dimensional factors k_2 for the same ratio of r/d.

Inspection of Fig. 13.24 shows that k_3, like k_2, approaches 2 as the lower limit, only k_3 reaches this limit more rapidly than k_2. Thus, at $r/d = 0.14$, k_3 is already equal to 2, whereas k_2 approaches this value only when r/d becomes infinite.

PART IV FILLETS AND GROOVES

§13.18 Shaft with Fillet in Tension, Fig. 13.27.

(*a*) *General Data:*

INITIAL DIMENSIONS

Diameters: $D = 0.996$ in., $d = 0.760$ in.
Radius of fillet: $r = 0.158$ in.
Depth of fillet: $h = (D - d)/2 = 0.118$ in.
$r/d = 0.208$, $h/r = 0.747$

FINAL DIMENSIONS

$D' = 0.988$ in.	$A_1 = 0.440$ sq. in.
$d' = 0.748$in.	$A/A_1 = 1.745$
$r' = 0.172$ in. approximately.	Load, $P = 16.2$ lb.
$r'/d' = 0.230$	$\sigma = 21.1$ psi.
$h'/r' = 0.698$	$\sigma_1 = 36.8$ psi.
Final $A = 0.767$ sq. in.	$N_{\text{unf.}} = 8.8$ in smaller shaft

$N_{\text{unf.}}' = 8.8/0.748 = 11.8$ fringes per inch.

(*b*) *Factor of Stress Concentration.* Fig. 13.28 shows a stress pattern obtained by means of a doubler from a thin central plate, $t = 0.1525$ in., cut from the shaft in Fig. 13.27. From this stress pattern the maximum fringe order at the fillet is found to be 5.07 (the average for both sides). Hence,

$$N_{\text{max.}}' = \frac{5.07}{2 \times .1525} = 16.6, \text{ approximately.}$$

From eq. (13.3) we have for the average fringe order in the minimum section

$$n_{\text{ave.}}' = \frac{36.8}{3.2} = 11.5.$$

Also, $n_{\text{ave.}}'$ is in this case directly equal to the uniform fringe intensity $N_{\text{unf.}}'$ in the smaller part of the shaft, which was found to be 11.8.

The two methods thus give essentially the same results.

Hence,

$$k_3 = \frac{16.6}{11.8} = 1.41.$$

We note that the two-dimensional factor for the same final r'/d' is 1.58 or slightly greater than k_3.

§13.19 Shaft with Semicircular Groove in Tension, Fig. 13.29.

(*a*) *General Data:*

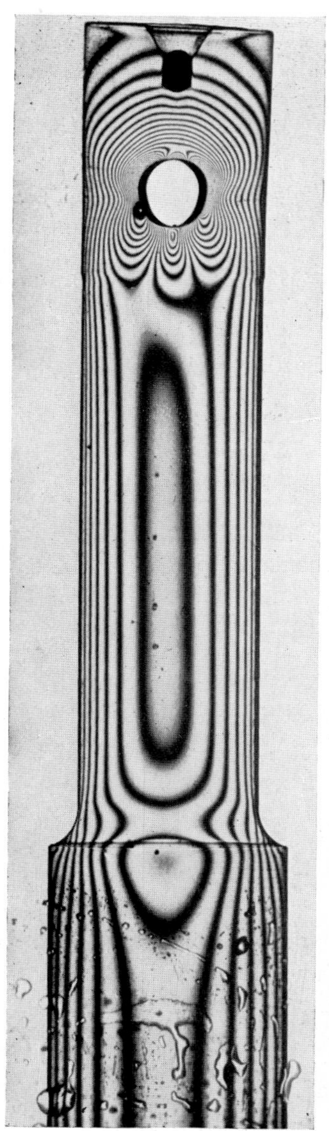

FIG. 13.27 Stress Pattern of a Solid Circular Shaft with a Fillet in Tension; $r/d = 0.208$ in. See §13.18.

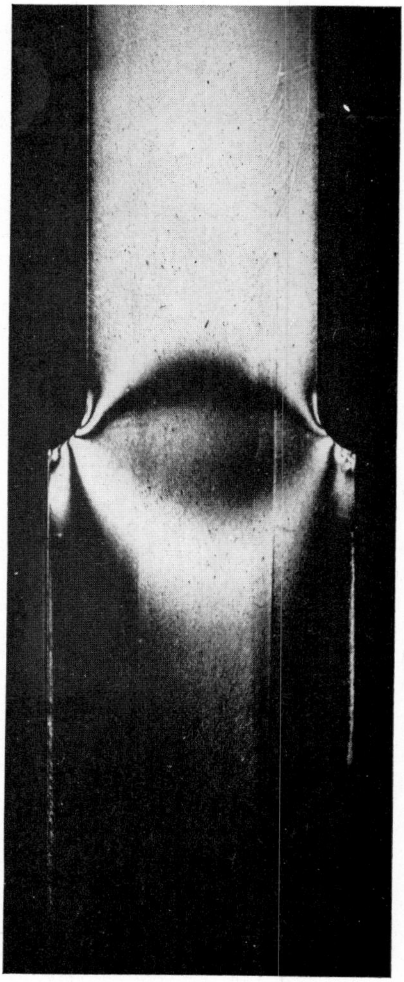

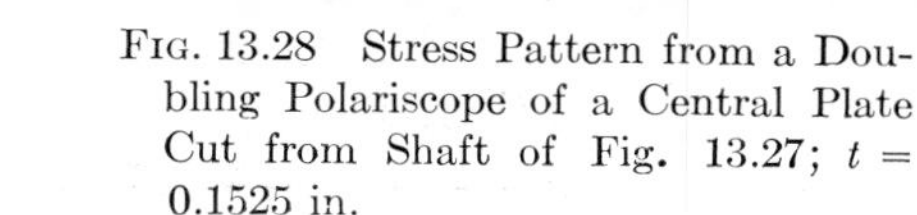

FIG. 13.28 Stress Pattern from a Doubling Polariscope of a Central Plate Cut from Shaft of Fig. 13.27; $t = 0.1525$ in.

FIG. 13.29 Stress Pattern of a Solid Circular Shaft with a Semicircular Groove in Tension; $r/d = 0.185$. See §13.19.

INITIAL DIMENSIONS

Diameters: $D = 0.968$ in., $d = 0.702$ in.
Radius of groove: $r = 0.130$ in.
Depth of groove: $h = (D - d)/2 = 0.133$ in.
$r/d = 0.185,\quad h/r = 1.02.$

FINAL DIMENSIONS

$D' = 0.953$ in.	$A_1 = 0.370$ sq. in.
$d' = 0.686$ in.	$A/A_1 = 1.93$
$r' = 0.151$ in.	$P = 22.2$ lb.
$r'/d' = 0.220$	$\sigma = 31.1$ psi.
$h'/r' = 0.88$	$\sigma_1 = 60$ psi.
Final $A = 0.714$ sq. in.	$N_{\text{unf.}} = 9.9$

$N_{\text{unf.}}' = 10.4$ fringes per inch.

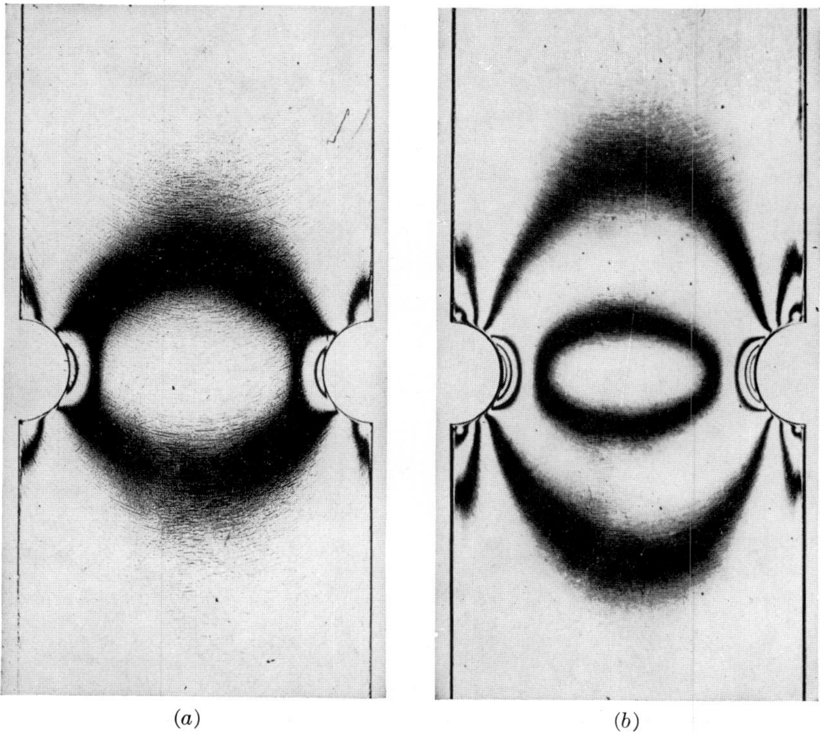

(*a*) (*b*)

FIG. 13.30. Stress Pattern of a Central Plate Cut from Shaft of Fig. 13.29; $t = 0.1095$ in.

Photographs obtained (*a*) using ordinary polariscope; (*b*) from a doubling polariscope.

(b) *Factor of Stress Concentration.* Fig. 13.30(b) shows a stress pattern of a central longitudinal section 0.1095 in. thick obtained by means of a doubling polariscope. From this stress pattern the maximum fringe order at the groove was found to be 6.5. This gives a maximum stress at the groove of

$$N_{\text{max.}}' = \frac{6.5}{2 \times 0.1095} = 29.7 \text{ approximately.}$$

Using eq. (13.3) we get

$$n_{\text{ave.}}' = \frac{60}{3.2} = 18.8 \text{ fringes per inch.}$$

Also by eq. (13.4)

$$n_{\text{ave.}}' = 10.4 \times 1.93 = 20 \text{ approximately.}$$

The minimum value of k_3 therefore is

$$k_3 = \frac{29.7}{20} = 1.5 \text{ approximately.}$$

The two-dimensional factor corresponding to the same final dimensions of r'/d' is 1.92.

§13.20 Circular Shaft with Three Adjacent Grooves in Tension. The object of this test was to see whether in three dimensions adjacent grooves exert a reinforcing effect similar to that found in two dimensions.

(a) *General Data.*

INITIAL DIMENSIONS

Diameter of shaft: $D = 0.9625$ in.
Diameter at central groove: $D_1 = 0.7125$ in.
Diameter at outside grooves: $D_2 = 0.736$ in.
Radii: small groove, $r_1 = 0.130$ in., larger grooves, $r_2 = 0.251$ in.
$r_1/D_1 = 0.183$, $r_2/D_2 = 0.34$, $h_1/r_1 = 0.96$.

FINAL DIMENSIONS

$D' = 0.947$ in., $D_1' = 0.697$ in., $D_2' = 0.722$ in.
$r_1' = 0.1425$ in., $r_2' = 0.273$ in. approximately.
$r_1'/D_1' = 0.205$, $h_1'/r_1' = 0.88$.
Final transverse areas in square inches: A — shaft $= 0.704$ sq. in., $A_1 = 0.382$ sq. in., $A_2 = 0.410$ sq. in. (outer groove).
$P = 20.54$ lb., $\sigma = 29.2$ psi., $\sigma_1 = 53.8$ psi., $\sigma_2 = 50.1$ psi.
$N_{\text{unf.}} = 8.75$, $N_{\text{unf.}}' = 8.75/0.947 = 9.24$ fringes per inch.

(b) *Factor of Stress Concentration.* Fig. 13.32 shows a central plate, 0.1705 in. thick, cut from the shaft in Fig. 13.31. From this stress

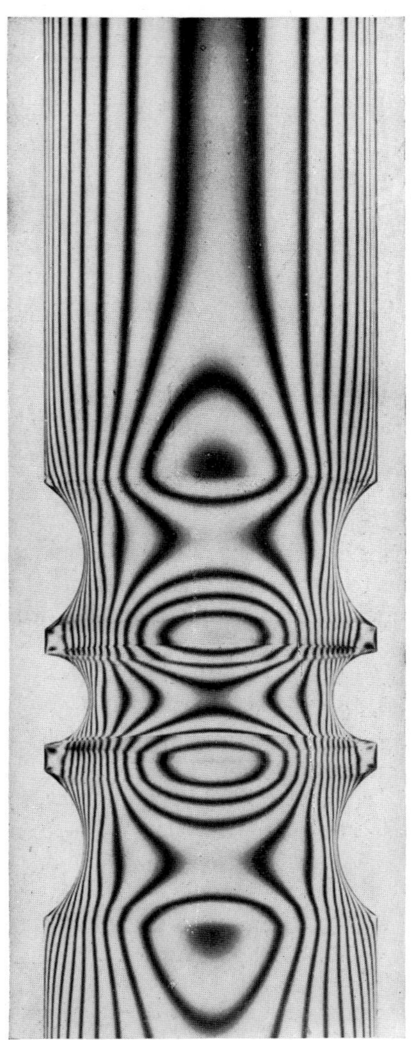

FIG. 13.31 Stress Pattern of a Solid Circular Shaft with Three Adjacent Grooves in Tension. See §13.20.

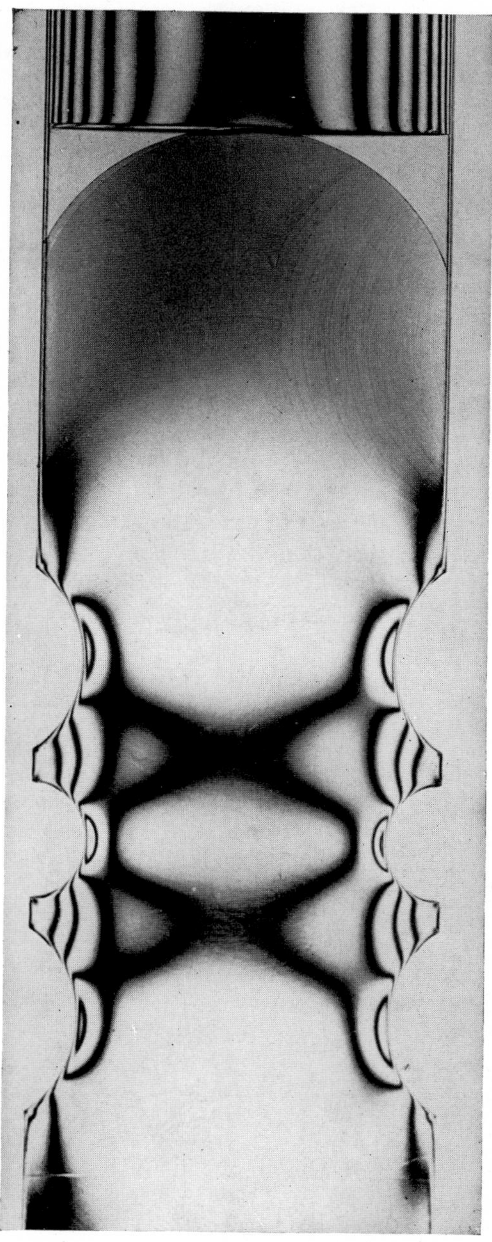

FIG. 13.32 Stress Pattern of a Central Plate Cut from Shaft of Fig. 13.31; $t = 0.1705$ in.

pattern we find that $n_{max.}$ equals 4.6 and 4 at the small and large grooves respectively. The maximum intensities at the grooves are

$$(N_{max.}')_1 = 27 \text{ fringes per inch at smaller groove}$$

and

$$(N_{max.}')_2 = 23.5 \text{ fringes per inch at larger groove.}$$

Also by eq. (13.3)

$$(n_{ave.}')_1 = 17 \quad \text{and} \quad (n_{ave.}')_2 = 15.7 \text{ fringes per inch.}$$

Hence,

$$(k_3)_1 = 1.59 \text{ at smaller groove}$$

and

$$(k_3)_2 = 1.5 \text{ at larger groove.}$$

The results indicate that for the particular grooves chosen there is no noticeable reinforcing effect. For in the preceding case, in which the shaft had a single groove, k_3 was found to be 1.5 for $r'/d' = 0.220$, whereas in the present instance the maximum factor is $(k_3)_1 = 1.59$ for $r_1'/D_1' = 0.205$. However, the test is inconclusive, and further work is indicated.

§13.21 Hollow Grooved Shaft, Fig. 13.33. (*a*) *General Data:*

INITIAL DIMENSIONS	FINAL DIMENSIONS
$D = 0.988$ in.	$D' = 0.978$ in.
$r = 0.094$ in.	$r' = 0.096$ in.
$d = D - 2h - b = 0.357$ in.	$d' = 0.356$ in.
Bore, $b = 0.4375$ in.	$b' = 0.432$ in.
$h = 0.0965$ in.	$h' = 0.095$ in.
$A = 0.604$ sq. in., $A_1 = 0.340$ sq. in.	$A/A_1 = 1.775.$
$P = 14.28$ lb., $\sigma = 23.6$ psi.	$\sigma_1 = 42$ psi.

$N_{unf.} = 4.10, \quad N_{unf.}' = N_{unf.}/(D' - b') = 4.10/0.546 = 7.5$ fringes per inch

(*b*) $N_{max.}'$. From Fig. 13.34 by extrapolation the maximum fringe order at the fillet was found to be 3.5 approximately. This gives a maximum stress of

$$N_{max.}' = \frac{3.5}{0.139} = 25 \text{ fringes per inch approximately.}$$

The average stress across the groove is

$$n_{ave.}' = 7.5 \times 1.775 = 13.3 \text{ fringes per inch.}$$

Hence,

$$k_3 = 25/13.3 = 1.88.$$

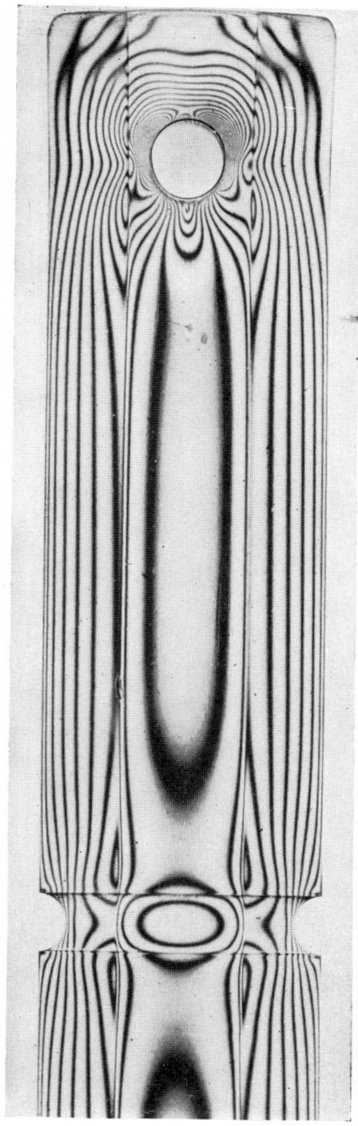

FIG. 13.33 Stress Pattern of a Hollow Circular Shaft with Semicircular Groove in Tension. See §13.21.

FIG. 13.34 Stress Patterns of Central Plate Cut from Shaft of Fig. 13.33; t = 0.139 in.; $n_{\text{max.}}$ = 3.5 fringes.

CHAPTER 14

SCATTERED AND CONVERGENT LIGHT

PART I SCATTERED LIGHT METHOD

§14.1 Scattering of Unpolarized Light. In Vol. I, §3.17, it was pointed out that when light travels through a material medium it is scattered in all directions transverse to the axis of propagation. Thus, the unpolarized collimated beam of light traveling in the Z direction, Fig. 14.1, would be visible to an observer looking along any direction in the XY plane. *A basic characteristic of the scattered light lies in the fact that it is always plane polarized.*

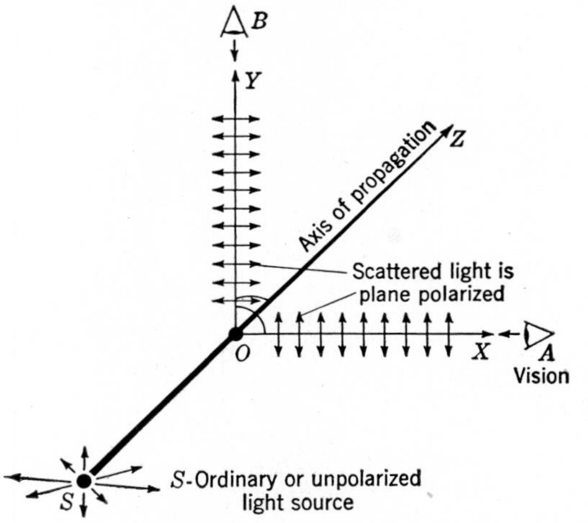

Fig. 14.1 Sketch Showing Polarization of Ordinary Light by Scattering.

For an unpolarized light source, the intensity of illumination of the scattered beam is essentially the same for all transverse directions of observation, Fig. 14.1.

§14.2 Scattering of Polarized Light. (*a*) *Plane-Polarized Light.* We consider next the scattering resulting from a plane-polarized source, Fig. 14.2. In all cases *the intensity of the scattered light is proportional to the square of its apparent amplitude*, i.e., to the square of the component of the amplitude normal to the line of sight. Thus, an observer at A looking in the X direction would see the beam at its maximum scattered intensity; an observer at B looking along the Y axis would not see it at

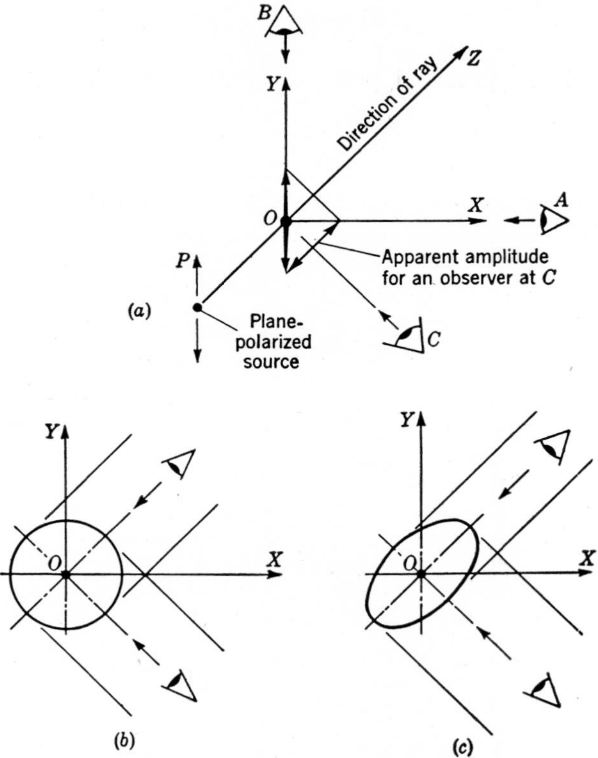

FIG. 14.2 Sketches Showing Scattering of Initially Polarized Beams in an Isotropic Medium.

all; and an observer at C would see the light in a diminished intensity. The scattered light is also here *plane polarized.*

(*b*) *Circularly Polarized Light.* If the main beam is circularly polarized the scattered light would be similar to that of an unpolarized source. Here the apparent amplitude is constant for all transverse directions of observation. The scattered light would therefore be plane polarized and of equal intensity.

(*c*) *Elliptically Polarized Light.* If the main beam is elliptically polarized the apparent amplitude varies from a minimum which is proportional to the minor axis to a maximum which is proportional to the major axis. The scattered polarized light would, therefore, vary in intensity.

§14.3 Scattering in Doubly Refracting Medium. In the preceding section we assumed the medium to be optically isotropic. We now consider the scattering resulting from a plane-polarized beam traveling through a doubly refracting medium, Fig. 14.3. For concreteness we assume that the principal planes of the doubly refracting plate are

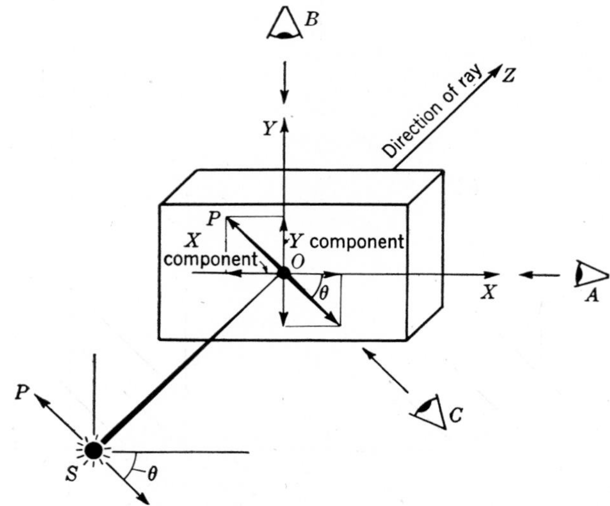

FIG. 14.3 Sketch Showing the Scattering of a Plane-Polarized Beam in a Doubly Refracting Medium.

parallel to the XZ and YZ planes, and that the direction of vibration P of the collimated plane-polarized beam makes an angle θ with the X axis as shown.

Upon entering the birefringent medium the polarized beam is resolved into two component vibrations $V \cos \theta$ and $V \sin \theta$, traveling respectively in planes parallel to the XZ and YZ planes, with different velocities.

An observer at A would see the Y component, but not the X component. Similarly, an observer at B would see the X component but not the Y component, whereas one looking in an arbitrary transverse direction, such as C, would perceive the combined effect of both components.

This effect is made up of the interaction of the two apparent amplitudes. Since the X and Y components travel with different velocities the scattered light beams which they produce will alternately reinforce and weaken each other. When θ equals 45°, there will be very distinct points along the path where the two scattered beams will completely cancel by interference. This will occur when the vibrations are out of phase. An observer looking in the direction of vibration P, or at right angles to it, will then see equally spaced bright bands separated by dark fringes.

There is, however, a difference in the visual effect resulting from the above two directions of observation. If the scattered light be viewed along the direction of vibration the components interfere at the point of entrance and a black fringe appears at the boundary. If, on the other hand, the observation is along a direction normal to that of vibration then the two beams reinforce each other and the entering boundary appears bright.

It is clear that the plane-polarized beam at 45° may be replaced by a circular beam. For clearest interference and reinforcement the direction of observation would have to bisect the angle between the principal planes of the plate and to be transverse to the axis of propagation.

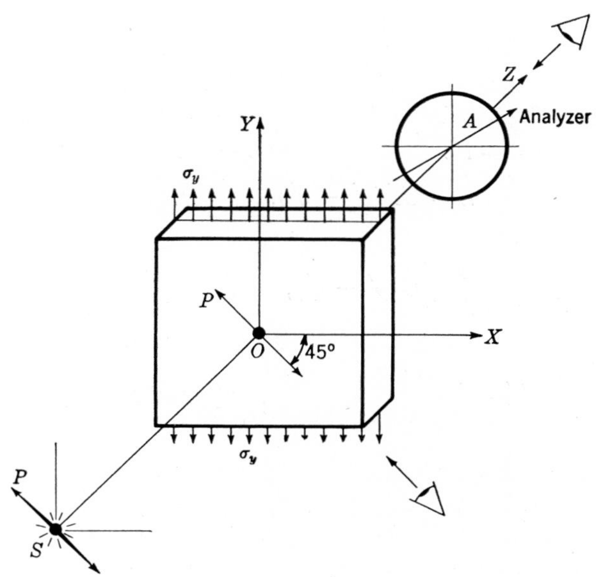

Fig. 14.4 Sketch Showing Scattering Resulting from the Transmission of a Plane-Polarized Beam through a Plate in Pure Tension.

§14.4 Scattering Acts as an Optical Analyzer. The optical effects described in the preceding section would clearly be the same if the birefringence were temporary such as that produced by stresses or strains in transparent materials. Thus, the plate shown in Fig. 14.4 may be thought of as being in pure tension parallel to either the X or Y axis. Let us assume that the magnitude of the tensile stress, say σ_y, is such that for the given plate of thickness t there would result ten fringes when viewed through a conventional crossed analyzer A. The accumulation or growth of these fringes could clearly be seen through this analyzer if the plate were viewed during the full interval of slow loading.

Observation of the scattered light viewed along the direction P, or at right angles to it, is thus equivalent to viewing the plate through an analyzer during the full loading period.

The effect of the scattering is thus similar to that of an analyzer; i.e., scattering acts as its own analyzer. There is, however, one difference. When viewed through the analyzer in an ordinary plane polariscope the accumulation of the total number of fringes can be observed only during the interval in which the loads are applied. At any one instant, only one uniform fringe order, representing the integrated effect, would cover the field. However, the image of the scattered light would at all times show the complete growth or accumulation of the fringes. Here all the bright and dark bands can be seen at once.

§14.5 The Stress-Optic Law for Scattered Light. In §10.3 it was shown that the basic relation between the retardation n and the secondary principal stresses p', q' corresponding to an arbitrary ray is

$$n = Ct'(p' - q'). \tag{10.1a}$$

From this we have

$$\frac{dn}{dt'} = C(p' - q'),$$

and

$$p' - q' = \frac{1}{C}\frac{dn}{dt'} = \frac{1}{C}\frac{\Delta n}{\Delta t'}, \text{ approximately,} \tag{14.1}$$

in which Δn is an increment in the fringe order corresponding to an interval $\Delta t'$ in the optical path.

Now, let Δn be chosen as one fringe. Then $\Delta t'$ denotes the distance between successive fringes in the scattered pattern. Remembering that $1/C = 2f$ we have from the last expression

$$p' - q' = \frac{2f}{\Delta t'}$$

or

$$\tau_{\text{max.}}' = \frac{f}{\Delta t'}, \tag{14.2}$$

where $\tau_{max.}'$ is the maximum secondary shear, and f is the usual fringe value of the material in shear, which for Bakelite is 43 psi. at room temperature.

This is the basic equation for the interpretation of a stress pattern resulting from scattering of a plane-polarized beam at 45° to the secondary principal stresses when the direction of observation is in a transverse plane and is either parallel or normal to the direction of vibration of the incident beam, and the effect of rotation is neglected.

In conventional photoelastic patterns the shear stress is directly proportional to the fringe order n. In scattered stress patterns the shear stress is inversely proportional to the spacings $\Delta t'$ between successive fringes.

The theoretical accuracy of eq. (14.1) increases with the number of fringes per unit length, for then the derivative dn/dt' approaches more nearly the value of $1/\Delta t'$. As the fringes get crowded, however, it is more difficult to measure $\Delta t'$ with good accuracy, although this difficulty can be largely eliminated by means of microphotometric traces.

§14.6 Photoelastic Stress Analysis by Means of Scattered Light. The first to suggest and to use the principles of scattered light in optical stress analysis was R. Weller.[1, 2] He stated the basic theory as well as the general experimental procedure. In the scattered-light method, Fig. 14.5, a plane-polarized beam is collimated, and a narrow sheet of it, which is formed by a slit of suitable width placed between the polarizer and the model, is allowed to pass through the specimen illuminating within it a section of approximately uniform thickness. Where the directions of the principal stresses are known, as for example in pure tension and bending, the application of the method is rather simple. The beam is directed so that the incidence is normal to the plane of the stresses, and the slit is adjusted to be parallel to a principal stress. The polarizer is then so oriented that the direction of vibration makes an angle of 45° with the direction of either one of the principal stresses. The resulting scattered pattern should be viewed along a direction either parallel or normal to that of the vibrations of the plane-polarized beam. Stress patterns of tension and bending are shown in Figs. 14.6 and 14.7 respectively.

A more interesting example is pure or Saint Venant torsion. The principal stresses at any point are in this case always in a plane normal to the radius of the shaft through the given point, and they make angles of

[1] See " A New Method for Photoelasticity in Three-Dimensions," by R. Weller, *Journal of Applied Physics*, Vol. 10, p. 266, 1939.

[2] See also his " Three-Dimensional Photoelasticity Using Scattered Light," *Journal of Applied Physics*, Vol. 12, No. 8, pp. 610–616, August, 1941.

45° with the line through the point which is parallel to the axis of the shaft, Fig. 14.8.

Two methods are available to obtain scattered stress patterns from pure torsion: in one method, the directions of vibration and observation are parallel to the axis of the shaft; in the other procedure they are normal to it, Fig. 14.5.

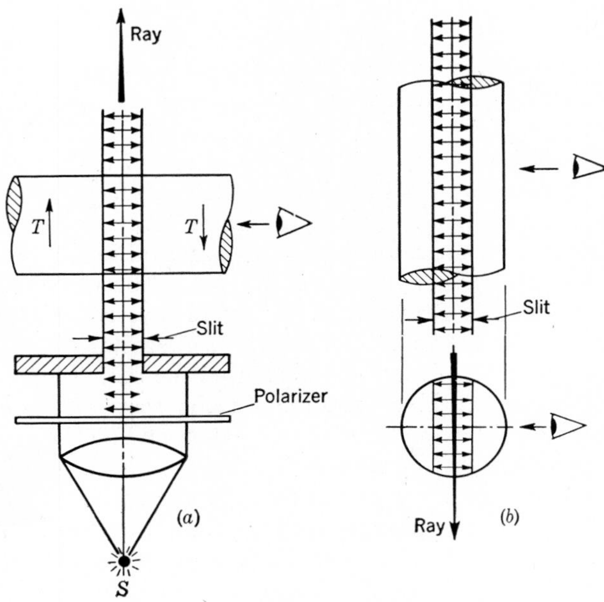

FIG. 14.5 Sketches Showing Necessary Elements and Their Arrangement in a Scattering Polariscope, with Particular Application to Torsion. See §14.6. Slits are much exaggerated in width.

Fig. 14.9 shows a stress pattern of a circular shaft in pure torsion.

Figs. 14.10 and 14.11 are two stress patterns of a circular shaft with a Woodruff keyway obtained in the manner shown in Figs. 14.5(*a*) and 14.5(*b*) respectively. In order to measure accurately the distances between the fringes Weller used the microphotometric traces of Fig. 14.12.

Several scattered stress patterns from rectangular shafts in torsion are shown in Figs. 14.13, 14.14, and 14.15. Weller has also studied a grooved circular shaft in tension.[1]

[1] See reference 2, p. 471.

It has recently been shown that the scattered patterns are in every way the same as membrane contours for pure torsion. Each fringe is a line of constant membrane elevation, and for a given cross section the

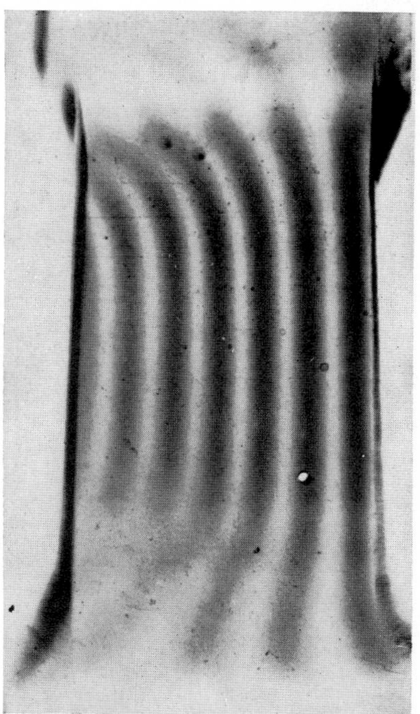

FIG. 14.6 Scattered Stress Pattern of a Bar in Tension.

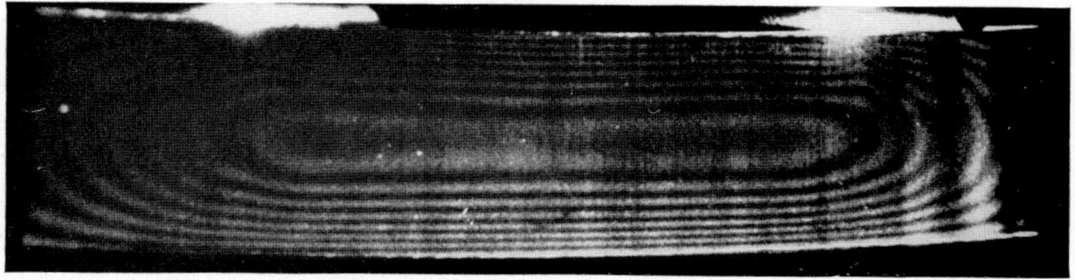

FIG. 14.7 Scattered Stress Pattern of a Beam in Pure Bending.

difference in elevation from one fringe to the next is a constant depending on the twisting moment and material constants only. *The pattern will not change if the shaft and the loading system are rotated as a unit about the axis of the shaft; i.e., the pattern is independent of the direction of the entering rays of parallel light* which may be plane or circularly polarized. The shearing stress at each point on the cross section is tangent to the fringe contour and has a magnitude proportional to the fringe gradient at the point.[1]

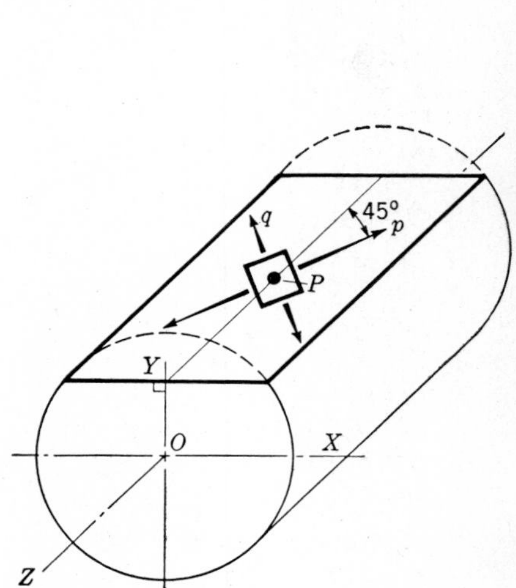

FIG. 14.8 Sketch Showing Principal Stresses in Pure Torsion.

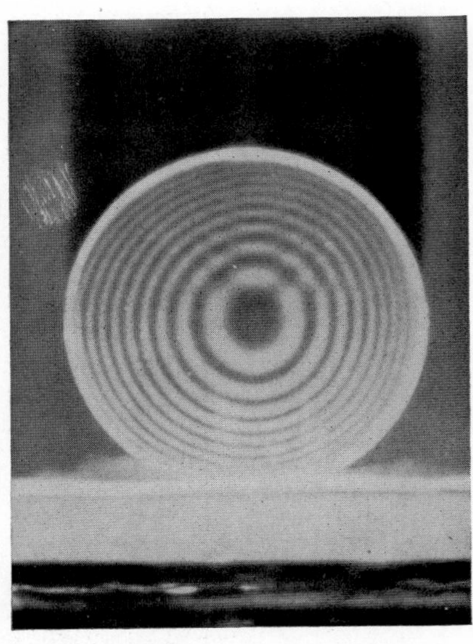

FIG. 14.9 Scattered Stress Pattern of a Circular Shaft in Pure Torsion. (Figs. 14.6–14.12 are from Weller.)

§14.7 Boundary Stresses. The plane tangent to a free boundary is always one of the three principal planes at the point of tangency, and the stress normal to this plane obviously vanishes. The three principal stresses at the point of tangency reduce to two components which lie in the tangent plane. Theoretically it should be possible to determine the two principal stresses at a free boundary by scattering. In order to do this one must first determine their directions. Referring to Fig. 14.16(a), let p and q be the unknown directions of the tangential principal stresses. We begin with a plane-polarized beam at normal incidence to the tangential plane for which the direction of vibration P makes an arbitrary angle θ with the principal stress p.

The scattered pattern for a direction of observation parallel to P

[1] See "Equivalence of Photoelastic Scattering Patterns and Membrane Contours for Torsion," by D. C. Drucker and M. M. Frocht, *Proc. Soc. for Experimental Stress Analysis*, 1947. See also paper by R. A. Frigon, *Proc. 15th Eastern Photoelasticity Conference*, p. 73.

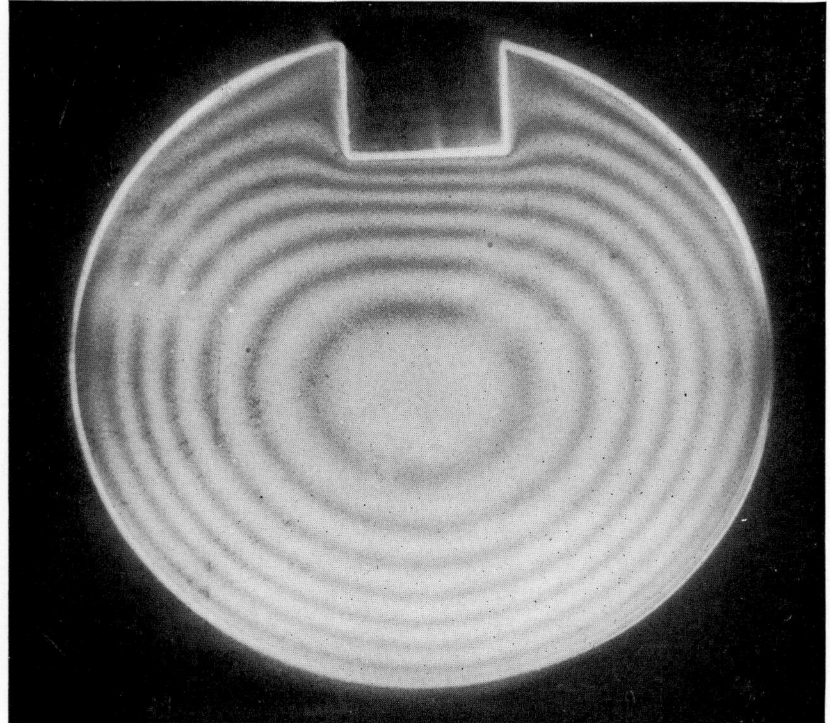

FIG. 14.10 Scattered Stress Pattern of a Circular Shaft with a Woodruff Keyway in Pure Torsion. Direction of light shown in Fig. 14.5(*a*).

would in general show bright and dark bands. The model is then revolved about the axis of propagation until the fringes disappear and the field seems uniform. *The principal tangential stresses are then parallel and perpendicular to the direction of observation giving this field.* If, without changing the direction of the beam, the model is rotated about the given axis of propagation through 45°, then the scattered pattern from a direction of observation either parallel to P or normal to it would give $(p - q)$.

Theoretically it is also possible to obtain p and q directly. To this end the axis of propagation is turned through 90° so that it lies in a tangential plane and is normal to one of the principal stresses, say p, the direction of vibration P being adjusted to make a 45° angle with the outward normal ON at the point O, Fig. 14.16(*b*). Observation along a direction parallel or perpendicular to P should give data for the calculation of p. The

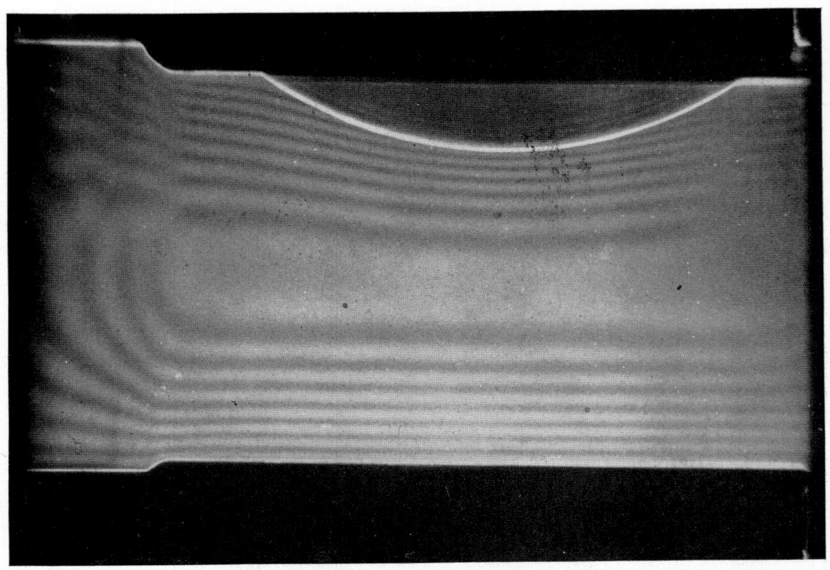

FIG. 14.11 Pattern of Same Shaft as Shown in Fig. 14.10 with Direction of Light Normal to Axis of Shaft. See Fig. 14.5(*b*).

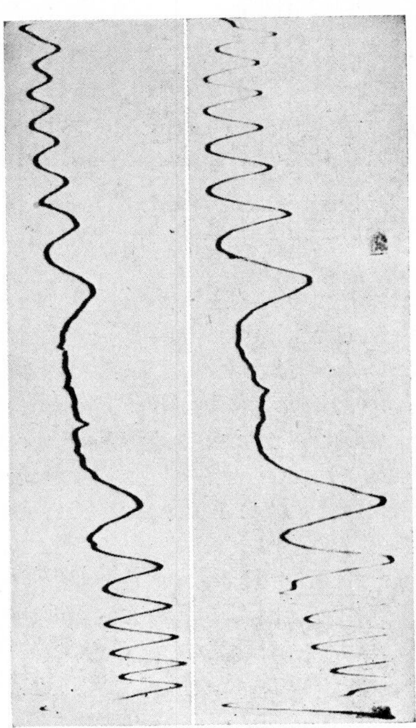

FIG. 14.12 Microphotometric Traces of Patterns Shown in Figs. 14.10 and 14.11.

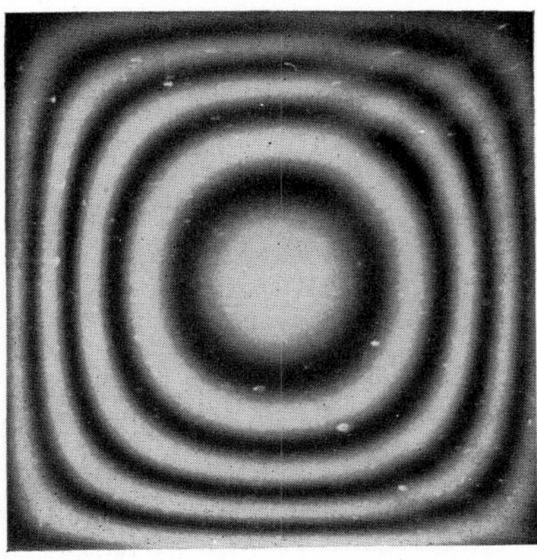

FIG. 14.13 Scattered Stress Pattern of a Square Shaft in Pure Torsion.

second principal stress can be determined in a similar manner, and the results can then be checked against the previously obtained value of $(p - q)$.

§14.8 The General Case. Weller also discusses the possibilities of evaluating the stresses at any arbitrary interior point by scattered light.

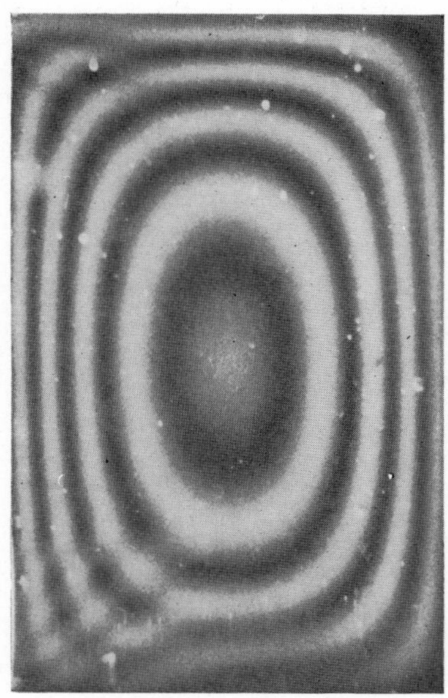

FIG. 14.14 Scattered Stress Pattern of a Rectangular Shaft in Pure Torsion.

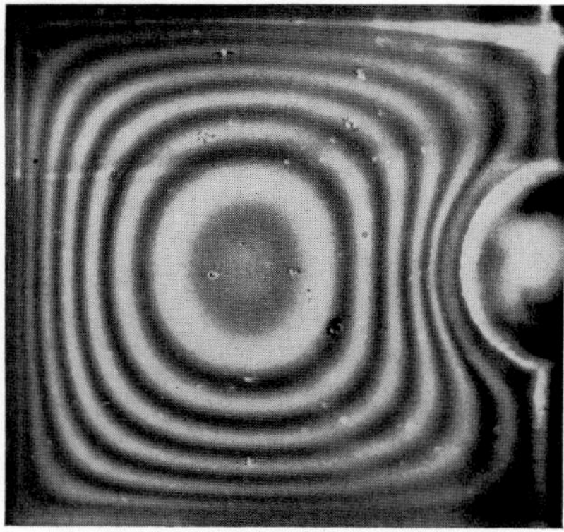

FIG. 14.15 Scattered Stress Pattern of a Square Shaft with a Semicircular Keyway in Pure Torsion.

This involves a point-by-point exploration in which that position of the model in relation to the ray is sought which gives the minimum spacing of the fringes at a point. If such a position could be determined with accuracy, the direction of the axis of propagation would be parallel to the intermediate principal stress, and the spacings between the corresponding fringes would be a measure of the difference between the maximum and minimum principal stresses, i.e., of the maximum shear. The directions of the maximum and minimum stresses could then be found by rotating the model about the intermediate stress until the fringes vanish. Another procedure in which the spacings between the fringes from several different directions are utilized has been suggested by Drucker and Mindlin.[1]

[1] See " Stress Analysis by Three-Dimensional Photoelastic Methods," by D. C. Drucker and R. D. Mindlin, *Journal of Applied Physics*, Vol. 11, p. 724, 1940.

Relatively little work has been done by the method of scattered light, and this field is fertile ground for future development. Practical considerations suggest that the method of scattering will have to be combined with that of freezing or fixation. It is rather impractical to immerse a complicated model and the straining fixtures in a suitable fluid for observation. Not only would this require large tanks and much

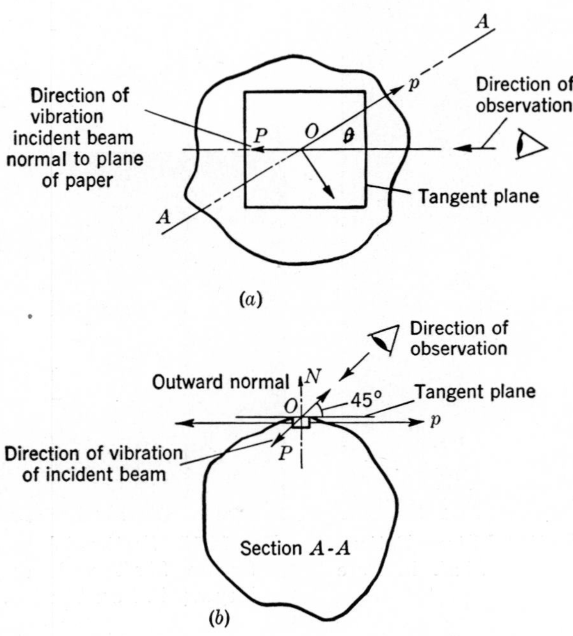

FIG. 14.16 Sketch Showing the Application of Scattered Light to the Possible Determination of Boundary Stresses.

fluid, but also the fixtures would, in most cases, interfere with the light. In order to obviate these difficulties it is more practical to fix or freeze the stress system into the model and to examine the model as a whole, or in part, by means of scattered light.

The necessity of resorting to the method of freezing, however, removes one theoretical advantage of scattering which was expected to result from the small deformations at room temperature. A general appraisal of the potentialities and practical value of the method involving scattered light must be postponed until much more work has been done with it. A special polariscope for scattering designed by Weller is shown in Fig. 14.17.

(*a*)

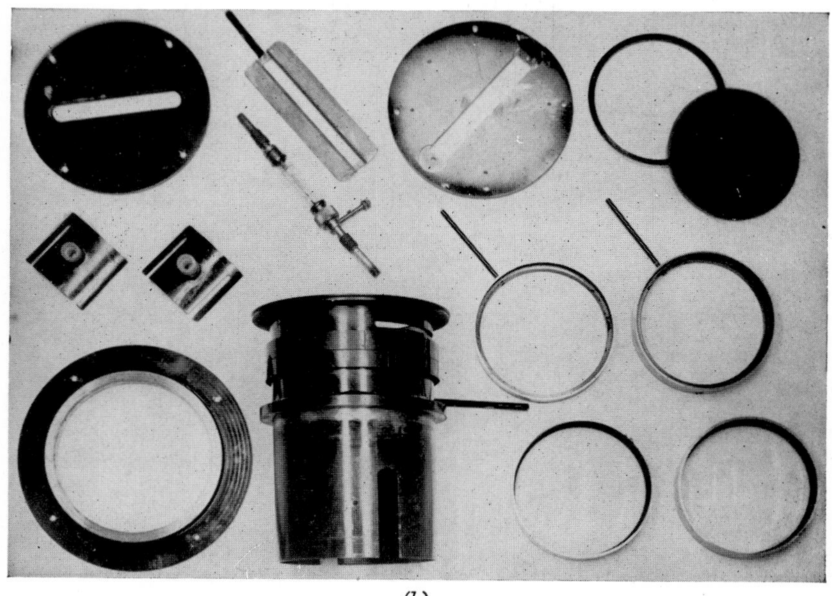

(*b*)

Fig. 14.17 Polariscope for Scattered Light. (*a*) Assembly; (*b*) Parts before assembly.

FIG. 14.18 Photographs of a Crankshaft Studied by Hiltscher by Means of Converging-Light Method.

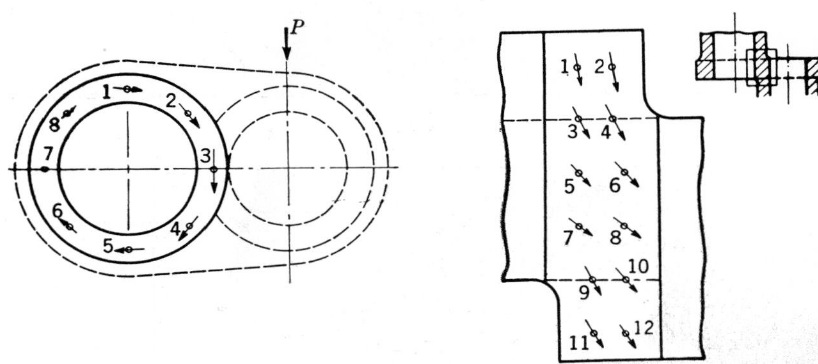

FIG. 14.19 Some Results Obtained by Hiltscher.

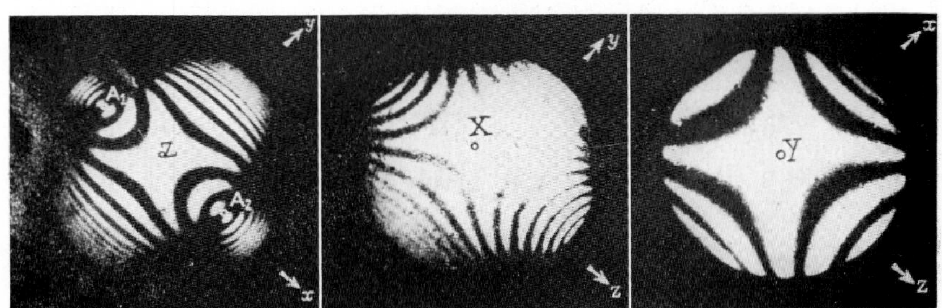

FIG. 14.20 Typical Stress Patterns from Converging Light.

§14.9 Hiltscher's Converging-Light Method. In 1937 Hiltscher proposed a procedure for three-dimensional photoelastic analysis which combines frozen stresses with converging light. The technique of converging light is widely used by petrologists in crystallographic investigations.

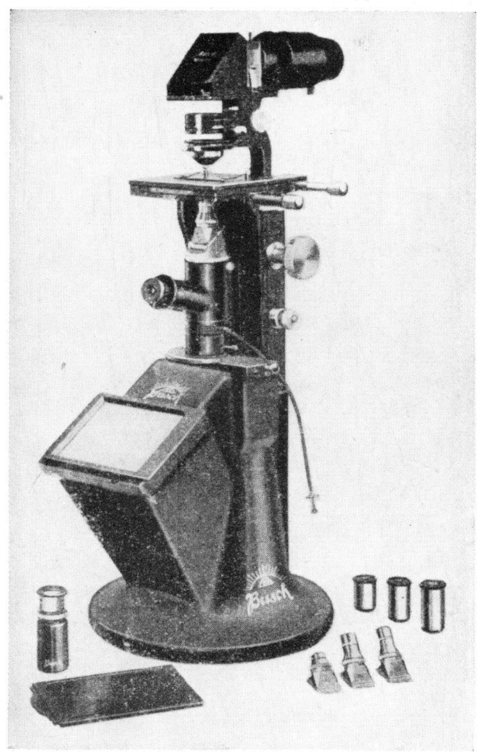

FIG. 14.21 Basic Apparatus in the Method of Converging Light.

By this method it is possible to obtain: (1) the directions of the principal stresses and (2) the three principal shear stresses. It is not possible, however, to obtain directly the principal stresses themselves. The procedure involves point-by-point explorations, and it is yet not clear whether the results are a function of the physical constants.

Thus far Hiltscher seems to have been the only one to have used this method in optical-stress analysis. He studied the stress distribution in a crankshaft of the type shown in Fig. 14.18. His results are shown in Fig. 14.19. Typical stress patterns from converging light on which the results are based appear in Fig. 14.20, and the apparatus used is shown in Fig. 14.21. For a detailed discussion of the method the reader is referred to the original paper by Hiltscher.[1]

[1] See " Polarisationsoptische Untersuchung des raumlichen Spannunszustandes im konvergenten Licht," doctor's dissertation by Rudolf Hiltscher, Technische Hochschule München, 1937, or *Forschung auf dem Gebiete des Ingenieurwesens*, Vol. 9, pp. 91–103, 1938.

APPENDIX[1]

FOSTERITE[2] — A NEW MATERIAL FOR THREE-DIMENSIONAL PHOTOELASTICITY

PART I GENERAL CHARACTERISTICS

§A.1 Introduction. A new material, known as Fosterite, particularly suitable for three-dimensional photoelastic stress analysis employing frozen stress patterns and free from the main limitations of Bakelite, was recently announced by the Westinghouse Research Laboratories.

§A.2 Chemistry. Fosterite is a general name for the resins of the styrene-alkyd type in which alkyds (alcohols and acids) are copolymerized with styrene. Only three of the many styrene alkyd resins which have been investigated for photoelastic properties by the Westinghouse Research Laboratories are described by Leven. These are adipic Fosterite, sebacic Fosterite, and fumaric Fosterite. The chemical components and curing time are given in Table A.1, in which the first three parts form the alkyd. Thus in adipic Fosterite the alkyd is composed of adipic acid, maleic acid, and diethylene glycol.

TABLE A.1

Adipic Fosterite	Sebacic Fosterite	Fumaric Fosterite
Adipic acid	Sebacic acid	Sebacic acid
Maleic acid	Maleic acid	Fumaric acid
Diethylene glycol	Diethylene glycol	Diethylene glycol
Styrene 54% (by weight)	Styrene 54%	Styrene 54%
Curing temperature 135° C.	Curing temperature 135° C.	Curing temperature 190° C.

§A.3 Time of Curing. The total time required to complete a Fosterite casting is approximately 30 days, whereas Bakelite requires roughly 18 months.

[1] This appendix is based on a paper of the same name by M. M. Leven from the Westinghouse Research Laboratories, which was presented before the Society of Experimental Stress Analysis at its meeting of December, 1947. All the curves and stress patterns in this appendix are from the above paper and are reproduced by the courtesy of the Westinghouse Research Laboratories. At the time of appearance of this paper, plates for the book had already been cast and further coordination with Chapter 11 where this material properly belongs was impracticable.

[2] Named after its inventor, N. C. Foster, Research Chemical Engineer, Westinghouse Research Laboratories. An early form of Fosterite was first used in photoelastic tests by M. Hetenyi.

§A.4 Size. Fosterite can be cast into large solid cylinders or flat plates. Fig. A.1 shows a Fosterite cylinder 30 in. long and 6 in. in diameter. It thus becomes possible to make relatively large models of

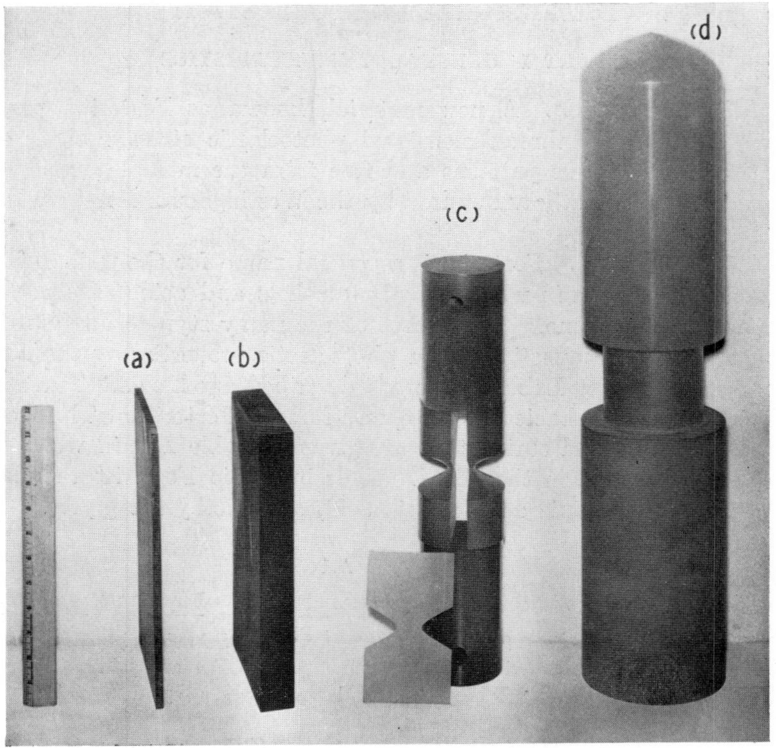

FIG. A.1 Comparison of Obtainable Bakelite with Fosterite.

(*a*) Bakelite plate, $t = 0.25$ in.; (*b*) largest Bakelite plate manufactured, 12 in. by 6 in. by $1\frac{1}{8}$ in. approximately; (*c*) Fosterite shaft with hyperboloidal notch showing slice removed for frozen pattern, $D = 3.4$ in.; (*d*) Fosterite cylinder, 30 in. long, 6 in. diameter.

complicated machine parts such as pistons, connecting rods, camshafts, and crankshafts. As yet, Fosterite cannot be cast into forms having holes or cavities.

§A.5 Machinability and Transparency. There is no greater difficulty in machining Fosterite than Bakelite. Fosterite is somewhat yellowish, but it is sufficiently transparent for all photoelastic uses. This can be clearly seen from the stress patterns in Fig. A.2.

§A.6 Strains in Fosterite at Elevated Temperatures. The strain behavior of Fosterite at elevated temperatures is rather anomalous.

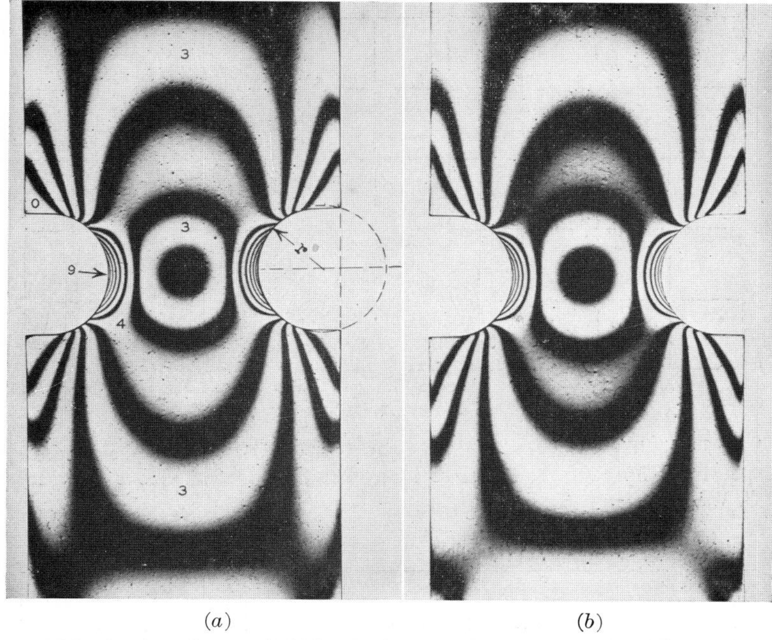

FIG. A.2 Frozen Stress Patterns of a Bar with Grooves in Tension Cut from Adipic Fosterite, Showing Absence of Time Stresses: (*a*) Immediately after Freezing; (*b*) 30 Days Later.

$P = 5.73$ lb. at 90° C. Initial dimensions: $r = 0.157$ in.; $d = 0.425$ in.; depth of grooves, $h = 0.235$ in. Final dimensions: $r = 0.179$ in.; $d = 0.420$ in.; depth of grooves, $h = 0.233$ in.

Inspection of Fig. A.3 shows that between 80° C. and 160° C. the strain decreases as the temperature increases. Thus, after 2 hours at a stress of 90.9 psi. the strains at 80° C., 97° C., and 100° C. are respectively 0.08, 0.074, and 0.066 approximately.

§A.7 Minimum Temperature for Elastic Behavior. Critical Temperature. At approximately 100° C. Fosterite seems to behave in a perfectly elastic manner. In pure tension the stress optic relation is linear up to about ten fringes for a thickness of ¼ in., Fig. A.4. At this temperature it is free from creep. Also, upon loading, the full deformations develop rapidly, and upon unloading, recovery is equally fast. The minimum temperature at which all these properties first develop is approximately 100° C. It is called the critical temperature. This temperature is of basic importance to photoelasticians. Since very high temperatures generally have a detrimental effect upon the chemical

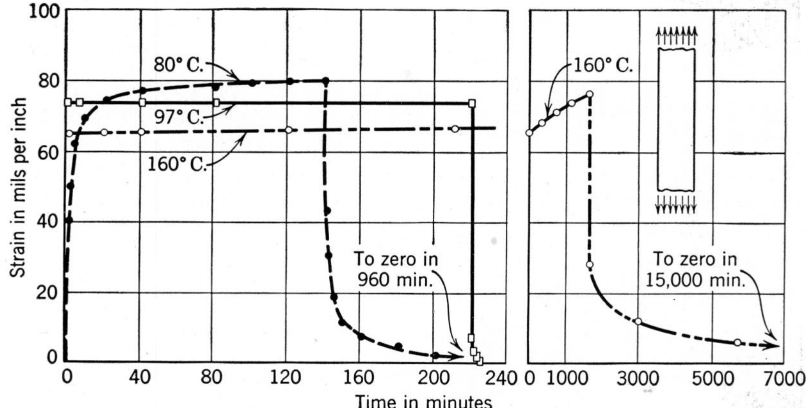

Fig. A.3 Strain-Time Curves from Adipic Fosterite at Constant Load and Different Temperatures, Showing the Absence of Creep and the Instantaneous Recovery at 97° C, Where $E = 1228$ psi.

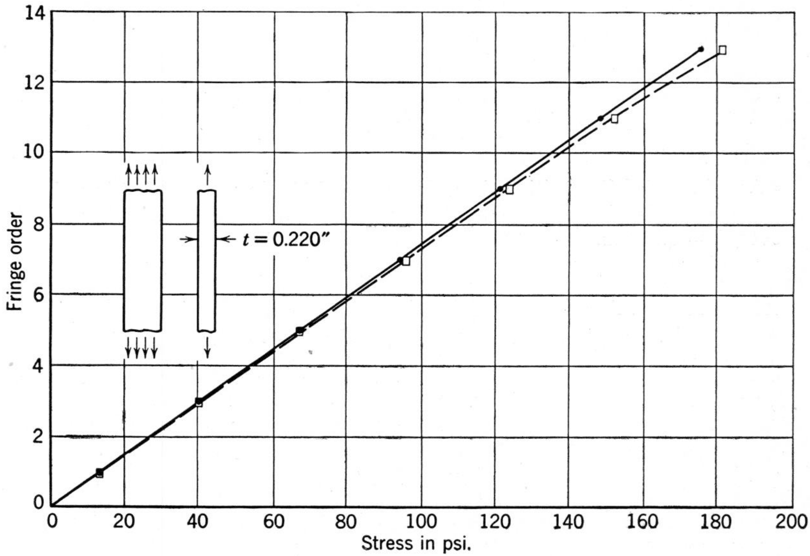

Fig. A.4 Basic Curves Showing the Linear Stress Optic Relation for Sebacic Fosterite at the Critical Temperature of 100° C.

Solid curve is based on dimensions at room temperature. Dashed curve is corrected for thermal expansion and lateral contraction. $2F = 13.66$ psi. tension; $2f = 3.00$ psi. tension.

stability of the Fosterite resins it is of course desirable to stay at the lowest possible temperatures which give elastic frozen stress patterns. (See also §A.12.)

§A.8 Frozen Patterns. At 100° C. Fosterite behaves like a diphase material. Excellent frozen stress patterns from Fosterite models have been obtained by Leven, Figs. A.2, A.8, and A.11. Frozen Fosterite models can be machined without disturbing the stress system.

§A.9 Time Stresses. For all practical purposes Fosterite may be said to be free from time stresses, which is a chief source of error in Bakelite. Fig. A.2 shows two stress patterns of one and the same model taken 30 days apart. Inspection of these patterns shows only negligible time effects.[1]

§A.10 Modulus of Elasticity and Fringe Value. At elevated temperatures Fosterite has a somewhat higher modulus of elasticity than Bakelite. Consequently, there are smaller distortions in the geometry of the model and therefore a greater accuracy in the final results. Fosterite also compares favorably with Bakelite in its optical sensitivity.

TABLE A.2

Material	Adipic Fosterite	Sebacic Fosterite	Fumaric Fosterite	Bakelite BT-61-893
Fringe value, $2f$ in psi. tension*	2.26	3.35	4.49	3.30
Modulus of elasticity, E in psi.	1155	2010	2865	1100
Figure of merit, $Q = \frac{E}{2f}$	511	600	660	334
Relative figure of merit, $Q' = \frac{Q\text{-Fosterite}}{Q\text{-Bakelite}}$	1.53	1.79	1.98	....

* Leven uses f for the tensile fringe value, whereas in this book the corresponding notation is $2f$.

The physical and optical properties of Fosterite seem to be determined entirely by the content of styrene and the curing temperature. In general the fringe value and modulus of elasticity increase with decreasing styrene content and increasing curing cycle temperature, while their

[1] The small time stresses which are developed are of signs opposite to those in Bakelite; i.e., the outside layers of the model are in tension and the interior in compression. This is indicated by the sudden reversal of direction of the fringes at the boundary.

ratio Q remains essentially constant.[1] Table A.2 shows the fringe values $2f$ in psi. tension and the modulus of elasticity E in psi. for the three types of Fosterite. The values for Bakelite are given for comparison.

§A.11 Creep in Fosterite. (*a*) At room temperature Fosterite shows a pronounced tendency to creep which would seem to make the material of doubtful value for photoelastic use.

(*b*) At elevated temperatures the tendency to creep diminishes. At approximately 100° C. the strain-time curve is essentially a straight horizontal line for a considerable range of stress and time.

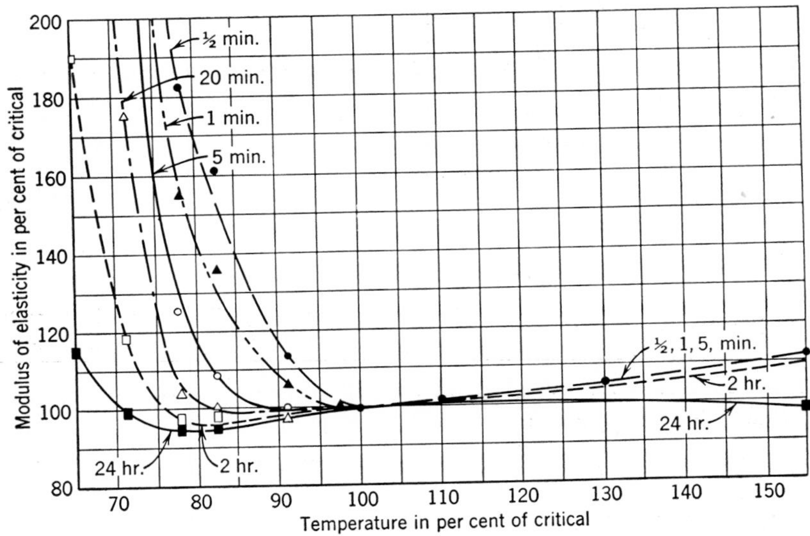

Fig. A.5 Curves of E/E_{critical} as a Function of T/T_{critical} Showing that at 100° C Fosterite is Free from Creep.

§A.12 Creep at the Critical Temperature. The curves in Fig. A.5 show conclusively that at 100° C. Fosterite is free from creep. This follows from the fact that all curves intersect at this temperature, which of course means that the modulus of elasticity is independent of time; i.e., for a constant stress the strain remains constant even in 24 hours of

[1] The quantity Q is called by Leven the *figure of merit*. It represents an index of suitability of the material for photoelastic research. The greater this index, the better the material, for clearly a larger modulus, a smaller fringe value, or both mean smaller distortions of the geometry and therefore smaller errors. It is seen that all three Fosterites have greater values of Q than Bakelite and that for fumaric Fosterite the relative index Q' is nearly 2; i.e., for the same fringe order n the distortions in Fosterite would be about half of those in Bakelite.

loading. Hence, there is no creep at this temperature.[1] At every other temperature E/E-critical is a variable depending on the time, which shows the presence of creep. The curves of Fig. A.6 are typical creep

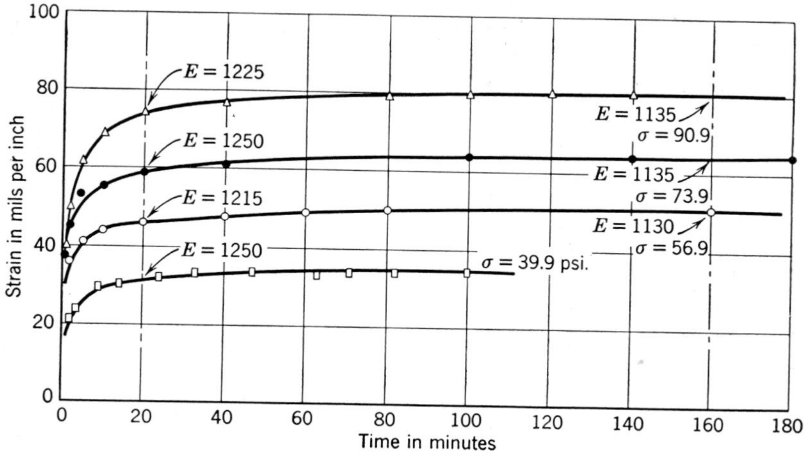

FIG. A.6 Typical Creep Curves of Fosterite at 80° C.

curves showing that the moduli of elasticity are independent of the magnitude of the stresses, provided they do not exceed the critical proportional limit, i.e., the proportional limit at 100° C.

§A.13 Fringe Order a Function of Strain. Fig. A.7 shows characteristic curves for the moduli of elasticity and the fringe values of Fosterite as a function of temperature. The results are given in terms of the critical values of E and f, which are obtained when the calibration member is still at 100° C. These values are slightly greater than those given in Table A.2 which correspond to the same calibration member after it was cooled down to room temperature. The curves of Fig. A.7 are identical in shape and almost coincide, showing that for the given range of temperature

$$\left.\begin{aligned} \frac{E}{E\text{-critical}} &= \frac{f}{f\text{-critical}}, && (a) \\ \text{or}\qquad \frac{f}{E} &= \frac{f\text{-critical}}{E\text{-critical}}. && (b) \end{aligned}\right\}(1)$$

[1] These curves further show that the critical temperature is not really very critical and that no serious errors would result from a small deviation from that temperature.

From eq. (1) it follows that for a given interval of loading time the fringe order n depends only on the strain ϵ and is independent of the temperature.[1] Thus, from eq. (1) we have

$$\frac{f\epsilon}{\sigma} = C, \quad \text{a constant.} \tag{2}$$

Remembering that

$$\frac{\sigma}{2f} = n, \tag{3}$$

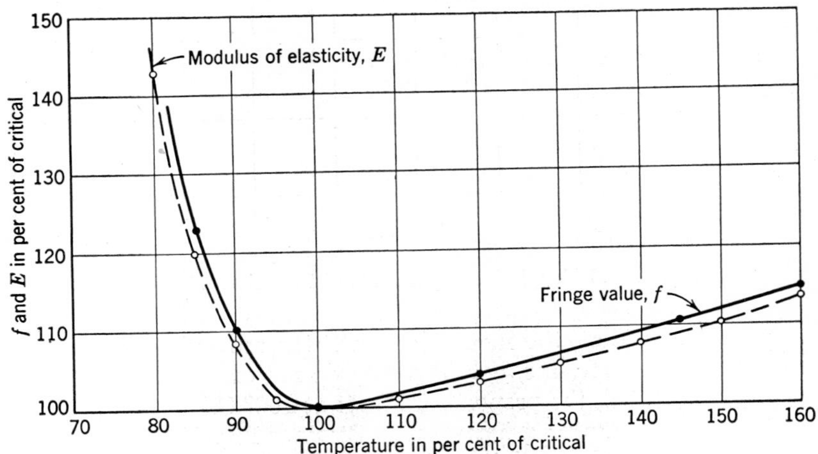

FIG. A.7 Curves of E/E_{critical} and f/f_{critical} as a Function of T/T_{critical} Showing that Shapes are Nearly Coincident.

where n denotes the fringe order for the stress σ, eq. (2) may be written as

$$\frac{\epsilon}{n} = C', \quad \text{a constant.}$$

Hence

$$n = \frac{\epsilon}{C'}\cdot \tag{4}$$

This would seem to show that as the temperature varies the optical effect is a function of the strain rather than stress. The full implications of this rather remarkable result have still to be explored.

[1] This observation was made by D. C. Drucker in a private conversation about the above results.

PART II QUANTITATIVE TESTS WITH FOSTERITE

§A.14 Flat Bar with a Central Circular Hole in Tension. In order to check the elastic character and the numerical accuracy of the results attainable from the new material, Leven froze a stress system into a flat

FIG. A.8 Frozen Stress Pattern of a Sebacic Fosterite Bar with a Circular Hole in Tension Used in Fig. A.9.

Initial dimensions: D = 1.046 in.; t = 0.230 in.; $2r$ = 0.156 in.; P = 7.53 lb.; $2f$ = 3.35 psi. tension.

bar of sebacic Fosterite having a central circular hole in tension, Fig. A.8. Fig. A.9 shows a comparison of the tangential stresses around the hole as obtained photoelastically from the Fosterite model with the corresponding theoretical vaules of Howland.[1] The results are expressed in terms of the uniform stress σ at infinity. The applied load P was 7.53 lb., which for a bar of width $D = 1.046$ in. and thickness $t = 0.230$ in. gives

$$\sigma = \frac{P}{tD} = \frac{7.53}{0.230 \times 1.046} = 31.25 \text{ psi.}$$

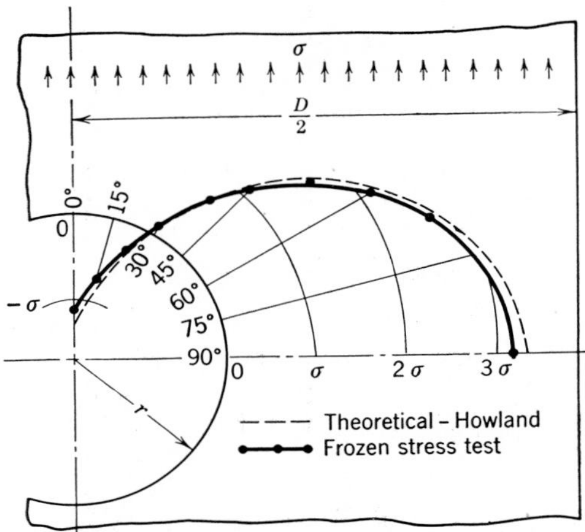

Fig. A.9 Comparison of Theoretical and Photoelastic Tangential Stresses around Hole in Bar of Fig. A.8.

The maximum observed fringe order is 6¾, occurring at the hole on the horizontal section. This gives

$$\sigma_{\text{max.}} = n2F = \frac{n2f}{t}$$

$$= \frac{6.75 \times 3.35}{0.230} = 98.4 \text{ psi.} = 3.15\sigma.$$

This compares with Howland's value of 3.33σ, giving an error of 5.4 per cent. It is to be remembered, however, that the above comparison is based upon the initial dimensions and shape of the model, no account being taken of the changes in shape and dimensions caused by the loading. Thus the radius of curvature has increased and the thickness of the model has decreased at the point of maximum tension. Both these

[1] See " On the Stresses in the Neighborhood of a Circular Hole in a Strip under Tension " by R. C. J. Howland, *Phil. Trans. Roy. Soc.*, **A229**, pp. 49–86, 1929.

factors would tend to decrease the maximum stress obtained photo-elastically.

§A.15 Shaft in Tension with a Deep Hyperboloidal Notch. As another test showing directly the applicability of Fosterite to three-dimensional problems a circular shaft with a deep circumferential external notch of hyperboloidal shape was chosen, Fig. A.10. The diameter of the straight part was 3.4 in., the minimum diameter at the

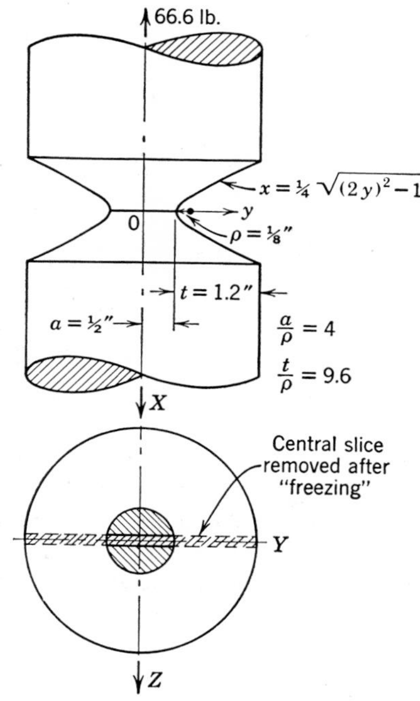

FIG. A.10 Sketch Showing Initial Dimensions of Circular Shaft with Deep Hyperboloidal Notch. $D = 3.4$ in.

base of the notch was 1 in., and the minimum radius of curvature was 0.125 in. The model was made of sebacic Fosterite, and the applied load, which included one-half of the weight of the model, was 66.6 lb. The loading temperature was 95° C., where $2f = 3.66$ psi., and the temperature drop was held to 2° C. per hour.

After the stress system was frozen into the model, a central slice parallel to the XY plane was removed for study, Fig. A.10. Fig. A.11 shows the frozen stress pattern when the thickness of the slice was reduced to 0.125 in., from which the maximum fringe order at the base of the notch was found to be 6. Remembering that at 95° C. the fringe value $2f$ is 3.66 psi. tension, we obtain

$$(\sigma_u)_{\text{max.}} = \frac{6 \times 3.66}{0.125} = 175.7 \text{ psi.},$$

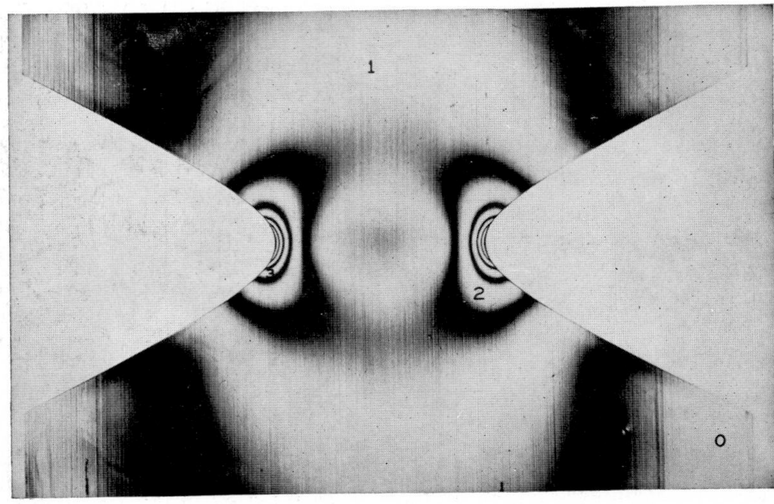

FIG. A.11(*a*) Stress Pattern of Central Slice from a Sebacic Fosterite Notched Circular Shaft in Tension.

t = 0.125 in.; $2f$ = 3.66 psi. tension; for initial dimensions of shaft see Fig. A.10.

where σ_u denotes the principal stress on the hyperboloidal surface, in the XY plane, Fig. A.12. The nominal stress σ then is

$$\sigma = \frac{\text{Load}}{\text{Min. area}} = \frac{P}{\pi a^2} = \frac{66.6}{3.14 \times 0.25} = 84.8 \text{ psi.}$$

Hence

$$(\sigma_u)_{\text{max.}} = \frac{175.7}{84.8}\sigma = 2.07\sigma.$$

Fig. A.12 shows a comparison of the surface stresses σ_u obtained photoelastically with the theoretical values of Neuber[1] for an infinitely deep notch. When the finite depth of the notch and the changes in the curvature of the root are considered Neuber's theory gives $(\sigma_u)_{\text{max.}} = 2.045\sigma$ as compared with the photoelastic value of 2.07σ from sebacic Fosterite. This is obviously an excellent agreement.

[1] *Theory of Notch Stresses* by H. Neuber, J. W. Edwards, Ann Arbor, Mich., p. 84, 1946.

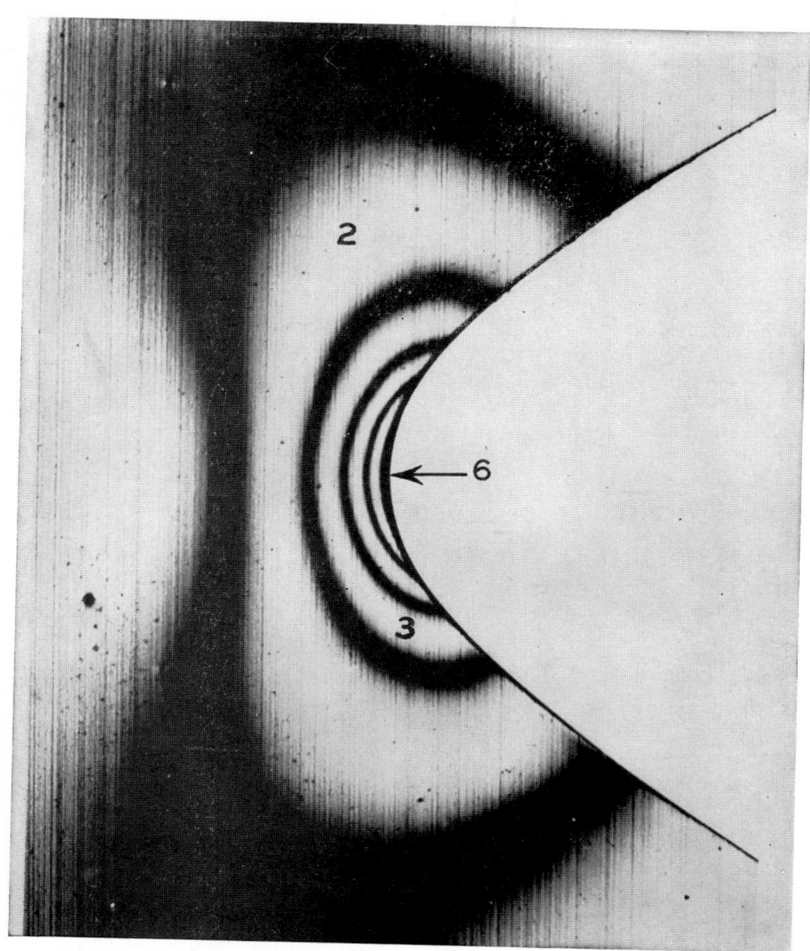

FIG. A.11(*b*) Enlargement of Fig. A.11(*a*).

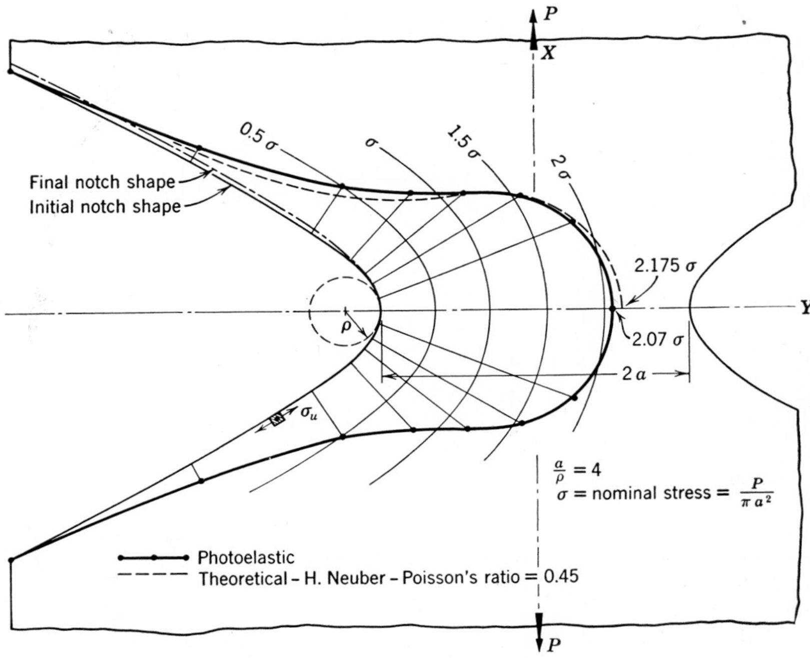

Fig. A.12 Comparison of Tangential Stresses Obtained Photoelastically from Sebacic Fosterite with Corresponding Theoretical Values of Neuber, for Shaft of Fig. A.10.

INDEX TO NAMES

SUBJECT INDEX*

*Photoelastic stress patterns are abridged to *patterns* or *stress patterns*.